The Regional
Geography
of Canada

Seventh Edition

Robert M. Bone

OXFORD
UNIVERSITY PRESS

OXFORD
UNIVERSITY PRESS

Oxford University Press is a department of the University of Oxford.
It furthers the University's objective of excellence in research, scholarship,
and education by publishing worldwide. Oxford is a registered trade mark of
Oxford University Press in the UK and in certain other countries.

Published in Canada by
Oxford University Press
8 Sampson Mews, Suite 204,
Don Mills, Ontario M3C 0H5 Canada

www.oupcanada.com

Copyright © Oxford University Press Canada 2018

The moral rights of the author have been asserted
Database right Oxford University Press (maker)

First Edition published in 2000
Second Edition published in 2002
Third Edition published in 2005
Fourth Edition published in 2008
Fifth Edition published in 2011
Sixth Edition published in 2014

Library and Archives Canada Cataloguing in Publication
Bone, Robert M., author
The regional geography of Canada / Robert M. Bone. – Seventh edition.

Includes bibliographical references and index. Issued in print and electronic formats.
ISBN 978-0-19-902129-1 (hardcover). – ISBN 978-0-19-902134-5 (PDF)

1. Canada–Geography–Textbooks. 2. Textbooks. I. Title.

FC76.B66 2017   917.1   C2017-904376-5   C2017-904377-3

Cover image: Insight Photography/First Light/Getty Images

Oxford University Press is committed to our environment.
This book is printed on Forest Stewardship Council® certified paper and comes from responsible sources.

Printed and bound in the United States of America
1 2 3 4 — 21 20 19 18

Brief Contents

Contents

④ Canada's Human Face   115

⑤ Canada's Economic Face   149

⑥ Ontario   175

⑦ Québec   213

(8) Western Canada   247

(9) British Columbia   283

(10) Atlantic Canada   321

Figures

Tables

Boxes

Vignette Boxes

Contested Terrain Boxes

Preface

The purpose of this book is to introduce university students to Canada's regional geography. In studying the regional geography of Canada, the student gains an appreciation of the country's amazing diversity; learns how its regions interact with one another; and grasps how regions change over time. By developing the central theme that Canada is a country of regions, this text presents a number of images of Canada, revealing its physical, cultural, and economic diversity as well as its regional complexity. Canada and its regions are involved in the global economy as never before. As a trading nation, Canada is affected by changes in world trade and prices. These changes impact each region differently. Also, Canada's population composition is now highly diverse as a result of immigrants arriving from around the world. These newcomers play a key role in Canada's population growth.

The Regional Geography of Canada divides Canada into six geographic regions: Ontario, Québec, Western Canada, British Columbia, Atlantic Canada, and the Territorial North. Each region has a particular regional geography, story, and population, and a unique location. These factors have determined each region's character, set the direction for its development, and created a sense of place. In examining these themes, this book underscores the dynamic nature of Canada's regional geography, which is marked by a shift in power relations among Canada's regions. World trade opened Canada to global influences, which, in turn, transformed each region and the relationships between the regions. This text employs a core/periphery framework. Such an approach allows the reader to comprehend more easily the economic relations between regions as well as modifications in these relations that occur over time. A simplified version of the core/periphery framework takes the form of "have" and "have-not" provinces.

At the same time, social cracks within Canadian society provide a different insight into the nature of Canada and its regions. Each faultline has deep historic roots in Canadian society. While they may rest dormant for some time, these raw tensions can erupt into national crises. Four such stress points exist between Indigenous and non-Indigenous Canadians; French and English Canadians; centralist (Ottawa and/or Central Canada) and decentralist (the other, less powerful regions) forces; and recent immigrants (newcomers) and those born in Canada (old-timers). This book explores the nature of these faultlines, the need to reach compromises, and the fact that reaching compromises provides the country with its greatest strength—diversity. While more progress in resolving differences is required, these faultlines are shown to be not divisive forces but forces of change that ensure Canada's existence as an open society within the context of a country of regions.

Organization of the Text

This book consists of 12 chapters. Chapters 1 through 5 deal with general topics related to Canada's national and regional geographies—Canada's physical, historical, and human geography—thereby setting the stage for a discussion of the six main geographic regions of Canada. Chapters 6 through 11 focus on these six geographic regions. The core/periphery model provides a guide for the ordering of these regions. The regional discussion begins with Ontario and Québec, which represent the traditional demographic, economic, and political core of Canada. The two chapters on the core regions are followed by our exploration of fast-growing, slow-growing, and resource hinterland regions: Western Canada, British Columbia, Atlantic Canada, and the Territorial North. Chapter 12 provides a conclusion.

Chapter 1 discusses the nature of regions and regional geography, including the core/periphery model and its applications. Chapter 2 introduces the major physiographic regions of Canada and other elements of physical geography that affect Canada and its regions. Chapter 3 is devoted to Canada's historical geography, such as its territorial evolution and the emergence of regional tensions and regionalism. This discussion is followed, in Chapter 4, by an examination of the basic demographic and social factors that influence Canada and its regions as well as its population. Chapter 5 explores the national and global economic forces that have shaped Canada's regions. To sharpen our awareness of how economic forces affect local and regional developments, four major themes running throughout this text are introduced in these first five chapters. The primary theme is that Canada is a country of regions. Two secondary themes—the integration of the North American economy and the changing world economy—reflect the recent shift in economic circumstances and its effects on regional geography. These two economic forces, described as continentalism and globalization, exert both positive and negative impacts on Canada and its regions, and are explored through the core/periphery model—a model introduced in the first edition back in 2000 that has had its basic premises shaken by the uneven effects of global trade on Canada's regions.

The regional chapters explore the physical and human characteristics that distinguish each region from the others and that give each region its special sense of place. To emphasize the uniqueness of each region, the concept of an advanced economy, discussed in Chapter 5, is examined in two ways: first by identifying leading or spearhead industries and second by a more in-depth discussion of the region's predominant or historic economic anchor. These economic anchors are the automobile industry in Ontario; Hydro-Québec in Québec; agriculture in Western Canada; forestry in British Columbia; the fisheries in Atlantic Canada; and megaprojects in the Territorial North. From this presentation, the unique character of each region emerges. In the concluding chapter we discuss the future of Canada and its regions within the rapidly changing global economy.

Seventh Edition

For Canada's regions, the consequences of recent global economic developments—notably the remarkable industrialization of Asian countries, especially China—are twofold. First, fluctuations in the global economy result in "boom-and-bust cycles," and these cycles affect Canada and its regions. Western Canada (led by Alberta and Saskatchewan) plus three other resource-dependent regions—Atlantic Canada, British Columbia, and the Territorial North—are currently suffering from low prices for their resources. During the last boom, the opposite happened. Then the economies of Alberta, Saskatchewan, and British Columbia attracted record numbers of newcomers: migrants from other parts of Canada and immigrants from abroad. High oil prices benefited Newfoundland and Labrador, though its population continued to decline. Since then, these regions have fallen into an economic slump.

Second, while Ontario and Québec remain the economic and population pillars of Canada, a shift of regional power is in the wind. Over the last decade, Ontario and Québec have suffered a decline in the number of workers in their manufacturing sectors. This decline began with the relocation of many firms offshore, where labour costs are significantly lower. Canadian manufactured goods also were troubled by the so-called "Dutch disease"—a combination of high energy prices and revenues and a rising Canadian dollar—which made their production and export more difficult, thus magnifying the problems facing the industrial heartland of Canada. All of these troubling trends came to an end in 2014. Since then, for example, Ontario's automobile industry has increased the value of its exports to the United States.

Reviews play an important role in crafting a new edition. How to recast Canada's regions within the global economic crisis was one challenge. Others were to restructure the book by splitting Chapter 4 into two chapters, one dealing with population and the other with economic matters; and to reorder the sequences of regional chapters by the population size of each region. All revisions had the goal of focusing on who we are, where we have been, and where we are headed—individually, collectively, and as a country of regions—all from a regional perspective.

Consequently, this new edition has experienced a major overhaul in content to account for changes both globally and within Canada. As well as features from the previous edition that helped students make connections and understand historical and contemporary processes, "Contested Terrain" boxes highlight controversial issues that make the regional geography of Canada dynamic and at times difficult for the major political actors to navigate. Many new photos, maps, vignettes, tables, graphs, further readings, websites, and glossary terms aim to facilitate and enrich student learning, and new essay questions have been added to each chapter.

Acknowledgements

With each edition, I have benefited from the constructive comments of anonymous reviewers selected by Oxford University Press. I especially owe a debt of thanks to one of those reviewers who spiced his critical comments with words of encouragement that kept me going. As Canada has changed, so has each edition of this book. When I look back at the first edition, I see a much different Canada from today. This transformation process is often captured in the constructive comments of reviewers.

I have called on the resources of *The National Atlas of Canada* and Statistics Canada to provide maps and statistics. As well, both organizations have created important websites for geography students. These websites provide access to a wide range of geographic data and maps that, because they are constantly updated, allow the student to access the most recently available information on Canada and its regions.

The staff at Oxford University Press, but particularly Phyllis Wilson, made the preparation of the seventh edition a pleasant and rewarding task. Peter Chambers, the developmental editor who worked with me in the initial phases of revising the text and selecting new photographs, deserves special thanks. Richard Tallman, who diligently and skilfully has edited my manuscripts into polished finished products for each of the last six editions, deserves special mention. As copy editor, Richard has become an old friend who often pushes me to clarify my ideas.

Finally, a special note of appreciation to my wife, Karen, is in order, as well as to our four wonderful grandchildren, Casey, Davis, Austyn, and Bodhi.

Important Features of this Edition

The seventh edition of *The Regional Geography of Canada* has been fully revised to incorporate the newest Statistics Canada data and reflect Canada's ever-changing role in the global economy. This is reflected in the new Chapter 4, Canada's Human Face, on the nation's demography, and in a new Chapter 5, Canada's Economic Face, on the economy. Building on the strengths of previous editions, the text takes into account key factors in human geography such as the slow but continuing recovery from the global economic crisis and the significant industrialization of Asian countries, which are contributing factors in shifting and reshaping the balance of power across the nation.

As in previous editions, the seventh edition incorporates a wide range of resources for students that complement and enhance the text. Features appearing throughout the text include:

- **New essay questions** at the end of each chapter that ask students to undertake research and think critically about important issues that have been introduced.
- **New and updated "Contested Terrain" boxes** that draw attention to specific issues in the regional geography of Canada.
- **New and revised vignettes** that focus on issues specific to each chapter.
- **New and updated "Think About It" questions** that prompt students to analyze the material both in and out of the classroom.
- **New and revised cross-chapter references** that highlight the interconnectedness of content across chapters to ensure a comprehensive study of the material.
- **Numerous new figures and tables** that help to delineate the changing social and cultural face of Canada and its regions.
- **New and updated maps** that highlight the characteristics of various regions across Canada.
- **New colour photographs** that engage the reader and provide strong visual references tied to the material.

The result is a new edition that retains the strengths that have made *The Regional Geography of Canada* a best-selling text while introducing new concepts and exploring topics of interest to today's student.

1 Regions of Canada

Chapter Overview

The study of Canada's regional geography provides an analysis and synthesis of Canada, and provides an intuitive grasp of the country's regional nature as well as the relationships between its regions. The following topics are examined in greater detail in Chapter 1:

- Geography as a discipline.
- Regional geography.
- Canada's geographic regions.
- The dynamic nature of Canada and its regions.
- Sense of place.
- Faultlines within Canada.
- Core/periphery theory.
- Understanding Canada's regions.

Introduction

Geography helps us understand our world. Since Canada is such a huge and diverse country, its geography is best understood from a regional perspective. In fact, the image of Canada as "a country of regions" runs deep in Canadian thought and literature, and even in the national psyche. This image is, in fact, political reality as geography and history have forged Canada into a complex and varied set of regions within a federal political framework. In its early years, railway building bound the country together and railways still play a unifying role (see Further Reading). Each region has its own political agenda and economic objectives that sometimes collide, causing tensions within the federation. The core/periphery model provides an overarching account of these regions and their economic relationship to each other.

Canada consists of six regions. Each differs by location, physical geography, resources, population, and historical development. From these differences, a strong sense of regional identity exists in each region. These identities, shaped over time as people came face to face with challenges presented by their economic, physical, and social environments, produced a unique sense of place in each region as well as a deep attachment to Canada. At the same time, each part of Canada contains powerful centrifugal forces that, from time to time, erupt into fractious disagreements between the federal government and particular regions, and these tensions pose challenges—some serious and other less so—to Canadian unity. So far, Canadians have overcome such friction through compromises and thus remain a strong and united country.

← A lake near Huntsville, Ontario, an area only a few hours by car from Canada's largest city, Toronto. The contrast between the two areas—not just physically but culturally as well—is striking. By closely examining the reasons for such differences in places across Canada, we can better understand country's geographic diversity.

Geography as a Discipline

THINK ABOUT IT

Does a sense of place still apply if a person moves from the region of his/her birth and resettles in another part of Canada?

Geography provides a description and explanation of lands, places, and peoples beyond our personal experience (Vignette 1.1). De Blij and Murphy (2006: 3) go so far as to state that "Geography is destiny," meaning that for most people, place is the most powerful determinant of their life chances, experiences, and opportunities. In that sense, geography sets the parameters for a person's life opportunities, and this concept transfers easily to regions and nations. The concept of "place" is much more than an area; rather, "place" refers to the community/region where one was born and raised, and emphasizes that this geographical fact combines the physical place with the local culture. In geography, this concept of place is known as a **sense of place**. Of course, within Canada, there are a variety of senses of place. An Inuk in Cambridge Bay has a different sense of place to a Québecer in Rimouski or a Vancouverite in British Columbia. Thus, sense of place reflects the attitudes and values of the inhabitants of particular communities. Yet, sense of place has a hierarchical feature whereby regional and national "layers" are added to this local palate, giving rise to both a sense of **regional consciousness** and a sense of national consciousness. As such, they combine to form a **regional identity** and a national identity, and these identities are the cornerstones of regional geography.

Regional Geography

The geographic study of a particular part of the world is called **regional geography**. In such studies, people, interacting with their economic, physical, and social environments, are perceived as placing their imprint on the landscape just as the landscape helps to determine their lives and activities. In layperson's terms, the goal of regional geography is to find out what makes a region "tick." By achieving such an understanding, we gain a fuller appreciation of the complexity and diversity of our world.

Regional geography has evolved over time.[1] Originally, geographers focused their attention on the physical aspects of a **region** that affected and shaped the people and their institutions. Today, geographers place more emphasis on the human side because the physical environment is largely mediated through culture, economy, and technology (Agnew, 2002; Paasi, 2003). The argument, based on a challenge and response paradigm, goes like this:

> A multitude of profound and often repeated extreme experiences mark people in a particular region, requiring them to respond. In turn, their responses help create a common sense of regional belonging and consciousness.

Vignette 1.1

Curiosity: The Starting Point for Geography

Curiosity about distant places is not a new phenomenon. The ancient Greeks were curious about the world around them. From reports of travellers, they recognized that the earth varied from place to place and that different peoples inhabited each place. Stimulated by the travels, writings, and map-making of scholars such as Herodotus (484–c. 425 BCE), Aristotle (384–332 BCE), Thales (c. 625–c. 547 BCE), Ptolemy (90–168 CE), and Eratosthenes (c. 276–c. 192 BCE), the ancient Greeks coined the word "geography" and mapped their known world. By considering both human and physical aspects of a region, geographers have developed an integrative approach to the study of our world. This approach, which is the essence of geography, separates geography from other disciplines. The richness and excitement of geography are revealed in Canada's six regions—each region is the product of its physical setting, past events, and contemporary issues that combine to produce a set of unique regional identities.

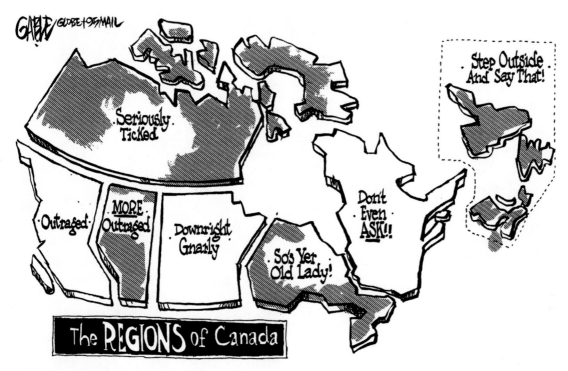

FIGURE 1.1 Gable's regions of Canada

Political cartoonist Brian Gable aptly captured the occasionally fractured relationships between provinces and territories with his map of Canada. In 1985, regional tensions reached the boiling point over the threat of Québec separating from Canada. The results of the 1995 referendum were very close, but afterwards the heated political scene cooled somewhat and political separation lost its appeal—at least for now. Fast-forward to 2017, and the stresses between regions have taken on a more economic tone: the crippled energy industry of Alberta has seen the Canadian dollar fall; the federal deficit has climbed; and the equalization payments are under fire.

Source: Brian Gable/The Globe and Mail/Canadian Press Images

Canada's Geographic Regions

The geographer's challenge is to divide a large spatial unit like Canada into a series of "like places." To do so, a regional geographer is forced to make a number of subjective decisions, including the selection of "core" physical and human characteristics that logically divide a large spatial unit into a series of regions and that distinguish each region from adjacent ones. Towards the margins of a region, its core characteristics become less distinct and merge with those characteristics of a neighbouring region. In that sense, boundaries separating regions are best considered transition zones rather than finite limits.

In this book, we examine Canada as composed of six geographic regions (Figure 1.2):

- Atlantic Canada
- Québec
- Ontario
- Western Canada
- British Columbia
- Territorial North

The six regions were selected for several reasons. First, a huge Canada needs to be divided into a set of manageable segments. Too many regions would distract the reader from the goal of easily grasping the basic nature of Canada's regional geography. Six regions allow us to readily comprehend Canada's regional geography

THINK ABOUT IT

Each region has had its struggles with Ottawa. What event(s) affected relations between your region and Ottawa?

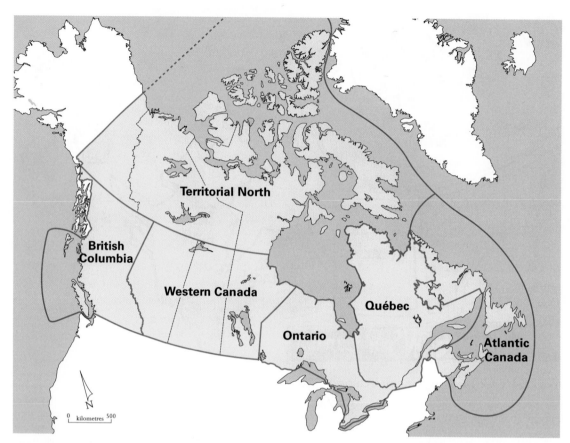

FIGURE 1.2 The six geographic regions of Canada

The coastal boundaries of Canada are recognized by other nations except for the "sector" boundary in the Arctic Ocean, which is shown as a dashed boundary. In the near future, the Territorial North may extend well into the Arctic Ocean and its seabed. In 2018, Canada plans to submit to the United Nations its claim to part of the "international" portion of the continental shelf of the Arctic Ocean. If successful, Canada may gain a portion of the Arctic Ocean's seabed as large as the Maritimes.

THINK ABOUT IT

Each of the six regions could be subdivided. For instance, a strong case could be made to divide Ontario into two parts—Southern and Northern Ontario. But even so, do you agree with the author's rationale to limit the number of regions to six?

For discussion of Canada's claim to the Arctic seabed, see Chapter 11, especially the section titled "Strategic Frontier, Arctic Sovereignty, and the Northwest Passage," page 376.

and to place these regions within a conceptual framework based on the core/periphery model, discussed later in this chapter. This is not to say that there are not internal regions or sub-regions. In Chapter 5, Ontario provides such an example. Ontario is subdivided into Southern Ontario (the industrial core of Canada) and Northern Ontario (a resource hinterland). Southern Ontario is Canada's most densely populated area and contains the bulk of the nation's manufacturing industries. Northern Ontario, on the other hand, is sparsely populated and is losing population because of the decline of its mining and forestry activities.

Second, an effort has been made to balance these regions by their geographic size, economic importance, and population size, thus allowing for comparisons (see Table 1.1). For this reason, Alberta is combined with Saskatchewan and Manitoba to form Western Canada, while Newfoundland and Labrador along with Prince Edward Island, New Brunswick, and Nova Scotia comprise Atlantic Canada. The Territorial North, consisting of three territories, makes up a single region. Three provinces, Ontario, Québec, and British Columbia, have the geographic size, economic importance, and population size to form separate geographic regions.

TABLE 1.1 General Characteristics of the Six Canadian Regions, 2015

Geographic Region	Area* (000 km²)	Area (%)	Population	Population (%)	GDP (%)
Ontario	1,076.4	10.8	13,850,090	38.5	38.5
Québec	1,542.1	15.4	8,284,656	23.0	19.1
Western Canada	1,960.7	19.6	6,654,345	18.5	24.8
British Columbia	944.7	9.5	4,703,939	13.1	12.7
Atlantic Canada	539.1	5.4	2,374,154	6.6	5.4
Territorial North	3,909.8	39.3	118,567	0.3	0.5
Canada	9,972.8	100.0	35,985,751	100.0	100.0

*Includes freshwater bodies such as the Canadian portion of the Great Lakes.

Source: Statistics Canada (2016a, 2016b).

Canadians understand this set of regions partly because of the following features:

- They are associated with distinctive physical features, natural resources, and economic activities.
- They reflect the political structure of Canada.
- They facilitate the use of statistical data.
- They are linked to regional identity.
- They are associated with reoccurring regional disputes.
- They replicate regional economic strengths and cultural presence.

The critical question is: What distinguishes each of Canada's six regions? Certainly geographic location and historical development play a key role. Equally important are contemporary elements such as variations in area, population, and economic strength (Table 1.1), while the proportions of French-speaking and Indigenous peoples in each region form another essential part of the puzzle (Table 1.2). These basic geographic elements provide a start to understanding the nature of the six regions. Further understanding is provided by analysis of an important economic activity—an "economic anchor"—found in each region. By examining these historically and currently important economic activities for each region we gain detailed insights into the nature and strength of each regional economy and are better able to identify the challenges they face. These economic anchors are:

- Ontario: automobile manufacturing
- Québec: hydroelectric power
- British Columbia: forest industry
- Western Canada: agriculture
- Atlantic Canada: fisheries
- The Territorial North: megaprojects

The task of interpreting Canada and its six regions poses a challenge. A spatial conceptual framework based on the core/periphery model helps us to understand the nature of this regional diversity within the national and global economies. At the same time, the social dimensions of Canada are captured in the concept of **faultlines** that identify and address deep-rooted tensions in Canadian society that sometimes stir negative feelings towards Ottawa and even other provinces. Such tensions present an obstacle to Canadian unity and often result in necessary adjustments to the regional nature of Canada. These faultlines require a reaction—a kind of challenge and response paradigm—that results in a continuous reshaping of Canada and its regions.

Geography of Political Power

Canada and its regions are dynamic entities. Population provides one indicator of this dynamism. Since Confederation, Canada's population has increased about tenfold. In 1867 Canada's population was 3.5 million and by 2015 it had reached 36 million (Statistics Canada, 2016a). Yet, this population increase was not distributed evenly across the country, and this fact leads to different levels of political power in each region (Figure 1.3). By 1871, Canada had expanded its territory and population, reaching 3.7 million people (Statistics Canada, 2012b). While the combined population of Ontario and Québec had increased to 21.9 million by 2015, their percentage of Canada's population had declined from 75 per cent in 1871 to 61 per cent (Statistics Canada, 2016a). Over the same span of time, the western half of the country saw its population jump from less than 100,000 to 11.3 million, forming 32 per cent of Canada's population. Atlantic Canada, on the other hand, had dropped from 21 per cent to 6.6 per cent over the same time span. This dramatic demographic shift mirrors the major realignment of Canada's economy caused by global forces. Such changes pull at the ropes holding the political balance of power, and in 2015 Alberta and British Columbia, along with Ontario and Québec, received more seats for the October 2015 federal election (see Chapter 4 for a more complete account of the geography of political power and electoral redistribution).

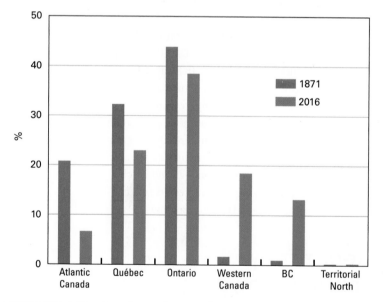

FIGURE 1.3 Regional populations by percentage, 1871 and 2016

In 1867, all Canadians lived in the original four colonies. Within four years, Canada gained sparsely populated lands, but its population geography changed little. However, by 2016, nearly one-third of Canada population was west of Ontario, marking the shift of the country's centre of population gravity westward, a trend that is likely to continue for the foreseeable future.

Source: Adapted from Statistics Canada (1871 and 2016a).

Sense of Place

In spite of our globalized world with its homogenized urban landscapes, the unique character of places still matters. The term "sense of place" embodies this perspective and provides a social cohesiveness. Sense of place has deep roots in cultural and human geography. Leading scholars in this area include Agnew, Cresswell, Paasi, Relph, and Tuan. While "sense of place" has been defined and used in different ways, in this text the term reflects a deeply felt attachment to a region by local residents who have, over time, bonded to their region and its resulting institutions and urban landscapes. As such, sense of place provides some protection from the predictable cityscapes produced by economic and cultural **globalization**. These urban features, such as McDonald's restaurants, are associated with a sense of **placelessness** (Relph, 1976). Distinctive cityscapes, on the other hand, provide an exclusive identity to a place that often evokes a powerful psychological bond between people and the locale. In sharp contrast, generic landscapes have global roots offering a standard product. For example, Tim Hortons coffee is the same from Vancouver to St John's. Physical location provides another form of sense of place. Yellowknife, located on the rocky shores of Great Slave Lake, exhibits a uniquely northern character (see Photo 1.1). Yellowknife is also noted for its large Indigenous population that, in 2011, accounted for 25 per cent of its residents.

A strong sense of place can evoke a negative reaction to the federal government. Such centrifugal energy flies awkwardly within the Canadian federal system. Québec provides such an example, where culture, history, and geography have had four centuries to nurture a strong sense of place and to give birth to a nationalist movement that has, from time to time, sought to separate Québec from the rest of Canada. On the other hand, natural disasters often place provinces in a difficult financial position, and provinces rely on Ottawa for support. One federal program, Disaster Financial Assistance Arrangements, eases the financial burden of the provinces and provides Ottawa an opportunity to demonstrate its commitment to national unity.

Winston Fraser / Alamy Stock Photo

Photo 1.1 Yellowknife, Northwest Territories, is no longer a rough-and-tumble mining town. This capital city also serves as a regional service centre, providing goods and services to surrounding villages and towns as well as to the mines and tourist camps. The public sector dominates the economy, with most workers employed by the territorial and federal governments. Expensive housing exists along its waterfront where, in the warm summer months, pleasure craft, sailboats, and float planes are moored along its sheltered coves on the north shore of Great Slave Lake.

For more information on the nationalist movement in Québec, see **Chapter 3**, "The French/English Fault-line," page 103.

A region, then, is a synthesis of physical and human characteristics that, combined with its distinctiveness from surrounding regions, produces a unique character, including a sense of place and power. People living and working in a region are conscious of belonging to that place and frequently demonstrate an attachment and commitment to their "home" region. Indeed, the theme of this book is that Canada is a country of regions, each of which has a strong sense of regional pride, but also a commitment to Canadian federalism.

Elenathewise/Thinkstock.com

Photo 1.2 Cityscape of St John's, Newfoundland and Labrador, as seen from Signal Hill. St John's is one of the oldest cities in North America. Its special relationship with the sea set it aside from other Canadian cities. Originally, the economy was based on the rich cod stocks, but now it focuses on offshore oil and on the mineral and hydroelectric resources of Labrador. The city is home to Memorial University, and by 2018 the Canadian Coast Guard Atlantic Region will be based in St John's.

Faultlines within Canada

Canada, like the earth's crust, has its weak points, making regional harmony an elusive commodity. In 1993, *Globe and Mail* columnist Jeffrey Simpson applied the term "faultlines"—the geological phenomenon of cracks in the earth's crust caused by tectonic forces—to the economic, social, and political cracks that divide regions and people in Canada and threaten to destabilize Canada's integrity as a nation. In this text, "faultlines" refers to four fractious tensions in Canada's collective psyche.

For long periods of time, these faultlines can remain dormant, but they can shift at any time, dividing the country into wrangling factions.

While many divisions in Canadian society emanate from the plight of the disabled, the homeless, the rural/urban divide, and the seemingly relentless growing gap between the very rich and the rest of Canada's people, our discussion is confined to four principal faultlines that have had profound regional consequences and that have, from time to time, challenged our national unity. These four faultlines represent struggles between centralist and decentralist visions of Canada; English and French; old and new Canadians; and Indigenous and non-Indigenous Canadians. Commencing in Chapter 3, specific examples of faultlines are explored within their regional setting.

Each faultline has played a fundamental role in Canada's historic evolution, and they remain critical elements of Canada's character in the twenty-first century. In extreme cases, these weak spots or cracks have threatened the cohesiveness of Canada and, by doing so, have shaken the very pillars of federalism. Under these circumstances, compromise was essential to Canada's survival. From these traumatic experiences, Canada, over time, has become what John Ralston Saul (1997: 8–9) describes as a "soft" country, meaning a society where conflicts, more often than not, are resolved through discussion and negotiations. The United States, on the other hand, would be considered a "hard" country where conflicts affecting minorities, for example, are more likely resolved by forceful means, such as threatening to deport millions of illegal Mexican immigrants now living in the United States and to build a wall along the Mexican border to prevent more Mexicans from entering the country, or, for that matter, by threatening to jail one's political opponent.[2]

Disagreement over the nature of Canada—is it a partnership between the two so-called French and English "founding" societies or is it composed of 10 equal provinces?—has troubled the country since Confederation in 1867. In recent years this disagreement came to a head twice with the sovereignty-association and independence referendums in Québec in 1980 and 1995, the latter of which was won by the federalist side by the narrowest margin—a mere percentage point. At the height of the referendum campaigns, uneasy relationships tore at the very fabric of Canada. But the ensuing dialogue and goodwill between Québec and the rest of the country have led to an unspoken and uneasy compromise that cements the country together. Still, tensions do arise, such as the appointment by the federal government in 2011 of two non-French–speaking Supreme Court judges, causing Québecers to ask: how can the Supreme Court properly evaluate cases that involve documents written in French if judges are not bilingual?

For discussion of the cultural divide between French- and English-speaking Canada, see Chapter 3, page 107, under the heading, "One Country, Two Visions."

Centralist/Decentralist Faultline

Of all the faultlines, the centralist/decentralist one leans the most heavily on Canada's geography and its political system. Canada's size and its varied physical geography provide the stage for regional differences that can—and have—led to bitter federal–provincial feuds. Adding another dimension to such feuds is provincial control over natural resources—until 2014, oil-rich provinces had an advantage over other provinces. This advantage disappeared with the dramatic drop in oil prices and may turn into a disadvantage with the federal government's effort to move Canada to a "low-carbon economy" that is less reliant on fossil fuels.

Disputes often flare up between particular provinces and Ottawa, or are reflected in the occasional volley of potshots between provincial political leaders. A closer examination of the underlying forces driving the centralist/decentralist faultline follows.

First, quarrels with Ottawa often revolve around federal transfer and equalization payments. Provincially administered post-secondary, health, and social programs far outstrip their financial capacity. Here we have contested ground with two different objectives. On the one hand, provinces constantly seek an increase in transfer payments, while on the other hand, Ottawa seeks ways to reduce its annual expenditures in order to balance its budget and to keep from sliding deeper into debt.

Second, another bone of contention exists between Central Canada, where the majority of national population and voters reside, and the rest of Canada over the extensive public support/subsidies for Central Canadian manufacturing. From the perspective of Ottawa and the provinces of Québec and Ontario, this public support is based on the long-held premise that economic success in Central Canada will benefit the nation as a whole. Not surprisingly, the premise is less well received in the rest of the country. Whether true or not, from this hinterland perspective Central Canada often benefits from federal policies that support industries representing the "national interest" while other provinces are left out in the cold. Federal support for Ontario's automotive industry and Québec's aerospace/rail industries are two examples.

⟳ Government support for the automotive industry in the form of financial loans to Chrysler and General Motors are described in Chapter 6, Contested Terrain 6.3, "The Bailout of Chrysler and GM: Sound Public Policy?"

Third, maybe Bob Dylan's 1964 song "The Times Are A-Changin" applies to the centralist/decentralist faultline? As the centre of population gravity edges westward, the population advantage of Central Canada is slowly eroding. Energy, the engine of growth in the past decade in Alberta, British Columbia, and Saskatchewan, added to this advantage, but energy has hit a bad patch in recent years with falling oil prices. Ottawa no longer sees the "national interest" taking the form of an "energy superpower" on the international stage, as former Prime Minister Stephen Harper imagined. With the Justin Trudeau Liberal government elected in late 2015, Canada has switched positions from posing as an energy superpower to one insisting on a carbon tax on fossil fuels.

Equalization payments shifted in the period of high oil prices. Given Ontario's long-standing position as the "powerhouse" of Canada, who would have thought that Ontario would have this "have-not" collar hung around its neck? With the sudden collapse of oil prices leading to the sharp devaluation of the Canadian dollar, the questions are: will Ontario regain it former status as a "have" province; and how will Alberta pay for equalization payments in 2016? Oddly enough, the calculation of annual equalization payments is based on a three-year calculation, thus keeping Ontario in the "have-not" group and Alberta, suffering badly from its weakened energy industry, forced to make equalization payments to Ottawa because the three-year calculation keeps it in the "have" group.

Fourth, faultlines do exist between provinces. The long-standing dispute between Québec and Newfoundland and Labrador over the 1969 Churchill Falls agreement illustrates this point. Within this contested terrain lurks the contentious boundary settlement made in 1927 when Newfoundland, still a British colony, was granted that part of the Labrador Peninsula from the "height of land" to the Atlantic coast, that is, all of the peninsular land within the Atlantic watershed. Québec has never accepted this boundary—the longest interprovincial boundary in Canada—and it acts like a burr in the psyche of the Québec nation. Could it be a hidden factor in preventing Hydro-Québec from reopening the 1969 agreement to seek a "fair" pricing arrangement, as well as a factor in Québec's denying space for the transmission of future hydroelectricity from Labrador along its transmission lines to Canadian and US markets? From the perspective of Newfoundlanders and Labradorians, the unfairness of the 1969 agreement sees billions flowing to Québec and only a pittance to them. Why is the agreement so one-sided?

The 1969 agreement gave a set amount of electric power—some 31 billion kilowatt hours per year—generated by Churchill Falls to Hydro-Québec

THINK
ABOUT IT
Given the sudden drop in oil prices, is the calculation of 2016–17 equalization payments based on a three-year average fair?

Contested Terrain 1.1

CETA and Canada's Dairy Industry: A Central Canada Issue?

Under a supply management system, Canadian dairy farmers enjoy a regulated production and sales system. Since most dairy farms are located in Central Canada (Canadian Dairy Information Centre, 2015), most opposition to free trade negotiations that call for the abandonment of the Canadian supply management system comes from Québec and Ontario. With the Comprehensive Economic and Trade Agreement (CETA) now in place between Canada and the European Union, Ottawa's promise of a compensation package for Canada's dairy farmers has yet to come (see Dairy Farmers of Canada, 2016).

for 65 years at a very low fixed price, which, instead of increasing over time, actually decreases. Shortly after the signing of this agreement, world oil prices more than doubled, and the jump in prices cascaded into much higher hydro prices. Hydro-Québec gained a huge windfall and this windfall will continue to 2041. To Newfoundland and Labrador, the agreement is a perfect example of exploitation by a bigger, more powerful province. Yet, as the Supreme Court determined in 1984, "a contract is a contract," and the dispute was legally settled—though Hydro-Québec held all the cards in negotiations and virtually dictated the terms.

> For extensive discussion of the Churchill Falls and Muskrat Falls hydroelectric developments in Labrador, see Chapter 10, "Muskrat Falls," page 331, and "Megaproject of the Century or a White Elephant?" page 340.

Fast-forward to 2016. The province is in the midst of another huge hydroelectric project, this one on the Lower Churchill River at Muskrat Falls. But the problem of transporting the power to markets in the United States would mean crossing Québec. The bitter experience of Churchill Falls has meant that Newfoundland and Labrador intends to build an expensive and risky underwater transmission system from Labrador to Newfoundland and then across the Cabot Strait to Nova Scotia and eventually to the huge market in New England. By mid-2016, cost overruns of several billion dollars and construction problems had called into question the feasibility of the megaproject.

English-speaking/French-speaking Canadians

Canada is a bilingual country. Yet, English is spoken in most parts of the country. History accounts for the two languages, though it was not until 1969 that the Official Languages Act recognized English and French as having equal status in the government of Canada. A few years later, in 1974, the Québec government passed its Official Language Act, making French the sole official language in the province. The rationale for this action was the desire to ensure and foster the French language and therefore the Québécois culture. In fact, only one province, New Brunswick, officially recognizes both official languages. The explanation for the distribution of languages across Canada is found in the geographic fact that relatively few French-speaking Canadians live outside of New

Vignette 1.2

Canadian Unity: A Powerful Force

The formation of Canada was a struggle from the beginning. But the federal government, through such national institutions as the Supreme Court of Canada, legislation, and a series of national programs, has provided the political glue to keep the country united. The first example was Ottawa's financial and political support for the building of the Canadian Pacific Railway that provided a much-needed physical link across the vast wilderness of the Canadian Shield, the Interior Plains, and the Cordillera to bind the western lands to Central Canada as well as ensuring that British Columbia joined Confederation (See Figure 2.1). More recent instances of nation-building have focused on ensuring a measure of equality among provinces through federal initiatives such as equalization payments to have-not provinces, multiculturalism legislation that supports a pluralistic society, and universal health care for all Canadians paid for through the tax system.

What federal programs do Canadians appreciate the most? A poll conducted for the Association for Canadian Studies in June 2014 indicates that the Charter of Rights and Freedoms, enshrined in the Constitution in 1982, and universal health care represent the two most popular expressions of Canada as a nation (Jedwab, 2014).

TABLE 1.2 Social Characteristics of the Six Canadian Regions, 2011*

Geographic Region	French	French (% of regional population)	Indigenous Peoples*	Indigenous Peoples (% of regional population)
Ontario	493,300	3.9	301,425	2.4
Québec	6,102,210	78.1	141,915	1.8
British Columbia	57,280	1.3	232,290	5.3
Western Canada	126,915	2.2	574,335	9.8
Atlantic Canada	272,315	11.9	94,490	2.6
Territorial North	2,970	2.8	56,225	52.4
Canada	7,054,975	21.3	1,400,685	4.3

In 2016 these population statistics were the most recent available from Statistics Canada. The release date for 2016 census French and Indigenous populations is 2017.

*The Indigenous identity question provided a lower figure than the ethnic-based census question known as Indigenous ancestry. In 2011, Indigenous population by identity was 1.4 million and by ancestry, it was 1.9 million. In 2011, Indigenous identity population was based on a census question that defined identity by three groups of Indigenous peoples—First Nations, Métis, and Inuit—while Indigenous ancestry is based on a self-declaration of ethnicity. In previous censuses, Indigenous population data were collected from the obligatory long-form census, but in 2011 census questions that determine Indigenous populations were modified and assigned to a voluntary survey known as the National Household Survey.

Source: Statistics Canada (2012a, 2013).

Brunswick and Québec. In the Québec case, this led to the political decision in 1974 to proclaim French as the province's official language. As seen in Table 1.2, the French presence in Canada is highly concentrated in Québec, where the francophone culture and French language thrive, thus allowing the province to form a distinct cultural region within Canada.

Language remains a sensitive issue and, because the proportion of French-speaking Canadians has declined over time, it forms a faultline. Back in 1867, the population of Canada consisted of two main groups: British, comprising 61 per cent, and French, making up 31 per cent, formed nearly 92 per cent of the population (*Atlas of Canada*, 2009). Today, though the total number of French-speaking Canadians has increased, reaching just over 7 million in 2011, their proportion of the total population has declined to 21.3 per cent. This drop represents a serious dilemma for that community and signals an erosion of their political position within Canada.

Not surprisingly, tensions between English- and French-speaking Canadians erupt over language issues. Within Québec, a faultline exists between the two language groups. The political and cultural desire to maintain French as a viable language in a principally English-speaking continent resulted in the controversial Bill 22 in 1974, followed by Bill 101 in 1977, which proclaimed French as the official language in

Québec for just about every facet of life: government, the judicial system, education, advertising, and business. In 1982, the Supreme Court of Canada struck down Bill 101. However, the Liberal government of Robert Bourassa overturned this ruling by employing the "notwithstanding clause" (section 33 of the 1982 Charter of Rights and Freedoms). While language is less of a hot-button issue in Québec today, some francophone leaders fear that the traditional Québécois way of life is slipping away, not because of any increased use of the English language but because of immigrants whose behaviour is not rooted in the cultural, historic, and linguistic factors that provide a sense of place for the majority of Québecers.[3]

For discussion of language and culture, see Chapter 4, "Language," page 136, Vignette 4.4, "Charles Taylor on Multiculturalism," and "French/English Language Imbalance," page 139.

Indigenous Minority and the Non-Indigenous Majority

As the first people to occupy the territory now called Canada, many Indigenous people—now legally referred to as "the Indian, Inuit and Métis peoples of Canada"—still find themselves stuck on the margins of Canadian society (Bone and Anderson, 2017). While Canada prides itself on its open society, upward social mobility, and economic opportunities, this open society was closed to Indigenous peoples who were (and remain) trapped in another world governed by the Indian Act. Change has come, first slowly and now in a more accelerated form, as more and more Indigenous people and reserves have followed a new path of engagement, including the current federal Minister of Justice, Jody Wilson-Raybould, a Kwakwaka'wakw woman of the We Wai Kai First Nation and the Liberal Member of Parliament for Vancouver Granville; the economically strong Onion Lake Cree Nation that straddles the Saskatchewan–Alberta border north of Lloydminster; and the Whitecap Dakota First Nation south of Saskatoon. Many other Indigenous people and groups, however, are geographically marginalized with seemingly little opportunity. There is no simple answer to this complex question, but for many people post-secondary education remains a key to open the door to full participation in Canadian society while retaining their Indigenous identity within a pluralistic society.

Pivotal events in the mid- to late twentieth century released Indigenous peoples from the bonds of the Indian Act, residential schools, and political activism. First and foremost, only in the mid-twentieth century did the doors to the economic and social opportunities available to other Canadians begin to open. Until then, the Indian Act served as the federal government's means to control, dominate, and manage First Nations peoples and their lands as well as to keep them restricted to reserves. The treaty land selection process in earlier centuries and the relocation of northern Indigenous peoples to settlements in the 1950s reinforced the segregation of Indigenous people from the rest of Canadian society. The relocation of those still on the land to trading posts in the 1950s produced mixed blessings. Access to public services and secure food supplies was a plus, but these villages had no economic foundation and therefore left the adults in no man's land—they were no longer self-sufficient hunters and trappers with a self-sustaining culture and way of life, nor could they become employed workers. Consequently, dependency on social assistance became the foundation of their new economic system.

Second, the first crack in the door took place in 1960 when First Nations men and women were allowed to vote in federal elections. Since then, civil and human rights common to Canadians have been extended to Indigenous peoples, especially through numerous landmark court cases; nonetheless, the Indian Act still leaves a role for the federal government in the affairs of Indigenous peoples. While the Métis and Inuit were not included in the Indian Act, they were, for the most part, treated equally badly and they also suffered from this quasi-apartheid policy. For instance, all three groups were subjected to the long period of the residential schools from the late nineteenth century to the late twentieth century. These schools were designed to equip young Indigenous students to find and accept a place on the bottom rungs of the larger society, and resulted in the loss of their language and culture as well as the connection to the land and their parents, many of whom continued a traditional life of hunting and trapping. In fact, the residential schools created "lost generations" who fitted into neither world.

Third, Indigenous peoples began to gain control of their traditional lands through favourable Supreme Court of Canada decisions and an acceptance of Aboriginal title to traditional lands by the federal and British Columbia governments. In turn, modern land claims, impact benefit agreements, and resource-sharing arrangements greatly benefited some, though certainly not all, Indigenous peoples (Vignette 1.3).

Barriers still exist. One is geographic isolation; another is the heterogeneous nature of the Indigenous population. The highly diverse population prevents a single voice and encourages divisions among Indigenous peoples. Then, too, Indigenous peoples are spread across Canada from the Arctic to temperate Canada in relatively small numbers. This geographic diversity includes 634 First Nations scattered across the country, many with populations under 1,000 and some near major urban centres, while many others are in remote locations far from such centres of economic opportunity. Linguistic diversity provides one measure of their heterogeneity; the legal definition of Indigenous peoples adds another component to their geographic diversity.

Without a doubt, the Indian Act limits the decision-making of First Nations band councils and their chiefs. Somehow a reconfiguration of this Act could open opportunities for First Nations—and, by extension, the Inuit and Métis—to grow. Clearly, the diversity of Indigenous peoples denies them a

Vignette 1.3

Indigenous Peoples, Modern Land Claims, and Resource-Sharing

The first break from old-style treaties took place in 1975 with the **James Bay and Northern Quebec Agreement (JBNQA)**, followed in 1984 by the Inuvialuit Final Agreement (IFA) in the western Arctic and then, in 1999, the establishment of Nunavut in the central and eastern Arctic. The JBNQA offered the James Bay Cree and the Inuit of northern Québec both cash compensation and a portion of their traditional lands. However, unlike the IFA and other comprehensive land claim agreements, the JBNQA did not spell out an economic side to the agreement; rather, the economic details were negotiated and managed by business corporations established by the Cree and Inuit, which have received and managed the compensation monies.

Impact benefit agreements (IBAs) emerged in the late 1990s as companies realized that settling traditional land claims was a necessary component of their mining operations. An IBA is a legal and confidential contract between the company and the impacted Indigenous community. The negotiation skills of Indigenous officials and their advisers vary. The Attawapiskat First Nation, for example, does not have a profit-sharing plan with De Beers Canada, which owns and operates the Victor diamond mine located on their traditional lands, while the Inuit of Nunavik in Arctic Québec, through the skilled negotiations of the Makivik Corporation, do receive annual profit-sharing payments from Glencore's nickel/copper Raglan mine located on their traditional lands.

Resource-sharing with Indigenous organizations of provincial and territorial royalties collected from mining companies varies from province to province (Coates, 2015). As of 2015, resource-sharing of provincial royalties existed in only six jurisdictions: three provinces (British Columbia, Québec, and Newfoundland and Labrador) and the three territories. But, in Canada's federal system, a uniform system of resource-sharing remains elusive; instead, various ad hoc resource revenue-sharing agreements exist (Coates, 2015). Still, Coates (2015: 5) argues that "governments can meet their treaty, legal, constitutional, and moral obligations to the Indigenous people of the country" through resource-sharing.

single path to the future, but the future paths will be defined not by Ottawa but by Indigenous youth, especially those who have completed their post-secondary education.

Newcomers and Old-Timers

While Canada is a land of immigrants, the first European immigrants, the British and, to a lesser degree, the French, established the economic, political, and social structure of Canada. Old-timers have also set the rules of the game—a secular state and, for more than three decades, a Charter of Rights and Freedoms governing the relationship between the state and its citizens. Newcomers must adjust to these political and structural facts. For newcomers, finding a job and a place to live provides a basic comfort level that can allow them to be themselves, support themselves

in families, and gain a sense of belonging. This challenge is not easy for the many non-white immigrants from the developing world. As well, a sense of belonging, so important to feeling part of the larger Canadian society, has been easier for English- and French-speaking immigrants, while the other immigrant groups often have left this search for belonging to the next generation, who would grow up in Canada speaking either English or French.

All cultures change with time. What is different in Canada are the continuous waves of newcomers, each bringing their own cultures, languages, and religions. The interaction between newcomers and old-timers represents a faultline. This social faultline involves a lively interaction: the cultural rubbing and bumping between those whose cultural roots are in distant overseas homelands and those whose roots developed in Canada. Of course, this

Vignette 1.4

Does Time Temper All?

On a few occasions, newcomers get involved in civil wars in their place of birth. Ten years ago, the civil war in Sri Lanka generated support for the rebel Tamil Tigers from recent Canadian immigrants from that war-torn country. Next, it was the struggle in Somalia. More recently, the ISIS terrorist organization has gone one step further by recruiting homegrown Canadian radicals to join its fight for territory in the Middle East and its aim to spread terror elsewhere. As a rule, the second and subsequent generations of immigrant groups, by being born and raised in Canada, have had a much easier time feeling connected to Canada, and, at the same time, they are less attached to the place of birth of their parents or grandparents. Yet, whether native-born or foreign-born, does this proposition apply to black Canadians, or is racism towards this group of people still a reality in Canada? Supporters of the Black Lives Matter movement think so, and point to racial profiling by police and violence directed by police towards blacks.

interaction necessarily requires adjustments and compromises from both groups. For the most part, old-timers are not always prepared to give ground and sometimes, as in the case of Québec, efforts have been made to establish a code of standards and values.

The public remains uncertain about the issue of accommodating newcomers with sharply different customs and religions. While the Charter of Rights and Freedoms protects minority groups from the tyranny of the majority, there are limits—one clear limit is honour killings; another is shariah law, which would replace the state justice system with that of a particular ethno-religious group.[4] The wearing of the burqa and the niqab by a small number of Muslim women—both cover the face—falls into the grey area of acceptance. Perhaps popular columnist Margaret Wente (2015) sums it up correctly:

> The truth is that our immigrant- and refugee-friendly ways are highly contingent on our capacity to absorb the newcomers—and their capacity to integrate successfully. Our lip service to multiculturalism is about a mile wide and an inch deep. We believe that people who come here are entitled to wear and eat and pray to whatever god they want. But in everything that matters, we expect them to behave like us.

The Core/Periphery Theory

The core/periphery theory offers an important framework for the study of Canada and its regions. To understand our complex country and its regional nature, a modified core/periphery model helps us grasp the broad economic relationships between regions.[5] This Canadian version has its roots in the Wallerstein model (1974) but is based on John Friedmann's 1960 adaptation of the core/periphery model to the market economy found in Venezuela over a half-century ago. One innovation was Friedmann's expansion of the number of periphery regions from one to three; another was a geographic shift from an abstract global model to a more realistic one based on Venezuela. These four regions—a core and three peripheries—are easily adapted to Canada's six geographic regions:

- core region centred on manufacturing (Ontario and Québec);
- rapidly growing region based on an expanding resource base (British Columbia and Western Canada);
- slow-growing region based on a declining resource base (Atlantic Canada);
- resource frontier region where many resources exist but few are viable for extraction and shipment to market (the Territorial North).

The application of the core/periphery model to explain Canada's internal workings has its limitations. For one, this model provides only a broad-brush interpretation of the spatial nature of Canada's economy. For example, the emergence of the "Fourth Industrial Revolution" discussed in Chapter 5, which is marked by the increased use of robotics and green energy, provides a more precise interpretation of Canada's place in the future global economy. Second, the model does not address social problems. To some degree, this issue is dealt with by the four faultlines. Then, too, the dynamic nature of Canada's regions is not well addressed by this model because each geographic region is assigned a designation as either a core region or a type of periphery region (defined as rapidly growing, slow-growing, or resource frontier), giving the impression of permanency. While the issue of shifting from one category to another is not directly addressed in this model, the historic development of Canada has several examples; i.e., British Columbia was, in 1867, a resource frontier and Atlantic Canada might have fallen into the rapidly growing or even core classification. The point is that geographic reality does change over time. Finally, the broad nature of the four types of economic regions in this theory makes the application to Canada challenging.

For instance, Ontario is described as a core region based on its relatively strong manufacturing sector; yet, not all of Ontario contains such economic activities. A case could be made that Northern Ontario is more closely aligned with a slow-growing resource economy than an industrial core one—not to mention that in recent years, as defined by equalization payments, Ontario has become a have-not province.

Without a doubt, theoretical models, including the Canadian version of the core/periphery model, provide only a partial representation of geographic reality. In spite of these blemishes, spatial theory has a place in geographic literature. As Nobel laureate Paul Samuelson observed (1976):

Every theory, whether in the physical or biological or social sciences, distorts reality in that it oversimplifies. But if it is a good theory, what is omitted is outweighed by the beam of illumination and understanding thrown over the diverse empirical data.

The core/periphery and the super cycle theories are discussed more fully in Chapter 5 under "Canadian Version of the Core/Periphery Model," page 168, and "The Super Cycle Theory," page 156.

SUMMARY

Canada's six regions provide a vehicle to explore the geographic essence of Canada. To simplify the complexities of space, regional geographers divide the world and countries into regions, which vary by scale but often are interrelated in a hierarchical order. A regional geographer selects critical physical, historic, and human characteristics that logically divide a large spatial unit into a series of regions. Towards the margins of a region, its main characteristics become less distinct and merge with those of a neighbouring region. For that reason, boundaries are best considered as transition zones. Canada is a country of regions. Shaped by its history and physical geography, Canada is distinguished by six geographic regions: Ontario, Québec, British Columbia, Western Canada, Atlantic Canada, and the Territorial North. Within Canada and its regions, four key tensions exist that, through their interaction, demonstrate the very essence of Canada as a "soft" nation, where conflicts are usually resolved or ameliorated through compromise rather than by political or military power.

The essential foundation for studying regional geography is to conceptualize places and regions as components of a constantly changing global system. The core/periphery model provides an abstract spatial framework for understanding the general workings of the modern capitalist system. It consists of an interlocking set of industrial cores and resource peripheries. This model can function at different geographic scales and serves as an economic framework for interpreting Canada's regional nature. In addition to the core region, three types of regions devised by Friedmann extend our appreciation of the diversity of the Canadian periphery. They are: (1) a rapidly growing region, (2) a slow-growing region, and (3) a resource frontier.

What does the future hold for Canada and its regions? Will the resource economy make a comeback or will Canada find its economic footing in the knowledge-based economy that is unfolding in the Fourth Industrial Revolution described in Chapter 5? Social change remains a factor in the years to come. For instance, the social fabric of Canada is responding to Indigenous peoples, who are on the move in both the economic and political arenas. The Indigenous faultline deals with this aspect of social change while the other three—centralist/decentralist, French/English, and newcomers/old-timers—tackle other social issues. One scenario where divisive relationships between regions and the federal government may once again flare up is over an imposed national carbon tax. This hinges on balancing Ottawa's "Green Canada" commitment with higher energy costs. Already, the Ontario government, a leader in a greener Ontario, sees its citizens facing higher electrical bills and, for low-income families, energy poverty.

Geography, in the form of the vast size of Canada and its diverse population, feeds both regionalism and factionalism. Yet, the country remains whole because Canada, through its system of governance and national institutions, offers its citizens freedom and dignity as well as opportunities and the prospects of well-being. More than that, a powerful current flowing through Canadian society expresses a willingness to seek compromises, consensus, and accommodation. These values are the hallmark of unifying forces that hold Canada together.

The central question for Canada and its regions is how best to respond to this rapidly evolving world. Opportunities and responses vary from one region to another. This critical topic is broached in each regional chapter and discussed further in the concluding chapter.

The next four chapters focus on Canada and, at the same time, set the stage for our discussion of Canada's six regions. These four chapters, respectively, examine Canada's physical geography, the country's historical geography, the social or human face of our country, and Canada's economy.

Challenge Questions

1. If you were designing this text, how would you divide the country into a set of regions?
2. Does a regional typology, like the six regions of Canada in this text, contain an element of subjectivity?
3. Table 1.1 shows the percentage of population and GDP by geographic regions for 2015. What is the significance, if any, of the fact that Western Canada's percentage of the national population is 18.5 per cent but its percentage of the national GDP is 24.8 per cent? Can you think of any reason why these two figures might change in the near future?
4. Do you agree or disagree with Professor Samuelson's views of theoretic models? More importantly, do you think the core/periphery model

provides a helpful interpretation of economic relations among Canada's six regions?

5. The glue that binds Canada together involves federal government programs and federal institutions. According to the Association of Canadian Studies, what two reflections of the Canadian state do Canadians rank as the most popular? What other federal programs and institutions are especially important or meaningful to you?
6. Over time, each of the four faultlines has posed a serious threat to Canada's unity, but then the fissures from these faultlines close up. In your opinion, which faultline is most likely to rip open in the coming years? Explain your choice.

Essay Questions

1. Louis-Edmond Hamelin introduced the concept of "Nordicity" in the 1970s, proposing five geographic regions. What are the names of these regions? Draw a map illustrating their geographic location, and present an argument that Hamelin's regions are better suited to explain Canada's geography than those

presented in this text by Bone. As well, offer a comment on why Bone's regions are better suited to using data from Statistics Canada than are Hamelin's regions.

References:

Hamelin, Louis-Edmond. 1979. *Canadian Nordicity: It's Your North, Too.* Trans. William Barr. Montreal: Harvest House.

Bone, Robert M. 2016. *The Canadian North: Issues and Challenges,* 5th edn. Toronto: Oxford University Press, pp. 9–11 and Appendix I.

Statistics Canada. 2015. "Geographical Region of Canada." 30 Nov. At: http://www.statcan.gc.ca/pub/92-195-x/2011001/geo/region/region-eng.htm.

2. Faultlines play a critical role in this text by focusing our attention on key social issues troubling this country. Each has a regional expression. Can you make a case for adding a fifth faultline based on the urban/rural split?

Reference:

Peck, Samantha. 2015. "Emergence of the Urban–Rural Divide in Canadian Federal Politics." *Global Public Affairs.* At:http://globalelectioninsights.ca/federal/emergence-of-the-urban-rural-divide-in-canadian-federal-politics/.

Further Reading

Berton, Pierre. 1970. *The National Dream: The Great Railway, 1871–1881.* Toronto: McClelland and Stewart.

Berton, Pierre. 1972. *The Last Spike: The Impossible Railway, 1881–1885.* Toronto: McClelland and Stewart.

Canadian unity, now and then, remains a central goal of the federal government. Pierre Berton, one of Canada's best-known authors and a strong nationalist, took on the task of popularizing this aspect of Canadian history. Berton recognized the political importance of the building of the Canadian Pacific Railway. He begins his story in 1871, when Canada's first Prime Minister, John A. Macdonald, was confronted with the dilemma of drawing British Columbia into Confederation or seeing it slip into American hands. With the natural north/south orientation of the Cordillera, the obvious choice for British Columbians was to join forces with the Americans settled along the Pacific Coast. Macdonald sought to trump this north/south physical connection with his east/west dream of a transcontinental railway that would cross two formidable physiographic barriers—the Canadian Shield and the Cordillera. Fearing American encroachment, Macdonald did not hesitate—he promised the colony of British Columbia a railway within 10 years if it agreed to join Confederation. Yet, the physical and political challenge of constructing a rail line across this unsettled land was both daunting and expensive. The Liberal opposition perceived the proposed railway as a reckless and ill-conceived adventure that would bankrupt the small nation of less than four million. The following year, a federal election was held and Macdonald sought and received money for his election from the railway syndicate, which, in return, expected to receive the contract to build the railway. The opposition learned of this arrangement, known as the Pacific Scandal, and Macdonald's Conservative Party lost the 1872 election and the successful Liberal government stopped the railway dream in its tracks. In 1878, however, Macdonald's Conservatives regained power, the construction of the Canadian Pacific Railway was approved, and it was completed in 1885. In overseeing this grand task, Macdonald united the former British territories, making Canada the second-largest country in the world.

A popular TV series, *The National Dream: Building the Impossible Railway*, was based on Berton's two books. In this short YouTube account, the larger-than-life Pierre Berton, who died in 2004, appears briefly (see www.youtube.com/watch?v=CtH6JAFkhzg).

Canada's Physical Base

2

Chapter Overview

This chapter provides a basic introduction to Canada's physical geography, emphasizing how it has shaped the regional nature of Canada. Until the emergence of climate change, physical geography was relatively stable. Now a new dimension has entered the picture that is affecting Canada's climate. At the same time, Chapter 2 lays the foundation for our discussion of the six regional chapters. In Chapter 2 we will examine the following topics:

- The geological structure, origins, and characteristics of Canada's physical base and its seven physiographic regions.
- The nature of Canada's climate, its seven climatic zones, and climate change.
- The concept of extreme weather events and how these events shape regional consciousness.
- Canada's cold environment as illustrated by the presence of permafrost in two-thirds of Canada's land mass.
- The five drainage basins that empty vast quantities of fresh water into Canada's three oceans—the Arctic, Atlantic, and Pacific.
- Environmental challenges caused by industrial pollution and climate change.

Introduction

The earth provides a wide variety of natural settings for human beings. For that reason, physical geography helps us understand the regional nature of our world. The basic question posed in this chapter is: *Why is Canada's physical geography so essential to an understanding of its regional geography?* Physical geography, but especially our physiography, presents a natural system that underlies Canada's national and regional character.[1] For instance, physical geography provides a fundamental explanation for Canada's **ecumene** that hugs a narrow zone just north of the border with the United States, leaving the less hospitable area of the country sparsely populated. Extending this argument, one can see that population differences between

Canada and the United States can be attributed, in part, to their very different physical geographies (Vignette 2.1).

In this text, physical geography provides the raison d'être for the basis of the core/periphery model. The argument is a simple one: regions with a more favourable physical base are more likely to develop into core regions that contain large populations. Regions with less favourable physical conditions have fewer opportunities to encourage settlement and economic development. As pointed out in Chapter 1, circumstances defining a favourable physical base can change over time and such changes have the power to alter the prospects for regional expansion and contraction.

← Lake Moraine, located in Banff National Park, Alberta, is a glacially fed lake within the Cordillera physiographic region.

Vignette 2.1

Two Different Geographies

Canada and the United States occupy the northern and central parts of North America, yet the two countries have strikingly different geographies. Canada, while larger in geographic area, has a much smaller area suitable for agriculture and settlement. A significant portion of Canada lies in high latitudes where polar climates and permafrost place these lands far beyond the limits of commercial agriculture and settlement. Consequently, most Canadians live in a narrow zone close to the border with the United States (see Figure 4.1). Here, more temperate climates prevail. Geography, therefore, has been kinder to the United States, if this is to be judged by carrying capacity—how many people the land can sustain—and economic potential. The US simply has more suitable physical space for settlement, which has allowed its population to reach 324 million by mid-2016, compared to 36 million for Canada. Thus, Canada has a population density of 4 people per km^2 compared to 30 in the United States. This physical reality, best described as Canada's northern handicap, limits the areas suitable for settlement. Immigrants to Canada have recognized this geographic fact and most have taken up residence in one of Canada's three largest cities (Toronto, Montréal, and Vancouver), though more and more are now settling in Calgary, Edmonton, Winnipeg, Saskatoon, and Regina.

Physical Variations within Canada

The physical geography varies across Canada. Climate provides one example. While our weather is warming, the types of climate vary from place to place, with temperate climates in southern Canada and polar ones in northern Canada. The Maritimes, for instance, has a mild, wet climate, while the Arctic has a cold, dry climate. Climate also affects the shape of landforms (mountains, plateaus, and lowlands) through a variety of weathering and erosional processes. Millions of years of weathering and erosion have produced the Appalachian Uplands, which in distant geological times was a young, rugged mountain range similar in many ways to the Rocky Mountains. Major landforms are the basis of seven physiographic regions in Canada and they illustrate the regional distinctiveness of Canada's physical geography. For instance, the flat to gently rolling topography of the Prairies is totally different from that found in the Canadian Shield, which consists of rugged, rocky, hilly terrain.

Geographers perceive an interaction between people and the physical world. This interactive two-way relationship is a fundamental component of regional geography. Favourable physical conditions can make a region more attractive for human settlement. The combination of a mild climate and fertile soils in the Great Lakes–St Lawrence Lowlands encourages agricultural settlement, while the St Lawrence River and the Great Lakes provide low-cost water transportation to local, American, and world markets. The favourable physical features of this region have allowed it to become Canada's industrial heartland.

As scientists who study the spatial aspects of nature and the processes that shape nature, physical geographers are concerned with all aspects of the physical world: **physiography** (landforms), bodies of water, climate, soils, and natural vegetation. Regional geographers, however, are more interested in how physical geography varies and subsequently influences human settlement of the land. The Rocky Mountains, for instance, offer few opportunities for agricultural settlement, but the spectacular scenery has led to the emergence of an economy based on tourism. Nature tends to work slowly and change may take centuries; but nature can work quickly. Floods and storms have had sudden and dramatic impacts on human occupation of the land, while **climate change** is an example of relatively rapid change to our environment that is affecting the human landscape.

Regional geographers also are concerned about the effect of human activities on the natural environment. In most cases, humans have a negative impact on the environment. For example, within the Bow Valley of the Rocky Mountains, extensive land developments have reduced the size of the natural habitat of wild animals such as bears and elk. Ironically, if more land is converted into golf courses, resort facilities, and housing developments, the animals that make this wilderness region so unique and attractive to tourists may no longer be able to survive. Another example is urban sprawl, which has gobbled up some of Canada's best farmland in the Niagara Peninsula, the Fraser Valley, and the Okanagan Valley. In our contemporary world, therefore, humans are the most active and, some would say, the most dangerous agents of environmental change.

The discussion of physical geography in this chapter and in the six regional chapters is designed to provide basic information about the natural environment and its essential role in the regional geography of Canada. To that end, the following points are emphasized:

- Physical geography varies across Canada.
- Physiographic regions represent one aspect of this natural diversity.

- Climate, soils, and natural vegetation provide other natural components and spatial patterns and, in doing so, provide the basis for a wide range of biodiversity across Canada.
- Human activity is changing the natural environment into an urban industrial landscape as well as causing air, soil, and water pollution for which there are long-term negative implications for all life forms; global pollution and climate change represent the major environmental challenges for the twenty-first century.
- Certain natural areas are more conducive for settlement.

We begin our discussion of physical geography by examining the nature of landforms.

The Nature of Landforms

The earth's surface features a variety of landforms. A simple classification of landforms results in three principal types: mountains, plateaus, and lowlands. These landforms are subject to change by various physical processes. Some processes create new

Vignette 2.2

The Earth's Crust and Major Types of Rocks

The earth's crust, which forms less than 0.01 per cent of the earth and is its thin solidified shell, consists of three types of rocks: igneous, sedimentary, and metamorphic. When the earth's crust cooled about 4.5 billion years ago, **igneous rocks** were formed from molten rock known as magma. Some 3 billion years later, **sedimentary rocks** were formed from particles derived from previously existing rock. Through denudation (weathering and erosion), rocks are broken down and transported by water, wind, or ice and then deposited in a lake or sea. At the bottom of a water body, these sediments form a soft substance or mud. In geological time, they harden into rocks. Hardening occurs because of the pressure exerted by the weight of additional layers of sediments and because of chemical action that cements the particles together. Since only sedimentary rocks are formed in layers (called **strata**), this feature is unique to this type of rock. **Metamorphic rocks** are distinguished from the other two types of rock by their origin: they are igneous or sedimentary rocks that have been transformed into metamorphic rocks by the tremendous pressures and high temperatures beneath the earth's surface. Metamorphic rocks are often produced when the earth's crust is subjected to folding and faulting. Lava from volcanoes constitutes a metamorphic rock and basalt is a product of the cooling of a thick lava flow.

Contested Terrain 2.1

The Northern Gateway Pipeline: Centripetal or Centrifugal Effect?

The Northern Gateway pipeline project would provide access to Asian markets for Alberta's oil sands. The National Energy Board recommended its construction and the Harper government agreed. Yet, this project generated fierce opposition from First Nations and environmental organizations. They feared that a bitumen spill, by either a pipeline rupture or a calamity at sea, could cause irreparable damage. In 2015, the Trudeau government banned crude oil tanker traffic along British Columbia's north coast, thus killing the Northern Gateway pipeline proposal. On this contested terrain, which position—that of Harper or of Trudeau—do you favour and why?

landforms while others reduce them. From a geological perspective, the earth, then, is a dynamic planet, and its surface is actively shaped and reshaped over thousands and millions of years (see Vignette 2.2 for more on the earth's origin and types of rocks). From a human perspective, however, the earth is relatively stable with few changes observable over a person's lifetime. For instance, the Appalachian Uplands in Atlantic Canada and Québec are undergoing the very slow process known as **denudation**, which is the gradual wearing down of mountains by erosion and weathering over millions of years. How did this happen? First, **weathering** broke down the solid rock of these ancient mountains into smaller particles. Second, **erosion** transported these smaller particles by means of air, ice, and water to lower locations where they were deposited. The result was a much subdued mountain chain from what once resembled the Rocky Mountains. Denudation and **deposition**, then, are constantly at work and, over long periods of time, dramatically reshape the earth's surface.

Physiographic Regions

The earth's surface can be classified into a series of physiographic regions. A **physiographic region** is a large area of the earth's crust that has three key characteristics:

- It extends over a large, contiguous area with similar relief features.
- Its landform has been shaped by a common set of geomorphic processes.

- It possesses a common geological structure and history.

Canada has seven physiographic regions (Figure 2.1). The Canadian Shield is by far the largest region, while the Great Lakes–St Lawrence Lowlands is the smallest. Perhaps the most spectacular and varied **topography** occurs in the Cordillera, while the Hudson Bay Lowlands has the most uniform **relief**. The remaining three regions are the Interior Plains, Arctic Lands, and Appalachian Uplands. Most significantly, three of these physiographic regions— the Cordillera, Interior Plains, and Appalachian Uplands—display a strong north–south orientation to the topography of North America.

Each physiographic region has a different geological age and structure. Some 4.5 billion years ago, the Canadian Shield emerged from the sea to form the core of North America. Much of the Canadian Shield lies under other physiographic regions, including the Interior Plains and Hudson Bay Lowlands. At the surface, the Canadian Shield remains the largest exposure of Precambrian-aged rock in the world. Its geological structure has produced a particular set of mineral resources that contain deposits of copper, diamonds, gold, nickel, iron, and uranium. Other physiographic regions were formed much later, as shown in the geological time chart (Table 2.1). The formation of the Interior Plains began about 500 million years ago when ancient rivers deposited sediment in a shallow sea that existed in this area. Over a period of about 300 million years, more and more material was deposited into this inland

THINK ABOUT IT

Geomorphic processes work steadily but slowly. The Appalachian Mountains found in Nova Scotia represent worn-down mountains. Some 500 millions years ago, these mountains looked more like the Rocky Mountains.

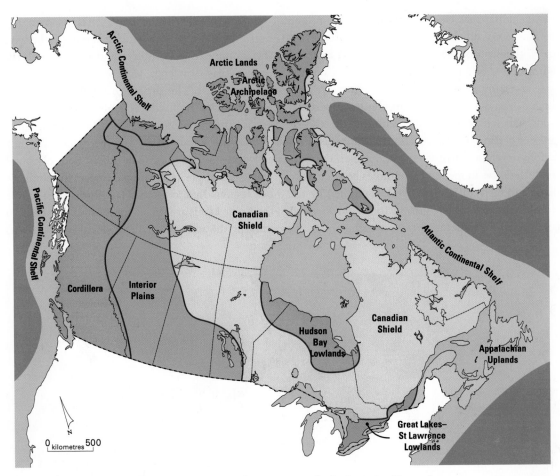

FIGURE 2.1 Physiographic regions and continental shelves in Canada

The seven physiographic regions are all different. The Arctic Lands is the most complex, consisting of a dozen large islands and numerous small islands that have been subjected to various geological events resulting in a mix of lowlands, uplands, and mountains. Together, these islands are known as the Arctic Archipelago. The Canadian Shield is the largest physiographic region and it extends beneath the Interior Plains, the Hudson Bay Lowlands, and the Great Lakes–St Lawrence Lowlands. The Cordillera and the Appalachian Uplands are products of plate tectonic activities—in the former case, less than 200 million years ago. The mountains of the Appalachian Uplands, on the other hand, formed nearly 500 million years ago.

TABLE 2.1 Geological Time Chart

Geological Era	Geological Time (millions of years ago)	Physiographic Region(s) Formed
Precambrian	600 to 4,500	Canadian Shield
Paleozoic	250 to 600	Appalachian Uplands, Arctic Lands
Mesozoic	70 to 250	Interior Plains
Cenozoic	0 to 70	Cordillera
Quaternary	0 to 2.5	The Great Lakes–St Lawrence Lowlands
Pleistocene	0.01 to 2.5	Hudson Bay Lowlands
Holocene	0.01 to present	

sea, including massive amounts of vegetation and the remains of dinosaurs and other creatures. Eventually, these deposits were solidified into layers of sedimentary rock 1 to 3 km thick. As a result, the Interior Plains have a sedimentary structure that contains vast oil and gas deposits plus the Alberta oil sands, which have propelled Canada into the leading ranks of global oil producers. Furthermore, as these regions developed their energy and mineral resources, differences in regional economies began to take shape and these differences were magnified by the global economy, which greatly increased demand (and prices) for these subterranean resources.

Each physiographic region has its own topography. The most dramatic difference is between the mountainous Cordillera and the relatively flat Hudson Bay Lowlands and, to a less degree, the Interior Plains. The surface material found in each region varies in hardness and thus resistance to erosional forces. Other factors affecting the rate of erosion are wind, water, and ice, which are more active in some regions than others, and, of course, gravity has a greater erosional impact in mountainous regions than on flatter landforms. In addition, the Arctic Lands are frozen for most of the year, thus limiting the activities of all erosional agents.

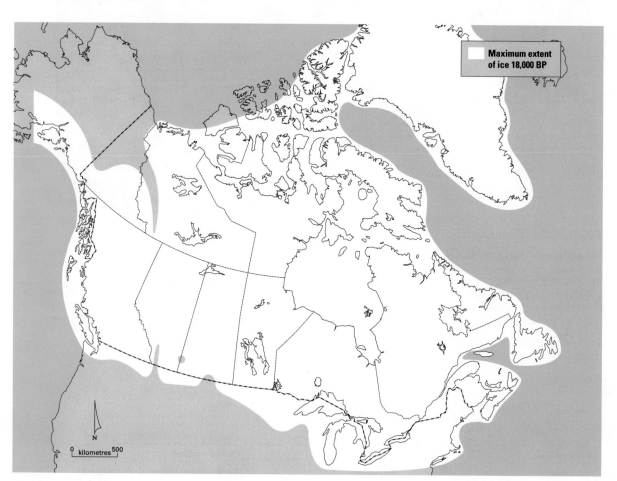

FIGURE 2.2 Maximum extent of ice, 18,000 BP

The last advance of the Late Wisconsin Ice Age (the combined Laurentide and Cordillera ice sheets) covered almost all of Canada and extended into the northern part of the United States around 18,000 years ago. As the climate warmed around 15,000 years ago, the massive ice sheets began to melt. During this Great Melt, huge amounts of fresh water surged to the oceans while some formed huge glacial lakes such as Lake Agassiz.

The series of advances and retreats of the Wisconsin ice sheets, but particularly the last one, shaped virtually all of the topography of Canada. These huge ice sheets spread out from their centre, which may have extended 4 km above the ground. Glacial movement is slow, behaving like a "stiff" liquid as it flows, oozes, and slides over the land. This Late Wisconsin advance began some 30,000 years ago and represents the end of the **Pleistocene epoch** (Table 2.1). The Late Wisconsin ice advance consisted of two major ice sheets, the Laurentide and the Cordillera. The Laurentide Ice Sheet was centred in the Hudson Bay area. As its mass increased, the sheer weight of the ice sheet caused it to move, eventually covering much of Canada east of the Rocky Mountains. In the Cordillera, a series of alpine glaciers coalesced into the Cordillera Ice Sheet, which spread westward into the continental shelf off the Pacific coast and eastward, eventually merging with the Laurentide Ice Sheet, which reached its maximum southern extent about 18,000 years ago (Figure 2.2). Gradually, the global climate began to warm and the grip of colossal ice sheets weakened. Ice sheets retreated first in the Interior Plains and much later in Ontario and Québec. The major remnants of these massive ice sheets are found as glaciers in the Cordillera and Arctic Lands.

Glaciation from these two huge ice sheets radically altered the geography of Canada. Glacial scouring and deposition took place everywhere (see Photo 2.1). The Laurentide Ice Sheet slowly pushed southward across the Canadian Shield, stripping away its surface material and depositing it much further south. When the ice sheet began to melt, it deposited material in situ, and meltwaters formed glacial lakes, including Lake Agassiz. As the world's greatest glacial lake, it created the nearly flat topography of the Manitoba Lowland in Western Canada. The Great Lakes provide another example of the impact of glaciation. They are remnants of glacial lakes that bordered the vast continental ice sheets. The bottoms of these lakes were formed by glacial scouring and then filled with meltwater from the receding ice sheet. Only a few remnants remain of these huge ice sheets. Today, the largest glaciers and ice fields are in the mountains of Ellesmere Island and in the Kluane National Park, Yukon.

Natural Resources Canada http://open.canada.ca/en/open-government-licence-canada

Photo 2.1 Beyond the treeline, the rugged nature of the Canadian Shield, stripped of most overlying material, exposes bare bedrock on Melville Peninsula, Nunavut. As observed in the photograph, the Laurentide Ice Sheet altered the surface by scouring, scratching, and polishing. Only a few rocks and boulders were deposited when the ice sheet melted. These boulders are called erratics.

The Canadian Shield

The Canadian Shield is the largest physiographic region in Canada. It extends over nearly half of the country's land mass and separates the densely populated area of the Great Lakes–St Lawrence Lowlands from the Interior Plains (Figure 2.1).

The Canadian Shield forms the ancient geological core of North America. More than 4.5 billion years ago, molten rock solidified into the Canadian Shield (Table 2.1). Today, these ancient Precambrian rocks not only are exposed at the surface of the Shield but also underlie many of Canada's other physiographic regions. Beneath this core rock is the molten heart of our planet.

The rock-like surface of the Canadian Shield consists mainly of a rugged, rolling upland. Shaped like an inverted saucer, the region's lowest elevations are along the shoreline of Hudson Bay, while its highest elevations occur in Labrador and on Baffin Island, where the most rugged and scenic landforms of the Canadian Shield are found. The Torngat Mountains in northern Labrador, for instance, provide spectacular scenery with a coastline of fjords (Photo 2.2). These mountains reach elevations of 1,600 m, making them the highest land in Canada

....

THINK ABOUT IT

Was the Canadian Shield a barrier to a united Canada? John Palliser, who headed an 1857 expedition sponsored by the Royal Geographical Society, recommended that the building of a railway across British territory should avoid what he called "the impregnable Canadian Shield" and take a more southerly route through American territory.

....

John Sylvester/All Canada Photos

Photo 2.2 Arctic landscape with tundra vegetation in the foreground, Saglek Fjord, Torngat National Park Reserve, Labrador.

east of the Rocky Mountains. The water divide of the Torngat Mountains represents the political boundary between northern Québec and Labrador.

As shown in **Chapter 10** (Photo 10.3, page 326), the Torngat Mountains form an impressive mountain chain extending in a north–south direction in Labrador and the adjacent area of Québec. The British Privy Council in 1927 used the Torngat water divide between Hudson Bay and the Atlantic Ocean to establish the Québec and Newfoundland and Labrador boundary. Québec still does not recognize this contentious decision (see Chapter 7, "Confederation to the Quiet Revolution," page 224).

During the last ice advance, the surfaces of the Canadian Shield and those of other physiographic regions were subjected to **glacial erosion** and deposition (Vignette 2.2). Giant ice sheets slowly grinding over the earth's surface changed its surface by glacial erosion and then glacial deposition (see Photo 2.1). As the ice sheet moved over the Canadian Shield, the ice scraped, scoured, and scratched the massive rock surface. During the movement of the ice sheet, huge quantities of various loose materials such as sand, gravel, and boulders were trapped within the ice sheet. As the ice sheet reached its maximum extent, its edge melted, depositing rocks, soil, and other debris. This debris is called **till**. Towards the end of the **ice age**, these ice sheets melted in situ, depositing whatever debris they contained. Sometimes the huge amount of water from the melting ice was blocked from reaching the sea by the retreating ice sheet.

These waters then formed temporary lakes. Once this ice was removed, these waters surged towards the sea.

Evidence of the impact of these processes on the surface of the Canadian Shield is widespread. Drumlins and eskers, both depositional landforms, are common to this region. **Drumlins** are low, elliptical hills (also called whalebacks or hogbacks) composed of till (material deposited and shaped by the movement of an ice sheet and subglacial megafloods), while **eskers** are long, narrow mounds of sand and gravel deposited by meltwater streams found under a glacier. There are also **glacial striations**, which are scratches in the rock surface caused by large rocks embedded in the slowly moving ice sheet.

The wealth of the Canadian Shield is in its vast and varied mineral resources. Along its southern fringe, huge deposits were sufficiently close to markets to permit exploitation. As an example, the rich nickel deposit near Sudbury has sustained that city for over 100 years and counting. In more remote areas, single-industry mining towns, such as the iron-mining town of Labrador City in Newfoundland and Labrador, were connected to global markets by rail and then sea transportation. While these towns flourished, those deposits beyond modern transportation networks employ a fly-in and fly-out labour force. For mines with a highly valued per unit product, such as diamonds, air transportation delivers the mineral to the marketplace. In the case of low-value per unit product, such as iron ore, the mine must have access to ocean transportation. The Raglan nickel mine in Arctic Québec falls into that category while the "Ring of Fire" mineral zone in Precambrian rocks in remote northern Ontario west of James Bay may well exceed the size and value of the Sudbury area, but transport issues have held up large-scale production except at the Victor Diamond Mine.

Like most of the Canadian Shield, the Laurentides, located just north of Montréal, contain many lakes and hills within a forested environment. Because of its close proximity to major cities in Québec, Ontario, and New England, the landscape, like that of the Muskoka region in Ontario, is principally exploited for recreation and tourism, with local residents and tourists enjoying these surroundings in both summer and winter.

The Cordillera

The Cordillera, a complex region of mountains, plateaus, and valleys, occupies over 16 per cent of Canada's territory. With its north–south alignment, the Cordillera extends from southern British Columbia to Yukon; its western border is the Pacific Ocean (Photo 2.3). The rugged nature of the Cordillera is illustrated in Figure 9.4, showing north–south aligned mountain ranges from the Vancouver Island Mountains on the Pacific coast to the Alberta border with the Rocky Mountains.

Plate tectonics played a critical role in the formation of the Cordillera. Beginning some 175 million years ago and ending around 85 million years ago, the Pacific and North American plates collided, uplifting the horizontal sedimentary rocks into a series of mountain ranges. During this time, tectonic movement was extremely slow, resulting in severe folding and faulting of the North American Plate that resulted in the series of mountains found in the Cordillera.

Along the fault line separating the Pacific and North American plates, tectonic movement continues, making the coast of British Columbia vulnerable to both earthquakes and volcanic activity. With the vast majority of the population and human-built environment of this region clustered along the coast in the cities of Vancouver, Victoria, New Westminster, and Nanaimo, the damage and loss of life from a major earthquake (measuring 7.0 or greater on the Richter scale) would be the worst natural disaster to strike Canada. The strongest earthquake ever recorded in Canada shook the sparsely populated Haida Gwaii (formerly called the Queen Charlotte Islands) in August 1949. This earthquake measured 8.1 on the Richter scale. Located along the Pacific Ring of Fire—a volatile expanse around the Pacific Ocean perimeter from New Zealand to southern South America, which is characterized by active volcanoes, fault lines, and shifting tectonic plates—the densely populated Lower Mainland of BC faces the threat of a powerful earthquake and possible tsunami sometime in the twenty-first century. The unknown question facing British Columbians is, when will the "Big One" strike?

Photo 2.3 Located along the Continental Divide between British Columbia and Alberta, the Athabasca Glacier forms part of the massive Columbia Icefield. Known as the "mother of rivers," the meltwaters from the Columbia Icefield nourish the Saskatchewan, Columbia, Athabasca, and Fraser river systems, the waters of which empty into three oceans—the Atlantic, Arctic, and Pacific oceans.

For earthquake risk in British Columbia, see Figure 9.8, "Earthquake hazard map for British Columbia." Discussion of earthquake danger in British Columbia is found in Chapter 9, page 295, "Waiting for the 'Big One'?"

In more recent geological times, the Cordillera Ice Sheet altered the landforms of the region. Over the last 20,000 years, alpine glaciation has sharpened the features of the mountain ranges in the Cordillera and broadened its many river valleys (Vignette 2.3). The Rocky Mountains are the best known of these mountain ranges. Most have elevations between 3,000 and 4,000 m. Their sharp, jagged peaks create some of the most striking landscapes in North America. The highest mountain in Canada—at nearly 6,000 m—is Mount Logan, part of the St Elias Mountain Range in southwest Yukon (Photo 2.4).

The Interior Plains

The Interior Plains region is a vast and geologically stable sedimentary plain that covers nearly 20 per cent of Canada's land mass. This physiographic region lies between the Canadian Shield and the Cordillera, extending from the Canada–US border to the Arctic Ocean. Within the Interior Plains, most of the population lives in the southern

THINK ABOUT IT

In 500,000 years, would the St Elias mountain range shown in Photo 2.4 look like the Appalachian Uplands shown in Photo 2.8?

Vignette 2.3

Alpine Glaciation, Glaciers, and Water for the Prairies

While glaciers still exist in the Rocky Mountains, they are slowly melting and retreating. During the Late Wisconsin ice advance about 18,000 years ago, these glaciers grew in size and eventually covered the entire Cordillera. At that time, alpine glaciers advanced down slopes, carving out hollows called **cirques**. As the glaciers increased in size, they spread downward into the main valleys, creating **arêtes**, steep-sided ridges formed between two cirques. As these glaciers advanced, they eroded the sides of the river valleys, creating distinctive U-shaped glacial valleys known as **glacial troughs**. The Bow Valley is one of Canada's most famous glacial troughs. Cutting through the Rocky Mountains, the Bow Valley now serves as a major transportation corridor. It has also developed into an international tourist area. The centre of this tourist trade is the world-famous resort town of Banff and its surrounding national park. While many rivers, especially the South Saskatchewan River, rely on these melting glaciers for fresh water that eventually flows to the cities and towns of the Canadian Prairies, as well as to irrigation works and industrial/mining operations, the concern is that, at some future time—perhaps in the last decades of the twenty-first century—these glaciers will disappear, thus greatly reducing the water supply for the Interior Plains.

area where a longer growing season permits grain farming and cattle ranching but low rainfall can affect yields and pastures. To those who are not native to this region, its topography often seems featureless, and bright sunshine does not offset the frigid winter months.

Millions of years ago, a huge shallow inland sea occupied the Interior Plains. Over the course of time, sediments were deposited into this sea.

Eventually, the sheer weight of these deposits produced sufficient heat and pressure to transform these sediments into sedimentary rocks. The oldest sedimentary rocks were formed during the Paleozoic era, about 500 million years ago (Table 2.1). Since then, other sedimentary deposits have settled on top of them, including those associated with the Mesozoic and Jurassic eras when dinosaurs roamed the earth. Unlike the Cordillera, the Interior Plains

John Zada/Alamy Stock Photo

Photo 2.4 Kluane National Park Reserve in southwest Yukon is the home of Canada's spectacular St Elias mountain range and the highest mountain in Canada, Mount Logan (5,959 m). Ice covers more than 80 per cent of the park. Glaciers were formed because of abundant snowfall from Pacific air masses plus cold temperatures through the year due to extremely high elevation and latitudes above 60°N. UNESCO in 1979 declared this park a World Heritage Site.

occupies a stable zone of the North American Plate where tectonic forces are not at play.

Tectonic forces associated with the collision of huge plates have had little effect on the geology of this region. For that reason, the Interior Plains is described as a stable geological region. For example, sedimentary rocks formed millions of years ago remain as a series of flat rock layers within the earth's crust. Geologists have used such sedimentary structures as geological time charts. In Alberta and Saskatchewan, rivers have cut deeply into these soft rocks, exposing Cretaceous rock strata. The Alberta Badlands provide an example of this rough and arid terrain (Photo 2.5). Archaeologists have discovered many dinosaur fossils within these Mesozoic rocks in southern Alberta and Saskatchewan.

Beneath the surface of the Interior Plains, valuable deposits of oil and gas are in sedimentary structures called **basins**. Known as fossil fuels, oil and gas deposits are the result of the capture of the sun's energy by plants and animals in earlier geologic time. The storage of this energy in the form of hydrocarbon compounds takes place in sedimentary basins. The Western Sedimentary Basin is the largest such basin. Most oil and gas production in Alberta comes from this basin, with the oil sands playing an increasingly important role. Fossil fuels are non-renewable resources, meaning that they cannot regenerate themselves. Renewable resources, such as trees, can reproduce themselves.

As the Laurentide Ice Sheet melted and began to retreat from the Interior Plains about 12,000 years ago, the surface of the region was covered with as much as 300 m of debris deposited by the ice sheet. Huge glacial lakes were formed in a few places. Later, the meltwater from these lakes drained to the sea, leaving behind an exposed lakebed. **Lake Agassiz**, for example, was once the largest glacial lake in North America and covered much of Manitoba, northwestern Ontario, and eastern Saskatchewan—its lakebed is now flat and fertile land that provides some of the best farmland in Manitoba, but as part of the Red River flood plain it is subject to frequent spring floods. When glacial waters escaped into the existing drainage system, they cut deeply into the glacial till and sedimentary rocks, creating huge river valleys known as **glacial spillways**.

Just north of Edmonton, the Interior Plains slopes towards the Arctic Ocean while east of Edmonton, the land tilts towards Hudson Bay and the Atlantic Ocean. Across this west–east cross-section of the Interior Plains, elevations decline from 1,600 m at Kicking Horse Pass of the Rocky Mountains to about 200 m near Lake Winnipeg and then to sea level at the mouth of the Nelson River. A south–north cross-section has a much smaller elevation drop—from 1,100 m at Yellowhead Pass to sea level at the mouth of the Mackenzie River. The principal rivers draining the Interior Plains

Photo 2.5 The sedimentary strata dating back to the late Cretaceous period remain virtually undisturbed in the Alberta Badlands, but these horizontal strata have been exposed by stream erosion when vast meltwaters associated with the melting of the two ice sheets flowed through the Red Deer River and its tributaries. These quick-moving waters easily cut through soft sedimentary rocks of the Interior Plains to reach rock layers that date back to the days of dinosaurs, some 70 million years ago. The Dinosaur Trail that explores these badlands and the Royal Tyrrell Museum of Paleontology are located near Drumheller, Alberta.

Wayne Lynch/All Canada Photos

are the northward-flowing Athabasca and Peace rivers, whose waters eventually enter the Mackenzie River and proceed to the Arctic Ocean, and the eastward-flowing North and South Saskatchewan rivers, which rise in the Rocky Mountains, join in central Saskatchewan, and empty into Lake Winnipeg. Then, by the Nelson River, these waters drain into Hudson Bay.

Three sub-regions based on sharp changes in elevations take place within the Canadian Prairies: the Manitoba Lowland, the Saskatchewan Plain, and the Alberta Plateau. Typical elevations are 250 m in the Manitoba Lowland, 550 m on the Saskatchewan Plain, and 900 m on the Alberta Plateau. The Cypress Hills, which reach elevations of nearly 1,500 m, provide a sharp contrast to the surrounding flat to rolling terrain of the Alberta Plateau (Vignette 2.4).

The Hudson Bay Lowlands

The Hudson Bay Lowlands comprises about 3.5 per cent of the area of Canada. Underlain by the Canadian Shield, this physiographic region consists of a thin cover of marine sediments deposited by the Atlantic Ocean some 10,000 to 12,000 years ago. The Hudson Bay Lowlands lies mainly in Northern Ontario, though small portions stretch into Manitoba

Natural Resources Canada http://open.canada.ca/en/open-government-licence-canada

Photo 2.6 The Hudson Bay Lowlands is a vast wetland where the lack of slope and the presence of permafrost restrict the development of a drainage system. Consequently, this lowland is dotted with myriad ponds and lakes. Muskeg prevails while black spruce occupies the higher, better-drained land made up of terraces (old sea beaches) and drumlins. The northern half of the Hudson Bay Lowlands lies beyond the treeline.

and Québec. This region extends from James Bay along the west coast of Hudson Bay to just north of the Churchill River. Permafrost is widespread and the northern half lies beyond the treeline.

Surface water is everywhere in the short summer but a frozen landscape exists in the long winter months. Muskeg, a type of peat, is the dominant ground cover, beneath which lies permafrost (Photo 2.6). Low ridges of sand and gravel—remnants of former beaches of the Tyrrell Sea—separate these extensive areas of muskeg. Because of its almost level surface, the presence of permafrost, and its immature drainage system, the Hudson Bay Lowlands is poorly drained. Underneath the muskeg are recently deposited marine sediments mixed with glacial till.

The Hudson Bay Lowlands, by far the youngest physiographic region, was formed around 10,000 years ago by three events. First, the huge Laurentide Ice Sheet covered the Hudson Bay Lowlands some 20,000 years ago and its weight depressed the land. Second, some 15,000 years ago, the climate warmed, causing the ice sheet to melt. By 12,000 years ago, the Hudson Bay Lowlands was ice-free, but because it was below sea level it was covered by waters from Hudson Bay. This body of sea water is called the Tyrrell Sea, which reached its maximum extent about 7,000 years ago. Third, with the tremendous weight of the ice gone from this submerged land, the Hudson Bay Lowlands slowly rose above sea level as the earth's crust began to rise. This process is called isostatic rebound (Vignette 2.5). Slowly, the isostatic rebound caused the seabed of the Tyrrell Sea to rise above sea level, thus exposing a low, poorly drained coastal plain (most of which is called the Hudson Bay Lowlands). This process of isostatic rebound began some 12,000 years ago and continues today, but at a slower pace. Some 12,000 years ago the rebound was around 600 cm per century, but this has gradually slowed—to around 100 cm in the twentieth century. This relatively recent geomorphic process makes the Hudson Bay Lowlands the youngest of the physiographic regions in Canada (Table 2.1).

With few resources to support human activities, the region has only a handful of tiny settlements. From this perspective, the Hudson Bay Lowlands is

Vignette 2.4

Cypress Hills

The Cypress Hills, a sub-region of the Interior Plains, consist of a rolling plateau-like upland deeply incised by fast-flowing streams. Situated in southern Alberta and Saskatchewan, this area is the highest point in Canada between the Rocky Mountains and Labrador. The hills are an erosion-produced remnant of an ancient higher-level plain formed in the Cenozoic era (see Table 2.1). With a maximum elevation close to 1,500 m, these hills rise 600 m above the surrounding plain. During the maximum extent of the Laurentide Ice Sheet about 18,000 years ago, the Cypress Hills were enclosed by the ice sheet but the higher parts remained above the ice sheet. Known as nunataks, these areas served as refuge for animals and plants. As the alpine glacier melted, streams flowing from the Rocky Mountains deposited a layer of gravel up to 100 m thick on these hills.

Today, the Cypress Hills area is a humid "island" surrounded by a semi-arid environment and has entirely different natural vegetation compared to the area surrounding it. Unlike the grasslands, the Cypress Hills have a mixed forest of lodgepole pine, white spruce, balsam poplar, and aspen. The Cypress Hills also contain many varieties of plants and animals found in the Rocky Mountains. For the Plains Aboriginal peoples, these hills were and are a sacred place.

one of the least favourably endowed physiographic regions of Canada. Moosonee (at the mouth of the Moose River in northern Ontario) and Churchill (at the mouth of the Churchill River in northern Manitoba) are the largest settlements in the region, each with a population of just over 1,000 people. These two settlements, formerly fur-trading posts, have an economic function as the termini of two northern railways (the Ontario Northland Railway and the Hudson Bay Railway, respectively). Regrettably, First Nation reserves have no similar economic functions and are a sad product of Ottawa's relocation policy of the 1960s.

Arctic Lands

The Arctic Lands region stretches over nearly 10 per cent of the area of Canada. Centred in the Canadian Arctic Archipelago, this region lies north of the **Arctic Circle**. It is a complex composite of coastal plains, plateaus, and mountains. The Arctic Platform, the Arctic Coastal Plain, and the Innuitian Mountain Complex are the three principal physiographic sub-regions. The Arctic Platform consists of a series of plateaus composed of sedimentary rocks. This sub-region is in the western half of the Arctic Archipelago around Victoria Island. The Arctic Coastal Plain extends from the Yukon coast and the adjacent area of the Northwest Territories into the islands located in the western part of the Beaufort Sea. The third sub-region, the Innuitian Mountain Complex, is located in the eastern half of the Arctic Archipelago. It is composed of ancient sedimentary rocks. Like the Rocky Mountains, its sedimentary rocks were folded and faulted. However, unlike the Rocky Mountains, the plateaus and mountains in the Innuitian sub-region were formed in the early Paleozoic era (Table 2.1). During this geological time, volcanic activity took place as the world island broke into North America, Eurasia, and Africa, leaving behind vast areas of basaltic rocks exposed at the surface (Photo 2.7). At 2,616 m, Mount Barbeau on Ellesmere Island is the highest point in the Arctic Lands region.

Across these lands, the ground is permanently frozen to great depths, never thawing, except at the surface during the short summer season. This cold thermal condition is called **permafrost**. Physical weathering, consisting mainly of differential heating and frost action, shatters bedrock and produces various forms of **patterned ground**. Patterned ground consists of rocks arranged in polygonal

David Nunuk/Science Photo Library

Photo 2.7 Basalt on Axel Heiberg Island, Nunavut. Basalt is a hard, black volcanic rock that, when cooled, can form various shapes, including tabular columns. Because they are resistant to erosion, basalt columns often form prominent cliffs. These weathered basalt columns date to the Paleozoic era (Table 2.1). At that geological time, North America, Greenland, and Eurasia broke into separate landmasses.

Except for primitive plants known as lichens, no vegetation grows. Aside from frost action, there are no other geomorphic processes, such as water erosion, to disturb the patterned ground.

Most people live in the coastal plain in the western part of this physiographic region. The three largest settlements are situated at the mouth of the Mackenzie River. Inuvik has a population of almost 3,000, while Aklavik and Tuktoyaktuk are smaller communities.

The Appalachian Uplands

The Appalachian Uplands region represents only about 2 per cent of Canada's land mass. Sometimes known as Appalachia, this physiographic region consists of the northern section of the Appalachian Mountains, though few mountains are found in the Canadian section. The Appalachians extend south in the eastern United States to northern Georgia and Alabama. With the exception of Prince Edward Island (Vignette 2.6), its terrain in Canada is a mosaic of rounded uplands and narrow river valleys. Typical Appalachian Uplands terrain is found in Cape Breton, Nova Scotia (Photo 2.8). These weathered uplands are either rounded or flat-topped. They are the remnants of ancient mountains that underwent a variety of weathering and erosional processes over a period of almost 500 million years. Together, weathering and erosion (including transportation of loose material by water, wind, and ice to lower elevations) have

forms by minute movements of the ground caused by repeated freezing and thawing. Patterned ground and **pingos** (ice-cored mounds or hills) give the Arctic Lands a unique landscape.

The climate in this region is cold and dry. In the mountainous zone of Ellesmere Island, glaciers are still active. That is, as these alpine glaciers advance from the land into the sea, the ice is "calved" or broken from the glacier, forming icebergs. On the plains and plateaus, it is a polar desert environment. The term "polar desert" describes barren areas of bare rock, shattered bedrock, and sterile gravel.

Vignette 2.5

Isostatic Rebound

At its maximum extent about 18,000 years ago, the weight of the huge Laurentide Ice Sheet caused a depression in the earth's crust. When the ice sheet covering northern Canada melted, this enormous weight was removed, and the elastic nature of the earth's crust has allowed it to slowly return to its original shape. This process, known as isostatic rebound or uplift, follows a specific cycle. As the ice mass slowly diminishes, the isostatic recovery begins. This phase is called a **restrained rebound**. Once the ice mass is gone, the rate of uplift reaches a maximum. This phase is called **postglacial uplift**. It is followed by a period of final adjustment called the **residual uplift**. Eventually the earth's crust reaches an equilibrium point and the isostatic process ceases. In the Canadian North, this process began about 12,000 years ago and has not yet completed its cycle.

worn down these mountains, creating a much subdued mountain landscape with **peneplain** features. The highest elevations are on the Gaspé Peninsula in Québec, where Mount Jacques Cartier rises to an elevation of 1,268 m. The coastal area has been slightly submerged; consequently, ocean waters have invaded the lower valleys, creating bays or estuaries, with a number of excellent small harbours and a few large ones, such as Halifax harbour. The island of Newfoundland consists of a rocky upland with only pockets of soil found in valleys. Like the Maritimes, it has an indented coastline where small harbours abound. The nature of this physiographic region favoured early European settlement along the heavily indented coastline where there was easy access to the vast cod stocks. With the demise of the cod stocks, these tiny settlements are declining or, like Great Harbour Deep, have been abandoned (see Chapter 10).

© iStock/shaunl

Photo 2.8 The Appalachian Uplands have sustained much erosion and the resulting landscape represents "worn-down" mountains. In rugged Cape Breton Highlands National Park, a table-like surface or peneplain lies between steep valleys carved by streams.

The Great Lakes–St Lawrence Lowlands

The Great Lakes–St Lawrence Lowlands physiographic region is small but important. Extending from the St Lawrence River near Québec City to Windsor, this narrow strip of land rests between the Appalachian Uplands, the Canadian Shield, and the Great Lakes.[2] Near the eastern end of Lake Ontario, the Canadian Shield extends across this region into the United States, where it forms the Adirondack Mountains in New York State. Known as the Frontenac Axis, this part of the Canadian Shield divides the Great Lakes–St Lawrence Lowlands into two distinct sub-regions.

As the smallest physiographic region in Canada, the Great Lakes–St Lawrence Lowlands comprises less than 2 per cent of the area of Canada. As its name suggests, the landscape is flat to rolling. This topography reflects the underlying sedimentary

Vignette 2.6

Prince Edward Island

Unlike other areas of the Appalachian Uplands, Prince Edward Island has a flat to rolling landscape. Sedimentary strata that underlie its surface consist of relatively soft, red-coloured sandstone that is quickly broken down by weathering and erosional processes. Occasionally, outcrops of this sandstone are exposed, but for the most part the surface is covered by reddish soil that contains a large amount of sand and clay. The heavy concentrations of iron oxides in the rock and soil give the island its distinctive reddish-brown hue. Prince Edward Island, unlike the other provinces in this region, has an abundance of arable land.

Vignette 2.7

Champlain Sea

About 12,000 years ago, vast quantities of glacial water from the melting ice sheets around the world drained into the world's oceans. Sea levels rose, causing the Atlantic Ocean to surge into the St Lawrence and Ottawa valleys, perhaps as far west as the edge of Lake Ontario. Known as the Champlain Sea, this body of water occupied the depressed land between Québec City and Cornwall and extended up the Ottawa River Valley to Pembroke. These lands had been depressed earlier by the weight of the Laurentide Ice Sheet. About 10,000 years ago, as the earth's crust rebounded, the Champlain Sea retreated. However, the sea left behind marine deposits, which today form the basis of the fertile soils in the St Lawrence Lowlands.

THINK ABOUT IT

Which physiographic region do you live in?

strata and its thin cover of glacial deposits. In the Great Lakes sub-region, flat sedimentary rocks are found just below the surface. This slightly tilted sedimentary rock, which consists of limestone, is exposed at the surface in southern Ontario, forming the Niagara Escarpment. A thin layer of glacial and lacustrine (i.e., lake) material, deposited after the melting of the Laurentide Ice Sheet in this area about 12,000 years ago, forms the surface, covering the sedimentary rocks.

In the St Lawrence sub-region, the landscape was shaped by the Champlain Sea, which occupied this area for about 2,000 years. It retreated about 10,000 years ago and left broad **terraces** that slope gently towards the St Lawrence River (Vignette 2.7). The sandy to clay surface materials are a mixture

Ian Cook/All Canada Photos

Photo 2.9 Rising sea levels following the last glaciation created the Champlain Sea, which extended up the Ottawa Valley, pictured here. Silt left behind by the receding waters formed the base for rich farm lands in the St Lawrence Lowlands. The gently rolling landscape is underlain by limestone.

of recently deposited sea, river, or glacial materials. For the most part, this sub-region's soils are fertile, which, when combined with a long growing season, allows agricultural activities to flourish.

The physiographic region lies well south of the forty-ninth parallel, which forms the US–Canada border from west of Ontario to Vancouver Island. The Great Lakes sub-region extends from 42°N to 45°N, while the St Lawrence sub-region lies somewhat further north, reaching towards 47°N. As a result of its southerly location, its proximity to the industrial heartland of the United States, and its favourable physical setting, the Great Lakes–St Lawrence region is home to Canada's main ecumene and manufacturing core.

Geographic Location

Canada occupies the northern portion of North America. As the two different geographies of Canada and the United States reveal (Vignette 2.1), this geographic fact has had profound implications for the course of development in the two countries. Simply stated, Canada's cooler climate translates into less area suitable for agriculture and settlement than is the case in the US.

A measure of geographic location on the earth's surface is provided by latitude and longitude. Because of the size of Canada, latitude and longitude vary enormously. Taking longitude as an example, the longitudinal distance between the westernmost area of Canada (as represented by Whitehorse, Yukon, at 135°08' west of the prime meridian in Greenwich, England) and the easternmost point (as represented by St John's at 52° 43'W) is nearly 83 degrees. In kilometres, the distance between the two cities is about 5,200 km. From a standard time perspective, five and a half time zones stretch across the country, from the Newfoundland Time Zone in the east to the Pacific Time Zone in the west (Figure 2.3).

How did the concept of standard time emerge? In fact, we have Sir Sanford Fleming, a Scottish-born Canadian civil engineer working on the construction of the Canadian Pacific Railway, to thank for inventing a system of standard time (as against individual time for each place as calculated from the sun). Fleming, in 1878, proposed the system of worldwide time zones based on the premise that

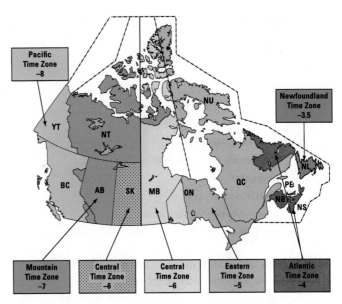

FIGURE 2.3 Time zones

Most of Saskatchewan observes Central Standard Time year-round. Lloydminster, which uses Mountain Standard Time and observes daylight saving time, is an exception. Some communities in Canada may choose not to observe official time zones and this map does not reflect all such variances.

Source: TimeTemperature.com, at: www.timetemperature.com/canada/canada_time_zone.shtml.

since the earth rotates once every 24 hours and there are 360 degrees of longitude in a sphere, each hour the earth rotates one-twenty-fourth of a circle or 15 degrees of longitude.

Because the earth is a spherical body, this measure is given in degrees (°) and minutes (') for both latitude and longitude. By longitude, we mean the distance east or west of the prime meridian. As the equator represents zero latitude, the prime meridian represents zero longitude. It is an imaginary line that runs from the North Pole to the South Pole and passes through the Royal Observatory at Greenwich, England. Canada lies entirely in the area of west longitude. Ottawa, for example, is 75° 28' west of the prime meridian. The distance between longitudes varies, being greatest at the equator and reaching zero at the North Pole.[3] Latitudes and longitudes for some other Canadian cities are found in Table 2.2.

By latitude, we mean the measure of distance north and south of the equator. For example, Ottawa is 42° 24' minutes north of the equator. How do we translate these latitudes into an understanding of Canada's northern location and its cold environment? One way is to examine the southernmost

TABLE 2.2 Latitude and Longitude of Selected Centres

Centre	Latitude	Longitude
Windsor, Ontario	42° 19'N	83°W
Montréal, Québec	45° 32'N	73° 36'W
St John's, Newfoundland and Labrador	47° 35'N	52° 43'W
Victoria, British Columbia	48° 27'N	123° 20'W
Winnipeg, Manitoba	49° 53'N	97° 10'W
Saskatoon, Saskatchewan	52° 10'N	106° 40'W
Edmonton, Alberta	53° 34'N	113° 25'W
Whitehorse, Yukon	60° 42'N	135° 08'W
Inuvik, Northwest Territories	68° 16'N	133° 40'W
Alert, Nunavut	82° 31'N	62° 20'W

latitudes near Windsor, Ontario, which is close to 42°N. Another way is to realize that over half of Canada lies north of the sixtieth parallel. Finally, we can look at the latitude of our capital. Ottawa is nearly 5,000 km north of the equator. Since the distance between each degree of latitude is about 111 km, the middle to high latitudes in Canada have considerable implications for the amount of solar energy received at the surface of the earth, and, hence, Canada's climate, and short summers and long, dark winters.

Climate

Our physical world encompasses more than just landforms, physiographic regions, and geographic location. **Climate**, for instance, is a central aspect of the physical world. Climate describes average weather conditions for a specific place or region based on past weather over a very long period of time, perhaps thousands of years. On the other hand, weather refers to the current state of the atmosphere with a focus on weather conditions that affect people living in a particular place for a relatively short period of time. In sum, climate is what we can expect while weather is what we get. Geography students can gain first-hand knowledge of current and historic patterns in climate and weather by using Climate Trend Mapper (Vignette 2.8)

"Coldness," wrote French and Slaymaker (1993: i), "is a pervasive Canadian characteristic, part of the nation's culture and history." They note that winter's effects include not only low absolute temperatures but also exposure to wind chill, snow, ice, and permafrost. As Canadians well know from personal experience, Canada has a cold environment. As seen on the map of climatic zones (Figure 2.4), the bulk of Canada's territory is associated with two northern climatic types, the Arctic and Subarctic zones. Both have extremely long, cold winters. Although the two maritime climatic types—along the coast of BC and in Atlantic Canada—have relatively short periods of cold weather, winter is a fact of life for Canadians. Artists, musicians, and novelists have found this northern theme appealing. In "Mon pays," Gilles Vigneault, one of Québec's best-known

Vignette 2.8

Prairie Climate Atlas

The Prairie Climate Atlas, developed by Professor Danny Blair and Ryan Smith at the University of Winnipeg, provides both historic and projected climate data. For more information, visit their Prairie Climate Centre website at: www.climateatlas.ca/home.html.

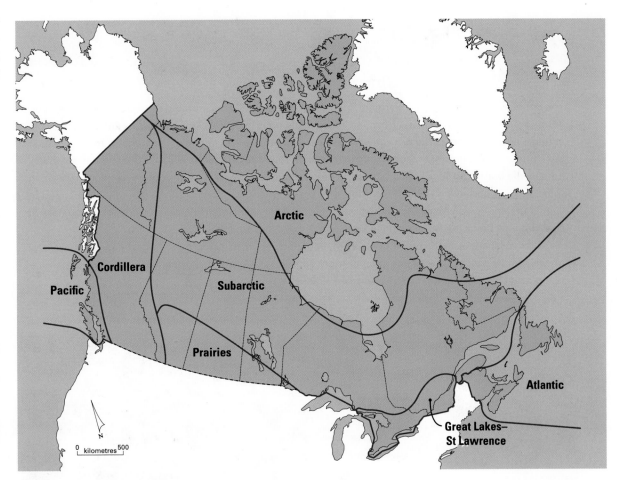

FIGURE 2.4 Climatic zones of Canada

Each climatic zone represents average climatic conditions in that area. Canada's most extensive climatic zone, the Subarctic, is associated with the boreal forest and **podzolic** soils.

chansonniers, refers to Québec, his country, in the opening line: *Mon pays ce n'est pas un pays, c'est l'hiver* (My country is not a country, it is winter). Stan Rogers's heroic song "Northwest Passage" has become one of Canada's unofficial anthems.

Climate Change and Global Warming

Canada, like other parts of the world, is caught in a warming trend referred to as **global warming**. Over the last 50 years, the average annual temperature has increased by 1.5°C (Warren and Lemmen, 2014: 6). In turn, this warming trend has led to **climate change**—a term that includes global warming and

the impact of higher temperatures on other components of weather as well as on the rest of the natural world (see Vignette 2.9). For instance, the average annual precipitation over a 40-year period (1956 to 1995) for Canada revealed an increase of 51 mm (Cutforth, Akinremi, and McGinn, 2000: 2177). Another example is the melting of ice in permafrost. In Photo 2.10, the narrow barrier known as a headwall prevented the lake from cascading downstream, but the ice in the headwall is thawing (CBC News, 2015). A week later, the headwall collapsed and the lake water plunged 200 m down slope into the Mackenzie Valley.

While annual temperature increases are relatively simple to measure and interpret, precipitation is more complicated (see Vignette 2.12). Evidence

Vignette 2.9

Global Warming and Climate Change: What Is the Difference?

The definitions of both "global warming" and "climate change" are centred on the premise that temperatures are increasing, which, in turn, contributes to changes in global climate patterns and an increase in extreme weather events. The principal difference between the two terms is that global warming focuses on temperature change that results from increased emissions of greenhouse gases from human activities, notably the burning of fossil fuels. Known as the greenhouse effect, this anthropogenic-caused warming trend began with the Industrial Revolution when great quantities of coal first began to be consumed to supply the energy necessary for industry. Originally, European countries were the major consumers of coal, but now China leads the world in consumption of coal with India not far behind.

Climate change, on the other hand, is not restricted to human-caused warming but considers natural forces, too. As well, climate change places more emphasis on other elements of climate, such as precipitation, wind patterns, and more frequent and violent weather events.

Scott Zolkos

Photo 2.10 This lake, near Fort McPherson, NWT, is poised to disappear—as it mostly did in July 2015 when a permafrost slump encroached on its edges. Repeated many times, this phenomenon represents one of many giant-sized permafrost slumps that are changing the North's landscape on a scale not seen since the last ice age.

shows that annual precipitation is increasing and even the drought-prone Canadian Prairies may be benefiting from greater precipitation (Cutforth, Akinremi, and McGinn, 2000; Zhang, Vincent, Hogg, and Niitsoo, 2000; Bonsal, Aider, Gachon, and Lapp, 2013). The basis of greater annual precipitation is the premise that warmer air masses have a greater capacity to hold moisture and produce

Vignette 2.10

Natural Factors Affecting Global Warming

The physics of global warming in the greenhouse model are elementary, but the actual process of climate change is extremely complex and remains unclear. The 2015 Paris Climate Change Conference declared a global warming goal for the twenty-first century of less than 2°C (UN, 2015). More specifically, the aim is to keep a global temperature rise this century well below 2°C and to drive efforts to limit the temperature increase even further, to 1.5°C above pre-industrial levels. But how each of the 195 nations that signed this agreement will implement measures within their political boundaries to reduce fossil fuel greenhouse gases entering the atmosphere remains an enormous task.

The groundswell from the Paris Conference suggests that the world is on an inevitable path towards a properly sustainable, low-carbon world (UN, 2015). But what does that mean? Has Canada committed to closing its low-cost thermal coal-burning plants? Can the federal government convince provinces to adapt a national carbon tax scheme? What will Ottawa do if President Trump decides to walk away from the US commitments made at the Paris Conference?

precipitation—and violent storms. On top of the interplay of global temperatures and precipitation, different parts of the world are affected differently. In Canada's Arctic, for instance, an indisputable indicator of warmer summers is the summer retreat of **sea ice**, leaving the possibility of an ice-free Arctic Ocean for part of the year. In another part of Canada, the Canadian Prairies, the jury is still out on how these two climatic elements of temperature and precipitation will play out. The semi-arid Prairies have long been subject to a cycle of wet and dry years. Now the question is whether, with longer and warmer summers, this region will turn into an arid environment or a more humid one.

As our planet warms, just how this increase will alter Canada is slowly unfolding before our eyes. Is a warmer Canada a better Canada? The jury is still out on this question. Are the melting of Arctic polar ice, the retreat of glaciers, and the thawing of permafrost benefiting Canada? Other changes take more time. The northward shift of climatic zones, for example, is followed by changes in natural vegetation and wildlife zones (Bouchard, 2001). Potential economic gains could be a reduction in costs for snow removal; a longer growing season for crops; and an extended navigation season for the St Lawrence Seaway and the **Northwest Passage**. Costs might see a shortage of water for Prairie cities as the glaciers feeding those rivers disappear;

preventing flooding of coastal cities might become a challenge of our changing natural world; winter supply routes via ice roads to remote mining sites and Aboriginal reserves already are threatened in some areas.

Climate Factors

While the addition of greenhouse gases into the atmosphere is causing global warming, the four traditional climatic factors require our attention. First, the energy from the sun sets the parameters for climate. The amount of this energy received at the earth's surface varies by latitude. Low latitudes around the

THINK ABOUT IT

Melt ice in permafrost causes massive ground **subsidence**, a form of irregular topography referred to by physical geographers as "thermokarst topography." With global warming, how might such subsidence in Canada's North affect housing and other infrastructure built on permafrost?

Photo 2.11 This NASA image shows Canada in the grip of winter, 28 February 2009. Canada is a northern nation with winter its dominant season.

NASA Goddard's Scientific Visualization Studio

equator have a net surplus of energy (and therefore high temperatures), but in high latitudes around the North and South poles, more energy is lost through re-radiation than is received, and therefore annual average temperatures are extremely low. Canada, lying in middle to high latitudes, is subject to great variation in the amount of solar energy. In turn, this variation results in wide differences in temperatures, climatic types, and zones (see Figures 2.5 and 2.6).

Second, the **global circulation system** redistributes this energy (i.e., energy transfers) from low latitudes to high latitudes through circulation in the atmosphere (system of winds and air masses) and the oceans (system of ocean currents). For example, the Japan Current warms the Pacific Ocean, bringing milder weather to British Columbia. On Canada's

east coast, the opposite process occurs as the Labrador Current brings Arctic waters to Atlantic Canada. While Halifax, at 44° 39'N, lies about 500 km closer to the equator than Victoria, at 48° 27'N, Halifax's winter temperatures, on average, are much lower than those experienced in Victoria.

Third, the global circulation system travels in a west-to-east direction in the higher latitudes of the northern hemisphere, causing air masses (Vignette 2.11) that develop over large water bodies to bring mild and moist weather to adjacent land masses. For Canada, air masses from the Pacific Ocean cross the Cordillera into the interior of Canada. Such air masses are known as **marine air masses**. In this way, energy transfers ultimately determine regional patterns of global weather and climate

THINK ABOUT IT

Which air mass dominates the summer climate where you live?

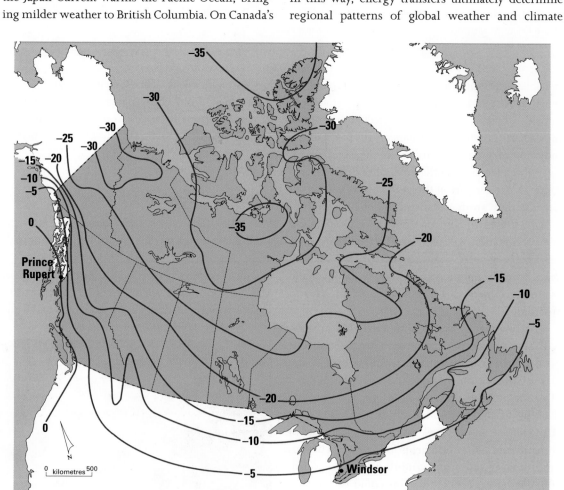

FIGURE 2.5 Seasonal temperatures in Celsius, January

The moderating influence of the Pacific Ocean and its warm air masses are readily apparent in the 0 to −5°C January isotherm. For example, Prince Rupert, located near 55°N, has a warmer January average temperature (0°C) than Windsor (−2°C), which is located near 42°N.

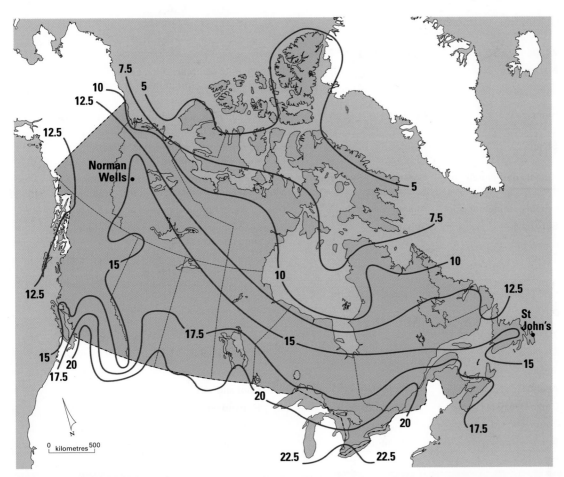

FIGURE 2.6 Seasonal temperatures in Celsius, July

The continental effect results in very warm summer temperatures that extend into high latitudes, as illustrated by the 15°C July isotherm. For example, Norman Wells, located near the Arctic Circle, has warmer July temperatures than St John's.

Vignette 2.11

Air Masses

Air masses are large sections of the atmosphere with similar temperature and humidity characteristics. They form over large areas with uniform surface features and relatively consistent temperatures where they take on these temperature and humidity characteristics. Such areas are known as source regions. The Pacific Ocean is a marine source region, while the interior of North America is a continental source region. During a period of about a week or so, an air mass may form over a source region. Canada's weather is affected by five air masses (Table 2.4).

(see Tables 2.3 and 2.4). Air masses originating over large land masses are known as **continental air masses**. These air masses are normally very dry and vary in temperature depending on the season. In the winter continental air masses are cold, while in the summer they are associated with hot weather.

The fourth factor is the so-called "continental effect." **Continental effect** refers to the fact that land

TABLE 2.3 Climatic Types

Köppen Classification	Canadian Climatic Zone	General Characteristics
Marine West Coast	Pacific	Warm to cool summers, mild winters Precipitation throughout the year with a maximum in winter
Highland	Cordillera	Cooler temperature at similar latitudes because of higher elevations
Steppe	Prairies	Hot dry summers and long cold winters Low annual precipitation
Humid continental	Great Lakes–St Lawrence Lowlands	Hot humid summers and short cold winters Moderate annual precipitation with little seasonal variation
Humid continental, cool	Atlantic Canada	Cool to warm humid summers and short cool winters
Subarctic	Subarctic	Short cool summers and long cold winters Low annual precipitation
Tundra	Arctic	Extremely cool and very short summers; long cold winters Very low annual precipitation

Source: Adapted from Christopherson (1998); Hare and Thomas (1974).

TABLE 2.4 Air Masses Affecting Canada

Air Mass	Type	Characteristics	Season
Pacific	Marine	Mild and wet	All
Atlantic	Marine	Cool and wet	All
Gulf of Mexico	Marine	Hot and wet	Summer
Southwest US	Continental	Hot and dry	Summer
Arctic	Continental	Cold and dry	Winter

Vignette 2.12

Types of Precipitation

As an air mass rises, its temperature drops. This cooling process triggers condensation of water vapour within the air mass. With sufficient cooling, water droplets are formed. When these droplets reach a sufficient size, precipitation begins. Precipitation refers to rainfall, snow, and hail. There are three types of precipitation. **Convectional precipitation** results when moist air is forced to rise because the ground has become particularly warm. Often this form of precipitation is associated with thunderstorms. **Frontal precipitation** occurs when a warm air mass is forced to rise over a colder (and denser) air mass. **Orographic precipitation** results when an air mass is forced to rise over high mountains. However, as the same air mass descends along the leeward slopes of those mountains (that is, the slopes that lie on the east side of the mountains), the temperature rises and precipitation is less likely to occur. This phenomenon is known as the **rain shadow effect**.

THINK ABOUT IT

Did Köppen uncover the fact that climate determines the global pattern of natural vegetation and soil zones?

masses heat up and cool more quickly than oceans. In turn, greater distance from an ocean affects temperature and precipitation; that is, as distance from an ocean increases, the daily and seasonal temperature ranges increase and the annual precipitation decreases. For example, Winnipeg experiences a much greater daily and annual range in temperature than does Vancouver, even though both lie near 49°N. The principal reason is the "continental effect."

Climatic Types and Zones

Since climate was relatively stable over thousands of year, the earth developed a series of climatic types and zones. But how many types and zones exist? It all depends on the criteria. In the nineteenth century, well before global climatic stations existed, Wladimir Köppen, a German scientist, developed a climatic classification scheme for the world based on natural vegetation zones. He assumed that these natural vegetation zones required certain temperatures and precipitation to thrive and therefore these zones were a surrogate for climatic types and zones. Based on world patterns of natural vegetation, Köppen created 25 climate types, each of which was assigned particular temperature regimes and seasonal precipitation patterns. Seven of Köppen's climatic types are found in Canada (Table 2.3).

A **climatic zone** is an area of the earth's surface where similar weather conditions occur. Long-term data describing annual, seasonal, and daily temperatures and precipitation are used to define the extent of a climatic zone.

Canada has seven climatic zones (Figure 2.4): Pacific, Cordillera, Prairies, Great Lakes–St Lawrence, Atlantic, Subarctic, and Arctic. The Arctic climate extends from the coast of Yukon to the Labrador coast. It dominates in Nunavut and Nunavik and is found along the Hudson Bay coastlines of Ontario and Manitoba. The Subarctic climatic zone, Canada's largest, extends over much of the interior of Canada and is found in each geographic region. The Subarctic climate prevails in northern areas

THINK ABOUT IT

Global warming has begun but so far the boundaries of the Canadian climate zones shown in Table 2.3 have not been altered. Does this mean that global warming has not yet had sufficient impact on our climate or is there a lag in updating these boundaries?

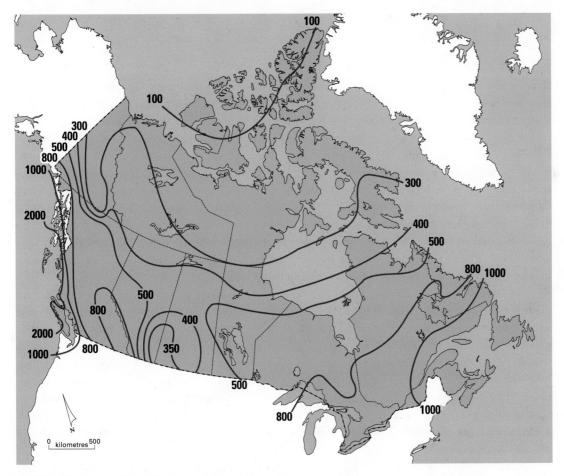

FIGURE 2.7 Annual precipitation in millimetres

The lowest average annual precipitation occurs in the Territorial North, indicating the dry nature of the Arctic air masses that originate over the ice-covered Arctic Ocean. The highest average annual precipitation occurs along the coast of British Columbia due to the moist marine air masses and the coastal mountains.

imageBROKER/Alamy Stock Photo

Photo 2.12 Glacial retreat of the Athabasca Glacier since 2000 can be attributed to warmer annual temperatures. Part of the Columbia Icefield in Jasper National Park, Alberta, the glacier is retreating at a rate of about 5 m per year (see Vignette 2.13).

of Atlantic Canada, Québec, Ontario, and Western Canada, and is present in northeast British Columbia. As well, the Subarctic climate is found in the Territorial North and is the principal climate in the Northwest Territories. The Subarctic reaches much higher latitudes in northwest Canada than in northeast Canada because of warmer temperatures in the northwest. In northwest Canada, the average July temperature often reaches or exceeds 10°C, thus permitting the growth of trees. In similar latitudes of northeast Canada, summer temperatures are much lower. In the extreme north of Québec, for example, the average July temperature is below 10°C, thus resulting in tundra rather than a tree vegetation cover. The Subarctic climatic zone therefore has a southeast to northwest alignment

Vignette 2.13

Fluctuations in World Temperatures

Our climate seems relatively constant, but geological history reveals otherwise. The last 10,000 years—the Holocene epoch—represents a relatively warm period in the earth's history. However, within that epoch, a series of shorter cycles of warm and then colder periods have occurred. We are currently in a warming period with the prospects of an increase in average global temperature of two or more degrees by 2100.

Each warm period in the Holocene epoch lasted about 500 years. For instance, the Medieval Warming Period took place between the tenth and fourteenth centuries. During this time, the Vikings established a settlement on the southern tip of Greenland and made voyages to neighbouring parts of Arctic Canada and southward to the northern tip of Newfoundland. At the same time, the Thule occupied much of the Canadian Arctic and were able to hunt the huge bowhead whales in the open summer waters. This warm spell was replaced by a cooler period known as the Little Ice Age, which lasted from about 1450 to around 1850. Since then, however, global warming has become the trend, with occasional interruptions of short periods of cooler weather such as occurred in the 1960s.

The Little Ice Age, perhaps triggered by volcanism and sustained by sea-ice/ocean feedback, chilled the northern hemisphere (Miller et al., 2012). Living on the edge of a cold climate, even a slight drop in annual temperatures had a dramatic impact on human beings. The Vikings were no longer able to sustain themselves in Greenland and the Thule had to make a drastic adjustment to their hunting economy. With a much more extensive and long-lasting ice cover over the Arctic Ocean, the bowhead whales no longer entered these waters for long periods of time. The consequences for the Thule inhabitants were devastating. They were forced to hunt smaller game—seals and caribou. The results were twofold: the new hunting system could not support as many people and it required smaller, more mobile hunting groups. Archaeologists believe that the Inuit, who were established in the Arctic by the mid-sixteenth century, are the descendants of the Thule people.

Today, much of the increase in world temperature is attributed to coal-burning thermal electric plants. Canada ranks thirteenth in the world in coal-fired energy production, far behind global "leaders" China, the United States, and India.

(Figure 2.4). This alignment is somewhat modified in Québec because of its proximity to the marine influences of the Atlantic Ocean.

Since environmental issues are the result of human actions, solutions are possible (Dearden and Mitchell, 2012: ch. 1). One solution involves establishing more protected areas and parks (Slocombe and Dearden, 2009). Another is for more stringent regulations that will reduce damage to the environment caused by both new and existing projects. But perhaps the most significant solution lies in "going green," which includes recycling waste products, moving towards electric automobiles, limiting discretionary air travel, and increasing the production of electricity from natural sources such as solar and wind rather than coal.

The section "Technological Gamble: Carbon Capture and Storage," in Chapter 8, page 263, discusses the efforts in Alberta and Saskatchewan to reduce greenhouse emissions from oil sands upgraders and coal-fired energy plants through carbon sequestration.

Extreme Weather Events

Extreme weather events—such as blizzards, droughts, and ice storms—are also part of climate and often have very powerful impacts on humans. In fact, extreme weather events constitute the most serious of natural hazards, whether they take the form of droughts, floods, ice storms, or tornados. The Intergovernmental Panel on Climate Change, which assesses and synthesizes the research of more than 2,000 climate scientists throughout the world, foresees an increase in extreme weather events because of rising world temperatures: a warmer atmosphere would have the capacity to hold increased moisture, thus supplying the fuel for heavier rainfalls, snowfalls, tornados, and other extreme weather events.

Often, extreme weather events occur with little warning and result in heavy losses of property and sometimes lives. Hurricanes are such extreme weather events. Atlantic Canada has been the site of many of these destructive tropical cyclones (Conrad,

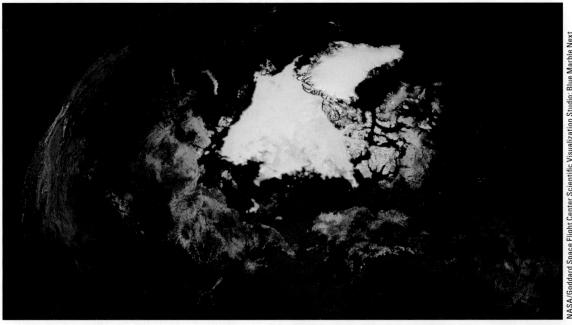

NASA/Goddard Space Flight Center Scientific Visualization Studio; Blue Marble Next Generation data courtesy Reto Stockli (NASA/GSFC)

Photo 2.13 Warm summer temperatures have caused the Arctic sea ice to shrink, thus exposing more open water. In September 2007, for example, Arctic sea ice coverage had reached its lowest extent for the year and the lowest amount recorded since satellite observations began some 30 years ago. Since then, this pattern of open water in the late summer has continued, with two routes through the Northwest Passage ice-free, but only for a short time. Differences do exist: the portion of the Arctic Ocean from the Beaufort Sea to the Bering Strait is ice-free for a longer time and its ice-free zone is much larger than in the central and eastern Arctic. The possibility of ocean-going vessels plying these western Arctic waters is more likely to occur before commercial cargo ships regularly use the entire Northwest Passage, although in 2014 the first unescorted bulk carrier transported nickel concentrate from a Chinese-owned mine in Arctic Québec through the Northwest Passage on a direct passage to China.

2009: 163–5). Conrad (2009: 1) places such weather in a broader context:

> Canada's climate is typified by extremes, and thus Canadians are interested in the weather out of necessity and concern. With the inevitable changes in our global climate, scientists as well as the general public are concerned with the impact such change will have on extreme weather events in Canada.

Not surprisingly, extreme weather events often have a cultural impact by providing a common threat and, as people struggle against this threat, creating a common bond. As indicated in Chapter 1, natural disasters have contributed to people's sense of belonging to a region, and often they are recurring phenomena, such as floods in a flood-prone area. As de Loë (2000: 357) explains, "Floods are considered hazards only in cases where human beings occupy floodplains and shoreland." Heavy rainfall combined with rapid snowmelt often triggers catastrophic floods. An excellent example is found in the flat Manitoba Lowland where the normally benign Red River winds its way from North Dakota in the United States northward to Lake Winnipeg. Since 1950, residents of Winnipeg and other communities along the Red River have suffered through nine major spring floods—in 1950, 1979, 1996, 1997, 2001, 2006, 2009, 2011, and 2013—and

THINK ABOUT IT

Even though the Red River floods regularly, Winnipeg is able to avoid serious flooding. Why?

THINK ABOUT IT

If our climate is warming, what are the consequences for the landscape if ice in the ground known as permafrost melts?

the frequency of these floods appears to be increasing, giving credence to the fears of the Intergovernmental Panel on Climate Change. In 1950, the Red River flood drove over 100,000 people from their homes. Following that disaster, the Red River Floodway, a wide channel nearly 50 km long, was constructed. Its purpose was to divert the flood waters around the city of Winnipeg. However, small communities in the Red River Basin remained vulnerable to flooding. In 1997, the largest flood in the twentieth century occurred (Rasid et al., 2000). While the Red River Floodway saved Winnipeg, the towns of Emerson, Morris, Ste Agathe, and St Adolphe and the surrounding farm buildings and lands were less fortunate. In April 2006, 2009, 2011, and 2013, waters overflowed the Red River (Photo 2.14).

Permafrost

Permafrost is a relic from a very cold Pleistocene climate (Table 2.1). This distinctive feature of Canada's physical geography is permanently frozen ground with temperatures at or below zero for at least two years. The vast extent of permafrost in Canada and, in places, its great depth provide a measure of the country's cold environment (Figure 2.8). Permafrost exists in the Arctic and Subarctic climatic zones and occurs at higher elevations in the Cordillera zone. Overall, permafrost is found in just over two-thirds of Canada's land mass.

In more northerly regions, permafrost extends far into the ground. North of the Arctic Circle, the permafrost may be several hundred metres deep. Further south, permafrost is less frequent, and where it occurs it rarely penetrates more than 10 m into the ground. Permafrost is found in all six of Canada's geographic regions and reaches its most southerly position along 50°N in Ontario and Québec. Along the southern edge of permafrost, there is a transition zone where small pockets of frozen ground have a depth of less than 1 m. Further south, these pockets of permafrost disappear.

Permafrost, like glaciers, is undergoing a retreat due to global warming. The most vulnerable permafrost lies mainly in the northern reaches of provinces where the permanently frozen ground is relatively warm at temperatures of zero to −5°C; its thickness

Joe Bryksal/Winnipeg Free Press

Photo 2.14 The town of St Jean Baptiste, 40 km north of the Canada–US border, is surrounded by a ring dike to protect it from the flooding Red River, 20 April 2011.

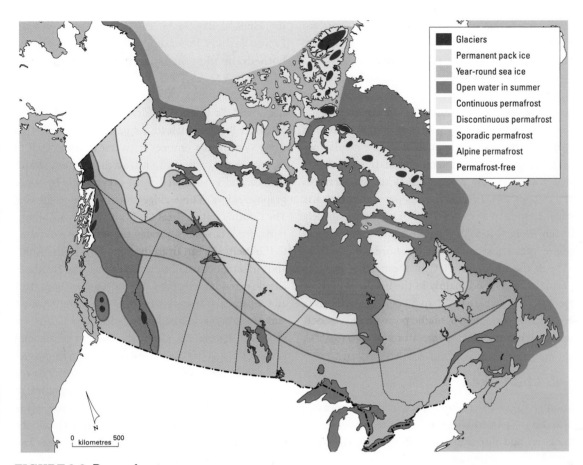

FIGURE 2.8 Permafrost zones

Canada's cold environment is best demonstrated by permafrost. Permanently frozen ground extends over two-thirds of the country.

is less than 5 m; and less than 30 per cent of the area contains permafrost (Warren and Lemmen, 2014: 37). This permafrost, described as "thin and warm," may disappear well before the end of the twenty-first century. In terms of permafrost zones, as shown in Figure 2.8, "thin and warm" permafrost dominates the sporadic zone and is widespread in the discontinuous zone. In sharp contrast, the temperature of the ground in the continuous permafrost zone is much lower (−15°C or colder) and its thickness exceeds 10 m. While this zone will remain intact for this century, its characteristics could take on those of the discontinuous zone.

The warming of permafrost is changing the northern landscape. One change involves the slumping of land and the disappearance of lakes (Kokelj et al., 2015). For example, on 15 July 2015, near Fort McPherson, NWT, the headwall that had kept the waters of a small, unnamed lake from plummeting into a valley below gave way (Photo 2.10). Reporter Bob Weber (2015) wrote:

> Within two hours, 30,000 cubic metres of water—the equivalent of a dozen Olympic-sized swimming pools—gushed over the edge in a waterfall up to five storeys high. Mud and debris filled more than a kilometre of the valley below and flowed for two days at the rate of 50 metres an hour.

Permafrost is divided into four types. **Alpine permafrost** is found in mountainous areas and takes on a vertical pattern as elevations of a mountain increase. Over most of Canada, however, permafrost follows a zonal pattern, which does not correspond to latitude but rather to the annual mean temperatures that fall below zero.[4] The zonal pattern has a northwest to southeast alignment, that is, from Yukon to central Québec (see Figure 2.8).

As the mean annual temperature varies, the type of permafrost also changes. **Continuous permafrost** occurs in the higher latitudes of the Arctic climatic zone, where at least 80 per cent of the ground is permanently frozen, although it also extends into northern Québec. Continuous permafrost is associated with very low mean annual air temperatures of –15°C or less. **Discontinuous permafrost** occurs when 30 to 80 per cent of the ground is permanently frozen. It is found in the Subarctic climatic zone where mean annual air temperature ranges from –5°C in the south to –15°C in the north. **Sporadic permafrost** is found mainly in the northern parts of the provinces, where less than 30 per cent of the area is permanently frozen. Sporadic permafrost is associated with mean annual temperatures of zero to –5°C.

Sea and Lake Ice

Another measure of the impact of climate change is found in sea and lake ice. While sea ice varies in thickness and duration across the North, the most durable and thickest ice is found in the permanent **Arctic ice pack**. Seasonal melting of lake and sea ice follows a temporal pattern: lake ice disappears first in the Great Lakes and sea ice in Hudson Bay; next, sea ice melts in the offshore waters of Atlantic Canada; and last, the pack ice in the Arctic Ocean diminishes in extent. Over the last several decades, satellite imagery has indicated that the extent of open water in the Arctic Ocean has gradually increased. An increase in open water does not occur each year. For example, a 14 per cent reduction in the volume of summer sea ice in the Arctic Ocean was recorded between 2010 and 2012, but the volume of ice jumped by 41 per cent in 2013, when the summer was 5 per cent cooler than the previous year (European Space Agency, 2015).

Major Drainage Basins

Canada, bounded by the Arctic, Atlantic, and Pacific oceans, is a maritime country (Figure 2.9). Canada has four major drainage basins: the Atlantic Basin, the Hudson Bay Basin, the Arctic Basin, and the Pacific Basin. The Atlantic and Hudson Bay basins both drain into the Atlantic Ocean (Figure 2.9 and Table 2.5).

In addition, a small portion of southern Alberta and Saskatchewan drains southward to the Missouri River, which forms part of the Mississippi River system that empties its water into the Gulf of Mexico. A **drainage basin** is land that slopes towards the sea and is separated from other lands by topographic ridges. These ridges form drainage divides. The Continental or Great Divide of the Rocky Mountains, for example, separates those streams flowing to the Pacific Ocean from those flowing to the Arctic and Atlantic oceans. On the east coast, the Northern Divide extends along the Labrador/Québec boundary and separates waters flowing into the Atlantic Ocean and Hudson Bay. Canada's five drainage basins are shown in Figure 2.9. Given its size and number of islands, Canada has the longest coastline in the world.

While the geographic extent of these drainage basins is fixed, the volume of water flowing through them varies by basin. As well, this volume is expected to increase due to climate warming and the resulting acceleration of the melting of glaciers and permafrost (Menounos, Osborn, Clague, and Luckman, 2009; Clarke, Jarosch, Anslow, Radić, and Menounos, 2015). Both glaciers and permafrost contribute meltwater containing organic and inorganic materials to freshwater systems and, with these additional waters added to the world's oceans, they play a role in the phenomenon of rising sea levels. In addition, the warmer climate is expected to produce more rainfall and less snowfall, especially in the Cordillera. In time, a tipping point will be reached

TABLE 2.5 Canada's Drainage Basins

Drainage Basin	Area (million km²)	Streamflow (m³/second)
Hudson Bay	3.8	30,594
Arctic	3.6	20,491
Atlantic	1.6	29,087
Pacific	1.0	24,951
Gulf of Mexico	<0.1	12
Total	10.0	105,135

Source: Laycock (1987: 32); Dearden and Mitchell (2012: 136).

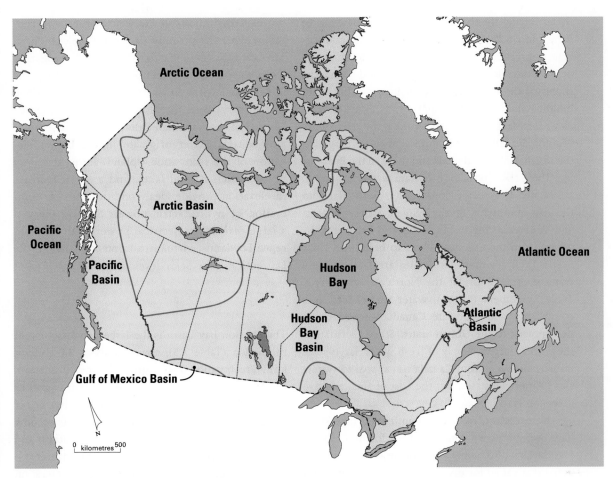

FIGURE 2.9 Drainage basins of Canada

The four divides determine Canada's drainage basins. They are the Continental or Great Divide, the Northern Divide, the Arctic Divide, and the St Lawrence Divide. The Hudson Bay Basin lies between three divides—the Continental Divide, the Arctic Divide, and the Northern Divide—and is by far the largest of the five basins in Canada. It also serves as a boundary between southern Alberta and British Columbia, and between northern Québec and Labrador.

and the volume of meltwater from glaciers and permafrost will decline, resulting in a drop in the volume of water passing through rivers and streams to the oceans, leading to a gradual stabilization of sea levels.

A few rivers cross the US–Canada border, and part of the Great Lakes lies in the United States. The Columbia River leaves British Columbia and continues its journey to the Pacific Ocean through the US states of Idaho, Washington, and Oregon. Two small rivers, the Milk and the Poplar, flow from southern Alberta and Saskatchewan into the Missouri River, which drains much of the northern half of the US Great Plains. The Red River flows from the US states of North Dakota and Minnesota into Manitoba and beyond to Lake Winnipeg and eventually to Hudson Bay by means of the Nelson River. The Richelieu River flows from Lake Champlain, which lies mainly in New York, and drains into the St Lawrence River near Sorel, Québec. The headwaters of the Saint John River partially originate in Maine, and this river empties into the Bay of Fundy at the city of Saint John, New Brunswick.

Historically, the rivers in each basin have played major roles in providing access to the interior of Canada and in the development of the country. For example, Aboriginal peoples and Europeans used the St Lawrence and Mackenzie rivers as transportation routes during the fur trade. Today, the St Lawrence River plays a key role in Canada's internal and foreign shipments of goods to and from Montréal and other cities along the St Lawrence and along the shores of the Great Lakes. River barges bring food, building materials, and other goods to settlements along the Mackenzie River and along the coast of the Beaufort Sea. Oil and gas equipment also is barged to the Norman Wells oil fields and those in the Beaufort Sea. These rivers remain important waterways today.

Water is a scarce commodity, particularly in the dry Southwest of the United States. Arizona and California, for instance, depend on water diverted from the Colorado River to help meet their needs. Even so, these two states are facing severe water shortages. Under the North American Free Trade Agreement (NAFTA), water was classed as a commodity and therefore Canadian water could be exported to the United States. Since Canada has the world's largest supply of fresh water, large-scale transfer of water from Canada has appeal to water-short American states, but the cost of such massive diversion is too great.

Nevertheless, two huge continental diversions have been proposed. One—first put forth in 1959—was the Great Recycling and Northern Development Canal that called for diversion of water from James Bay to the Great Lakes and then, by pipelines, to the water-short American Southwest. Another continental scheme, the North American Water and Power Alliance, was conceived by the US Army Corps of Engineers in the 1950s and proposed diverting the Yukon River and the two major tributaries of the Mackenzie River, the Liard and the Peace, to the US along the Rocky Mountain Trench. Neither proposal has ever come to fruition.

The Atlantic Basin

The Atlantic Basin is centred on the Great Lakes and the St Lawrence River and its tributaries, but the basin also includes Labrador. The Atlantic Basin has the third-largest drainage area and also the second-greatest streamflow. As seen in Figure 2.9, the Atlantic Basin receives considerable precipitation, making it second only to the Pacific Basin. The largest hydroelectric development in this

drainage basin is located at Churchill Falls in Labrador, with the promise of more development at Muskrat Falls on the Lower Churchill River. Earlier hydroelectric developments took place along the St Lawrence River in southern Québec and along its tributary rivers that flow out of the Laurentide Upland of the Canadian Shield. Rivers such as the Manicouagan River originate in the higher elevation of the Laurentide Upland. Here, abundant precipitation, natural lakes, and a sharp increase in elevation provide ideal conditions for the generation of hydroelectric power. Because there is a large market for electrical power in the St Lawrence Lowlands, virtually all potential sites in the Laurentides have been developed.

The Hudson Bay Basin

The Hudson Bay Basin is the largest drainage basin in Canada (Table 2.5), covering about 3.8 million km². Precipitation varies greatly across this basin. In the West, precipitation is low while it is greater in the East (Figure 2.7), where the headwaters of its rivers in the uplands of northern Québec flow westward into James Bay. In northern Ontario and Manitoba, rivers drain into James and Hudson bays.

The large rivers and sudden drops in elevation that occur in the Canadian Shield make this part of the basin ideal for developing hydroelectric power stations. In fact, most of Canada's hydroelectric power is generated in the Canadian Shield area of the Hudson Bay Basin—the largest installations are on La Grande Rivière in northern Québec and on the Nelson River in northern Manitoba. La Grande Rivière's hydroelectric developments are the first stage in the James Bay Project. The Great Whale River Project was to follow the completion of the hydroelectric projects on La Grande Rivière, but a variety of circumstances (low energy demand, low prices in New England, and strong opposition from environmental groups and the Cree of northern Québec) stalled its development. Instead, Québec focused its attention on the Eastmain Diversion Project and the Romaine Hydro Complex.

For further discussion of Québec's hydroelectric developments, see Chapter 7, "Québec's Economic Anchor: Hydro-Québec," page 232.

THINK ABOUT IT

Examine Figures 2.8 and 2.9, which illustrate the extent of glaciers, permafrost, and drainage basins, to determine which drainage basin would benefit the least from the melting of glaciers and permafrost.

THINK ABOUT IT

If the price of water in Arizona and California reaches the point where water diversion from Canada becomes a viable operation, would you support such a project?

The Arctic Basin

The Arctic Basin is Canada's second-largest drainage basin but this basin has the largest coastline, thanks to the many islands in the Arctic Ocean. The Mackenzie River dominates the drainage system in this basin. Along with its major tributaries (the Athabasca, Liard, and Peace rivers), the Mackenzie River is the second-longest river in North America. However, because of low precipitation in the Arctic, this basin has only the fourth-largest streamflow. There are few hydroelectric projects in the Arctic Basin because of the long distance to markets, with the exception of the hydroelectric development on the Peace River in British Columbia. Here, power from the Gordon M. Shrum generating facility is transmitted to the population centres in southern British Columbia and to the United States, primarily to the states of Washington, Oregon, and California.

The Pacific Basin

The Pacific Basin is the smallest basin. However, it has the third-highest volume of water draining into the sea. Heavy precipitation along the coastal mountains of British Columbia accounts for this unusually high streamflow. As a result, the Pacific Basin is the site of one of Canada's largest hydroelectric projects. Located at Kemano, this facility is owned and operated by Rio Tinto, which uses the electrical generating station to supply power to its aluminum smelter at Kitimat. The ice-free, deep-water harbour at Kitimat and low-cost electric power generated at Kemano make Kitimat an ideal location for an aluminum smelter. Kitimat at some point may become a terminal port for natural gas and bitumen pipelines, although shortly after taking office in 2015 Prime Minister Justin Trudeau imposed a ban on oil tanker traffic along BC's north coast, thereby apparently ending the plans for the Northern Gateway pipeline (see Chapter 8). This was confirmed in November 2016 when the government definitively rejected the Northern Gateway pipeline.

Canada and Pollution

In our contemporary world, humans are the most active and dangerous agents of environmental change (Pacheco-Vega, 2015). All human activities affect the environment. Cultivation of the land, building of cities, burning of coal, exploitation of renewable and non-renewable resources, and processing of **primary products** have forever changed our natural environment into an industrial landscape. The mining industry represents a major polluter of our lands and waters while the burning of fossils fuels by coal-burning thermal generating plants and by the operation of vehicles and planes pollutes our air and atmosphere.

Waste affects Canada's regions. Governing waste is a complex and risky activity involving all three levels of government. Their regulations extend over transportation, recycling, and ultimately, disposal. Nuclear waste disposal, for instance, tops the list in terms of dangerous waste products. Mining wastes stored in tailing ponds are less dangerous, but the risk of leakage or rupture in containment structure dams is always present.

Mining and Pollution

Mining, before environmental regulations were in place, left behind toxic wastes. The Giant Yellowknife mine left behind toxic waste that will cost the public millions to neutralize. Even now, mining operations remain major polluters. For example, toxic chemicals from Alberta's vast oil sands tailing ponds have been leaching into groundwater and seeping into the Athabasca River for years. In 2012, Canada's Commissioner of the Environment and Sustainable Development estimated that the cost to the federal government for removing wastes from abandoned mining sites would exceed $4 billion and could reach $7.7 billion (Vaughan, 2012). In 2014, the spectacular breach of the Mount Polley tailing pond at a gold/copper mine in central British Columbia is cause for concern (Photo 2.15). Mining operations across Canada have hundreds of tailing ponds, all containing toxic solutions. Minor breaches are not that uncommon, but the Mount Polley disaster spewed out tonnes of polluted water and toxic sludge. The scope of this disaster is revealed in the report of the Mount Polley Review Panel (2015) and in videos and reports from Global News (2015).

Canada's greenhouse gas emissions peaked in 2007 (Figure 2.10). The Alberta oil sands are a major contributor. In fact, oil sands extraction

THINK ABOUT IT

Ottawa, our capital city, lies in which drainage basin? What about Winnipeg and Calgary?

THINK ABOUT IT

One reason why Canada has the longest coastline in the world is its physical size. But since Russia has an even larger territorial area, why does Russia not have a longer coastline? The answer lies in the fact that Canada has more islands than Russia. Most are found in the Arctic Archipelago.

Photo 2.15 An aerial view shows the damage caused by a tailing pond breach at the Mount Polley mine near the town of Likely, BC. The containment dam broke, discharging 25 million m³ of contaminated water and mining waste into nearby creeks and rivers. The BC government is now strengthening the rules for construction and maintenance of tailing ponds. Is this a case of closing the barn door after the horse has gone?

takes place at several sites, including the Suncor mine (Photo 2.16). As well, oil sands extraction is the primary reason why Alberta is the leading province in greenhouse emissions and why Alberta's emissions increased from 2006 to 2012. Environmental organizations, ranging from international ones such as Greenpeace and the Sierra Club to local ones such as the Pembina Institute, have long targeted the oil sands as a major source of greenhouse gas emissions and therefore one of the industrial culprits affecting global warming. Politicians, too, have entered the fray, with US President Barack Obama finally rejecting approval for the Keystone XL pipeline, his main argument being that the pipeline would lead to an expansion in oil sands production and therefore would increase the amount of greenhouse gases entering the atmosphere (Photo 2.16) at a time when national economies should be transitioning away from fossil fuels as an energy source.

is the primary reason why Alberta accounts for most of Canada's greenhouse gas emissions. Extraction of bitumen also poses risks both to the local environment and to global warming. Open-pit mining is the worst offender and such mining

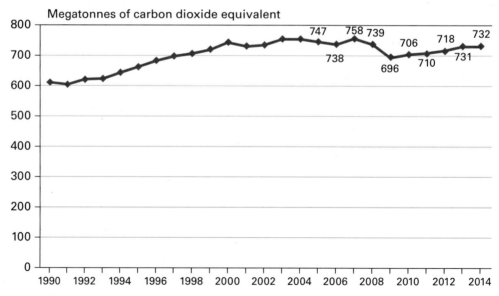

FIGURE 2.10 Greenhouse gas emissions, Canada, 1990–2014

Source: Environment Canada and Climate Change Canada (2016a).

Aurora Photos/ Alamy Stock Photos

Photo 2.16 Alberta's oil sands are a major source of greenhouse gases, both in the extraction and refining processes and in the ultimate burning of the oil produced. Decisions over economic growth or environmental sustainability usually favour economic growth. The oil sands and vast tailing ponds, such as those serving the Suncor oil sands operation near Fort Mc-Murray, Alberta, are a consequence of production. While the oil sands produce the bulk of Canada's oil, the environmental cost is high, including huge greenhouse gas emissions from the upgrading of bitumen.

Air Pollution

Canadians are all too familiar with smog and other forms of **air pollution**. Most air pollution results from industrial emissions and from automobile and truck exhaust. Coal-burning plants and oil sands production account for most industrial pollution, followed by the internal combustion engines found in cars and trucks. The TransAlta Plant in Alberta is the largest coal-burning electric power station in Canada. In 2014, the top three provinces by industrial emissions were Alberta, Ontario, and Québec. Since Ontario closed its Nanticoke Station in December 2013, the province has reduced its emissions while Alberta's emissions have continued to climb (Environment and Climate Change Canada, 2016b). Automobile manufacturers, under government pressure, have decreased the amount of carbon dioxide released into the air from the operation of their vehicles.

For urban dwellers in Canada's larger cities, air pollution can be a serious health problem. Smog, a mixture of smoke, sulphur dioxide, and other contaminants, takes the form of a brownish haze over cities. Vehicles account for over half of urban air pollution. Coal-burning plants are the second principal source of urban air pollution. Densely populated areas like southern Ontario contain millions of automobiles and trucks. Furthermore, southern Ontario is an energy-deficient area. For years, coal thermal plants produced much of the region's electricity at a relatively low cost. Now that urban air pollution has become a health problem, Ontario has sought to limit sulphur dioxide emissions by closing its coal-burning plants, replacing the electrical production with natural gas, nuclear power, and water power. At one time, Ontario was considering importing electricity from Québec, Michigan, New York, and Manitoba. However, a drop in demand that began in 2007, due to more energy-efficient houses and factories and fewer large manufacturers, ended any thought of importing electricity.

SUMMARY

Physical geography varies across Canada. This spatial variation is critical in understanding Canada's regional character. Added to this spatial dimension, climate change is altering key components of our physical geography. Physiography, however, is immune to climate change. Physiographic regions—large areas with similar landforms and geological structures—represent a basic measure of Canada's physical diversity and provide a broad and simple geomorphic framework for understanding Canada. Climate adds to that geography by creating a zonal arrangement of weather patterns, soils, natural vegetation, and wildlife. Climate, therefore, influences land use. This link between the physical and human worlds identifies those regions having a more favourable mix of physical characteristics for settlement and economic development, and translates the abstract core/periphery model into a geographic reality. The Great Lakes–St Lawrence Lowlands region is the most favoured physical region in Canada. Physical barriers, such as the Rocky Mountains, and extreme climatic conditions, such as the very long and cold winters in northern Canada, have also affected the historical settlement of the country and continue to influence contemporary economic activities.

Challenge Questions

1. The Cordillera and the Appalachian Uplands are products of plate tectonic activities but have strikingly different landscapes. The explanation lies in the geological age of the two physiographic regions, which means that geomorphic processes have had longer to work on the Appalachian Uplands. What are these geomorphic processes and how would you describe the two landscapes as shown in photos 2.4 and 2.8?

2. Physiographic regions could replace the six geographic regions as the terms of reference for understanding Canada's geography. Discuss the advantages and disadvantages of using physiographic regions over the geographic regions.

3. What personal evidence do you have to suggest that climate change is affecting the area where you live?

4. Climatologists have determined that over the last 50 years the annual precipitation in Canada has increased. How do they explain this phenomenon?

5. Does Prince Rupert at latitude 54°N have a warmer January than Windsor at 42°N (see Figure 2.5)? Explain.

6. Was the Mount Polley catastrophe a classic example of the old idiom, "closing the barn door after the horse has gone"?

7. Why does the thawing of permafrost cause subsidence of the land?

Essay Questions

1. What is the conceptual model of vulnerability and, applied to Arctic communities, what are the implications of future climate change?

   Reference:

   Ford, James D., Barry Smit, and Johanna Wandel. 2006. "Vulnerability to Climate Change in the Arctic: A Case Study from Arctic Bay, Canada." *Global Environmental Change* 16: 145–60. At: http://citeseerx.ist.psu.edu/viewdoc/download?doi=10.1.1.472.1321&rep=rep1&type=pdf.

2. Richard Muller makes a powerful case for climate change. In his concluding sentence (see "Further Reading" below), Muller states that "the difficult part remains: agreeing across the political and diplomatic spectrum about what can and should be done." Is Canada's national climate change plan—which includes

Prime Minister Trudeau's October 2016 imposition on the provinces of mandatory carbon pricing to take effect by 2018 if provinces have not developed their own plans by then—an impossible dream because of regional/provincial differences?

References:

Donner, Simon, and Kirsten Zickfeld. 2016. *Canada's Contribution to Meeting the Temperature Limits in the Paris Climate Agreement.* At: http://blogs.ubc.ca/sdonner/files/2016/02/Donner-and-Zickfeld-Canada-and-the-Paris-Climate-Agreement.pdf.

Harris, Kathleen. 2016. "Justin Trudeau Gives Provinces until 2018 to Adopt Carbon Price Plan" CBC News, 3 Oct. At: http://www.cbc.ca/news/politics/canada-trudeau-climate-change-1.3788825.

Further Reading

Muller, Richard A. 2012. "The Conversion of a Climate-Change Skeptic." *New York Times*, 28 July. At www.nytimes.com/2012/07/30/opinion/the-conversion-of-a-climate-change-skeptic.html?pagewanted=all; and Berkeley Earth, at BerkeleyEarth.Org.

In a startling release, Richard Muller, a professor of physics at the University of California, Berkeley, who for long had been an outspoken skeptic of global warming, announced that he had become a believer. His change of heart was based on the scientific findings of his research team, Berkeley Earth. Their key finding is that the rise in average world land temperature is approximately 1.5°C in the past 250 years, and about 0.9 degrees in the past 50 years.

In his *New York Times* article, Dr Muller muses about the future. As carbon dioxide emissions increase, temperatures should continue to rise. Furthermore, Muller expects the rate of warming to proceed at a steady pace, about one and a half degrees over land in the next 50 years. However, if China's development and use of its vast coal reserves continues at the current high pace, then that same amount of warming could take place in less than 20 years. (In 2012, China accounted for 49 per cent of world coal consumption, at about 4 billion tons, and 46 per cent of production, followed by the United States at 11 per cent of global consumption and 12 per cent of production [USEIA, 2014]; Canada produces less than 1 per cent.) Finally, Dr Muller hopes that "the Berkeley Earth analysis will help settle the scientific debate regarding global warming and its human causes." He observes that "the difficult part remains: agreeing across the political and diplomatic spectrum about what can and should be done."

3 Canada's Historical Geography

Chapter Overview

In this chapter we will consider the following topics:

- The arrival of Canada's first people.
- The colonization of Canada by the French and the British.
- The settlement of Canada's West by peoples from Central Europe and czarist Russia.
- The territorial evolution of Canada.
- The four faultlines as they have developed in the context of Canada's geography and history.
- The notion of "One Country, Two Visions."
- Two power struggles: economic and political.
- Possible "solutions" to complex problems.

Introduction

In one sense, Canada is a young country. Its formal history began in 1867 with the passing of the British North America (BNA) Act by the British Parliament. In another sense, Canada is an old country with a human history that goes back perhaps as far as 40,000 years. As an old country, its history has followed many twists and turns, but three events stand out because they continue to have a profound impact on the nature of Canadian society. These events are the arrival of the first people in North America and, most importantly, the capacity of their descendants to survive and endure the colonization and assimilation efforts of European settlers and, after 1867, the actions of the federal government; the colonization of North America by France and England and the establishment of British institutions, laws, and values; and, in the early twentieth century, the influx of people from Central Europe and czarist Russia, many of whom settled the prairie lands. In later years, these "outsiders" provided the political push behind government-backed multicultural programs and policies and, at the same time, challenged the previous vision of a French/English Canada.

Given these circumstances, tensions between regions and groups were inevitable. Disagreements arose. The search for solutions to these tensions is a dominant feature of modern Canadian society and, to a large degree, this process of seeking a middle ground accounts for Canadians' high degree of acceptance of various religious and ethnic groups as well as their desire to resolve regional disagreements. However, this tolerance did not magically appear; rather, it was "learned" over time—often after reconsidering past intolerant acts towards minority groups, especially towards Indigenous people and visible minorities. Using John Ralston Saul's metaphor, an underlying theme in this chapter is that Canada evolved from a "hard" country to a "soft" country.

← Indigenous people have deeply influenced the historical geography in all regions of Canada. Carved mortuary and memorial poles at an unoccupied Haida village in the Haida Gwaii archipelago known as SGang Gwaay LInagaay provide one example.

The First People

The first people to set foot on North American soil were <u>Old World hunters</u> who, as early as 40,000 years ago, crossed a land bridge (known as Beringia) into Alaska and Yukon. Beringia was exposed with each ice advance when so much water was contained in the continental ice sheets that the sea level dropped by at least 100 m, thus exposing the ocean bottom between Siberia and Alaska. At the time of the Late Wisconsin ice advance some 18,000 years ago, the Old World hunters in Alaska and Yukon were blocked from proceeding south by an ice sheet that was perhaps 4 km thick (Figure 2.2).

Beginning around 15,000 years ago, the climate warmed and the Great Melt began. Why the climate warmed remains a puzzle, but the result was clear—the ice sheets began their retreat and eventually the Old World hunters migrated into the heart of North America (Dickason with McNab, 2009: 15). But just when these hunters arrived in the south and then evolved culturally into Paleo-Indian peoples poses one question. A second question involves which migration route they took.

Old World hunters penetrated beyond the ice sheets perhaps as early as 15,000 years ago. But what

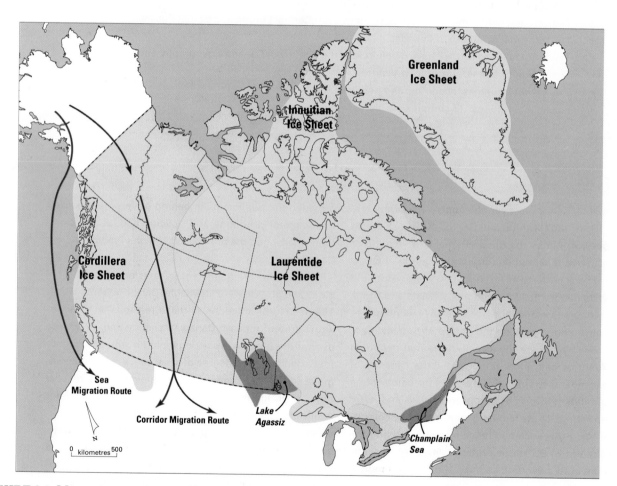

FIGURE 3.1 Migration routes into North America

Archaeologists originally believed that the Corridor Route along the eastern edge of the Rocky Mountains was exposed by 14,000 years ago, allowing the descendants of the Old World hunters to reach the heart of North America. More recently, the Sea Route has gained favour because it explains how human beings could have arrived south of the ice sheet before the Great Melt created the ice-free corridor between the two ice sheets (Pedersen et al., 2016).

is the archaeological evidence? Solid evidence indicates that, some 13,500 years ago, the Paleo-Indians known as Clovis culture inhabited New Mexico. In 2016, archaeological finds in Florida revealed that descendants of the Old World hunters occupied the Americas at least a thousand years earlier (Halligan et al., 2016).

Until the evidence became clear that Old World hunters had reached the interior of North America before 13,500 years ago, the Corridor Route seemed to provide the answer. Accordingly, the Old World hunters who had been blocked from proceeding south by the ice sheet were now able to migrate south through the narrow ice-free route between the Cordillera and the Laurentide ice sheets (Figure 3.1). Archaeologists estimated that this ice-free corridor appeared about 14,000 years ago. However, Pedersen and colleagues (2016) demonstrate that natural vegetation and wildlife took another 1,000 years or so to make the Corridor biologically sustainable for human migration. As a result of this recent finding, the Corridor Route was clearly not the first passage taken by Old World hunters to the heart of North America. Nevertheless, this passage to the unglaciated lands of North America remained an important natural route for more recent migrations from the Old World.

The Sea Route theory provides the most plausible explanation for the peopling of the Americas before 14,000 years ago. The Old World hunters used an island-hopping system just off the sea edge of the Cordillera Ice Sheet. Once they reached the unglaciated US Pacific coast, these Old World hunters had access to the interior of North America and its rich flora and fauna well before 14,000 years ago. However, archaeological evidence of such a route is lacking because these ancient island campsites, if they existed, are now well below the current sea level, as is Beringia, where generations of Old World hunters likely lived before migrating further east to the North American continent.

Paleo-Indians

The **Paleo-Indians**, the people who devised the fluted spear points characteristic of Clovis culture, were descendants of the Old World hunters. The oldest fluted points found in North America are about 13,500 years old. These spearheads, along with the bones of woolly mammoths, have been discovered in the southern part of the Canadian Prairies. By 11,000 years ago, many of the large species, such as the woolly mammoths and the mastodons, had become extinct, possibly as a result of excessive hunting and/or climatic change. Later Paleo-Indian cultures, which archaeologists refer to collectively as Folsom and Plano, developed a variety of unfluted stone points with stems for attachment to spear shafts. These technological changes made weapons more suitable for hunting buffalo and caribou. About 8,000 years ago, hunters in the grasslands of the interior of Canada pursued the buffalo, while those in the tundra and forest lands of northern and eastern Canada depended on caribou for most of their food.

These smaller prey species could not support large numbers of people, so the Paleo-Indians had to develop new survival strategies. These strategies involved remaining in one area (and presumably keeping other peoples out of that area), developing effective hunting techniques for the local game, and making extensive use of fish and plants to supplement their principal diet of game. The time frame provided by Thomas (1999: 10) divides Paleo-Indians into three groups:

- Clovis culture from 13,500 to 12,500 thousand years ago;
- Folsom culture from 11,000 to 10,200 thousand years ago;
- Plano culture from 10,000 to 8,000 thousand years ago.

This link between geographic territory and hunting societies marked the development of Paleo-Indian culture areas with the following two characteristics: (1) a common set of natural conditions that resulted in similar plants and animals; and (2) inhabitants who used a common set of hunting, fishing, and food-gathering techniques and tools. Under these conditions, Paleo-Indians formed more enduring social units that became the forerunners of the numerous Indigenous North American tribes at the time of contact with Europeans.

Indigenous Peoples

Most archaeologists support the idea that Algon-quians (e.g., Cree, Ojibwa) are direct descendants of Paleo-Indians, but they are less certain about Athapaskans (e.g., Dene, Chipewyan, Gwich'in), whose ancestors may have arrived from Asia some 10,000 years ago. Since the Paleo-Indian culture had emerged some 13,500 years ago, the Athapaskans represent a distinct Indigenous culture. But how did the early Athapaskans cross waters of the Bering Strait? Archaeologists suggest that the ancient ancestors of the Athapaskans either walked across the frozen Bering Strait or crossed it in small, primitive boats.

Around 12,000 years ago, the Laurentide Ice Sheet had retreated from the Interior Plains and the Great Lakes. At that time, climatic zones ranged from a tropical climate in Mexico to an Arctic climate just south of the Laurentide Ice Sheet. These climatic zones provided different agricultural opportunities for Indigenous tribes in North America. About 5,000 years ago, Indigenous peoples living in the tropical climate of Mexico began to domesticate plants and animals. This agricultural system and its people gradually

TABLE 3.1 Timeline: Old World Hunters to Contact with Europeans

Date	Events: Possible and Actual
(BP = years before present)	
40,000–35,000 BP	Old World hunters from Asia may have crossed the Beringia land bridge into the unglaciated areas of Alaska and southern Yukon but were blocked by the Cordillera Ice Sheet from moving into the rest of North America.
35,000–32,000 BP	Corridor Route became ice-free in this interglacial period, and, in pursuing the woolly mammoth, the Paleo-Indians may have found their way further south.
24,000–18,000 BP	Late Wisconsin Ice Age: Old World hunters from Asia crossed the Beringia land bridge into the unglaciated areas of Alaska and southern Yukon, but were blocked by the ice sheet from moving into the rest of North America.
20,000 BP	The Wisconsin ice sheets reach a maximum geographic extent, covering virtually all of Canada.
15,000 BP	As the climate warmed, the ice sheets retreat rapidly in western Canada, exposing a narrow ice-free area along the foothills of the Rocky Mountains known as the Corridor Route. At the same time, the Cordillera Ice Sheet withdrew from the Pacific coast, making island-hopping along the Sea Route more amenable.
13,500 BP	Carbon dating of stone points from the Clovis culture provides solid evidence of Paleo-Indian presence in New Mexico some 13,500 years ago.
11,000 BP	Mammoths and mastodons become extinct, forcing early inhabitants of North America to adjust their hunting practices and thereby become more mobile and less numerous.
5,000 BP	As the Arctic coast became ice-free, Paleo-Eskimo (known as the Denbigh) hunters were the first people to cross the Bering Strait to the Arctic coast of Alaska. Within 2,000 years, they moved eastward along the Canadian section of the Arctic coast and eventually reached Greenland.
3,000 BP	The Dorset people represented another wave of Arctic immigrants and, with a more advanced technology suited for an Arctic marine environment, they either absorbed or replaced the Denbigh hunters. What are believed by some scholars to be the last Dorset people, known as Sadlermiut, lived in isolation principally on Southhampton Island in Hudson Bay and became extinct around 1902.
1,000 CE (common era)	A third wave of Arctic hunters, known as the Thule, migrated across the Arctic, eventually reaching the coast of Labrador. Their primary source of food was the bowhead whale. At the same time Vikings reached Greenland and North America, where they established a settlement on the north coast of Newfoundland (L'Anse aux Meadows).
1450 CE	Climate cooling marked the onset of the Little Ice Age. Both Thule and Vikings suffered in the colder environment with the Viking settlement disappearing and the Thule culture evolving from hunters of bowhead whales to the Inuit culture of small-game hunters (see Vignette 2.13).
1497 CE	John Cabot lands on the east coast (Newfoundland or Nova Scotia).
1534 CE	Jacques Cartier plants the flag of France near Baie de Chaleur.
1576 CE	Martin Frobisher sails to Baffin Island and makes contact with Inuit.

spread northward into areas with more restrictive growing conditions. These climatic differences required Indigenous peoples to adapt their agricultural system accordingly. About 3,000 years ago, Indigenous peoples in what is today the eastern United States planted corn, beans, and squash (known as "the three sisters"), which supplemented their diet of game and fish. Table 3.1 outlines significant events in the peopling of what is today Canada to the time of contact with Europeans.

Agriculture was not possible north of the Great Lakes–St Lawrence Lowlands because of the shorter growing season for corn and other crops. Algonquian-speaking Indigenous peoples who lived north of the Great Lakes had to hunt big-game animals, particularly caribou, for sustenance. They also traded with those more sedentary Indigenous peoples, such as the Huron and Iroquois, who practised a form of slash-and-burn (swidden) agriculture in the Great Lakes–St Lawrence Lowlands and in the Ohio Valley. By the sixteenth century, the Huron controlled the agricultural lands between Lake Simcoe and the southeastern corner of Georgian Bay, where about 7,000 acres were under cultivation and where Indigenous villages with populations as large as 1,500 persons, and in some cases considerably larger, were commonplace (Dickason with McNab, 2009: 46–7). In western North America, agriculture spread northward along the valleys of the Mississippi River and its major tributary, the Missouri River. Tribes on the Canadian Prairies engaged in trade for agricultural products with tribes along the upper reaches of the Missouri River. In the Northwest, Athapaskan-speaking Indigenous peoples, whose ancestors probably came from Asia much later (perhaps between 7,000 and 10,000 years ago), continued to practise a nomadic lifestyle of hunting and gathering. They moved about in the forest lands stalking big-game animals and made summer hunting trips to the tundra where the caribou had their calving grounds.

Arctic Migration

Arctic Canada became a human habitat much later than the forested lands of the Subarctic. Before people could occupy the Arctic Lands, two developments were necessary. The first was the melting of

Photo 3.1 A tent ring located near Igloolik, Nunavut. The stone ring indicates the edges of the tent's skin walls, which were weighted down with rocks. Tent rings similar to this one mark sites where Thule families located their tents.

Alec Aitken

the ice sheets that covered this physiographic region. About 8,000 years ago, the western Arctic was ice-free and only small remnants of the great Laurentide Ice Sheet remained in mountains found in northeastern Canada. The second development was the emergence of a hunting technique that would enable people to live in an Arctic marine environment. About 5,000 years ago, the Paleo-Eskimos had developed an Arctic sea-based hunting tradition. Shortly thereafter, they began to move eastward from coastal Siberia to the marine environment of Alaska and then into Arctic Canada. This Paleo-Eskimoan hunting culture is known as the Denbigh. Unlike previous marine hunting societies, these people invented a harpoon and other tools that enabled them to hunt seals and other marine mammals, though they also relied heavily on terrestrial game such as the caribou. About 3,000 years ago, a second migration from Alaska took place. Known as the Dorset culture, this culture replaced the Denbigh. The third and final Arctic migration took place roughly 1,000 years ago, when the Thule people, who had developed a sophisticated sea-hunting culture, spread eastward from Alaska and gradually succeeded their predecessors. The Thule, the ancestors of the Inuit, hunted the bowhead whale and the

THINK ABOUT IT

In all societies, food security is a critical element. Which of the two groups—the hunters or the agriculturalists—would have better food security and thus be less likely to face starvation?

walrus. However, the climate began to cool (known as the Little Ice Age) and whales no longer entered the Arctic Ocean in large numbers because the ocean was covered by ice for most of the year (Vignette 2.13). The Inuit became more nomadic and hunted smaller game such as the seal and the caribou.

A fuller discussion of the Little Ice Age and its impact on the Thule is found in Vignette 2.13, "Fluctuations in World Temperatures," page 46.

Initial Contacts

Long before the time of European contact, the descendants of Old World hunters occupied all of North and South America. Yet, Europeans considered the New World terra nullius or empty lands. North American First Nations and Inuit tribes met the European explorers searching for a trade route to the Orient. While the total population of these tribes can only be estimated, many scholars now believe there may have been as many as 500,000 First Nations people and Inuit living in Canada at the time of first contact. The greatest concentrations were found along the Pacific coast, where marine resources provided abundant food, and in the Great Lakes–St Lawrence Lowlands, where agriculture supported relatively large sedentary populations. Following contact, their numbers dropped sharply, perhaps declining to 100,000. By 1871, the Census of Canada reported an Indigenous population of 122,700 (Romaniuc, 2000: 136). Loss of hunting grounds to European settlers and the spread of new diseases by explorers, fur traders, and missionaries greatly contributed to this depopulation.

In the early seventeenth century, the sudden collapse of Huronia, the most powerful Indigenous group in the region, took place shortly after contact with the French. Their numbers dropped from 21,000 to less than half this number within a decade. This demographic catastrophe was not unique to Huronia, but it does provide one example of the deadly impact of European diseases and the cost of colonial alliances on the Indigenous peoples. French missionaries unwittingly brought diseases to the Huron villages, while the Iroquois, who opposed the French–Huron alliance, attacked the Huron villages and eventually destroyed the Huron Confederacy in 1649. In little more than a generation, Huron villages were abandoned, the cornfields of Huronia reverted to forest, and its people were greatly reduced in numbers and scattered across the land, some finding their way to the north shore of the St Lawrence in Québec, others being captured and assimilated by the Iroquois, and another remnant joining related tribes in what are today Michigan and Ohio.

John Cabot, the first European explorer to land in Canada after the brief settlement of the Norse at the tip of Newfoundland around AD 1000, reached the east coast in 1497. Cabot was followed by others, including Jacques Cartier and Martin Frobisher. In 1534 Cartier made contact with two Indigenous tribes along the Gaspé coast, and in 1576 Frobisher encountered an Inuit encampment along the Arctic coast of southern Baffin Island. Both explorers were searching for a

Photo 3.2 Relationships between explorers and Indigenous peoples were not always peaceful. In this painting by John White, the artist, a member of Frobisher's second expedition in 1577, records a fight between Frobisher's crew and Baffin Island Inuit.

route to Asia, but instead discovered a new continent and peoples. In both instances, contact with North Americans ended badly. Lives were lost on both sides, some Native North Americans were captured and brought to Europe as "prizes" and proof of discovery, and ore that the explorers took back to Paris and London, respectively, proved worthless. Instead of gold, they had found fool's gold (iron pyrites).

Culture Regions

At the time of contact with Europeans, Indigenous peoples occupied specific territories (cultural regions). Within each cultural region, these first human inhabitants developed distinct techniques suitable for the local environment and wildlife. The seven culture regions in present-day Canada are the Eastern Woodlands, Eastern Subarctic, Western Subarctic, Arctic, Plains, Plateau, and Northwest Coast (Figure 3.2). The Inuit occupied the Arctic cultural region. In the Eastern Subarctic, the Cree were the principal Algonquian tribe, and further east the Innu (Naskapi and Montagnais) resided. The Cree in this region had developed a technology—snowshoes—to hunt moose in deep snow. In the Western Subarctic, the Athapaskans, including a number of Dene tribes, hunted caribou and other big-game animals. Indigenous peoples of the Northwest Coast harvested the rich marine

THINK ABOUT IT

Imagine yourself to be Captain Martin Frobisher. How would you communicate with the Baffin Island Inuit who held several of your sailors?

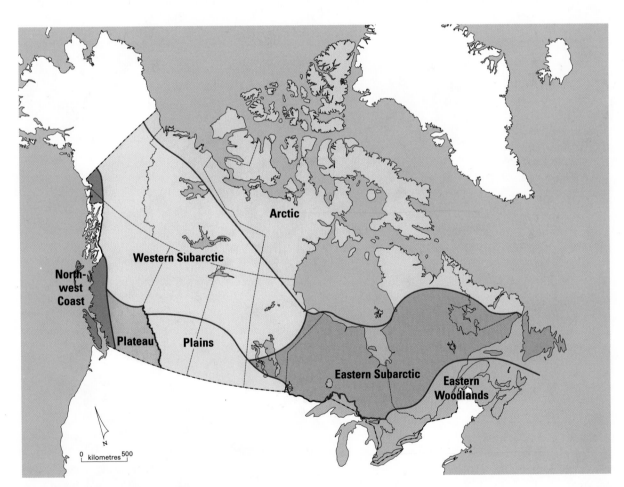

FIGURE 3.2 Culture regions of Indigenous peoples

Resources and natural conditions found in culture regions provided the foundation for the formation of unique spatial versions of Indigenous hunting systems and social organizations, and accounted for varying population densities. For example, the reliable and rich sea resources found along the Northwest Coast supported one of the densest Indigenous populations, while the opposite was true for the Indigenous peoples in the Subarctic and the Inuit in the Arctic.

THINK ABOUT IT

European countries claimed various parts of North America. What was the basis of their claim of sovereignty over lands they "discovered"?

life found along the Pacific coast. Tribes such as the Haida, Nootka (Nuu-chah-nulth), and Salish comprised the Northwest Coast cultural region. In the southern interior of British Columbia, the Plateau peoples—including the Carrier, Lillooet, Okanagan, and Shuswap—occupied the valleys of the Cordillera, forming the Plateau cultural region. Across the grasslands of the Canadian West, Plains peoples such as the Assiniboine, Blackfoot, Sarcee, and Plains Cree hunted bison. The Iroquois and Huron were among those living in the Eastern Woodlands of southern Ontario and Québec, although the Iroquois were primarily based further south, in present-day New York State. Both groups combined agriculture with hunting. In the Maritimes, the Mi'kmaq and Maliseet also occupied the Eastern Woodlands, where they hunted and fished. The complexity and diversity of Indigenous peoples can be gleaned from the spatial arrangement of their languages (Figure 3.3).

The Second People

The colonization of North America by the French and the British set the stage for Canada's early history. France and England established colonies in North America in the seventeenth century. Québec City, founded in 1608 by Samuel de Champlain, was the first permanent settlement in Canada. By 1663, the French population in New France was about 3,000 compared to a population of about

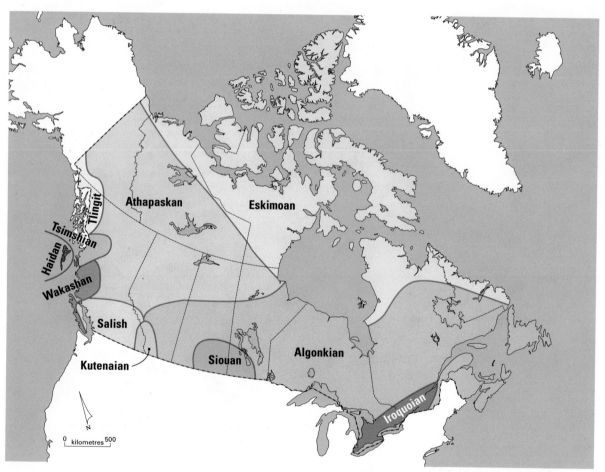

FIGURE 3.3 Indigenous language families

Indigenous peoples in Canada form a very diverse population. At the time of contact, there were over 50 distinct Indigenous languages spoken. These languages formed 11 language families, five of which were in one natural cultural region, the Northwest Coast. Following contact, language loss was swift. By the end of the twentieth century, only three Indigenous languages, Cree, Inuktitut, and Ojibwa, had over 20,000 speakers.

Photo 3.3 The American Revolution (1775–83) divided the residents of the Thirteen Colonies. With the defeat of British forces, those British subjects who did not support the revolutionary cause were forced to leave, losing their property and sometimes their lives. Considered traitors by Americans, Loyalists were often subjected to mob violence.

10,000 Indigenous people (mainly Huron and Iroquois), who lived in the same area of the St Lawrence Valley, the Great Lakes, and the Ohio Basin. By 1750, the French Canadians numbered about 60,000, while the Indigenous population continued to drop because of disease and warfare. Following the British Conquest of New France in 1759, the flow of French colonists ceased and British immigrants began to move to what used to be New France. Meanwhile, the French-Canadian population depended entirely on natural population increase.

The first large contingent of British immigrants to Canada consisted of Loyalists who had supported Britain during the American War of Independence (1775–83). After the defeat of the British army, they sought refuge in other parts of the British Empire, including its North American possessions. In North America, most Loyalists settled in Nova Scotia, while a smaller number moved to the **Eastern Townships** of Québec and to Montréal. Others settled in what is now southern Ontario. At the end of the American War of Independence, the forty-fifth parallel was established as the border between Lower Canada (Québec) and New York State and Vermont. The St Lawrence River and the Great Lakes became the boundary between Upper Canada and the United States.

The Second Wave of British Immigrants

The second wave of British immigrants occurred in the first half of the nineteenth century. Almost a million people migrated from Britain to British North America. In the 1840s, for example, the potato famines in Ireland caused terrible hardships for the Irish people. Thousands fled the countryside and many left for North America, settling in the towns and cities of British North America and the United States.

British immigrants greatly changed Canada, by turning the demographic balance of power from a French-Canadian majority to an English-speaking one. At the time of Confederation in 1867, the population of British North America had reached 3 million, with over 60 per cent of British descent. While the French Canadians were concentrated in Québec and New Brunswick, most English-speakers lived in Upper Canada, the major cities in Québec, and the Maritimes. Across the rest of British North America, Indigenous people made up most of the population. In the Red River Settlement, a new Indigenous people, the Métis, who were of Native and European descent, had emerged. By 1869, the Métis, who were split between French- and English-speaking, greatly outnumbered white settlers and fur traders in the settlement, which had a population of nearly 12,000. The Métis formed over 80 per cent of this population (Table 3.2).

Immigration changed the ethnic composition of the English-speaking population from almost entirely English to a mixture of English, Irish, Scottish, and Welsh. Moreover, by the 1860s, Canada's ethnic character varied by region. In Atlantic Canada, the Scottish and Irish outnumbered the English. In Québec, the English and Irish formed a sizable minority in the towns and cities, though rural Québec remained solidly French-speaking except in the Eastern Townships. Ontario, like Atlantic Canada, was decidedly British.

Canada began as a collection of four small British colonies—Upper and Lower Canada, New Brunswick, and Nova Scotia—with a population under 4 million. In sharp contrast, the United States had a population of nearly 10 times that of Canada.

Further discussion of two visions of Canada is found later in this chapter in the section "The French/English Faultline," page 103.

The Death of Brock at Queenston Heights C. W. Jefferys c. 1908 watercolour on paper Government of Ontario Art Collection, 619871

Photo 3.4 The death of General Brock at Queenston Heights. On 13 October 1812, the first major battle of the War of 1812 took place when American troops crossed the Niagara River with the objective of establishing a military base on Canadian soil before winter set in. These invaders were repelled by British troops, Canadian militia, and Mohawk warriors, forcing the Americans to retreat to the American side of the river. Early in the battle, General Isaac Brock was mortally shot while he led a charge on American forces who had taken a strategic position at the top of Queenston Heights. The War of 1812 was a stalemate, though both the British/Canadians and the Americans claimed victory. As Laxer (2012: 1) points out, however, the Indigenous forces led by Tecumseh lost, as the war failed to halt the unyielding westward march of settlers, first in America and later in Canada. This C.W. Jefferys painting, c. 1908, romantically and heroically depicts Brock's death.

TABLE 3.2 Population of the Red River Settlement, 1869

Ethnic Group	Population Size	Population Percentage
Whites born in Canada	294	2.5
Whites born in Britain or a foreign country	524	4.4
First Nations	558	4.7
Whites born in Red River	747	6.2
English-speaking Métis	4,083	34.1
French-speaking Métis	5,757	48.1
Total population	11,963	100.0

Source: Adapted from Lower (1983: 96).

The Third People

In 1870, Ottawa obtained the vast land of the Hudson's Bay Company and was faced with the question of settling this territory. Little progress was made until after the signing of treaties with various Plains tribes, the completion of a land survey, and the driving of the final spike in the Canadian Pacific Railway in November 1885 (Vignette 3.1).

The Land Survey System was crucial to the settling of the Prairies and, in turn, this system organized the human landscape into townships and sections. In 1872, the federal government passed the Dominion Lands Act. This legislation established a survey system that divided the land into square townships made up of 36 sections, each measuring 1 mile by 1 mile, with allowances for roads. Each section was further subdivided into four quarters, each quarter section measuring one-half mile by one-half mile and comprising 160 acres. This survey system gave the Canadian Prairies a distinctive "checkerboard" pattern.

The last large area of arable lands in North America was opened to settlers. A free grant of one quarter section was available to persons 21 years or older with the payment of a $10 fee. Upon fulfilling cultivation

Vignette 3.1

Unity through the CPR

Prime Minister John A. Macdonald envisioned a transcontinental railway that would unite the four provinces with the newly acquired territories from the Hudson's Bay Company. Macdonald realized that those living in the Red River Valley saw St Paul, Minnesota, as their natural market for trade and this north/south linkage could cause the West to drift into the orbit of the United States. Without such a railway, Macdonald feared that American settlers would turn to the fertile lands in the Red River Valley and then beyond into the Canadian Prairies—a repeat of the annexation of the Oregon Territory in 1846 (Vignette 3.4). He knew that British Columbia, isolated on the Pacific coast, felt the same north/south pull of the United States. In 1871, Macdonald made a daring—some would say reckless—promise to build a railway across Canada to unite the country. The CPR remains one of Macdonald's greatest legacies and has been the subject of numerous books and songs. These include Pierre Berton's books, *The National Dream* (1970) and *The Last Spike* (1972), Gordon Lightfoot's well-known song, "Canadian Railroad Trilogy," which was commissioned by the CBC for a Centennial celebration broadcast in 1967, and Harold Innis's *A History of Canadian Pacific Railway* (1923).

Source: http://web.archive.org/web/20070410201902/http://www8.cpr.ca/cms/nr/cprinternet/images/cprchildrenshistory.pdf.

THINK ABOUT IT

Homesteaders far from the railway had to use local resources for building materials. What resource was readily available in the prairie landscape?

and residency requirements within three years of acquiring the property, the homesteader would receive title to the land. Since Ottawa had made substantial land grants to the Canadian Pacific Railway (CPR) and to the Hudson's Bay Company (HBC), not all the land was free. Both the CPR and the HBC sold their land at market prices, thus making a considerable profit.

For Canada, occupying the Prairies allowed the country to expand its population and to remove the threat of America annexing these lands. Also, the creation of a grain economy would provide freight for the Canadian Pacific Railway, thereby helping turn it into a viable operation. But where to find such people? Some came from Ontario, Québec, and Atlantic Canada to claim their 160 acres as homesteaders; others came from Britain and the United States. But the bulk came from non-English-speaking countries in Continental Europe and czarist Russia. As these settlers came west, the hegemony of the British and French was broken and Western Canada became a mixture of British, French, and non-English-speaking people.

By the end of the nineteenth century, much of Western Canada still was not occupied. Clifford Sifton, the Minister of the Interior, accepted the challenge to settle the West. By the beginning of the twentieth century, Sifton had launched an aggressive and innovative advertising campaign to lure people from Britain and the United States to "The Last Best West," but this effort failed to bring sufficient immigrants. At that point, he recognized the need to go beyond these two countries. In a break with past immigration policy, Sifton turned his attention to the people of Central Europe, Scandinavia, and czarist Russia. Land-hungry peasants from Ukraine formed the largest single group of immigrants but Doukhobors and German-speaking Mennonites also came from czarist Russia, giving Western Canada a distinct and different mix of ethnic groups and landholdings, with communal rather than individual landholdings the norm among some groups. From 1901 to 1921, Western Canada's population increased from 400,000 to 2 million, and Saskatchewan became the third-most populous province by 1921 (Table 3.3). As these ethnic groups and individuals spread across the Prairies, their impact was enormous on a landscape that only recently had been populated largely by vast herds of buffalo and semi-nomadic Indigenous tribes (see Kerr and Holdsworth, 1990: Plate 17).

By opening the door for immigration from European countries without a French or British background, Sifton's immigration policy changed the face of Canada. His goal of settling the West

TABLE 3.3 Canada's Population by Provinces and Territories, 1901 and 1921

Political Unit	Population 1901	%	Population 1921	%
Ontario	2,182,947	40.6	2,933,662	33.4
Québec	1,648,898	30.7	2,360,510	26.9
Nova Scotia	459,574	8.6	523,837	6.0
New Brunswick	331,120	6.2	387,876	4.4
Manitoba	255,211	4.8	610,118	6.9
Northwest Territories*	20,129	0.4	8,143	0.1
Prince Edward Island	103,259	1.9	88,615	1.0
British Columbia	178,657	3.3	524,582	6.0
Yukon	27,219	0.5	4,147	>0.1
Saskatchewan	91,279	1.7	757,510	8.6
Alberta	73,022	1.3	588,454	6.7
Canada	5,371,315	100.0	8,787,949**	100.0

*Saskatchewan and Alberta did not become provinces until 1905 and were officially included in the population of the Northwest Territories.

**Includes 485 members of the armed forces.

Source: Adapted from Statistics Canada (2003).

was accomplished, and a new dimension had been added to Canada's social fabric—people with neither a French nor a British background. The immigration to the Canadian Prairies from 1896 to 1914 forms the topic for more detailed discussion later in this chapter under the subheading "The Immigration Faultline."

The Territorial Evolution of Canada

Canada's formal history as a nation began with the proclamation of the British North America Act on 1 July 1867. This Act of the British Parliament united the colonies of New Brunswick, Nova Scotia, and the Province of Canada (formerly Upper Canada and Lower Canada) into the Dominion of Canada.[1] Canada soon acquired more territory. In 1870, the Deed of Surrender transferred Rupert's Land and the North-Western Territory to the federal government, at which time this large expanse that had been under HBC control was renamed the North-West Territories. In 1871, British Columbia joined Confederation, and Prince Edward Island followed two years later. In 1880, Ottawa acquired the Arctic Archipelago from Great Britain. Thus, while Canada began as a small country, consisting of what is now known as southern Ontario, southern Québec, New Brunswick, and Nova Scotia, it quickly became one of the largest in the world (Figures 3.4 and 3.5).

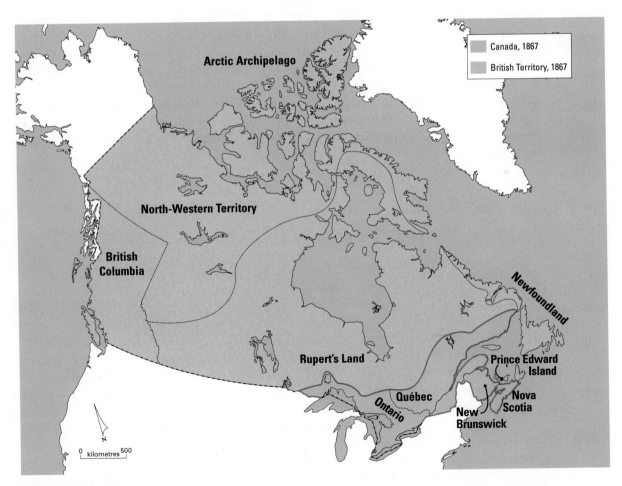

FIGURE 3.4 Canada, 1867

At Confederation, Canada, consisting of Ontario, Quebec, Nova Scotia and New Brunswick, was only a fraction of its current territorial extent. The Hudson's Bay Company controlled most of British North America, including Rupert's Land and the North-Western Territory. With the transfer of these British lands to Canada, a transcontinental nation was born (Table 3.4).

What was behind these real estate deals? For Britain, the American doctrine of **Manifest Destiny** (Vignette 3.2), first expressed in the early nineteenth century, lurked in the political background of British–American diplomacy. More specifically, the union of its North American colonies had three advantages for Britain: (1) a better chance for the political survival of these colonies against the growing economic and military strength of the United States; (2) an improved environment for British investment, especially for the proposed trans-Canada railway; and (3) a reduction in British expenditures for the defence of its colonies.

The British colonies perceived unification differently. The Province of Canada, led by John A. Macdonald, pushed hard for a united British North America because it would have a larger domestic market for its growing manufacturing industries and a stronger defensive position against a feared American invasion. The Atlantic colonies showed little interest in such a union. As they were part of the British Empire, the attraction of joining the Province of Canada had little appeal. Furthermore, unlike the Canadians, Maritimers continued to base their prosperity on a flourishing transatlantic trading economy with Caribbean countries and Great Britain. From 1840 to 1870, the backbone of the Maritime economy was the construction of wooden sailing-ships. Shipbuilding was so important that this period was known as the "Golden Age of Sail" in the Maritimes. Even diplomatic pressure from Britain to join Confederation had little effect on Maritime politicians. But the Fenian raids into New Brunswick in 1866 and the termination of the Reciprocity Treaty with the United States quickly changed public opinion in the Maritimes.[2] Shortly after the Fenian raids, the legislatures of both New Brunswick and Nova Scotia voted to join Confederation.

Within a decade, the territorial extent of Canada expanded from four British colonies to the northern half of North America. The new Dominion grew in size with the addition of other British colonies and territories and the creation of new political jurisdictions (Figure 3.5), while the British government transferred its claim to the Arctic Archipelago to Canada in 1880. Negotiations between Ottawa and the British colonies in British Columbia and Prince Edward Island soon brought them into the fold of Confederation, in 1871 and 1873, respectively, and the "numbered treaties" were signed with Indigenous tribes of the West beginning in 1871. No such

Vignette 3.2

America's Manifest Destiny

The doctrine of Manifest Destiny was based on the belief that the United States would eventually expand to all parts of North America, thus incorporating Canada into the American republic. From its beginnings along the Atlantic seaboard, the United States had greatly increased its territory by a combination of force, negotiation, and purchase. In 1803, the United States purchased the Louisiana Territory (a vast land west of the Mississippi and east of the Rocky Mountains) from France; in 1846, the US gained the Oregon Territory in negotiations with Great Britain; and in 1867 the country bought Alaska from Russia. To Americans, such expansion was an expression of their right to North America. As well, it would rid North America of the much-hated European colonial powers.

Not surprisingly, the Fathers of Confederation were concerned about American designs on British North America. First, in 1866, the Fenians raided Upper Canada, Lower Canada, and New Brunswick with the grandiose intention of seizing British North America and holding it for ransom until Ireland was free of British rule. Second, in 1867, the American purchase of Alaska left British Columbia wedged between American territory to its north and south, and the exact boundary along the coastline south of 60°N was uncertain. Canada and the United States settled this final border dispute in 1903.

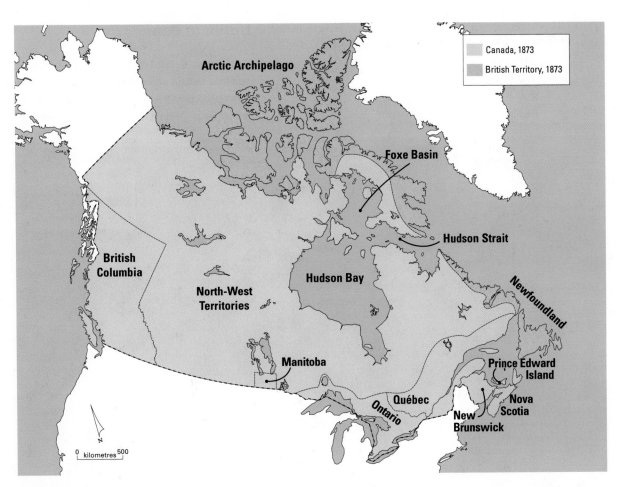

FIGURE 3.5 Canada, 1873

Canada's geographic extent increased between 1867 and 1873. During that short span of time, Canada had obtained the vast Hudson's Bay Company lands (including the Red River Settlement and a small part of the Arctic Archipelago whose streams flow into Hudson Bay and Foxe Basin) as well as two British colonies (British Columbia and Prince Edward Island). For the North-Western Territory and Rupert's Land, the Crown paid the HBC £300,000, granted the Company one-twentieth of the lands in the Canadian Prairies, and allowed it to keep its 120 trading posts and adjoining land. In 1870, these lands were renamed the North-West Territories. In 1880, Britain transferred the Arctic Archipelago to Canada (see Vignette 3.3).

negotiations took place with the Red River Métis. The result was the Red River Rebellion of 1869–70, the formation of the Métis Provisional Government, and then negotiations with Ottawa that led to the Manitoba Act of 1870 and entry into Confederation of an initially tiny Manitoba, consisting of the Red River Settlement and a small surrounding area.

For further discussion of the first Riel-led resistance, see "The First Clash: Red River Rebellion of 1869–70," page 96.

By 1880, Canada stretched from the Atlantic to the Pacific and north to the Arctic. However, political control over its western lands was limited for two reasons—very small populations and no transportation link between the western regions and Central Canada (Vignette 3.1). Still, Canada had begun the slow journey to independence and nationhood. By 1882, its political geography took on a new look with four districts in what is now Alberta and Saskatchewan. These administrative districts were Athabasca, Alberta, Saskatchewan, and Assiniboia (Figure 3.6). At the same time, Manitoba and Ontario vied for the land known as the "disputed area." In 1899, this land was awarded to Ontario. In 1905 the provinces of Alberta and Saskatchewan were created, and much later, in 1949, Newfoundland joined Canada, completing the union of British North

America into a single political entity. (The territorial evolution of Canada is illustrated in Figures 3.4 to 3.9 and Table 3.4.)

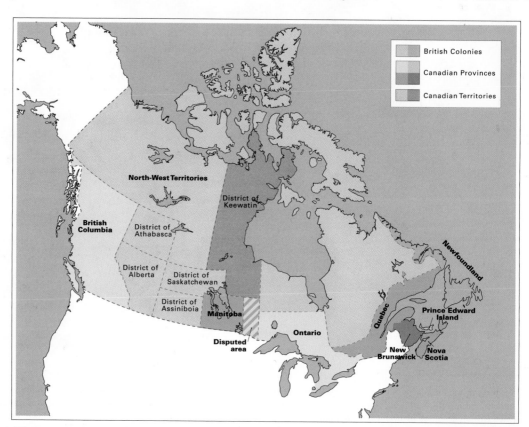

See **Vignette 11.3**, "The Northwest Passage and the Franklin Search," for discussion of the lost Franklin expedition and the search that only ended in 2016.

National Boundaries

Well before Confederation in 1867, wars and treaties between Britain and the United States shaped many of Canada's boundaries. The southern boundary of New Brunswick, Québec, and Ontario was settled in 1783

FIGURE 3.6 Canada, 1882

Governance west of Ontario consisted of two provinces, Manitoba and British Columbia, plus four districts designed to provide a minimum of administrative services to the yet-to-be settled Prairies. The key to settlement and later two more provinces would be the construction of the Canadian Pacific Railway. By the start of 1882, the prairie section of the CPR extended from Winnipeg to just west of Brandon. This and other railway building bound Canada together (see Morrison, 2003).

Source: http://www.rootsweb.ancestry.com/~abcalgar/maps.htm.

TABLE 3.4 Timeline: Territorial Evolution of Canada

Date	Event
1867	Ontario, Québec, New Brunswick, and Nova Scotia unite to form the Dominion of Canada.
1870	The Hudson's Bay Company's lands are transferred by Britain to Canada. The Red River Colony enters Confederation as the province of Manitoba.
1871	British Columbia joins Canada.
1873	Prince Edward Island becomes the seventh province of Canada.
1880	Great Britain transfers its claim to the Arctic Archipelago to Canada.
1949	Newfoundland joins Canada to become the tenth province.

Vignette 3.3

The Transfer of the Arctic Archipelago to Canada

As with the transfer of Hudson's Bay lands in 1870, the territorial size of Canada was greatly increased when Great Britain transferred the Arctic Archipelago to Canada in 1889. Ten years earlier, Canada had acquired the small portion of these lands that drained into Hudson Bay, which included the western half of Baffin Island and several islands located in Hudson Strait, Hudson Bay, and Foxe Basin. Britain's claim to this vast archipelago was based on its naval exploration of the Arctic Ocean. The first venture by Britain into these waters took place in 1576 when Martin Frobisher and his crew sailed to southern Baffin Island. The most intensive exploration took place in the mid-nineteenth century with the search for the lost British naval expedition led by Sir John Franklin.

when Britain and the United States signed the Treaty of Paris. Under this treaty, the United States gained control of the Indigenous lands of the Ohio Basin, with Britain controlling Québec lands draining into the St Lawrence River. Earlier, Britain had formally recognized the rights of "Indians" to the lands of the Ohio Basin, and to the north and west, in the Royal Proclamation of 1763, which provided the constitutional framework for negotiating treaties with Indigenous peoples. This recognition was the basis of **Indigenous rights** in Canada (see "Indigenous Rights" in this chapter). Based on the fur trade route to the western interior, the boundary of 1783 passed through the Great Lakes to Lake of the Woods. In 1818, Canada's southern boundary was adjusted; it was set at 49°N from Lake of the Woods to the Rocky Mountains. As for the northwestern boundary, Britain and Russia set the northern boundary at 141° W (the Treaty of St Petersburg, 1825). In Atlantic Canada, the boundary between Maine and New Brunswick had not been precisely defined in 1783 and, in 1842, Britain and the United States finalized the boundary in the Webster-Ashburton Treaty.

In the early nineteenth century, the border separating Canada's western territories from the United States was not well defined. In fact, it depended on the natural boundary between Rupert's Land and the Louisiana Territory. Rupert's Land was defined by those lands whose waters flow into Hudson Bay while the geographic extent of the Louisiana Territory was determined by the rivers draining into the Mississippi River system. Some oddities resulted—Rupert's

Land included the Red River, which rises in Minnesota and forms much of the North Dakota–Minnesota boundary as it flows north to Manitoba, while the Louisiana Territory had the Milk and Poplar rivers flowing from what are now Alberta and Saskatchewan into the Missouri River. In 1818, Britain and the United States decided on a compromise of the forty-ninth parallel west of Lake of the Woods because it was easier to delineate, and this was extended to the Pacific coast by the Oregon Boundary Treaty of 1846 (Vignette 3.4). With the establishment of the North American Boundary Commission in 1872, the boundary in the West was surveyed and marked (see Photo 3.5).

Internal Boundaries

Since Confederation, the internal boundaries of Canada have changed (Figures 3.4–3.9). These changes have created new provinces (Alberta and Saskatchewan) and territories (Yukon and Nunavut). As well, the boundaries of Manitoba, Ontario, and Québec were extended. In all cases, these political changes took land away from the Northwest Territories.

In 1870, the boundary of Manitoba formed a tiny rectangle comprising little more than the Red River Settlement. The province's western boundary, while extended in 1881 and 1884, did not reach its present limit until 1912. By this time, Manitoba spread north to the boundary with the Northwest Territories (now Nunavut) and east to Lake of the Woods.

THINK ABOUT IT

Why did Canada and the US set the boundary from Lake of the Woods to the Pacific coast at the forty-ninth parallel rather than use the natural boundary between the Mississippi/ Missouri River Basin and the Hudson Bay drainage basin? As a result, the upper reaches of the Red River went to the United States and the headwaters of the Milk and Poplar rivers were assigned to British North America.

Vignette 3.4

The Loss of the Oregon Territory

The last major territorial dispute between Britain and the United States took place over the **Oregon Territory**, which included present-day Oregon, Washington, Idaho, and small portions of Montana and Wyoming, as well coastal British Columbia and Vancouver Island. Britain's claim to the Oregon Territory hinged on exploration and the fur trade while the American claim was based on the large number of recent settlers who cultivated the fertile soils of the Willamette Valley. In the final outcome, there was no doubt that occupancy was a more powerful claim to disputed lands than that based on exploration and the presence of a fur-trading economy. Too late, the British urged the HBC to bring settlers from Fort Garry to the Oregon Territory (the **Red River migration**). With the Oregon Boundary Treaty of 1846, the boundary between British and American territory from the Rockies to the Pacific coast was set at 49°N with the exception of Vancouver Island, which extended south of this parallel.

Royal Canadian Mounted Police/Library and Archives Canada/C-073304

Photo 3.5 A crew from the North American Boundary Commission building a sod mound marking the border between Canada and the United States, August or September 1873. Without a natural feature dividing the two countries, sod mounds marked the boundary between the two countries. Until the completion of the CPR in 1885, these prairie lands remained largely empty of European settlers.

Québec, too, received northern territories. In 1898, its boundary was extended northward to the Eastmain River and then eastward to Labrador. In 1912, Ottawa assigned Québec more territory that extended its lands to Hudson Strait. Canada also believed that the province of Québec should extend to the narrow coastal strip along the Labrador coast, while the colony of Newfoundland contended that Newfoundland owned all the land draining into the Atlantic Ocean. In 1927, this dispute between two British dominions (Canada and Newfoundland) went to London. The British government ruled in favour of Newfoundland (Figure 3.8). The Québec government has never formally accepted this ruling, and though Québec has respected this ruling of nearly a century ago it still impacts relations between the two provinces, especially in regard to hydroelectric development and transmission.

🔁 Contested Terrain 10.1, "Churchill Falls: Bonanza for Québec," page 342, discusses the hydroelectric relationship between Québec and Newfoundland and Labrador.

In the years following Confederation, Ontario gained two large areas. In 1899, its western boundary was set at the Lake of the Woods (previously this area belonged to Manitoba); at the same time, its northern boundary was extended to the Albany River and James Bay. Then, in 1912, Ontario obtained its vast northern lands, which stretch to Hudson Bay.

THINK ABOUT IT

Examine Figures 3.7 and 3.8. Did the decision of King Charles II in 1670—that the Hudson's Bay Company was given control over lands draining into Hudson Bay—affect the determination by the British Privy Council of the 1927 border between Québec and Labrador?

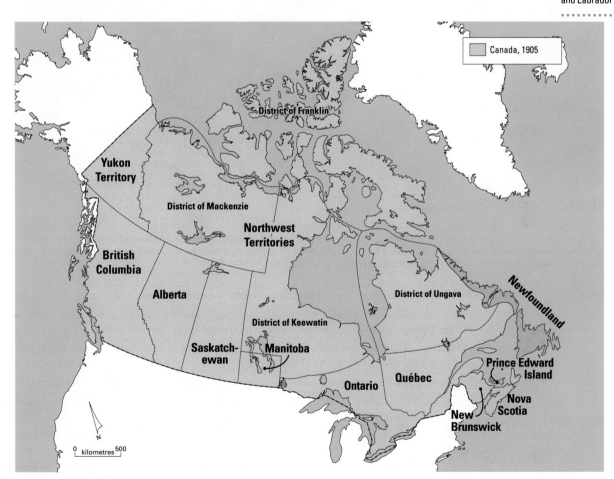

FIGURE 3.7 Canada, 1905

By 1905, two new provinces (Alberta and Saskatchewan) and two territories (Yukon and the Northwest Territories) were created out of the North-West Territories and the Arctic Archipelago, which was ceded to Canada in 1880 and later formed the District of Franklin. As well, the provinces of Ontario, Québec, and Manitoba expanded their boundaries into the former North-West Territories.

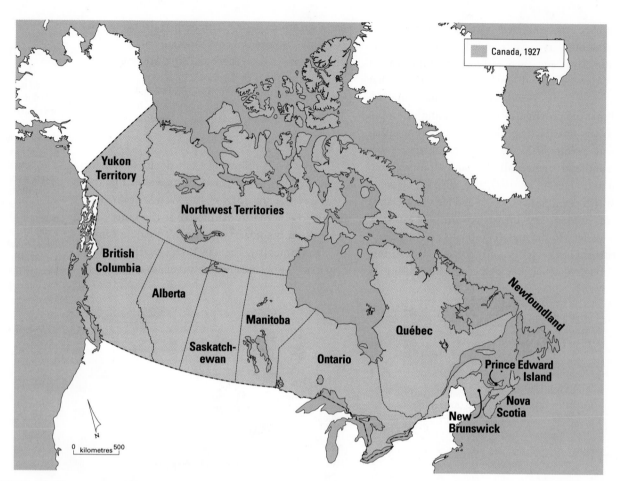

FIGURE 3.8 Canada, 1927

The complicated history of Lower Canada and Newfoundland provided ample justification for both parties to claim the land between the Northern Divide and the coastal strip associated with the fisheries. In 1927, the Privy Council of the British Parliament ruled in favour of Newfoundland by selecting the watershed boundary, a decision that dated back to 1670 when King Charles II created Rupert's Land. In 1912 Ontario, Québec, and Manitoba gained additional northern lands to reach their current geographic size.

In 1905, Canada formed two new provinces, Alberta and Saskatchewan. The final adjustment to Canada's internal boundaries occurred in 1999 with the establishment of the territory of Nunavut (Figure 3.9 and Table 3.5), which was hived off from the Northwest Territories in the eastern Arctic.

Faultlines in Canada's Early Years

Canada's regional geography has always been defined by its faultlines, a notion introduced in Chapter 1. For better or worse, this aspect of regionalism is a fact of life in Canada and it may well be the most telling characteristic of Canada's changing national character over the centuries. Four faultlines described in this text have their roots in Canada's historical geography. In all cases, these cracks in Canada's unity pose powerful challenges to the federal government. The federal government, because it is charged with establishing national policies and programs, tries to keep the country united—but what a task. Even so, the national political parties are most aware that the political power (the number of seats in the House of Commons) is concentrated in Central Canada. Whether real or not, federal policies have seemed to favour the two largest provinces,

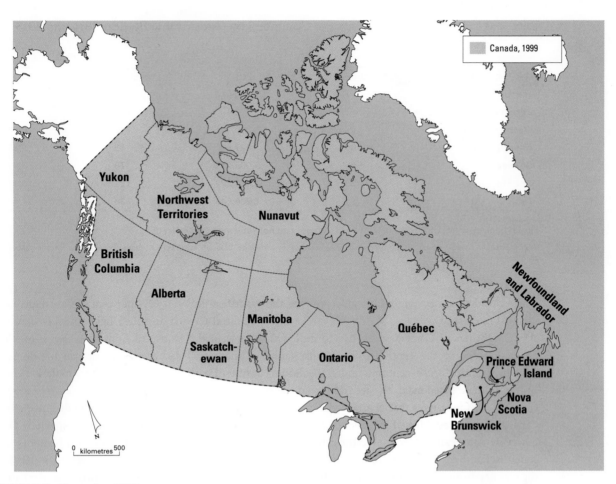

FIGURE 3.9 Canada, 1999

On 1 April 1999, Nunavut became a territory. In 2001, Newfoundland officially added "and Labrador" to its provincial name.

TABLE 3.5 Timeline: Evolution of Canada's Internal Boundaries

Date	Event
1881	Ottawa enlarges the boundaries of Manitoba.
1898	Ottawa approves extension of Québec's northern limit to the Eastmain River.
1899	Ottawa decides to set Ontario's western boundary at Lake of the Woods and extend its northern boundary to the Albany River and James Bay.
1905	Ottawa announces the creation of two new provinces, Alberta and Saskatchewan.
1912	Ottawa redefines the boundaries of Manitoba, Ontario, and Québec, extending them to their present position.
1927	Great Britain sets the boundary between Québec and Labrador as the Northern Divide. Québec has never accepted this decision.
1999	A new territory, Nunavut, is hived off from the Northwest Territories in the eastern Arctic.

TABLE 3.6 Members of the House of Commons by Geographic Region, 1911 and 2015

Geographic Region	1911		2015	
	Members (no.)	Population	Members (no.)	Population
Territorial North	1	15,019	3	111,663
British Columbia	7	392,480	42	4,573,321
Western Canada	27	1,328,121	62	6,087,811
Atlantic Canada*	35	937,855	32	2,357,325
Québec	65	2,005,776	78	7,979,663
Ontario	86	2,527,292	121	13,372,996
Total	221	7,206,543	338	34,482,779

*In 1911, the province of Newfoundland and Labrador had not yet joined Confederation.

Source: Elections Canada, *House of Commons Seat Allocation by Province*, 2015, at: http://www.elections.ca/content.aspx?section=res&dir=cir/red/allo&document=index&lang=e.

Québec and Ontario, under the guise of "in the national interest."

The Fathers of Confederation had to deal with an early form of the centralist/decentralist fault-line. In the nineteenth century, under the leadership of John A. Macdonald, the federal government launched two initiatives that changed the course of Canada's history, established the basis of a core/periphery structure, and added fuel to the centralist/decentralist faultline. The first initiative, the CPR, linked the country from the Atlantic to the Pacific and thus sought to overcome Canada's vast space and link its regions east to west (Vignette 3.1). The second initiative established an industrial core in Central Canada through the **National Policy**, which set high tariffs on imported goods and encouraged a home market for the manufactures of the core. These two federal efforts provided the basis of a national core/periphery economic structure that endured for over 100 years. From a regional perspective, the chief beneficiaries were Ontario and Québec and the major loser was the Maritimes.

Rightly or wrongly, Canadians living outside Central Canada believed that Ontario and Québec had an unfair influence over national policies and therefore Ottawa would favour economic development in Central Canada over that in the rest of the country. From a different perspective, given that the majority of voters continue to live in these two provinces, their concerns often translate into national concerns that federal governments must address. In 1911, 62.9 per cent of Canadians lived in Central Canada and they held 68.3 per cent of the seats in the House of Commons. By 2014, Central Canada still had a stranglehold on the democratic system with 61.6 per cent of the population and 58.8 per cent of the seats in the Commons (see Table 3.6). Even though their political weight declined over this span of time, Central Canada and especially Ontario still held sway. Atlantic Canada suffered both demographic and political losses over this period—its share of Canada's population dropped from 10.4 per cent in 1911 to 5.5 per cent in 2011 while its political representation in the House of Commons declined from nearly 16 per cent to just under 7 per cent.

The Centralist/Decentralist Faultline

In a federation like Canada, the role of the central government is to unify the country. A strong central government must advocate national policies that benefit provinces and provide the environment for a strong national economy. The initial premise in Ottawa was that a viable manufacturing sector in Central Canada required economies of scale, which translates into a large local market and access to distant markets. National policies do not always lead to harmony among regions. In 1980, the federal Liberal government intervened in the marketplace by imposing the **National Energy Program** on oil-producing provinces, stoking the fires of **western alienation**. Ottawa claimed the program was in the national interest. It had four goals:

- increase national energy security;
- expand Canadian private and public ownership of the oil industry;
- provide Ottawa with a larger share of oil revenues;
- maintain lower oil prices in Central Canada.

The National Energy Program lasted only four years (1980–4), but it altered the political landscape in Canada by deepening western alienation and was instrumental in causing the Liberal Party to lose its western base for the next 35 years and perhaps longer. This political divide surfaced again in 2016 when the federal government asked the provinces to agree to a carbon tax. Three provinces, Québec in October 2007, BC in July 2008, and Alberta in May 2016, have committed to such a tax, but other energy-rich provinces and the opposition parties in Alberta are opposed to such a tax.

The Indigenous/Non-Indigenous Faultline

Without a doubt, the Indigenous/non-Indigenous divide represents the most complex and troubling one facing the nation. Historically, Ottawa's ethnocentric programs were based on the assumed superiority of Western culture. One such program created residential schools, which have been described as a form of cultural genocide. The price of this failed assimilation program that targeted school-aged Indigenous children was extremely high. As pointed out by the report of the Truth and Reconciliation Commission (Sinclair, 2015), the damage caused to survivors and their descendants still haunts the Indigenous community.

The diversity of Aboriginal peoples, the scattered nature of their reserves and settlements, the erosion of their cultures and languages, and, for many, their educational and geographic disadvantages on the margins of the larger society have produced

different needs for different groups, as well as calls for a variety of responses by Ottawa. Two general, overarching points must first be understood:

- The federal government's responsibility for Indigenous peoples has been uneven. It began in 1867 with First Nations; in 1939, this responsibility was extended to Inuit; finally, in 2016, Métis and non-status Indians were recognized as a federal responsibility (Vignette 3.5).
- As Canadian society has changed, the federal government has shifted its direction from advocating assimilation policies, such as residential schools, to a more accommodative approach, as exemplified by modern treaties and the duty to consult over resource projects.

By the beginning of the twenty-first century, the question had become whether, in a sovereign state such as Canada, there is political room for Indigenous peoples *on their terms*. So far, two main examples exist for accommodating Canada's First Peoples.

- *Reserves*. In the nineteenth and twentieth centuries, treaties created over 3,100 reserves that are governed by just over 600 band councils, in many cases under the ever-lessening control of the federal Indian Act.
- *Territory*. Nunavut represents a territory. Nunavut blends an existing Canadian political unit within an Inuit environment. Although an Inuit initiative, the result was not an ethnic territory. Earlier, in 1975, the Dene Nation proposal for their own homeland called Denendeh, within the Northwest Territories, was rejected by Ottawa (Bone, 2016: 226).

The current federal accommodation of Indigenous peoples, guided by rulings of the Supreme Court of Canada, has launched the redefining of the relationship between Indigenous peoples and the nation-state of Canada. For Indigenous peoples, the question has become whether any redefinition will provide the political control and territorial space sought by them. Some scholars think not (Nadasy, 2003; White, 2006; Kulchyski, 2013; Willow, 2014). With Indigenous education reform and funding on the table, the process of redefining the relationship will be put to the test in 2016–17 when negotiations between the federal government and the Assembly of First Nations take place. Still, this could lead to a dead end for Indigenous peoples because the process is inevitably dominated by Canada. In other words, any resulting agreements could smother Indigenous cultures and values while slowly but quietly integrating the people into Canadian society.

A third path has been described by Manuel (1974) and Dyck (1985). In their view, Indigenous peoples must find their own path within a nation-state. In Canada, this path could take the form of a third level of government. Such a path is possible but difficult to achieve. For example, Nunavik was on such a path but the Québec Inuit rejected the proposition for self-government in a 2011 referendum (CBC News, 2011; Bone, 2016: 232).

Canada's Indigenous citizens are seeking a new place in Canada and a new relationship. Some First Nations, such as the Onion Lake Cree First Nation and the Whitecap Dakota First Nation in Saskatchewan, have come a long way to finding that place and relationship.[3] Others, such as the Innu Nation in Labrador, the Attawapiskat First Nation in northern Ontario, and the Lubicon Cree in northern Alberta, have struggled because of government actions and inaction, remote and resource-poor geographic location, and, sometimes, weak or divided local leadership. Each Aboriginal community and individual will define this new place and relationship, and those in remote areas have different needs and goals than those in urban Canada.

Three key events have laid the groundwork for change. One is the recognition by the federal government of past wrongs, reflected in the formal apology by Prime Minister Stephen Harper in Parliament in 2008, along with Ottawa's ongoing promise to negotiate from a respectful appreciation of Indigenous peoples' place in Canada. The Truth and Reconciliation Commission, created in 2008 as part of the Residential Schools Settlement Agreement, represents the second key event. In 2015, this Commission presented its report after holding many meetings with survivors of the residential schools. The Commission's goal is to provide closure for these former students and, through this process, better educate the broader Canadian public of past wrongs. A third significant change involved the rise of the Idle No More grassroots movement, founded in 2012 by three First Nations women and one non-Indigenous woman in response to a Conservative government omnibus bill that, among other things, aimed to gut important environmental protections, as well as their concern for a lack of accountability among First Nations leadership. Time will tell if these actions and events help to turn the

Vignette 3.5

The Federal Government and Indigenous Peoples

Who are the Indigenous peoples? In the Constitution Act of 1982, three Aboriginal groups are recognized: First Nations, Métis, and Inuit. Yet, under the Indian Act of 1876, the federal government was only responsible for First Nations. One reason for Ottawa's reluctance to recognize the other two groups was the desire to keep the cost to the federal treasury at a minimum. Over the years, rulings by the Supreme Court of Canada forced Ottawa to expand its acceptance of responsibility to include the Métis and Inuit. In 1939, Inuit were considered "Indians" by the Court and therefore fell under the responsibility of the federal government. In 2016, the Supreme Court ruled that the federal government was responsible for Métis and non-status Indians. This responsibility varies for each group. However, as of October 2016 negotiations with Ottawa to determine the exact nature of these obligations and benefits had not yet begun.

corner for Indigenous peoples. A First Nations columnist for the Saskatoon *StarPhoenix*, Doug Cuthand (2012), concluded:

> I realize that you can't bury the past, but we need to move on. It's said that if you can't get over something the best you can do is get through it. We have to think of future generations, and I hope that time is now.

The Elusive Nature of the Indigenous/Non-Indigenous Faultline

Both Indigenous and non-Indigenous Canadians in the twenty-first century remain puzzled about this faultline, asking questions like: Why can't Indigenous people adapt to Canadian ways like immigrants from foreign countries? Why does Canada need so many temporary foreign workers when unemployment rates are so high among Indigenous workers? And why are there so many missing and murdered Indigenous women, as the Royal Canadian Mounted Police and Indigenous groups have brought to public attention in recent years (and for which a federal inquiry was formed in 2016)?

While some progress on the narrowing of this divide has begun, closing it proves elusive. First, we are dealing with two distinct cultures, each with a different set of values and different views on what that relationship should be. Second, for too long, Indigenous peoples were the invisible Canadians. The fact that treaty Indians only obtained the vote for federal elections in 1960 is but one example of their long-term isolation from Canadian society.

Equally important, moving on is not easy when the two sides have different means of decision-making. The federal government, for example, has a hierarchical structure with power concentrated with cabinet and the Prime Minister. In contrast, Indigenous cultures, by and large, have operated on an egalitarian system of decision-making based in consensus and individual autonomy (including the freedom to opt out of a group decision). Unlike the federal government, for example, the **Assembly of First Nations (AFN)** is "a national advocacy organization" with no power to make decisions that bind the more than 630 First Nations.

So how do the federal government and the AFN negotiate? In 2014, a contentious issue faced the AFN—whether or not to support Bill C-33, the First Nations Control of First Nations Education Act, which the federal Conservative government believed would improve the performance of Indigenous youth in First Nation schools. The Assembly of First Nations waffled on the issue: the AFN leadership initially seemed to support the bill when Shawn Atleo was National Chief, but strong dissent among many of the constituent First Nations and leaders led to Atleo's resignation, and the AFN position was quickly reversed when Perry Bellegarde replaced him in 2014. Leaders believed Bill C-33 was merely another assimilation attempt that, according to Manitoba Chief Derek Nepinak, aimed to make "indigenous peoples more like them" (CBC News, 2014). This political drama has consequences because, with the change in government, not only is the original funding of nearly $2 billion gone from the previous Conservative file, but also the Liberal government is reviewing its position (Galloway, 2016).

In all of this, the larger questions remain unanswered:

- What role does the federal government have in shaping the delivery of education for Indigenous children on reserves?
- Given the diversity of First Nations across the country, how do First Nations and Ottawa arrive at a decision?

Now, our attention turns to past relations, to a time when alliances were the order of the day—with each partner having different goals. Only with some historical background can we begin to understand the complexity of current and ongoing Indigenous/non-Indigenous issues.

An Overview

The tangled historical relations between Indigenous peoples and European settlers, first in New France and through the British Crown and then between Indigenous peoples and Ottawa, place a cloud over the search for accommodated solutions. In the nineteenth century and much of the twentieth century, the forced assimilation policies of the federal government solidified an Indigenous distrust of the Canadian state and the Crown and removed any opportunity for an accommodated solution. These failed policies created an enormous divide between Indigenous peoples and the rest of Canadian society. The net result was a disaster for Indigenous peoples who, pushed to the margins of Canadian society, were caught in a dependency relationship with Ottawa. They faced unrelenting forms of racism and became the ignored members of Canadian society, shunted to the social and geographic margins.

The recognition by the federal government of past wrongs and an increased (though far from complete) awareness by the general population of the circumstances facing Indigenous peoples marked this turnaround. An initial step in that direction was federal funding for post-secondary education for status Indians. First begun in a limited fashion in the 1960s, the Post-Secondary Student Support Program (PSSSP) now provides financial assistance to status Indian and Inuit students who are enrolled in eligible post-secondary programs. By fostering a more educated Indigenous population, a new leadership class has emerged and greater upward mobility within Indigenous communities has become a possibility. Unfortunately, this progressive federal policy has not included non-status Indians and those of Métis descent—though a 14 April 2016 decision of the Supreme Court of Canada in *Daniels v. Canada* could find both groups falling under Ottawa's responsibility for land, education, and health programs (Galloway and Fine, 2016).

The Royal Proclamation and the Haldimand Grant

History sometimes makes strange allies. Shortly after Pontiac, chief of the Odawa, led a successful uprising against the British in 1763, Britain decided to form an alliance with him and other Indigenous leaders.[4] Pontiac's goal was to keep the Ohio Valley lands free of settlers from New England, and the British knew they could not hold these lands without the support of Pontiac. For strategic reasons, then, to keep colonists along the eastern seaboard

from further encroaching on Indigenous territory and to maintain a peace with the Indigenous peoples, George III issued the Royal Proclamation of 1763, which identified a part of British territory west of the Appalachian Mountains as Indian lands. The British also believed that Indigenous peoples had a limited ownership over the forested lands they inhabited, and that therefore such lands could not be occupied by settlers but must be purchased from the Indigenous "owners." This somewhat ambiguous concept remains the basis of land claims by Canadian Indigenous peoples.

With the colonists' victory in the American Revolution 20 years later, the concept of Indian lands in the Ohio Valley quickly disappeared as a flood of land-hungry settlers poured across the Appalachian Mountains. Indigenous forces that had been loyal to and fought for the King during the Revolutionary War retreated to Canada following the war, where they received the first major Indian land grant, the Haldimand Grant of 1784. The purpose was to reward the Iroquois who had served on the British side during the American Revolution. In his proclamation, the Governor of Québec, Lord Haldimand, prohibited the leasing or sale of land to anyone but the government in the tract extending from the source of the Grand River in present-day southwestern Ontario to the point where the river feeds into Lake Erie.

For further discussion of the Iroquois Confederacy, see "The Six Nations of the Iroquois Confederacy," page 104.

However, Joseph Brant, the leader of the Iroquois, insisted that they had the same rights as the colony's Loyalist settlers, that is, freehold land tenure. And so the waters were muddied by the early sale and lease of plots of land in the original Haldimand Grant. This issue has been part of the contemporary conflict between non-Indigenous residents and Six Nations Iroquois at Caledonia, Ontario.

For further discussion of the Haldimand Grant and a map illustrating the area of the original grant in 1784 and the current size of the reserve of the Six Nations of Grand River, see "Ontario's Historical Geography," page 182, and Figure 6.6, "The Haldimand Tract." Additional information is available on the Six Nations website at: www.sixnations.ca/index.htm.

See Vignette 6.3, "Timeline of the Caledonia Dispute," page 187.

Canada Takes Over with the Indian Act

In 1867, the British North America Act transferred the responsibility for the Indigenous tribes from Great Britain to Canada. Nine years later, in 1876, the government pulled together the various pieces of colonial legislation and regulations to create the repressive Indian Act.

The Indian Act had the effect of isolating Indigenous communities from the rest of Canada and stripping them of the power to govern themselves. Basing its action on the premise that Indigenous communities could not manage their affairs, Ottawa, through the federal Department of Indian Affairs, served as their guardian until First Nations were fully integrated into Canadian society—as defined by Ottawa. As a result, the federal department intervened in band issues, including managing Indigenous lands, resources, and moneys, with the objective of assimilating Indigenous peoples into Canadian society. This Act promoted a dependency on Ottawa and left control of band affairs in the hands of local Indian agents, thus stifling Indigenous initiatives. While Indigenous people were living in Canada, they were isolated from other Canadians and did not have the rights of citizenship, including the right to vote. Perhaps the only positive outcome of the Act was, unlike the situation of the Métis, Indian land could not be sold to private individuals unless approved by Ottawa—though over the years the government frequently did downsize reserves by selling and leasing reserve lands. Oddly enough, the Métis and Inuit did not fall under this Act, but they too fell into this twilight zone of living in Canada but not being fully accepted. Today, Inuit have a homeland in the territory of Nunavut, as well as in the northern extremes of the Northwest Territories, Québec, and Labrador, and in March 2013 the Manitoba Métis Federation won a landmark case in the Supreme Court in regard to the government's failure—in 1870 and ever since—to provide the Métis a proper land base.

For further discussion of treaty making, see "The Second Clash: Making Treaty," page 98.

Residential Schools: An Assimilation Tool

From the beginning, Ottawa's objective was the assimilation of Indigenous peoples into Canadian society (Milloy, 1999). Education was an important tool in federal efforts to "civilize" Indigenous people. One such effort, residential schools, stands out. Spread across Canada but concentrated in the West, the residential schools were operated by the major religious groups, especially the Roman Catholic Church. Without a doubt, residential schools were the most painful experience for many Indigenous children and their parents, and this learning experience has had long-term effects (Vignette 3.6). After a detailed examination of Indigenous–white relations, J.R. Miller (2000: 269) concludes that:

> While some students of these residential schools were thoroughly converted by the experience, many more absorbed only enough schooling to resist still more effectively. It would be from the ranks of former residential school pupils that most of the leaders of Indian political movements would come in the twentieth century. By any reasonable standard of evaluation, the residential school program from the 1880s to the 1960s failed dismally.

Not only did this assimilation program fail, but many students were abused, some sexually, by their religious teachers. By the 1990s some residential school survivors began to seek reparation for harms through the courts, and the Canadian legal system demanded financial compensation. The churches claimed that they were unable to pay for these claims and Canada offered to pay 70 per cent of compensation in respect of joint government and church liabilities to victims of sexual and physical abuse at residential schools. The churches involved—Roman Catholic, United, Methodist, Presbyterian, and Anglican—negotiated separate financial agreements with Ottawa. The Anglican Church, in 2003, was the first to reach a settlement, for payment of up to $25 million. It had also been the first church to formally apologize,

Vignette 3.6

The Failure to Create "Good Little Indians"

In 1892, the federal government entered a formal arrangement with several Christian churches—Roman Catholic, Anglican, Methodist, and Presbyterian—to provide a boarding school education for young Indigenous children. The churches ran the schools; Ottawa paid the bills. The plan was to quickly assimilate these young children into society by removing them from their families and home communities and by insisting that they not use their native languages. The effect was to destroy their culture and leave them between two worlds without roots in either one. While some parents wanted their children to attend these schools, many others were forced to send their children. From 1931 to 1996, about 150,000 First Nations, Inuit, and Métis children attended boarding schools; at least 3,000 students died at the schools, largely from diseases such as the Spanish flu (CBC News, 2013a). And, as we now know, many of the children were subjected to physical and sexual abuse.

The federal government (and society in general) believed that Indigenous children could be successful in modern society if they abandoned their culture and language and adopted Christianity, learned English or French, and had a basic education—though only enough to fit onto the lower rungs of the economy, as manual labourers, farm workers, seamstresses, and domestic workers. Attendance was mandatory and this rule was enforced by Indian agents and other federal officers as well as by missionaries. By the 1980s the failure of this assimilation program was self-evident, although First Nations families and communities had lived with this failure for generations. The last school was closed in 1996.

in 1993, for its part in the tragic residential schools history. On 23 November 2005, the Canadian government announced a $1.9 billion compensation package to benefit tens of thousands of survivors of the residential schools. The settlement provides for a lump-sum payment to former students: $10,000 for the first school year plus $3,000 for each additional year. The average payout has been about $28,000. Those who suffered sexual or serious physical abuses, or other abuses that caused serious psychological effects, could apply for additional compensation or seek redress through the courts. Finally, on 11 June 2008 the Prime Minister made a formal apology in the House of Commons for the harm done to individuals, families, and cultures by the residential schools.

Since the 1970s, Ottawa has adopted a more enlightened policy towards resolving issues related to Canada's First Peoples, stressing three elements: settling outstanding land claims; recognizing Indigenous right to self-government; and accepting that the concerns and rights of each Indigenous people (First Nations, Métis, and Inuit) are different and that such concerns and rights require specific solutions.

Defining Indigenous Peoples

The Indigenous peoples of Canada—First Nations, Métis, and Inuit—are those now living in Canada who trace their ancestry to the original inhabitants who were in North America before the arrival of Europeans in the fifteenth century and who identify with that ancestry. From a cultural perspective, the legal terms used to describe First Nations people as status, non-status, and treaty Indians have little meaning in regard to their traditional or current lifeways or their relationship with the land. People legally defined as status (registered) Indians are recorded by the federal government as "Indians," according to the Indian Act as amended in June 1985, and have certain rights acknowledged by the federal government, such as tax exemption for income generated on a reserve. According to data compiled by the federal department responsible for Indigenous affairs,[5] the number of status Indians—from over 600 First Nations—had grown to 868,206 by end of 2011 (AANDC, 2013).

Non-status Indians are those of Indigenous ancestry who are not registered as status Indians and therefore have no rights under the Indian Act. Treaty Indians are status or registered Indians who are members of (or can prove descent from) a band that signed a treaty. They have a legal right to live on a reserve and participate in band affairs. Less than half live on reserves. The Métis are people of European and North American First Nations ancestry. The Inuit are Indigenous people located mainly in the Arctic.

Statistics Canada records Indigenous people by their identity as declared by those individuals on census day. In 2011, the National Household Survey recorded 1,400,685 Indigenous people: 851,560 First Nations people; 451,795 Métis; and 59,445 Inuit (Statistics Canada, 2013b). The principal reason for the difference in population size of registered Indians recorded by Indigenous and Northern Affairs Canada (INAC) and the census figure for First Nations population is due to the two data collection methods. The registry kept by INAC is based on the list of people recognized as status Indians compiled by each of the bands, while the census records the self-identity of people. Some people are missed in the census survey and a few bands have refused to allow a census enumeration.

First Nations, Inuit, and Métis constitute a highly diverse population. One indication of their cultural diversity is linguistic classification. As noted earlier, there were approximately 55 distinct Indigenous languages (of 11 language families) spoken in Canada at the time of original contact (Figure 3.3). The largest language family is Algonkian. There are 15 distinct Algonkian-based languages, the most common of which are Cree and Ojibwa. Inuktitut, the Inuit language, has regional dialects and is spoken across the Canadian Arctic.

Another measure of Indigenous diversity is self-identification. Many people prefer to identify themselves using the name of their nation, while others prefer the name of their band, For example, the Cree nation occupies a vast territory that stretches from northern Québec to Alberta. There are many Cree bands within that territory. A Cree living in northern Saskatchewan might identify himself or herself as a member of a Cree band, such as the Lac La Ronge band.

The population of each band is recorded by the federal department. The largest First Nations are southern Ontario's Six Nations of the Grand River (Iroquois) with a population of 24,384; Qalipa Mi'kmaq of Nova Scotia (21,424); the Mohawk of Akwesasne (11,466) at St Regis on the Ontario–Québec border near Cornwall; the Kainai (Blood) (11,448) in southern Alberta; Kahnawake (Mohawk) (10,053) near Montréal; the Saddle Lake Cree reserve (9,574) outside Edmonton; and the Lac La Ronge Cree in northern Saskatchewan (9,408). Approximately half of First Nations people live on reserves (51 per cent) while the rest live off-reserve, mainly in cities. The number of First Nations people living on reserves has increased but the percentage has declined. In 1984, for instance, 223,169 or 64 per cent lived on reserves, compared to 441,891 or 51 per cent in 2011 (AANDC, 2013). The growing number of urban Indigenous people is a significant economic and political factor and the original source of the Idle No More movement.

Indigenous peoples are reclaiming their identity and place names. Some bands are relinquishing the names given to them by Europeans in favour of their original names, such as Anishinabe (for Ojibwa) and Gwich'in (for Kutchin). The landscape is also being reclaimed. For example, the Arctic community of Frobisher Bay, named after the English explorer Martin Frobisher, is now Iqaluit ("the place where the fish are"), the capital city of Nunavut ("our land"). On the west coast, the Queen Charlotte Islands have been renamed Haida Gwaii.

Indigenous and Treaty Rights

Indigenous rights are group or collective rights that stem from Indigenous peoples' occupation of the land before contact. Such rights apply most readily to status Indians and Inuit, while Métis are less well protected in regard to rights.

Métis Rights

In 1870, Ottawa, in an effort to quell the resistance at the Red River Settlement, accepted that the Métis, by virtue of their Indian ancestry, had Indigenous rights. However, the government viewed these rights in the narrowest possible manner by offering

THINK ABOUT IT

While the high birth rate of First Nations people allows the number of First Nations people living on-reserve and off-reserve to increase, the rate of population increase is higher for the off-reserve population. Today, more First Nations people live off-reserve, i.e., in cities, than on-reserve.

THINK ABOUT IT

Why did the Métis sell their scrip instead of converting it to farmland? When did the "responsibility" for Inuit fall to Ottawa?

individual land grants to the Métis. The agreement had three components. First, land occupied before 1870 became private property. Second, the children of the Métis were eligible for a land grant of 140 acres. Third, each head of a Métis family received 160 acres in scrip, which could be either claimed or sold. The federal government set aside 1.4 million acres for the Métis children, estimated in 1871 at around 10,000. Based on these figures, each Métis child, at adulthood, could claim 140 acres. Before the actual land allocation began, the government ordered a census of the Métis population and this 1872 census identified just over 5,000 eligible Métis children. Accordingly, their individual allocation was increased to 240 acres (Library and Archives of Canada, 2012).[6] Unfortunately for the Métis, much of the land on offer was marginal for agriculture and it certainly did not provide the basis for a homeland; plus, the government was slow to act while settlers from the east continued to take up land in the region. Consequently, many adults sold their land scrip to speculators, sometimes at half its value, or accepted a one-time payment from the government (money scrip) for the value of the land they might have taken (Dickason and Newbigging, 2015: 217). By 1880, the outcome was clear—the dream of a Métis land base was dead. In March 2013 the Supreme Court overturned a lower court decision, ruling in *Manitoba Métis Federation v. Canada (Attorney General)* that the Canadian government in 1870 and the ensuing years did not act in good faith in its dealings with the Métis. The focus of the dispute is the 1870 federal commitment to set aside 5,565 km[2] for 7,000 children of the Red River Métis. In 2013, the president of the Manitoba Métis Federation stated that some kind of compensation, not necessarily land, is most important to the Métis (CBC News, 2013b). In 2016, the Liberal government and the Manitoba Métis Federation signed a Memorandum of Understanding that sets the stage for exploratory talks on the reconciliation of this 1870 promise (CBC News, 2016).

⟳ For more on the subject of land allotments to the Métis, see page 96, "The First Clash: Red River Rebellion of 1869–70."

Treaty Rights

Treaty rights are the most generous of Indigenous rights. Treaties set aside reserve land, held collectively by and for the benefit of the band, and define other negotiated rights (benefits).

The reasons for signing treaties varied depending on the historical context. During the late nineteenth century, treaties were signed throughout the Prairies to remove Indigenous communities from the land and make way for European settlement; at the same time, this helped ensure that the Indian Wars, which were common south of the border between the US military and various Indigenous groups, would not erupt in Canada. For Indigenous peoples, treaties promised land (reserves) that would not be available to settlers, as well as support to shift from nomadic hunting to sedentary farming. The numbered treaties for the Plains peoples therefore offered protection from the anticipated flood of settlers and some guarantee that the federal

Contested Terrain 3.1

The Supreme Court and the Métis

The Supreme Court of Canada began hearing the case brought by the Manitoba Métis Federation in December 2011. With the Court ruling in favour of the Métis claim that the federal government of the day did not safeguard the interest of the Métis, Ottawa will likely favour a cash settlement. Although David Chartrand, president of the Federation, stated in the immediate aftermath that land was not at issue after so many years, that sentiment might not be true for many of the Métis, especially those whose forebears were affected by the government's foot-dragging of almost a century and half ago and who, consequently, migrated to the west and north of the original "postage stamp" province of Manitoba. See also Vignette 3.7.

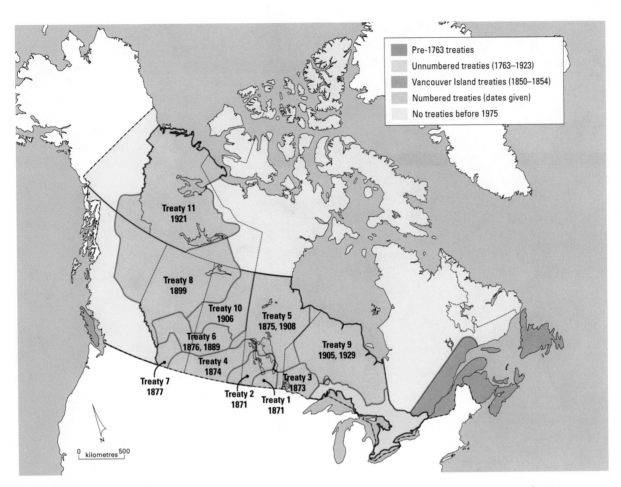

FIGURE 3.10 Historic treaties

The first treaties, made between the British government and Indigenous tribes, were "friendship" agreements. In Upper Canada the Robinson treaties of 1850 set aside reserve lands in exchange for the title to the remaining lands. With the settlement of lands in the Canadian West, Indigenous peoples became concerned about their future, so many of the 11 numbered treaties, which spanned a half-century from 1871 to 1921, included provisions for agricultural supplies. When the last numbered treaty was signed, many Indigenous peoples in Atlantic Canada, Québec, and British Columbia were without treaties.

government would care for them now that their principal source of food, the buffalo, was gone (Figure 3.10). However, treaty assurances of federal assistance were often not met (see Brownlie, 2003; Carter, 2004).

The terms of each treaty varied, although they generally included cash gratuities and presents at the signing of the treaty, annual payments in perpetuity, the promise of educational and agricultural assistance, and the right to hunt and fish on Crown land until such land was required for other purposes, as well as land reserves to be held by the Crown in trust for the First Nations. In Treaty No. 6 of 1876, for example, which covered much of central

Saskatchewan and Alberta, each tribe was assigned land based on the size of its population, i.e., each family of five received one square mile. Reserves represent land collectively owned by First Nation bands, though legally the Crown holds the land in trust.

Conflicting ideas as to the significance of treaties between the signing parties largely shaped Indigenous and non-Indigenous relations in Canada during the twentieth century. When treaties were signed, Crown authorities viewed them as vehicles for extinguishing Indigenous rights and titles to land and thus for opening the land to agricultural settlement. First Nations, however, understood them as

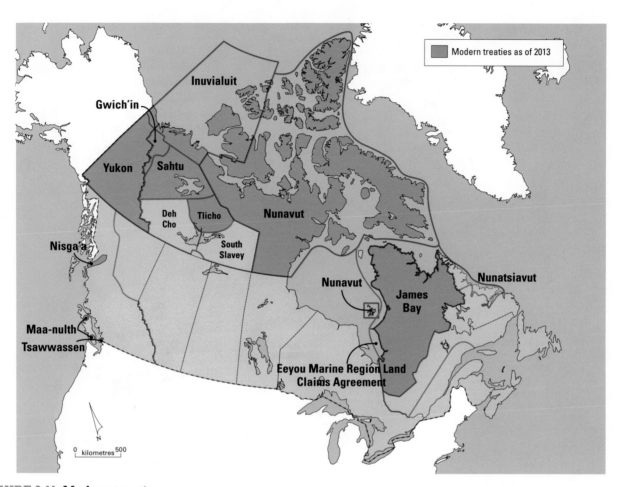

FIGURE 3.11 Modern treaties

The first modern treaty was the James Bay and Northern Québec Agreement, signed in 1975. By 2015, the main areas without treaties were much of BC, part of Labrador and the Northwest Territories, and lands in central and southern Québec.

agreements between "sovereign" powers to share land and resources. With such diverging perceptions, disagreements were inevitable.

Modern or comprehensive treaties came about in the latter part of the twentieth century, the first being the James Bay and North Québec Agreement of 1975, and have continued to be negotiated into the twenty-first century (Figure 3.11). Comprehensive treaties or agreements extend rights to those Indigenous groups, especially in northern Canada and British Columbia, that had never signed treaties, and generally include large cash settlements, a portion of the group's traditional lands, surrender of the larger portion of traditional lands, self-governance agreements, and environmental/natural resource co-management agreements.

Modern Treaties

The legal meaning of Indigenous title to land has evolved over time. Until the 1970s, Ottawa recognized two forms of land rights. Reserve lands were one type of right or ownership, which the Canadian government held for First Nations people. The second type was a usufructuary right to use Crown land for hunting and trapping, in other words, to freely use and enjoy Crown lands without any claim to ownership of these lands. At that time, Crown lands (both provincial and federal) included most of Canada's unsettled areas. First Nations, Inuit, and Métis families lived on Crown lands, continuing to hunt, trap, and fish. However, federal and provincial governments could sell such lands to individuals and corporations or grant them a lease to use the land for a specific purpose, such as mineral exploration or logging, without compensating the Indigenous users of those lands. By the 1960s, many Indigenous groups still did not have treaties with the Canadian government. Atlantic Canada, Québec, the Territorial North, and British Columbia contained huge areas where treaties had not been concluded. As a consequence, Indigenous peoples had no control over developments on these lands.

A combination of events radically changed this situation. One factor was the emergence of Indigenous leaders who understood the political and legal systems. They used the courts to force the federal and provincial governments to address the issue of Indigenous rights and land claims. The first major event took place in 1969, when Ottawa proposed reforms to the Indian Act in its White Paper on Indian Policy. This galvanized treaty First Nations into action. The White Paper proposed to treat all Canadians equally. For First Nations, it meant the abolition of their treaty rights and the reserve land system. At about the same time, the Nisga'a in northern British Columbia took their land claim, known as the *Calder* case, to court.

In 1973, the Supreme Court of Canada narrowly ruled (by a vote of four to three) against the Nisga'a argument that the tribe still had a land claim to territory in northern British Columbia. However, in their ruling, six of the seven judges agreed that Indigenous title to the land had existed in British Columbia at the time of Confederation. Furthermore, three judges said that Indigenous title still existed in British Columbia because the British Columbia government had not extinguished Indigenous title, while three other judges stated that the various laws passed by the British Columbia government since 1871 served to abolish Indigenous title. The seventh judge ruled against the Nisga'a claim on a legal technicality. Even though the judgement went against the Nisga'a, the course of Indigenous land claims in Canada changed because three judges agreed that Indigenous title was not extinguished. In the same year, 1973, the federal government agreed that Indigenous peoples who had not signed a treaty may very well have a legal claim to Crown lands, and in 1974 an Office of Native Claims was first established

to deal with both specific and comprehensive land claims.

In the early and mid-1970s the James Bay Project in northern Québec and the proposed Mackenzie Valley Pipeline Project in the Northwest Territories added fuel to the political fire over Indigenous rights. The possible impact of these industrial projects on Indigenous peoples was made clear through the Mackenzie Valley Pipeline Inquiry of 1974–7 (the Berger Inquiry) into possible environmental and socio-economic impacts and in the media. Indigenous organizations obviously were prepared to take action to defend their land claims. Their position in the 1970s was "no development without land claims settlements." All these events changed both the public's views of Indigenous rights and the government's position. At first grudgingly and then more willingly, governments, corporations, and Canadian society recognized the validity of Indigenous land claims.

A **comprehensive land claim agreement** is sought when a group of Indigenous people who have not yet signed a treaty can demonstrate a claim to land through past occupancy. Such agreements are considered modern treaties (Table 3.7). The James Bay and Northern Québec Agreement is regarded as the first modern treaty, although negotiations between governments and the James Bay Cree and the Inuit of northern Québec had begun before the government policy was established. As well, the 1978 Northeastern Québec Agreement, signed between the Innu (Naskapi) and governments, can be considered a part of the James Bay and Northern Québec Agreement.

In 1984, the Inuvialuit of the Western Arctic became the first Indigenous people to settle a comprehensive land claim with the federal government under the comprehensive land claim process. Since then, 26 comprehensive claims have been finalized in Canada, involving well over 90 Indigenous communities. Negotiations can be extremely slow and complex, and approximately 60 comprehensive claims are in various stages of negotiation at present. Most of these claims involve First Nations in British Columbia. Virtually the entire province of British Columbia, except for Vancouver Island (where 14 treaties—the Douglas treaties—were

TABLE 3.7 Modern Land Claim Agreements, 1975–2014

Name of Agreement	Year
James Bay and Northern Québec Agreement	1975
Northeastern Québec Agreement	1978
Inuvialuit Final Agreement	1984
Gwich'in Comprehensive Land Claim Agreement	1992
Nunavut Land Claims Agreement	1993
Yukon First Nations Final Agreements:	
Champagne and Aishihik First Nations	1993
First Nation of Nacho Nyak Dun	1993
Teslin Tlingit Council	1993
Vuntut Gwitchin First Nation	1993
Little Salmon/Carmacks First Nation	1997
Selkirk First Nation	1997
Tr'ondek Hwechin'in First Nation	1998
Ta'an Kwach'an Council	2002
Kluane First Nation	2003
Kwanlin Dun First Nation	2005
Carcross/Tagish First Nation	2005
Sahtu Dene and Métis Comprehensive Land Claim Agreement	1993
Nisga'a Final Agreement	2000
Tlicho Land Claims and Self-Government Agreement	2003
Labrador Inuit Land Claims Agreement	2005
Nunavik Inuit Land Claims Agreement	2007
Tsawwassen First Nation Final Agreement	2009
Eeyou Marine Region Land Claims Agreement	2010
Maa-nulth Final Agreement	2011
Yale First Nations Final Agreement	2016
T'amin Final Agreement	2016

Source: Land Claims Agreement Coalition, "Modern Treaties," 2016, at: www.landclaimscoalition.ca/modern-treaties/.

signed between First Nations and the Hudson's Bay Company in the early 1850s), is claimed by First Nations. In BC, progress has been extremely slow. Until 1992, the provincial government claimed that British occupancy had extinguished Indigenous title. However, in 1992 the British Columbia government accepted the principle of Indigenous land claims. The following year, Ottawa and Victoria agreed to a formula for settling outstanding claims. The federal government would pay 90 per cent of the money needed to settle outstanding claims and the province would provide the land. In 2000, the Nisga'a Agreement was finalized, followed by two more—the 600-strong Tsawwassen First Nation

signed their final agreement in 2007 and it became law in 2009; the Maa-nulth First Nation signed their final agreement in 2008, which was approved by Parliament in 2011.

For more on BC land claims, see page 298, Vignette 9.3, "Aboriginal Title: Who Owns BC?"

Those Indigenous groups that have concluded modern treaties are moving forward. They are able to focus on economic and cultural developments rather than expending their energies on land claim negotiations. In 1993, the Nunavut agreement broke new ground by effectively establishing self-government over an entire territory. Since then, modern land claim agreements, such as the Nisga'a Agreement, have included arrangements for self-government. As a result, a gap is emerging within the Indigenous community between those with a modern treaty and those without, as well as between those on reserve and those who live in urban areas among Canada's increasingly pluralistic majority society. Also, as with countries and with regions, some Indigenous groups reside on lands rich in natural resources, resource developments, and development potential (e.g., oil and gas deposits, oil sands, pipelines, prime timber land) that provide a base for economic growth and considerable wealth, while many other groups live in areas with little resource potential where even subsistence from the land is marginal if not impossible.

Bridging the Indigenous/Non-Indigenous Faultline

Indigenous peoples are taking the control of their affairs away from Ottawa (Vignette 3.7). Some First Nations and Inuit have made substantial advances in economic development, while others have gained increasing control over their own affairs through self-government and sovereignty. Unfortunately, some Indigenous peoples, including the Métis, have not yet begun this self-government process and remain on the political margins of Canadian society. For most, the process of change has started.

In 1996, the Report of the Royal Commission on Aboriginal Peoples identified two major goals: Aboriginal economic development and self-government. The gap between Indigenous and non-Indigenous societies will not be bridged until these goals are achieved. The principal factor is transferring power from Ottawa (the political power core) to the various Indigenous communities (the politically weak periphery). The economic and social well-being of Indigenous reserves varies widely. Some, such as the Whitecap Dakota First Nation near Saskatoon with its casino and top-tier golf course, have gained a high level of economic and social stability. The Labrador Inuit provide another example since they gained a share of the royalties from the Voisey's Bay nickel mine within their land claim agreement. Many

others remain trapped in poverty and, without an economic base, breaking the dependency on the federal government seems an impossible task. Many individuals and families have made a choice, relocating to cities where a variety of opportunities and amenities are available.

According to 2011 census, Indigenous people residing off-reserve constitute the fastest-growing segment of Canadian society (AANDC, 2014b).The pull of cities is a worldwide phenomenon and its impact on Indigenous peoples is ongoing. Most significantly, this demographic movement is shifting the geographic location of First Nations people, Inuit, and Métis from their cultural homes on reserves and in small communities to the multicultural major urban centres. In 2011, 56 per cent of Indigenous people lived in urban areas, up from 49 per cent in 1996. The cities with the largest Indigenous populations in 2011 were Winnipeg (78,420), Edmonton (61,765), Vancouver (52,375), Toronto (36,995), Calgary (33,370), Ottawa–Gatineau (30,570), Montréal (26,280), Saskatoon (23,895), and Regina (19,785). These figures, however, mask a degree of "churn" or back and forth of individuals between urban places and reserves.

But for those who remain within their cultural homes, developing an economic base on a reserve or in a remote community is not an easy task. Some have benefited from resource development through impact benefit agreements (IBAs) but most have not. One of the most successful IBA negotiations took place in Arctic Québec, where Makivik Corporation obtained a 4.5 per cent share of the profits of the Raglan mine as well as the standard commitments to employment and business opportunities (Lewis and Brocklehurst, 2009: 21–9). Yet, most Indigenous communities do not have the business experience and expertise of Makivik, which is a product of the James Bay and Northern Québec Agreement of 1975. Leadership in remote communities and reserves, while improving, is ill-equipped to negotiate impact benefit agreements with international mining companies.

Consider Attawapiskat First Nation, whose IBA negotiators focused on an annual cash payment of $2 million per year from De Beers. While that is a substantial amount of money, it pales in comparison

THINK ABOUT IT

Why have modern treaty agreements resulted in more benefits and powers for the groups involved than have the earlier numbered treaties?

Vignette 3.7

From a Colonial Straitjacket to Indigenous Power

Until 1969, Canada's Indigenous peoples were largely invisible to other Canadians. Most were geographically separated, as many status Indians lived on reserves, Métis were in isolated communities, and Inuit, in the previous two decades, had been moved by government to small settlements in the Far North. By and large, all were outside the political process and thus denied access to political decision-making. In fact, status Indians did not receive the right to vote in federal elections until 1960. Shunned by Canadian society, these marginalized peoples had been subjected to assimilation policies for many years.

However, the political and social landscape began to change in 1969. Ottawa made one last attempt to assimilate the First Nations people of Canada through its "Statement of the Government of Canada on Indian Policy," more popularly known as the White Paper. The Liberals under Pierre Trudeau proposed to eliminate the legal distinction between First Nations people living in Canada and other citizens of Canada by repealing the Indian Act and amending the British North America Act to remove those parts that called for separate treatment for status Indians, and to abolish the Department of Indian Affairs. Ottawa believed that the separation of First Nations people from other citizens not only was divisive but made the First Nations people dependent on government and thereby held them back. The remedy was individual "equality." In the context of the 1960s, when oppressed people in other countries, including blacks in the United States and in South Africa, fiercely sought equality and the American Indian Movement railed against colonial oppression, Prime Minister Trudeau believed that the White Paper was the answer to Canada's Indigenous problem. Some Indigenous leaders—soon labelled "Uncle Tomahawks" by their less conciliatory peers—supported this solution, but many others did not.

Reaction was swift. In the same year, Harold Cardinal published *The Unjust Society*, and the following year, under his leadership, the Alberta chiefs published a formal rebuttal to the White Paper, commonly known as the "Red Paper" and titled *Citizens Plus: A Presentation by the Indian Chiefs of Alberta to the Right Honourable P.E. Trudeau.* In brief, the vast majority of First Nations and their leaders were unwilling to be assimilated and to give up their status as "citizens plus," meaning that they might be Canadian citizens but they also had certain inalienable rights as Canada's First Peoples. In 1970 Trudeau reluctantly withdrew the White Paper, and by 1973, despite being a fierce believer in *individual rights*, he began to recognize that Canada had to begin to find a place within its polity for the *collective rights* of its Indigenous peoples.

During the 1970s, the debate over the place of Indigenous people in Canadian society took several different directions. First, there was legal support for the First Nations position, beginning with the *Calder* case in 1973 when the Supreme Court held that the Nisga'a had Indigenous rights. Second, the election of the Parti Québécois in 1976 called for "nation-to-nation" discussions between the province and the federal government. Indigenous leaders seized the opportunity to present their demands in the same constitutional language. Third, recognition of the Indigenous peoples and their rights in the 1982 Constitution Act dramatically enhanced their status and bargaining power. Fourth, the Constitution Act did not define Indigenous rights, leaving that task to negotiations or the courts. The courts have been active in this regard. In 1997, the Supreme Court's landmark decision in the *Delgamuukw* case overturned the earlier decision denying that First Nations in British Columbia had Indigenous title. Furthermore, the Court ruled that Indigenous title means that First Nations have the right to the resources on their lands.

to a percentage of the annual revenue, estimated at $400 million in 2012 (Porter, 2013), and amounts to only 0.5 per cent of what De Beers was gaining each year from its Victor Diamond Mine in northern Ontario. As more negotiations for IBAs take place, the sharing of the wealth generated by resource projects will likely increase as Indigenous leaders gain more experience.

The Immigration Faultline

The history of non-British immigration to Canada is complex and sometimes controversial. Most importantly, immigration has been a continuous stream of people coming to Canada, with each wave having a distinct impact on the land and society. Before 1867, immigration was often an instrument of colonial power. After the British Conquest of New France, for example, the British government set the immigration policy and the French-speaking majority in Canada did not have a say in shaping this policy. The British government's objective was to offset the large French-speaking population by encouraging large-scale immigration from the British Isles and curtailing immigration from France. In the case of the Acadians, the British, beginning in 1755, deported many of these people to England and to the English colonies to the south, and many others fled to Québec, sheltered in northern New Brunswick, or found their way to the Louisiana Territory. At the same time, the British sought to resettle the area with British subjects. Colonial-style immigration, therefore, not only generated tensions between the existing population and the newcomers, but it also imposed a way of life and a set of institutions on the existing population and often marginalized these people.

After 1867, the Dominion of Canada remained closely tied to the British Empire, and its immigration policies continued to reflect the "imperialist" attitude displayed in London, namely that Europeans but especially the British were superior to non-European peoples. However, needs often trump attitudes. The CPR line across the Cordillera where few people lived, for instance, was largely built by 15,000 Chinese labourers, who came from California and China and who worked for half the wages of white workers. As well, the Chinese were prepared to undertake the very dangerous mountain/tunnel blasting.

While the existing colonial populations asked how the newcomers would benefit them and their society, the colonial power took a rather different view, asking how the colonies would benefit the imperial centre. The economic, military, and social relationship between New France and the Huron Confederacy illustrates this point. In 1609, the Huron chiefs met with Samuel de Champlain to discuss both trade and a military alliance. The Huron had three objectives: (1) to gain access to European goods, including firearms, by supplying the French with beaver pelts; (2) to improve their material well-being with the trade goods and, in turn, trade these goods to more distant Indigenous people for profit; and (3) to strengthen their military position against their traditional enemies, the Iroquois, who were allied with the Dutch and later the English traders based in New York. The French had two objectives: (1) to secure a supply of furs; and (2) to convert the Huron to Christianity. At the height of the fur trade in the seventeenth century, New France greatly prospered and the Huron accounted for around half of the furs shipped to France (Dickason with McNab, 2009: 101). Trade was so important to the Huron tribes that when the French insisted that the Huron allow Jesuit missionaries to live among them as a condition for continued trade, the Huron reluctantly agreed. Unfortunately, the missionaries brought with them smallpox and other diseases that quickly swept through the Huron tribes, causing a sharp decline in their population.

Here, our focus is on the impact of immigration on the settling of Western Canada. The story begins with the purchase of Hudson's Bay lands by Ottawa, the reaction of the Métis in the Red River Settlement, the making of treaties, and then the subsequent settling of the Canadian Prairies by many people who were not of British ancestry. This historic period stretches from 1870 to 1914. During this time, although the face of British colonialism had changed from London to Ottawa, it had not softened. Immigrants and those being incorporated into the expanding Canada had to conform to the legacy of the British colonial society. The experiences of the original occupants of Western Canada—the Plains peoples and the Métis—and then of the Doukhobors, who were very clearly not British immigrants, ended badly. Even the **Manitoba Act of 1870** did not protect the hard-fought gains of the **Provisional Government** of the Métis led by Louis Riel.

In all instances, the pressure to conform to the majority society was both overt and covert; and in each case, the outcome pushed these peoples to the margins of Western Canadian society. The leader of the Métis, Louis Riel, was forced into exile in the

United States. Later, Riel returned to lead the second Métis uprising in 1885, which was suppressed, and he was convicted of treason and hanged on 16 November 1885. The final irony was that Riel's death came only nine days after the driving of the last spike on the Canadian Pacific rail line at Craigellachie, British Columbia. Of these two events, one drove a wedge between Ottawa and Québec; the other, redolent in symbolism, united the new nation from sea to sea.

The First Clash: Red River Rebellion of 1869–70

With the transfer of the vast lands administered by the Hudson's Bay Company, Canada changed from a small territory to a truly continental country. While the boundary between Western Canada and the United States had been determined earlier, the survey of lands for agricultural settlement took place in the 1880s. The land survey system, based on a township and range model, stamped a rectangular-shaped grid on the cultural landscape, thus determining the shape and placement of farms, roads, and towns. As Moffat (2002: 204) points out, this survey system "enabled the division of western lands among the HBC, the Canadian Pacific Railway (CPR) and homesteaders, and set aside two sections in each township for the future of local education."

The land grant to the CPR was one way Ottawa was able to help finance its construction. However, when the federal surveyors set foot in the Red River Colony in 1869, Ottawa had failed to acknowledge the presence and rights of the Métis. As well, the federal government had not yet begun negotiations with the Indigenous peoples of the prairie. In fact, Ottawa did not inform the residents of the Red River Colony of its

Photo 3.6 The confluence of the Red and Assiniboine rivers is known as the Forks. Today, the Forks lies in the heart of Winnipeg. In times past, the strategic location of the Forks provided Plains peoples with ready access by canoe to the lands south of the forty-ninth parallel and to the vast western interior. In 1738, the French explorer La Vérendrye established Fort Rouge at the Forks. With the founding of the Red River Settlement in 1812, the Forks became its focal point.

Ron Garnett/AirScapes.ca

plans for the Hudson's Bay lands, nor did the government signal that it recognized local landholdings. With the clash between the surveyors and the Métis, events quickly spun out of control, resulting in the Métis Provisional Government and the Red River Rebellion.

The Red River Rebellion pitted the existing population of the Red River Colony against Ottawa, whose land survey and agricultural plans posed a potentially fatal threat to the existing Métis settlement and its hunting economy. Even before the arrival of settlers, surveyors sent by Ottawa ignored the long-lot holdings of the Métis along the Red and Assiniboine rivers. In 1869, the Red River Colony was the only settled area of any size in the North-Western Territory, with a population of nearly 12,000 evenly divided between French- and English-speaking residents (Table 3.2). Most consisted of mixed-blood people, born of French and British fur traders and First Nations, who had settled in long lots along the banks of the two major rivers, and whose economy was based on the buffalo hunt and subsistence farming (Vignette 3.8).

By early 1869, news of the pending transfer of Hudson's Bay Company lands to Ottawa had reached the colony, and the arrival of land surveyors resulted in open hostility. When Canadian surveyors began to survey Métis-occupied lands, the Métis feared for their rights to those lands and even for their place in the new society. Matters came to a boil when, in October 1869, Louis Riel put his foot on a surveyor's chain and told them to leave. Thus, the Red River Rebellion began, during which the Métis took control of Upper Fort Garry and the HBC headquarters, and William McDougall, who had been appointed lieutenant-governor of the HBC lands soon to be passed over to Canada, was turned back at the border in his attempt to claim Canadian sovereignty over the territory.

Two months later, the Métis under Riel formed their Provisional Government and soon began to negotiate with Canada over the terms of entry into Confederation. The three-man delegation sent to Ottawa by Riel's Provisional Government gained much of what they sought, including agreement to the establishment of a new province, but anti-Roman Catholic Orange Order elements from Ontario who had come to the Red River area were not pleased that Catholic and French-speaking Métis "half-breeds" were in charge, and one man, Thomas Scott, who had been arrested by the Métis but persisted in being belligerent and unruly, was summarily executed after a brief trial. This inevitably led to further difficulties.

One advantage Riel had had in his negotiations with the Canadian government was "remoteness." Without rail connection to the settlement, Ottawa could not rush troops to quell the resistance, which, with the execution of Scott, seemed on the verge

THINK ABOUT IT

Is it more accurate historically to refer to the Red River Rebellion as the Red River Resistance?

Vignette 3.8

The Origin of the Métis Nation

The fur trade and the Métis are part of the historical fabric of Western Canada. With their command of English/French and First Nations languages, the Métis were logical intermediaries in the fur trade. Over the centuries, the fur trade absorbed the mixed-blood offspring of Cree, Ojibwa, or Saulteaux women with French fur traders from the North West Company or Scottish and English fur traders from the Hudson's Bay Company. In the early nineteenth century, the settlement near the confluence of the Red River and the Assiniboine River consisted mainly of French and Scottish "half-breeds" and Scottish settlers brought from Scotland to fulfill Lord Selkirk's dream of an agricultural community. By 1821, the two fur-trading empires had amalgamated, throwing many of the mixed-race Indigenous people out of work. Many gathered in the Red River Settlement, which provided the cultural melting pot for the formation of the Métis Nation. The Métis culture was neither European nor First Nations, but a fusion of the two.

**THINK
ABOUT IT**

Why do you think
the Métis chose
to negotiate with
Ottawa rather than
to declare their
independence from
Canada?

of full-scale warfare. Although a rail line reached St Paul in Minnesota, the US government refused to allow Canadian troops to cross the border. In April 1870, Macdonald authorized a military force of 1,000 troops—the Wolseley Expedition—to advance on Red River and assert Canada's sovereignty over the colony. The Canadian troops followed an old fur trade route and took four months to finally reach the Red River in August 1870. Fearing for their lives, Riel and his lieutenants fled to the United States. On 15 July 1870, Manitoba became a tiny province of Canada with an area of about 2,600 km² (1,000 square miles). The Métis had obtained most of their demands (the use of English and French languages within the government and a dual system of Protestant and Roman Catholic schools); at the same time, Prime Minister Macdonald had begun to ensure Canadian control over Western Canada.

The Second Clash: Making Treaty

After Manitoba became part of the Dominion, Ottawa sought to expand its control into the empty Prairie lands. Making treaty with the peoples of this "empty land" was essential before these potential farmlands were filled with homesteaders from Canada, the United States, and Great Britain. From 1871 to 1877, seven treaties—the so-called numbered treaties 1 to 7—were negotiated to open the West to settlement.

The objective of Ottawa was to extinguish Indigenous rights to the land, as it had in Ontario with the Robinson treaties in 1850, and to promote the assimilation of Plains peoples into Canadian society. The formula was simple—cash, a small annual payment, and land for the exclusive use of Indigenous peoples (now known as reserves). The assimilation goal soon enough took the form of residential schools. But what were the goals of the various Indian tribes? While they did not speak with one voice, they were aware of the Robinson treaties, the Indian Wars in the United States, and the threat of agricultural settlement on their way of life. More importantly, their main source of food, the buffalo, was disappearing. Word from their cousins in the United States made them very aware of the impact of

settlement and railways on their way of life. Few options remained and their main goal was to survive as a people, but the path was not clear.

Treaty negotiations provided a small window of opportunity to improve the terms over the Robinson treaties. Of course, tribes were acutely aware of earlier settlements, and by Treaty No. 3 they knew all the cards played by the federal negotiators and were able to use this information to gain additional concessions. In this way, the Indigenous peoples forced the federal government to consider issues far beyond the Robinson treaties. For instance, some Indigenous leaders hoped that agriculture might provide the basis for a new economy and they were able to have training in farming/ranching plus supplies and tools included in the treaties. Then, too, Indigenous leaders were able to include "the medicine chest" in Treaty No. 6, which became the basis for subsequent free health care for First Nations people.

While both Canada and the Prairie peoples agreed to these seven treaties, the federal government and the First Nations saw treaties as necessary elements in achieving their very different goals. Ottawa, for instance, gained ownership of the land but it was not happy with the cost of the "unanticipated concessions" granted to the tribes by federal negotiators. First Nations peoples felt the fulfillment of their treaty rights, especially with regard to help in developing an agricultural base on reserve lands, was not forthcoming. Matters turned from bad to worse, culminating in the 1885 Northwest Rebellion.

The Third Clash: The Northwest Rebellion of 1885

While treaties had been signed, Indigenous peoples faced desperate conditions, and those bands that were not docile in the face of drought and starvation found their meagre treaty provisions cut by federal officials. At the same time, the many Métis from Red River who had migrated north and west into present-day Saskatchewan in the years following the 1869–70 rebellion felt threatened once more by the advancing wave of settlers and by difficult conditions. A delegation went to Montana in 1884 and convinced Louis Riel, in exile as a schoolteacher and an American citizen, to return to Canada to lead their quest for their rights. Late in 1884, Riel sent a petition to Ottawa with various demands for all the inhabitants of the North-West—First Nations people, Métis, and whites—effectively asking that they be treated with the dignity deserving of loyal British subjects. Eventually, when no remotely supportive government response was forthcoming, Métis soldiers, with a few warriors from local bands, ambushed a North West Mounted Police (NWMP) contingent at Duck Lake on 26 March 1885, killing 12 men and losing six of their own. Big Bear, a Plains Cree chief, was seeking a peaceful solution to the plight of his people, but a few of his warriors, too, went on the warpath. On 2 April 1885 Cree warriors led by Wandering Spirit rode to Frog Lake to demand food. When the local Indian agent refused them, he was shot. The warriors then looted the settlement and left nine dead.

The Métis, under the leadership of Riel but led militarily by Gabriel Dumont, were prepared to fight the advancing Canadian army, which had arrived quickly from Ontario by means of the Canadian Pacific Railway. Attempts to unite with the Cree failed. Still, the Métis and a few warriors from nearby reserves were successful in surprising the Canadian troops, led by Major-General Frederick D. Middleton, at Fish Creek, but the larger and well-equipped Canadian army eventually wore down the smaller and less well-equipped Métis and First Nations forces at Batoche (see Figure 3.12). From Ottawa's perspective, the Northwest Rebellion was crushed. Louis Riel and eight First Nations leaders were hung while **Big Bear** and **Poundmaker** were sent to prison. But the uprising had an enduring effect on the Prairie tribes and the Métis, and soured Ottawa's relations with Québec.

For more on the reasons for the souring of relations between Ottawa and Québec, see "Strained Relations," page 106.

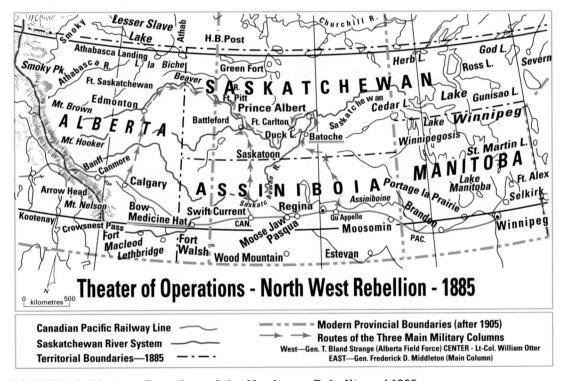

FIGURE 3.12 Western Canada and the Northwest Rebellion of 1885

The Canadian Pacific Railway played a key role in the Northwest Rebellion by transporting the Canadian forces quickly from Ontario to Qu'Appelle, Saskatchewan. In 1885, the political boundaries in Western Canada (except for Manitoba) still were part of the North-West Territories. The provinces of Alberta and Saskatchewan were formed in 1905 while Manitoba reached its current size in 1912.

Source: Based on Rattlesnake Jack's Old West Clip Art Parlour, Font Gallery, North West Rebellion Emporium and Rocky Mountain Ranger Patrol, at: members.memlane.com/gromboug/P5NWReb.htm.

The Making of Canada

THINK ABOUT IT

John Ralston Saul calls Canada a "soft country" where middle ground to conflicts is sought. Was this true in the late nineteenth century when the faultline between Ottawa and Québec widened over events surrounding the Métis and the hanging of Riel?

After the completion of the CPR, Canada became a country linked together by the "iron horse," which in turn brought thousands to its western territories. Not only was the migration to Western Canada one of the greatest world immigrations, it also placed a "British/Canadian" brand on the landscape, and, with Indian treaties and the dispersal of the Métis, Canada relegated the earlier occupants to the margins. The emerging cultural landscape of Western Canada took three forms—the rectangular appearance of its rural landholdings, the orientation of villages and cities to the railways, and the symbols of ethnic/religious diversity as expressed by farm buildings and churches. By 1895, Western Canada had a predominantly British population that had established its own land survey and ownership system, local governments and police to ensure "law and order," and a variety of social institutions.

As evident from the experience of the Métis pattern of landownership, elements of the landscape that did not conform ran into serious problems. During a 10-year span from 1870 to 1880, the Métis lost their majority due to an influx of immigrants from Ontario, many of whom either belonged to or supported the views of the Orange Order. Some newcomers saw no place for the Métis and First Nations peoples in the emerging society, thus creating tensions between the existing population and the newcomers. From 1871 to 1881, Manitoba's population increased from 25,228 to 62,260, with most immigrants coming from Ontario, the British Isles, and the United States (Table 3.8). At this time, those

of British ancestry formed 54 per cent of the population; other Europeans made up 17 per cent; Métis, 17 per cent; and First Nations, 11 per cent (Canada, 1882: Table III). The newly formed English-speaking majority focused their attention on the dual school system. By 1891, Manitoba's population exceeded 150,000 (Table 3.8). In an example of the tyranny of the majority, the English-speaking population argued that with so few French-speaking students, funding for the Catholic school was not warranted. In 1890, the government of Manitoba abolished public funding for Catholic schools. This decision took on national significance by becoming a critical issue between Québec and the rest of the country.

What caused this initial influx of settlers? One reason was that Ontario no longer had a surplus of agricultural land and sons of farmers looked to the unsettled lands on the Great Plains of the United States and to Manitoba. A second reason was that the promise of a railway would make farming in Manitoba more viable. With completion of the CPR line from Fort William on Lake Superior to Selkirk, Manitoba, in 1882, grain could be transported by rail and ship to eastern Canada and Great Britain rather than by the more circuitous steamship route to St Paul and then by rail to New York. Wheat farming in Manitoba had become a profitable business because of advances in agricultural machinery and farming techniques, and rising prices for grain. Equally important, new strains of wheat, first Red Fife and then Marquis, both of which ripened more quickly than previous varieties, lessened the danger of crop loss due to frost. Marquis wheat, which matured seven days earlier than Red Fife, allowed wheat cultivation

TABLE 3.8 **Population in Western Canada by Province, 1871–1911**

Year	Manitoba	Saskatchewan	Alberta
1871	25,228		
1881	62,260	21,652	9,875
1891	152,506	40,206	26,593
1901	255,211	91,279	73,022
1911	461,394	492,432	374,295

Note: The boundaries of Manitoba did not reach their present limits until 1912, and Saskatchewan and Alberta became provinces in 1905. Their populations for 1881, 1891, and 1901 have been calculated from the censuses of Canada for 1881 and 1891.

Source: Canada (1882: 93–6; 1892: 112–13); Statistics Canada (2003).

to take place in the parkland belt of Saskatchewan and Alberta where the frost-free period was shorter than in southern Manitoba.

Sifton Widens the Net

By the end of the nineteenth century, Canada's West still needed more settlers. Clifford Sifton of Manitoba, the federal minister responsible for finding settlers, realized that he had to expand his recruitment area beyond Great Britain into Central Europe and Russia. Even though this ran against the creation of a British-populated Western Canada, Sifton (1922) took a pragmatic approach, which he summed up in later years: "I think a stalwart peasant in a sheepskin coat, born on the soil, whose forefathers have been farmers for ten generations, with a stout wife and a half-dozen children is good quality." Under Sifton, the pattern of immigration took a sharp turn from the main sources of immigrants to the West, namely Canada, the British Isles, and the United States. Within two decades of entering Confederation, Manitoba's population had increased by just over 600 per cent (Table 3.8). Most were of British stock, but substantial numbers of Mennonites and Icelanders had also come to Manitoba. At the same time, few settlers had reached Saskatchewan and Alberta, though many of the Métis had relocated in Saskatchewan, primarily around the settlement of Batoche on the South Saskatchewan River just north of Saskatoon. In the next decade, the volume of immigrants from Central Europe, Scandinavia, and Russia increased substantially. As peasants, they were prepared for the harsh physical conditions associated with breaking the virgin prairie land and were willing to deal with the psychological stress of living on isolated farmsteads in a foreign country where their native tongue was not accepted. As the numbers of these European immigrants grew, the anglophone majority became concerned about the newcomers and their possible effect on the existing social structure. The demographic impact of the non-British migration to Western Canada is shown in the 1916 census (Table 3.9).

This wave of Central Europeans had tremendous implications for Western Canada. While most newcomers assimilated into the English-speaking society, a few did not. Often these ethnic groups settled in one area where they were somewhat insulated from the larger society and where they attempted to maintain their traditional customs, language, and religion. The federal government, by providing land reserves for ethnic groups such as the Mennonites and Doukhobors, reinforced this tendency.

While they were successful farmers, the cultural differences between the more conservative Doukhobors and Canadian society were too great for the majority society to accept. Some Doukhobors were able to integrate into local society, but the Community Doukhobors simply were not prepared to adapt. They remained faithful to their religious beliefs that emphasized communal living. In choosing to settle in Canada, they were granted blocks of land and exemption from military service.

Through negotiations with the Canadian government, Doukhobor leaders had obtained four large blocks of land totalling 750,000 acres. In 1899, the Doukhobors—7,500 in total—arrived in Canada and took possession of pre-selected lands where they built 57 villages. The four colonies were located just west of Swan River, Manitoba (North Colony), and at Prince Albert (Saskatchewan Colony) and Yorkton, Saskatchewan (South Colony and Good Spirit Lake Annex).

Farming was not only an economic activity, but it was also central to their religious beliefs, which emphasized the value of a simple, communal life. For example, Doukhobors shared in the returns from farming, and no one person owned the land or the tools. In a land of individual landholdings and the pursuit of profit, the Doukhobors were seen as "out of step" with the surrounding community. As public resentment increased, the federal government took action. In 1905, Frank Oliver succeeded Clifford Sifton as Minister of the Interior. Oliver decided to enforce the Dominion Lands Act, so when the Doukhobors refused to swear an oath of allegiance to the King, Oliver had his excuse to deny them homestead lands.

Failure to take such an oath had two implications. First, it suggested that these people were disloyal to the monarch. Second, it meant that the Doukhobors could not obtain title to their homestead lands. Under this pretext, Oliver used the

THINK
ABOUT IT

Does the open discrimination against Indigenous peoples and non-British newcomers that was common in the nineteenth century and much of the twentieth century reflect Saul's concept of a "hard" country? If so, why?

TABLE 3.9 Population of Western Canada by Ethnic Group, 1916

Ethnic Group	W. Canada Population	% of W. Canada Population	% of Manitoba Population	% of Sask. Population	% of Alberta Population
British	971,830	57.2	57.7	54.5	60.2
German	136,968	8.1	4.7	11.9	6.8
Austro-Hungarian	136,250	8.0	8.2	9.1	6.4
French	89,987	5.3	6.1	4.9	4.9
Russian	63,735	3.7	2.9	4.5	3.8
Norwegian	47,449	2.8	0.6	4.2	3.4
Indigenous	39,147	2.3	2.5	1.7	2.9
Ukrainian	39,103	2.3	4.1	0.7	1.8
Swedish	37,220	2.2	1.4	2.5	2.7
Polish	27,790	1.6	3.0	1.0	0.9
Jewish	23,381	1.4	3.0	0.6	0.6
Dutch	22,353	1.3	1.3	1.4	1.3
Icelandic	15,800	0.9	2.2	0.5	0.1
Danish	9,556	0.6	0.3	0.5	0.9
Belgian	9,084	0.5	0.8	0.4	0.4
Italian	5,348	0.3	0.3	1.0	0.9
Other	26,219	1.5	0.9	1.5	2.3
Total	1,701,220	100.0	100.0	100.0	100.0

Source: Census of Prairie Provinces, 1916, Table 7. Data adapted from Statistics Canada, at: www12.statcan.ca/English/census01/products/analytic/companion/age/provpymds.cfm.

Dominion Lands Act to cancel their right to land. Most of the Doukhobors who remained committed to the communal way of life eventually moved to British Columbia; others abandoned the village life and took title to homesteads. The villages gradually lost members and lands. The South Colony just north of Yorkton, Saskatchewan, was the last holdout, but by 1918 it ceased to exist on Crown land. It persisted in a much reduced area on purchased land until 1938, as did other communal settlements established in the Kylemore and Kelvington areas.

One explanation for the ultimate failure of the Doukhobor experiment was that Canada's model of individual settlement was simply too rigid to accept a communal one. Primarily for that reason, the Community Doukhobors were unable to find a place in Western Canada. They represent a classic example of a people being too different—too "other"—from the majority to be allowed a comfortable space within the predominately British landscape.

Ironically, the village model of settlement was perhaps the most effective way of settling the Prairies in the late nineteenth and early twentieth centuries. Carl Tracie (1996: xii) puts it this way:

At the very time when the individual homesteader was struggling with the very real problems of isolation and loneliness, the Doukhobor settlements, whose compact form allayed these problems, were being dismantled by forces which could not accommodate the communal aspects of the group. Also, although the initial government concern was the survival of the Doukhobors, their very prosperity, based as it was on communal effort, may have worked against them since it illustrated the success of a system diametrically opposed to the individualistic system dictated by government policy and assumed by mainstream society.

The French/English Faultline

Although the ancestors of Indigenous peoples were the first to occupy North America, the colonization of the continent pushed them to the margins, leaving the two European powers—the French and the British—to place their mark on the land. Following the British military victory at Québec in 1759, the Treaty of Paris (1763) confirmed British hegemony over a French-Canadian majority and its control over the lands of New France. This historic fact underscores the dominant position of the British and their impact on later Canadian institutions and governments. Also, the British way of life was established across Canada, though rural Québec retained its French character, the seigneurial agricultural system, and the Roman Catholic religion. Differences between these two cultures have come to represent a major faultline in Canadian society.

Nonetheless, the union of Lower Canada (Québec) and Upper Canada (Ontario) in 1841 meant that French and English had to work together in a single parliament, which made each dependent on the other and was instrumental in the 1867 Confederation. This balance of political power between the French and English has done much to shape the political nature of Canada, particularly the need to find a middle ground. Over the years, they have accomplished much together. Yet, significant differences between the two communities exist, and from time to time these differences flare into serious misunderstandings. Without a doubt, Canadian unity depends on the continuation of this relationship and the need for compromise, which has become a feature of modern Canadian political life and is a basic aspect of Canadian tolerance between the two official language groups and towards newcomers.

The serious nature of the French/English rift has profound geopolitical consequences for Canada. While blowing hot and cold over the years since Confederation, the rift was boiling hot in the last three decades of the twentieth century. In 1993, a well-known Canadian political columnist, Jeffrey Simpson, captured this moment:

We can also hope that, in the 1980s, Canadians gained a deeper understanding of the faultlines running through their society, and that they will avoid measures that widen them, thereby concentrating on making new arrangements and reforming old ones, so that what the rest of the world rightly believes to be a successful experiment in managing diversity will endure and prosper. (Simpson, 1993: 368)

Origin of the French/English Faultline

The British Conquest of the French on the Plains of Abraham in 1759 marks the origin of this faultline. An event that remains a dark page in French-Canadian history culminated in the battered remnants of the French army and the French colonial elite boarding ships to return to their mother country. The French Canadians had no thought of leaving, but what would happen to them under British military rule? Would they, like their Acadian brethren, be deported to other British colonies? Britain did not need to take such drastic action by this time—the Acadian deportations had occurred in the 1750s when there still was a French threat to Britain's North American possessions. In the Treaty of Paris, France ceded New France to Britain, which placed the French-Canadian majority under the British monarchy. While the English lived in cities in Québec and dominated the Québec economy and politics, French Canadians lived mostly in rural areas where they successfully maintained their culture within a British North America. This relationship between British rulers and the French Canadians would be strengthened with the Québec Act of 1774.

The Québec Act, 1774

With the Québec Act of 1774, the unique nature and separateness of Québec were recognized, thus affirming its place in British North America. This Act is sometimes described as the Magna Carta for French Canada.[7] Its main provisions ensured the continuation of the aristocratic seigneurial landholding system and guaranteed religious freedom for the colony's Roman Catholic majority and, by implication, their right to retain their native language.[8] This gave the most powerful people in New France a good reason to support the new rulers. The Roman Catholic Church was placed in a particularly strong position. Not only was the Church allowed to collect tithes and dues but its role as the protector of French culture went unchallenged. Therefore, the clergy played an extremely important role in directing and maintaining a rural French-Canadian society, a role further enhanced by the Church's control of the education system. The **habitants** (farmers) were at the bottom of French-Canadian society's hierarchy. They formed the vast majority of the population and continued to cultivate their land on seigneuries, paying their dues to their lord (seigneur) and faithfully obeying the local priest and bishop. The British granted another important concession, namely, that civil suits would be tried under French law. Criminal cases, however, fell under English law.

The seigneurial system formed the basis of rural life in New France and, later, in Québec. In 1774, there were about 200 seigneuries in the St Lawrence Lowland. This type of land settlement left its mark on the landscape (the long, narrow landholdings extending to the river and the vast estate of the seigneur) and on the mentality of rural French Canadians—close family ties, a strong sense of togetherness with neighbouring rural families (the long-lot system of land tenure meant that rural neighbours were not so far away), and staunch support for the Church. A habitant's landholding, though small, was the key to his family's prosperity, and by bequeathing the farm to his eldest son the habitant ensured the continuation of this rural way of life. In 1854, the habitant was allowed to purchase his small plot of land from his seigneur, but the last vestiges of this seigneurial system did not disappear until a century later. Even today, the landscape along the St Lawrence shows many signs of this type of landholding.

While the heart of this new British territory was the settled land of the St Lawrence Lowland, its full geographic extent was immense. Essentially, the Québec Act of 1774 recognized the geographic area of former French territories in North America. Québec's territory in 1774 was extended from the Labrador coast to the St Lawrence Lowland and beyond to the sparsely settled Great Lakes Lowland and the Indigenous lands of the Ohio Basin. After the British defeat in the American Revolution, the geographic size of Québec shrank with the southern part of the Great Lakes Lowland and the Indigenous lands of the Ohio Basin ceded to the Americans.

The Loyalists

The American War of Independence changed the political landscape of North America. Within the newly formed United States, a number of Americans, known as the **Loyalists**, remained loyal to Britain. Like the French-speaking people in North America, most of these Loyalists were born and raised in the New World. For them, North America was their homeland. During the revolution, they had sided with the British. They were hounded by the American revolutionaries and many lost their homes and property. Most resettled in the remaining British colonies in North America, where Britain offered them land. The majority (about 40,000 Loyalists) settled in the Maritimes, particularly in Nova Scotia. About 5,000 relocated in the forested Appalachian Uplands of the Eastern Townships of Québec. A few thousand, including Indigenous peoples led by Joseph Brant, took up land in the Great Lakes Lowland in present-day Ontario.

Within a few decades, more English-speaking settlers arrived in the Great Lakes region. As their numbers grew, they felt frustrated as a small part of the sprawling Québec colony. Its capital city, Québec, was too far away and these English-speaking settlers sought to control their own affairs so they could have a more "British" government with British civil law, British institutions, and an elected assembly. In the Constitutional Act of 1791, Québec was split into Upper and Lower Canada.

The Six Nations of the Iroquois Confederacy

The Mohawk, Oneida, Onondaga, Cayuga, Seneca, and Tuscarora formed the Six Nations of the Iroquois Confederacy. Centred in New York, the Confederacy blocked European settlers from entering the Ohio Valley. During the American Revolution the Confederation split, with the Oneida and Tuscarora joining the American cause, while the rest of the league, led by Chief Joseph Brant's Mohawk, sided with the British. After the end of the American Revolution in 1783, those loyal to the British moved from New York to Ontario and settled along the Grand River in southwestern Ontario on a vast tract—the Haldimand Grant—given to them in 1784 by the Governor of Québec, Lord Haldimand.

See Figure 6.6, "The Haldimand Tract," page 186, for more details about the Haldimand Grant.

The Constitutional Act, 1791

The Constitutional Act of 1791 represented an attempt by the British Parliament to satisfy the political needs of the French- and English-speaking inhabitants of Québec. These were the main provisions of the Act: (1) the British colony of Québec was divided into the provinces of Upper and Lower Canada, with the Ottawa River as the dividing line, except for two seigneuries located just southwest of the Ottawa River; and (2) each province was governed by a British lieutenant-governor appointed by Britain. From time to time, the lieutenant-governor would consult with his executive council and acknowledge legislation passed by an elected legislative assembly.

In 1791, Lower Canada had a much larger population than Upper Canada. At that time, about 15,000 colonists lived in Upper Canada, most of whom were of Loyalist extraction, plus about 10,000 Indigenous people, some of whom had fled northward after the American Revolution. Lower Canada's population consisted of about 140,000 French Canadians, 10,000 English Canadians, and perhaps as many as 5,000 Indigenous people.

Following the Constitutional Act, Upper and Lower Canada each had an elected assembly, but the real power remained in the hands of the British-appointed lieutenant-governors. In Lower Canada the lieutenant-governor had the support of the Roman Catholic Church, the seigneurs, and the Château Clique. The Château Clique, a group consisting mostly of anglophone merchants, controlled most business enterprises and, as they were favoured by the lieutenant-governor, wielded much political power. In Upper Canada the Family Compact—a small group of officials who dominated senior bureaucratic positions, the executive and legislative councils, and the judiciary—held similar positions in commercial and political circles. While these two elite groups promoted their own political and financial well-being, the rest of the population grew more and more dissatisfied with blatant political abuses, which included patronage and unpopular policies that favoured these two groups. Attempts to obtain political reforms leading to a more democratic political system failed. Under these circumstances, social unrest was widespread.

In 1837 and 1838, rebellions broke out. In Lower Canada Louis-Joseph Papineau led the rebels, while William Lyon Mackenzie headed the rebels in Upper Canada. Both uprisings were ruthlessly suppressed by British troops. The goal of both insurrections was to take control by wresting power from the colonial governments in Toronto and Québec and putting government in the hands of the popularly elected assemblies. In Lower Canada the rebellion was also an expression of Anglo-French animosity. While both uprisings were unsuccessful, the British government nevertheless sent Lord Durham to Canada as Governor General to investigate the rebels' grievances. He recommended a form of responsible government and the union of the two Canadas. Once the two colonies were unified, the next step, according to Durham, would be the assimilation of the French Canadians into British culture.

The Act of Union, 1841

In response to Durham's report, in 1841 the two largest colonies in British North America, Upper and Lower Canada, were united into the Province of Canada. This Act of Union gave substance to the geographic and political realities of British North America. The geographic reality was that a large French-speaking population existed in Lower Canada, while a smaller English-speaking population was concentrated in Upper Canada (Table 3.10). The political reality was twofold. Both groups had to work together to accomplish their political goals and neither group could achieve all of its goals without some form of compromise. When the two cultures were forced to work together in a single legislative assembly, a new beginning to the French/English faultline surfaced.

Demographic Shifts

In a democracy, political power is based on population numbers. During the early days of the Act of Union most people lived in Lower Canada, but by 1851 the reverse was true (Table 3.10). In this way, the balance of power shifted to Upper Canada and this shift continues. In 1841, Québec's population stood at 45 per cent of British North America's population, but after Confederation, in 1871, Québec represented 34 per cent of the total population.

Strained Relations

During these formative years, several events seriously strained relations between the Dominion's two founding peoples:

- the Red River Rebellion, 1869–70;
- the Northwest Rebellion, 1885, and its aftermath, with the execution of Riel;
- the Manitoba Schools Question, 1890.

The Red River Rebellion, 1869–70

As we have seen, the Métis uprising, led by Louis Riel, soon became a national issue, reopening differences between English, Protestant Ontario and French, Roman Catholic Québec.[9] Québec considered Riel a French-Canadian hero who was defending the Métis, a people of mixed blood who spoke French and followed the Catholic religion.

Protestant Ontario, on the other hand, considered Riel a traitor and a murderer. For Canada, the larger issue was the place of French Canadians in the West. A compromise was achieved in the Manitoba Act of 1870. Accordingly, the District of Assiniboia became the province of Manitoba. Under this Act, land was set aside for the Métis, although a number of them sold their entitlements (scrip) to land allotments for a cheap price to incoming settlers and moved further west or sought to continue their former hunting lifestyle in Manitoba. The elected legislative assembly of Manitoba provided a balance between the two ethnic groups with 12 English and 12 French electoral districts. Equally important, Manitoba had two official languages (French and English) and two religious school systems (Catholic and Protestant) financed by public funds.

The background to the Red River Rebellion is presented earlier in "The First Clash: Red River Rebellion of 1869–70," page 96.

The Northwest Rebellion, 1885

During the 1870s, many Ontarians settled in Manitoba while some Métis sought a new home on the open prairie. Seeking to remain hunters, one group settled along the South Saskatchewan River where they established a Métis colony around Batoche, about 60 km northeast of present-day Saskatoon. Batoche became the new centre of the French-speaking Métis in Western Canada. As settlers spread into Saskatchewan, the Métis again feared for their future. In 1884, when a party of Métis went to Montana to plead with Louis Riel to return to Batoche and lead them again, Riel, convinced of his destiny, accepted this challenge. As we have seen, this uprising ended

TABLE 3.10 Population by Colony or Province, 1841–1871 (%)

Colony/Province	1841	1851	1861	1871
Ontario	33.0	41.1	45.2	46.5
Québec	45.0	38.5	36.0	34.2
Nova Scotia	13.0	12.0	10.7	11.1
New Brunswick	9.0	8.4	8.1	8.2
Manitoba				< 0.1
British Columbia				< 0.8

Source: McVey and Kalbach (1995: 38). © 1995 Nelson Education Ltd. Reproduced by permission. www.cengage.com/permissions.

in failure for the Métis and their First Nations allies. For Québec, the defeat of the Métis and the subsequent hanging of their leader not only represented a defeat for a French presence in the West but also widened the gulf between French and English Canadians. Riel's link to Québec and the Roman Catholic Church made him a powerful symbol of language, religious, and racial divisions for over 100 years. Indeed, to this day historians remain divided about Louis Riel's legacy, his place in the story of Canada, and even his sanity as the messianic leader of a doomed rebellion.

The background to the Northwest Rebellion is presented earlier in "The Third Clash: The Northwest Rebellion of 1885," page 98.

The Manitoba Schools Question, 1890

The British North America Act of 1867 established English and French as legislative and judicial languages in federal and Québec institutions. The remaining three provinces (New Brunswick, Nova Scotia, and Ontario) had only English as the official language. The question of French-language and religious rights in acquired western territories first arose in Manitoba.

The French/English issue became the focal point for the entry of the Red River Settlement (now Manitoba) into Confederation. Local inhabitants—mostly French-speaking Roman Catholic Métis and the less numerous English-speaking Métis—were determined to have some influence over the terms that would include their community as part of Canada. One of their concerns was language rights, an issue ultimately resolved when a list of rights drafted by the Riel's Provisional Government became the basis of federal legislation. When the settlement and surrounding territory of Red River entered Confederation in 1870 as the province of Manitoba, it did so with the assurance that English- and French-language rights, as well as the right to be educated in Protestant or Roman Catholic schools, were protected by provincial legislation.

During the 1870s and 1880s, with the influx of a large number of Anglo-Protestant settlers from Ontario, the proportion of Anglo-Protestants in the Manitoba population increased and the proportion of French and Roman Catholic inhabitants decreased. This demographic change created a stronger Anglo-Protestant culture in Manitoba. In 1890, the provincial government ended public funding of Catholic schools. From Québec's perspective, this legislation shook the very foundations of Confederation. Sir Wilfrid Laurier became Prime Minister in 1896 and, in the following year, Laurier negotiated a compromise agreement with the government of Manitoba. The compromise allowed for the teaching of Catholic religion in a public school when there were sufficient Catholic students. Similarly, if there were sufficient French-speaking students, classes could be taught in French.

One Country, Two Visions

The greatest challenge to Canadian unity comes from the cultural divide that separates French- and English-speaking Canadians and their respective visions of the country. The two predominant visions are (1) a partnership between French and English Canada, and (2) equality of the 10 provinces.

In the early years of Confederation, events such as those outlined above widened the French/English faultline. For French Canadians these events demonstrated the "power" of the English-speaking majority and their unwillingness to accept a vision of Canada as a partnership between the two founding peoples. The root of each vision lies in the history of Canada and the division of powers by the Fathers of Confederation.

Partnership Vision

One vision of Canada is based on the principle of two founding peoples. This vision originated in French-Canadian historical experiences and compromises that were necessary for the sharing of political power between the two partners. This vision began with the Conquest of New France, but its true foundation lies in the formation of the Province of Canada in 1841. From 1841 onward, the experience of working together resulted in a Canadian version of cultural dualism.

Henri Bourassa, a French-Canadian politician and journalist (and Canadian nationalist) in the early twentieth century, was a strong advocate of cultural dualism. He wrote, "My native land is all of Canada, a federation of separate races and autonomous provinces. The nation I wish to see grow up is the Canadian nation, made up of French Canadians and English Canadians" (quoted in Bumsted, 2007: 307). Bourassa argued that a "double contract" existed within Confederation. Even today, Bourassa's "double contract" is an essential element in the concept of two founding peoples. He based the notion of a double contract on a liberal interpretation of section 93 of the BNA Act, which guarantees denominational schools. Bourassa expanded the interpretation of the religious rights to include cultural rights for French- and English-speaking Canadians. In more practical terms, Bourassa regarded Confederation as a moral contract that guaranteed French/English duality, the preservation of French-speaking Québec, and the protection of the language and religious rights of French-speaking Canadians in other provinces.

From a geopolitical perspective, Canada is a bicultural country. In one part the majority of Canadians speak English, and in another part French is the majority language. Thus, French culture dominates in Québec and has a strong position in New Brunswick. In addition to provincial control over culture, two other geopolitical factors ensure the dynamism of French in those provinces. One factor is the large size of Québec's population—the vitality of Québécois culture is one indication of its success. The second factor is the geographic concentration of French-speaking Canadians in Québec and adjacent parts of Ontario and New Brunswick. In New Brunswick the French-speaking residents, known as Acadians, constitute over one-third of the population.

The Royal Commission on Bilingualism and Biculturalism was designed to bridge the gap between English and French Canadians. This Commission, set up in 1963, examined the issue of cultural dualism, that is, an equal partnership between the two cultural groups. But by the 1960s, Canada's demographics revealed a third ethnic force and the concept of duality no longer reflected reality. English-speaking Canada had changed. English-speaking Canada had evolved from a predominantly British population to a more diverse one with several large minority groups who also spoke other languages besides English, especially German and Ukrainian. Ottawa, in searching for a compromise, established two policies, bilingualism (1969) and multiculturalism (1971).

The Vision of Equal Provinces

In the second vision, Canada consists of 10 equal provinces—yet this, too, is misleading. On the one hand, it represents the simple notion based on provincial powers granted under the British North America Act, which ensured that Canada consists of a union of equal provinces, all of which have the same powers of government. Nonetheless, by assigning provinces powers over education, language, and other cultural matters within their provincial jurisdictions, the BNA Act ensured that Québec's French culture was secure from political tampering by the anglophone majority in the rest of Canada. Thus, Confederation provided a form of collective rights for French culture within Québec. Under Canada's federal system, the powers of government are shared between the federal government and 10 provincial governments. But are all provinces really equal? As noted earlier, population size, geographic extent, and financial strength vary considerably, which is reflected in the need for equalization payments.

The vision of 10 equal provinces may reflect English-Canadian nationalism. For some time, English-speaking Canadians have been searching for their cultural identity and a sense of national belonging. Before World War I, English-speaking Canadians saw themselves as part of the British Empire, but with Canadian troops fighting as a unit in Europe the first signs of nationalism appeared. Canada's efforts during World War II pushed the sense of nationalism to new heights. In the years following, symbols of nation-building took the form of the Maple Leaf flag, adopted by Parliament in 1964, and "O Canada," the new national anthem approved by Parliament in 1967 and officially adopted in 1980. While the Québécois culture was flourishing, thanks in part to generous provincial funding for the arts, English-speaking Canadians continued to lean heavily on American culture. Some looked with envy at the cultural accomplishments of the Québécois and wondered aloud if similar achievements in English-speaking Canada were possible. The answer could be yes, providing the provincial governments offered similar financial support for the arts, and providing that English-speaking Canadians supported their artists at the same level as the Québécois public supported francophone artists and cultural producers.

Compromise

Given the incompatibility of the two visions—two founding peoples versus 10 equal provinces—and the historical development of the country, Canadian politicians have had the unenviable task of trying to accommodate demands from different groups—especially French Canadians, new immigrants, and Indigenous peoples—and from different regions without offending other groups or regions. As in the past, politicians have continued to struggle with this Canadian dilemma, but in reality there is no perfect solution, only compromise. With this object in mind the federal government has made many efforts in search of the elusive middle ground.[10] It seems the search for an acceptable compromise between the two opposing visions of Canada will never end, and perhaps that is a good thing because the process is more important than the end result. To understand the current struggle for compromise, it is important to understand the political, economic, and cultural developments that have taken place in Québec over the past five decades.

Resurgence of Québec Nationalism

After World War II, Québec broke with its past. A rise of Québec nationalism had begun much earlier but gained political momentum during the **Quiet Revolution** of the early 1960s. This development was the result of four major events. The most important was the resurgence of ethnic nationalism, that is, a pride in being Québécois. The second was Québec's joining the urban/industrial world of North America and the subsequent expansion in the size of its industrial labour force and business class. The third was the removal of the old elite. This reform movement was profoundly anticlerical in its opposition to the entrenched role of the Church in Québec society, particularly the Church's control over education. In many ways, this reform was based on the aspirations of the working and middle classes in the new Québec economy. The fourth was the state's aggressive role in the province's affairs.

With the election of Jean Lesage's Liberal government in 1960, which held power until 1966, the province moved forcefully in a new direction. It created a more powerful civil service that allowed francophones access to middle and senior positions often denied them in the private sector of the Québec economy, which was controlled by English-speaking Québecers and American companies. It nationalized the province's electricity system, thereby creating the industrial giant known as Hydro-Québec, now a powerful symbol of Québec's revitalized economy and society. In turn, Hydro-Québec built a number of huge energy projects that demonstrated the province's industrial strength. By 1968, this Crown corporation had constructed one of the largest dams in the world on the Manicouagan River. Called Manic 5, this dam demonstrated Hydro-Québec's engineering and construction capabilities. To Québecers, Hydro-Québec was a symbol of Québec's economic liberation from the years of suffocation associated with Maurice Duplessis and his Union Nationale government, which had been closely tied to big businesses owned by English-speaking Canadians and Americans. Clearly, Lesage's political goal of becoming "maîtres chez nous" (masters in our own house) had materialized with the success of Hydro-Québec, thus sparking a growth in Québec nationalism. Québec's desire for more autonomy in its own affairs intensified with increased confidence. In short, a new society had arisen in Québec, a society that wanted to chart its destiny. Charles Taylor (1993: 4) summed up this new feeling as "a French Canada which, after a couple of centuries of enforced incubation [under London and then Ottawa], was ready to take control once more of

THINK ABOUT IT

Is the demand for Québécois culture within Québec driven by the threat of drowning in a sea of American culture?

its history." The political question Taylor raised is a simple one: Would this "control" take place within the framework of Canada's political system or outside it?

Separatism

Separatism—the desire for an independent francophone nation in North America—grew out of the Quiet Revolution. The embers of nationalism were ignited in 1967 by French President Charles de Gaulle, who, when visiting the province for Expo '67, uttered the incendiary words, *"Vive le Québec. Vive le Québec libre"* (Photo 3.7), during a speech from a balcony at Montréal City Hall. Soon, René Lévesque, who as a member of the Lesage government had been the architect of the nationalization of electricity generation in the province, had formed a new separatist political party, the Parti Québécois. By 1976, the PQ had won a stunning election victory, and since that time separatism, though waxing and waning in public support, has taken on a mainstream political form. By the time of the first referendum on independence in 1980, the separatists made up a substantial minority within Québec's population, with perhaps 20 per cent dedicated separatists and

another 40 per cent strongly dissatisfied with their place within Canada.

In the 1980 referendum, Québec voters rejected the **sovereignty-association** option, with almost 60 per cent voting to remain in Canada, which suggests that just over half of the francophone voters stood with the "Non" side, along with almost all of the English-speaking residents. The rest of Canada responded with a collective sigh of relief, but separatism was far from dead.

The dream of an independent Québec remained a strong political force. In fact, the 1995 referendum vote on independence almost succeeded. "No—by a Whisker!" screamed the headline of the *Globe and Mail* on the morning after the referendum of 30 October 1995. Québec came within 40,000 votes of approving the separatist dream of becoming an independent state (Vignette 3.9).

For historical background on the French/English faultline in Québec, see Chapter 7, "British Colony, 1760–1867," page 222.

Moving Forward

The 1995 referendum was a low point in French–English relations, and its after-effects were many and varied. English Canada was dazed by the outcome, but the separatists appeared to be a spent force. In 1996, provincial premiers added their voice to the discussion in the Calgary Declaration, stating: "the unique character of Québec society with its French-speaking majority, its culture and its tradition of civil law is fundamental to the well-being of Canada." In the typical fashion of Canadian provincial leaders, the premiers remained clearly in the camp of 10 equal provinces by adding to their conciliatory Declaration that "any power conferred to one province in the future must be available to all." This Declaration was the third attempt at reconciliation with Québec since the patriation of the Constitution in 1982.[11] The next step was for each provincial government to pass the appropriate legislation, giving the Calgary Declaration legal status. By July 1998, all provinces (except Québec) and territories had passed this resolution in their legislatures.

Archives de la Ville de Montreal VM94_ED37

Photo 3.7 French President Charles de Gaulle during his incendiary "Vive le Québec libre" speech in Montréal, 24 July 1967.

Vignette 3.9

The Results of the 30 October 1995 Referendum

The Question: "Do you agree that Québec should become sovereign, after having made a formal offer to Canada for a new Economic and Political Partnership within the scope of the Bill respecting the future of Québec and of the agreement signed on June 12, 1995?"

The Answer (at 10:30 p.m. Eastern Time, 21,907 of 22,427 polls):

	Number	Per cent
No	2,294,162	49.5
Yes	2,254,496	48.7
Rejected	83,340	1.8
Total	4,631,998	100.0

Source: *Globe and Mail* (1995).

Since the 1995 referendum, separatism, while not gone, has lost its spark, in part because the threat of being absorbed by English-speaking North America has subsided for Québecers, who are more confident in the security of their language and culture than had been the case in the immediate post–World War II period. Equally important, Ottawa is more comfortable with the idea of Québécois being recognized as a "distinct cultural group" or nation within Canada. In November 2006, the House of Commons overwhelmingly passed a motion by Prime Minister Harper that recognized Québécois as a nation within Canada. But Québécois nationalism, while somewhat dormant for now, remains deep inside Québécois culture and language.

THINK ABOUT IT

Why won't separatism go away?

SUMMARY

History and geography explain the nature and complexity of contemporary Canada. Canada is both a young and an old country. Complexities are reflected in its four faultlines. The newcomer/old-timer faultline hinges on the "accommodation" issue. The centralist/decentralist argument has taken a twist with Ontario in recent years having become a "have-not" province. Indigenous peoples are settling their outstanding issues with the Crown—the land claim settlement process continues to function and the deep sores caused by Indian residential schools, one can hope, have begun to heal. History teaches Canadians that differences will continue to emerge but compromises are necessary for national unity, regional harmony, and social justice.

Over the course of its short history as a nation of regions Canada, has learned "tolerance" the hard way, and, it would seem, has chosen a "soft" path into the twenty-first century.

Challenge Questions

1. Why did the doctrine of "terra nullius" allow Europeans to consider North America "unoccupied" and therefore open to European ownership and settlement?

2. What does Saul mean when he distinguishes between a "hard" country and a "soft" country?

3. Do you believe that demographic reality forces federal governments to favour Ontario and Québec over other parts of the country? Can you supply an example?

4. Why does Québec support the concept of Canada as "two founding peoples" rather than the concept of Canada as "10 equal provinces"?

5. If the separatists had won the 1995 referendum, would a geographically split country inevitably drift into the political orbit of the United States?

6. Why is the Indigenous/non-Indigenous divide the most complex one facing Canada?

Essay Questions

1. World War I was a turning point. But did the valiant efforts of the Canadian troops result in a surge in Canadian nationalism among English-speaking Canadians and alter Canada's "national" identity?

References:

Canada History. 2013. "Nationalism." At: http://www.canadahistory.com/sections/eras/the%20great%20war/Nationalism.html.

Nelles, H.V. 2017. "Dominion Limited." Chapter Three in Nelles, *A Little History of Canada*, 3rd edn. Toronto: Oxford University Press.

2. World War I divided the nation into two parts: those English-speaking Canadians who jumped to support Britain's war effort and the French-speaking Canadians who felt less loyalty to Britain. The straw that broke the back of a united Canada was conscription. Conscription forced French-speaking Canadians of military age to join the army and this political decision bolstered the French/English divide. Provide the historical evidence to support this view.

References:

Bumsted, J.M. 2014. "The Great War and Its Aftermath, 1914–1919." Chapter 9 in Bumsted, *The Peoples of Canada: A Post-Confederation History*, 4th edn. Toronto: Oxford University Press, 198–219.

Canada History. 2013. "Conscription Act." At: http://www.canadahistory.com/sections/eras/the%20great%20war/Conscription.html.

Further Reading

Harris, R. Cole, ed. 1987. *Historical Atlas of Canada, Volume I: From the Beginning to 1800*. Toronto: University of Toronto Press.

Gentilcore, R. Louis, ed. 1993. *Historical Atlas of Canada: Volume II: The Land Transformed 1800–1891*. Toronto: University of Toronto Press.

Kerr, Donald, and Deryck W. Holdsworth, eds. 1990. *Historical Atlas of Canada, Volume III: Addressing the Twentieth Century 1891–1961*. Toronto: University of Toronto Press.

The historical geography of Canada recalls past events. Maps play a large role in this rediscovery of Canada's past. In 1970, several geographers and historians explored the idea of preparing a major Canadian historical atlas focused on social and economic themes. These three volumes, which parallel the discussion in this chapter, are the successful outcome. The editors weave together the various strands that constitute Canada's historical geography and provide a rich legacy for Canadian scholars and students. Four more recent major events, however, are not covered—the rise of Indigenous political power; the threat of separation of Québec from the rest of Canada; the influx of non-European immigrants; and the Canada–US Free Trade Agreement. These issues are discussed in Chapter 4.

4 Canada's Human Face

Introduction

Human geography provides a broad framework for examining Canada's human face. In this chapter, two major elements of human geography are examined: population and culture. Population geography lays the foundation for this discussion while cultural geography provides a sense of its social character and a vision of the future. In both cases, the emphasis is divided between the national picture and the six geographical regions.

Canada is home to over 36 million people. While its rate of natural increase has fallen, Canada's population size continues to grow due to the arrival of large numbers of immigrants. Most population increase has taken place in Ontario, British Columbia, and Western Canada. Looking to the future, if these demographic trends continue, Canada's population could reach 40 million by 2025 or sooner, with BC and Western Canada experiencing the greatest rates of population increase among the six geographic regions but with Ontario receiving the largest increase in population.

Canada has evolved into a pluralistic society. This transformation began in the 1970s. At that time, most immigrants came from Europe. Now, a significant majority come from Asia, with the Philippines, India, China, Iran, and Pakistan providing Canada with almost 50 per cent of its newcomers in 2015, thus injecting fresh cultural, ethnic, and religious elements into Canadian society. In a humanitarian gesture, Canada opened its doors to Syrian refugees in November 2015, and a year later, by the end of October 2016, the number of these refugees who had entered Canada as permanent residents totalled 33,723.

Over the past 25 years, 200,000 or more immigrants have arrived each year, and about 300,000 were projected to enter the country in 2016. As a result, a more cosmopolitan and "international" society has emerged. Since most newcomers settle in large cities where economic opportunities are perceived to be the highest, Ontario has received the greatest number of newcomers, though in recent years Alberta has attracted large

← Crowds enjoy Vancouver's seawall at the height of summer. Nearly all of Canada's recent population growth has taken place in the country's major urban centres.

BrendanHunter/Getty Images

numbers. The streetscapes of our metropolitan cities have changed, and while hockey and Tim Hortons still resonate with Canadians, cricket and somas are no longer strangers to the playgrounds and street-scapes of these cities.

Cultural change is not without its challenge as accommodation of newcomers remains near the top of the national political agenda, as Prime Minister Trudeau emphasized in an address to the United Nations General Assembly in September 2016. For the most part, however, such adjustment to a new way of life occurs relatively smoothly. The federal government's response to cultural diversity takes the form of its multicultural policy and programs. Yet, the troubled relationship between Indigenous peoples and Ottawa has made the accommodation of Canada's First Peoples far from smooth. Past government policies, such as Indian residential schools, were so harsh that Chief Justice Beverley McLachlin (2015) categorized them as "cultural genocide."[1]

Canada's Population

Canada's population reached 36 million at the start of 2016. Such growth is not surprising. Since Confederation, the country's population has increased steadily (Figure 4.1). In the twenty-first century the nation continues to grow, thanks in large measure to the annual flow of newcomers. By 2025, Canada's population may reach 40 million (Statistics Canada, 2015c).

Two key features mark Canada's population geography: (1) the concentration of Canadians near the US border; and (2) the shift of the centre of population gravity to the West. In terms of the six geographic regions, Ontario and Québec remain the two most populous regions, though the fastest-growing region is now Western Canada, led by Alberta (Table 4.1).

In demographic terms, Canada is aging. Its age dependency ratio is increasing, making the burden to support the very young and the very old fall on fewer and fewer workers. Bucking that national trend, Indigenous peoples and recent immigrants provide a striking exception with their high fertility

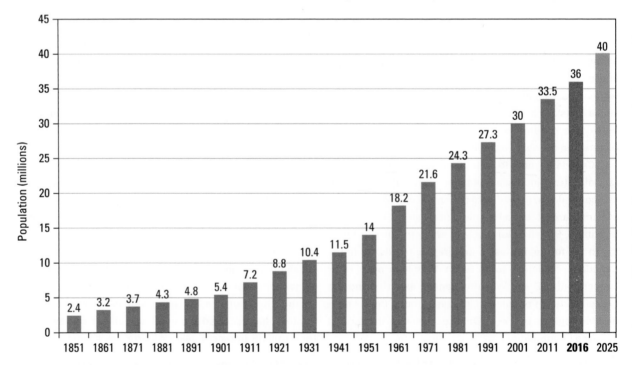

FIGURE 4.1 Population of Canada, 1851–2016, with an estimate for 2025

Sources: Statistics Canada (2012d, 2015c, 2016).

TABLE 4.1 Population Size, Increase, and % Change by Geographic Region, 2001–2016

Geographic Region	Population 2001	Population 2016	Population Increase 2001–2016	% Change, 2001–2016
Territorial North	92,779	118,658	25,879	27.9
Atlantic Canada	2,285,729	2,375,828	90,099	3.9
British Columbia	3,907,738	4,707,021	799,283	20.5
Western Canada	5,073,323	6,678,425	1,605,102	31.6
Québec	7,237,479	8,294,656	1,057,177	14.6
Ontario	11,410,046	13,873,933	2,463,887	21.6
Canada	30,007,094	36,048,521	6,041,427	20.1

Sources: Adapted from Statistics Canada (2002, 2016a).

rates and resulting youthful populations. Yet, participation in the workforce differs sharply between young immigrants and Indigenous youth; and this critical subject is discussed in depth in Chapter 6.

Population Increase

Canada's population is driven by two components: natural increase and immigration. As Figure 4.2 illustrates, immigration now accounts for most of Canada's annual population increase. In 2014, the crude birth rate and crude death rate per 1,000 population were 10.9 and 7.3, respectively, giving a rate of natural increase of 3.6 per 1,000 persons (Table 4.2).

Until 1986, most of Canada's population growth was due to natural increase (Figure 4.2). With changes in Canada's immigration regulations, two key elements emerged: immigration began to replace natural growth as the principal factor causing Canada's population growth; and immigrants from outside of Europe and the United States were more easily admitted than before.

How do we explain these shifts in Canada's demography? The demographic transition theory provides a general framework for all countries that pass from a pre-industrial economy to an industrial one. Most significantly, this theory calls for the death rate to decline well before the birth rate, resulting in a population explosion. According to this

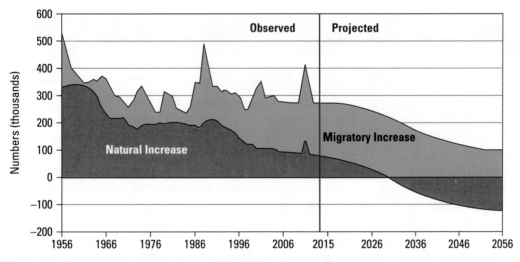

FIGURE 4.2 Population increase, 1956–2056: Immigration, an increasingly important component

Sources: Statistics Canada (2009k, 2012a).

TABLE 4.2 Phases in the Demographic Transition Theory

Phase	Birth and Death Rates	Rate of Natural Increase	Percentage Urban
Late pre-industrial	High birth and death rates	Little or no natural increase but possible fluctuations because of variations in the death rate	Extremely low
Early industrial	Falling death rates	Extremely high rates of natural increase	Low
Late industrial	Falling birth rates	High but declining rates of natural increase	Medium
Early post-industrial	Low birth and death rates	Little or no natural increase; stable population	High
Late post-industrial	Birth rate at or below zero	Declining population	Extremely High

theory, these demographic changes occur in five phases, each of which has a distinct set of vital rates that coincide with the phases in the process of industrialization and urbanization (Table 4.2).

A cursory examination of Canada's birth and death rates over the last 150 years reveals strong similarities to the early industrial, late industrial, and post-industrial phases of this theory. Assuming that Canada is now in the early post-industrial phase, the theory makes sense when applied to Canada's natural increase (i.e., the difference between births and deaths for a given year) (Table 4.3). Supporting that position, demographers argue that Canada's rate of natural increase has fallen below its replacement level (Vignette 4.1). Furthermore, Statistics Canada

projects that natural increase will drop below zero by 2030 (Figure 4.2).

Projections of Canada's natural increase are based on past vital statistics and therefore are not always accurate predictors of the future. The baby boom that took place after World War II presents a perfect example. During the late 1940s and lasting to the early 1970s, birth rates ceased to decline and, instead, increased sharply. The result was a bulge in the age structure of Canadian society that continues to have both economic and social implications (Foot with Stoffman, 1996). As consumers of goods and services, baby boomers have had a decided impact on the economy as they move through their life cycle. Companies have geared their products to meet

Vignette 4.1

The Concept of Replacement Fertility

The concept of replacement fertility refers to the level of fertility at which women have enough daughters to replace themselves. If women have an average of 2.1 births in their lifetime, then each woman, on average, will have given birth to a daughter and a son. The number 2.1 was determined to represent the minimum level of replacement fertility because, on average, slightly more boys than girls are born. In 1961, the Canadian total fertility rate was 3.8 births per woman of child-bearing age (15–49). By 2000, it had dropped to 1.51 but since then has slowly increased, reaching 1.59 in 2013 (Statistics Canada, 2016h).

Nature has ensured that slightly more male than female babies are born. However, male **mortality rates** are higher than those for females. The net result is a population with more females than males. In 2014, females in Canada totalled 17.9 million compared to males at 17.6 million. The **sex ratio**, defined as the number of males per 100 females in the population, was 98.3 in 2014, meaning that there were just over 290,000 fewer males than females in that year (Statistics Canada, 2014a).

TABLE 4.3 Canada's Rate of Natural Increase, 1851–2015

Year	Crude Birth Rate	Crude Death Rate	Natural Increase (%)	Natural Increase (000s)
1851	45.0	20.0	2.5	61
1871	42.0	20.0	2.2	81
1891	38.0	18.0	2.0	97
1911	32.0	14.0	1.8	129
1921	29.3	11.6	1.8	160
1941	22.4	10.1	1.2	145
1961	26.1	7.7	1.8	335
1981	15.2	7.0	0.8	200
2001	10.5	7.1	0.3	108
2011	11.3	7.2	0.4	134
2014	10.9	7.3	0.4	126
2015*	10.9	7.5	0.7	124

*Author's estimates based on Statistics Canada (2016d, 2016e: Q4).

Sources: Adapted from Statistics Canada (1997, 2003a, 2006b, 2007b, 2007c, 2012a, 2015b); McVey and Kalbach (1995: 268, 270).

THINK ABOUT IT

If more women are having children, why is the birth rate not increasing more rapidly? The answer lies in the nature of measuring birth and fertility rates. See "fertility rate" in the Glossary for the answer to this question.

the strong demand created by baby boomers. In the early 1950s, the emphasis was on baby products and larger houses. In the 1960s, a similar age-related pressure was exerted on school facilities, creating a demand for more schools and teachers. As the baby boomers enter old age, the demand for health-care services has risen. Governments, on the other hand, are concerned about rising health-care costs associated with the increase in senior citizens.

Immigration and Population Increase

Immigration keeps Canada growing. The federal government encourages immigration for three reasons:

1. Newcomers keep Canada's population increasing, which is believed necessary for economic growth (see Figure 4.3).
2. Newcomers add valuable members to Canada's workforce and invest capital in Canadian enterprises.
3. Canada takes in a limited number of refugees who are fleeing oppressive sociopolitical conditions in their homelands.

As shown in Figure 4.2, immigration accounts for two-thirds of Canada's annual population increase.

This remarkable flow of people to Canada is central to understanding Canada's population increase and its changing identity. From 1971 to 2015, the proportion of immigrants born in Europe and Asia has reversed. In 2015, the countries providing the most immigrants to Canada were the Philippines (50,816), India (39,495), People's Republic of China (19,512), Iran (11,665), and Pakistan (11,320) (Canadian Magazine of Immigration, 2016). In that year, these five countries accounted for nearly half of the 271,660 new permanent residents. Upon arrival and once in Canada, these newcomers often have large families. As Bélanger and Gilbert (2006) observe, the next generation tends to have fertility rates closer to the national average, a sign of adjusting to Canadian culture norms.

The destination of these newcomers follows the economic strength of Canada's six geographic regions. Up to 2006, around 55 per cent of newcomers chose Ontario as their destination; British Columbia welcomed about 18 per cent; Québec around 14 per cent; Western Canada, 12 per cent; and the remainder settled in Atlantic Canada and the Territorial North (Statistics Canada, 2007a).

Since 2007, more newcomers have selected Western Canada and British Columbia as their primary destinations, reaching 34 per cent for Western Canada and 17 per cent for British Columbia in 2015

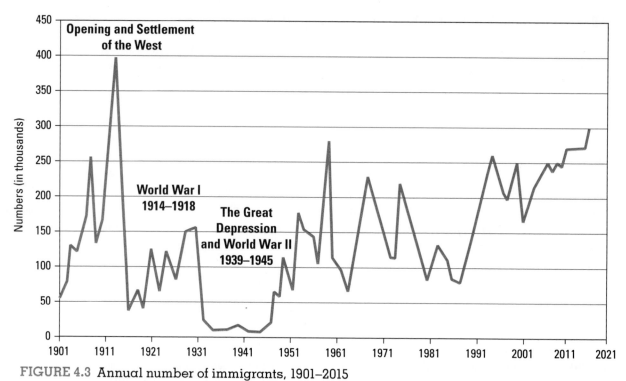

FIGURE 4.3 Annual number of immigrants, 1901–2015

Since 1991, Canada's natural increase has declined from around 200,000 per year to around 130,000 per year. Over the same time span, immigration numbers, while fluctuating from year to year, are now more than double the annual figure for natural increase. By 2015, the number of immigrants reached 271,660 with a projection for 2016 of about 300,000.

Sources: Statistics Canada (2003a: 2; 2009b); Citizenship and Immigration Canada (2011a and 2016).

THINK
ABOUT IT

Laurence C. Smith's *The World in 2050: Four Forces Shaping Civilization's Northern Future* predicts that global migration will greatly increase due to global warming. Could the recent surge of migrants into Europe be a harbinger of an even more dramatic and uncontrolled global movement of people in the future?

(Citizenship and Immigration Canada, 2016). On the other hand, Ontario dropped to 28 per cent and Québec showed some increase, to 19 per cent. Atlantic Canada and the Territorial North remained unchanged.

Population Density

As the second-largest country in the world, Canada's **population density** is one of the lowest. The explanation is simple—relatively few people inhabit its vast northern lands of Arctic and Subarctic climates (Figure 2.4). Canada has a population density of 3.7 persons per km^2, which means the country has an extremely low population density (but not as low as Australia and Mongolia). The United States, by comparison, has 32 persons per km^2. But are population density figures more meaningful if they are expressed as the amount of arable land per person? This measure is called physiological density. By eliminating non-productive agricultural land, Canada's physiological density is similar to that found in the United States.

The explanation for these variations between countries is that land varies greatly in its capacity to support human settlement. Capacity depends heavily on two factors: the suitability of land for agriculture, and the degree of industrialization. When we look at Canada's six geographic regions, the Territorial North falls short on both accounts. Not surprisingly, then, the Territorial North accounts for less than 1 per cent of Canada's population (Table 1.1). In sharp contrast, Ontario scores well on both accounts and thus is home to nearly 40 per cent of Canada's population (Table 1.1). The 2016 population densities of the six geographic regions varied, but only two—the Territorial North and Western Canada—fell below the national average of 3.6 persons per km^2, as shown in Table 4.4.

Population Distribution

Canada's population is extremely unevenly spread across the country. One interpretation describes Canadians as "huddling" near the border with the United States. This observation was made half a

TABLE 4.4 Population Density by Region, Canada, 2016

Region	Population Density (persons per km²)
Territorial North	0.03
Western Canada	3.4
Atlantic Canada	4.4
British Columbia	4.9
Québec	5.4
Ontario	12.9
Canada	3.6

Source: Adapted from Table 1.1.

century ago in a well-known American geography text, which explained that Canada's population is "drawn by a magnet toward the giant neighbor on the south, for they [Canada's inhabitants] are strikingly concentrated along the United States border" (Trewartha, Robinson, and Hammond, 1967: 542). Underlying this understanding are two key factors: Canadian agricultural lands are found near the US border, and trade with the United States dictates that Canada's industrial economy is closely linked with—and close to—that of the United States.

Canada's **population distribution** is reflected by six geographic regions (Table 1.1 and Table 4.1) and by population zones (Figure 4.4). A more geographic view involves classifying Canada's population into four zones.

Led by Vancouver, Calgary, and Edmonton, the two western regions of British Columbia and Western Canada are growing more rapidly than the national average (Table 4.1). On the other hand, Atlantic Canada and Québec are the slowest-growing regions of the country. Paradoxically, the Territorial North, the largest geographic region, contains the smallest number of residents. Added to its distinctive demographic character, the Territorial North had the second-highest rate of **population increase** of the six geographic regions over the last 15 years (Table 4.1).

Population Zones

Canada's population falls into four zones. Its two more densely populated zones are described as Canada's **ecumene** or national population core. Beyond the Canadian ecumene lies a population hinterland consisting of two sparsely populated areas—one nearly empty and the other virtually empty (Figure 4.4).

Population zones provide a more exact geographic picture of Canada's population distribution. As shown in Figure 4.4 and Table 4.5, the four population zones vary in population size from very large (nearly 22 million, or 60 per cent of Canada's population, in zone 1) to very small (the fewer than 100,000 people in zone 4 account for less than 1 per cent of Canada's population). Similarly, the four zones vary considerably in population density, from about 80 persons/km² in zone 1 to 0.01 person in zone 4. The overall spatial pattern reinforces the image of a highly concentrated population core surrounded by more thinly populated zones.

Canada's core population zone lies in the Great Lakes–St Lawrence Lowlands. As the most naturally favoured physiographic region, the Great Lakes–St Lawrence Lowlands contains 21.6 million people and almost three-quarters of Canada's major cities. This population core includes Toronto, Montréal, Ottawa–Gatineau, Québec City, Hamilton, Oshawa, London, and Windsor, to name only some of the largest cities in the region. As Canada's most densely populated area, its economy is based on manufacturing and its agriculture lands are the most fertile in Canada.

The secondary core zone extends in a narrow band across southern Canada. In general, its northern boundary corresponds with the polar edge of arable land. As the second-most favoured zone, it occupies the more southerly portions of the Appalachian Uplands, the Canadian Shield, the Interior Plains, and the Cordillera. About 14 million Canadians, or nearly 40 per cent, live in this moderately populated zone. Canada's remaining major cities are located within this zone, including Vancouver, Edmonton, Calgary, Winnipeg, and Halifax. Within the secondary zone, some areas, such as southern Alberta and British Columbia, are growing quickly while other areas, such as Newfoundland and Labrador, have experienced much slower growth and even population losses. As a result, the population of the secondary zone is increasing slowly and unevenly.

The sparsely populated or tertiary zone contains about 1 per cent of all Canadians (just under 400,000). This zone is associated with the boreal forest that stretches across mid-Canada. Only one of Canada's major cities, Fort McMurray, Alberta, is situated in

THINK ABOUT IT

While Ontario has a population density of 12.9 persons per km², the 2015 figure for southern Ontario is much higher—nearly 95 persons per km²—while northern Ontario's figure is less than 1 person per km². Do the other five geographic regions contain similar internal population density variations?

TABLE 4.5 Population Zones, 2016

Zone Description	Population (millions)	Percentage of Canada's population	Major City	Population of Major City
1. Core zone: densely populated	21.6	60	Toronto	6,129,900
2. Secondary zone: moderately populated	14.0	39	Vancouver	2,504,300
3. Tertiary zone: Sparsely populated	0.3	1	Fort McMurray*	78,000
4. Empty zone: Isolated settlements	<0.1	<1	Labrador City	9,000

*Wood Buffalo Regional Municipality.

Source: Statistics Canada (2016a, 2016b).

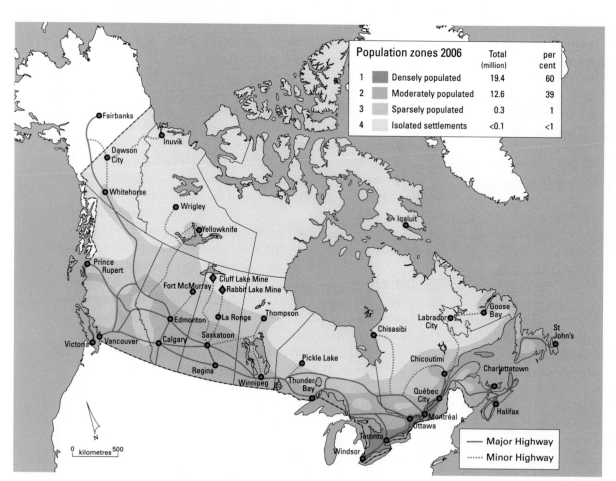

FIGURE 4.4 Canada's population zones and highway system

Canada's population is heavily concentrated in southern Ontario and southern Québec, where a favourable physical geography and an advantageous geographic location have resulted in a dense population of nearly 80 persons/km². A secondary belt of population spans a southern strip of Canada with a population density close to 15 persons/km². Together, the densely and moderately populated zones account for 99 per cent of Canada's population. Population zones 3 and 4 contain only 1 per cent of Canada's population

© iStock/espiegle

Photo 4.1 Founded in 1642, Montréal, Québec, is one of Canada's oldest cities. Located on the St Lawrence River, Montréal is a transportation hub for international shipping. With a 2015 population just over 4 million, the city has the largest francophone urban population in North America and is the second-largest French-speaking city in the world, behind only Paris, France.

this zone. Fort McMurray is an outstanding example of a resource town. As the hub of northern Alberta's oil sands extraction and exploration, Fort McMurray (which is within the Wood Buffalo Regional Municipality) is the largest city in the tertiary zone with a population exceeding 78,000. Other larger urban centres range in size from 10,000 to 20,000. Whitehorse and Yellowknife, as the capital cities of

Bufflerump/Shutterstock.com

Photo 4.2 Toronto, Ontario, with a population of 6.1 million in 2015, is Canada's most populous city and serves as the economic engine for Ontario and as the financial capital for Canada. Toronto has also become the nation's most culturally diverse city. Toronto is the major destination for immigrants.

David Nunuk/All Canada Photos

Photo 4.3 Vancouver, British Columbia, is Canada's leading ocean port, with most goods coming and going to China and other Asian countries, and is the third-largest Canadian city, with a 2015 population of 2.5 million in 2015. Many Vancouverites are concerned about potential oil spills in Vancouver's harbour and consequently have opposed a twinning of the existing oil pipeline from Alberta's oil sands. In the foreground, the Cambie Street Bridge spans False Creek and leads to BC Place; to the west of the bridge, at the bottom of the photo, is Granville Island with its public market.

Contested Terrain 4.1

Social Engineering Often Backfires

In the 1950s, the federal government faced a dilemma—how should it begin to provide basic public services to Indigenous people living on the land? One choice was to provide financial support, possibly taking the form of a fur subsidy. A second one could have been a direct payment to hunters/trappers and their families, similar to the Quebec Income Security Program for Cree Hunters and Trappers. Ottawa elected the more culturally risky strategy, the relocation solution that drew hunters and their families to existing outposts, such as fur trading posts and missions, and turned them into permanent urban dwellers. The attraction of relocation into settlements was that this would end the threat of starvation, allow access to medical services, and, through the schooling system, begin the process of "modernization" and "assimilation" of Indigenous people into Canadian society. Ottawa's strategy had two fatal flaws. First, the birth rate of the new "urban" dwellers shot up, creating a population explosion and a new round of challenges for Ottawa. Second, these artificially created settlements had few employment opportunities, but within a generation the sedentary lifestyle led to the erosion of a traditional way of life, to an unhealthy change in diet, and to a life of dependency on government handouts. Given what you know now, if you were the Prime Minister back in the 1950s, would you still choose the "relocation" strategy?

Yukon and the Northwest Territories, are administrative centres and regional service centres, since they also provide most of the service functions for their areas. These two cities, with estimated populations of 28,000 and 21,000, respectively, in 2015, also mark the poleward edge of zone 3.

The last population zone has fewer than 100,000 inhabitants. Most reside in resource towns, Indigenous settlements, or regional centres. Most of its territory lies in the Arctic and the northern edge of the boreal forest. The challenging cold climate limits settlement possibilities. One exception is resource towns and administrative centres. The iron-mining town of Labrador City is the largest centre, with a population of just over 9,000. Iqaluit, the capital of Nunavut and the second-largest town, has a population approaching 7,000. As described in Contested Terrain 4.1, the Indigenous settlements that dot zone 4 resulted from an initiative of the federal government back in the 1950s. Unlike in the other zones in Canada, Indigenous people form the majority in this zone.

Urban Population

Canada has evolved into an urban country. Before World War I, most Canadians lived in a rural setting and farming was the principal activity (Figure 4.5). The reverse is now true. In 2015, almost 7 in 10 Canadians—over 25 million people—were living in census metropolitan areas (CMAs) with populations over 100,000. Not only do large cities dominate the population landscape, but the bulk of Canada's population growth is in these cities (Table 4.6). From 2006 to 2015, 86 per cent of Canada's population increase of 3.7 million took place in CMAs. Furthermore, urban dwellers are concentrated in six CMAs: Toronto, Montréal, Vancouver, Calgary, Edmonton, and Ottawa-Gatineau (Table 4.6). Not surprisingly, the highest percentage of urban population is found in Ontario, Québec, and British Columbia, with the lowest percentage in Atlantic Canada.

Urban population has increased because of two primary factors:

1. The arrival of immigrants has greatly added to urban growth, especially in the larger cities.

Photo 4.4 With the Parliament Buildings (left) and the Château Laurier in the background, the Rideau Canal provides a winter skating experience in Ottawa, Canada's capital. The canal, completed in 1832, was originally built as a military supply route between Kingston and Ottawa. Metropolitan Ottawa in 2015 had more than 1.3 million residents.

2. The stream of rural Canadians abandoning the countryside for urban places remains a powerful factor. More recently, Indigenous people have added to the growth of cities.

Census Metropolitan Areas

CMAs serve as the economic and cultural anchors of their hinterlands. Statistics Canada defines census metropolitan area (CMA) as an urban area (known as the urban core) together with adjacent urban and rural areas that have a high degree of social and economic integration with the urban core. The urban

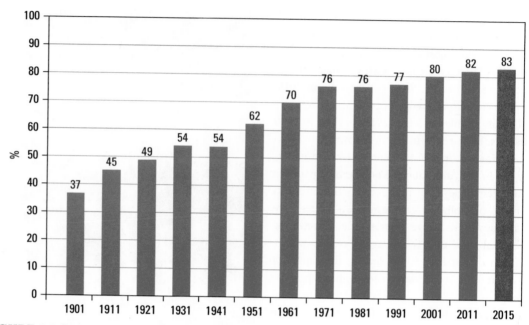

FIGURE 4.5 Percentage of Canadian population in urban regions, 1901–2015

Sources: Adapted from Statistics Canada (2007d, 2013a, 2016b).

core population of a CMA must be at least 100,000. On this basis, no city in the Territorial North qualifies as a CMA.

These large cities are a barometer for urban population increases in the six geographic regions. In 2015, the percentage change in CMAs over the last nine years (2006 to 2015) varied from highs above 30 per cent to lows below 5 per cent. Four CMAs in Western Canada (Calgary, Saskatoon, Edmonton, and Regina) were at the top, with each recording increases exceeding 20 per cent over the nine-year period. In British Columbia, only Kelowna had such an increase, though Vancouver was close to this threshold. No CMAs in Atlantic Canada and Québec experienced such a rise in population, while in Ontario, Toronto saw a 20 per cent increase. At the other end, Ontario had the largest number of CMAs with population increases over these nine years of under 5 per cent (St Catharines–Niagara, Greater Sudbury, Windsor, and Thunder Bay), while Atlantic Canada (Saint John) and Québec (Saguenay) each had one. Western Canada did not have any CMAs falling into this category (Table 4.6).

What is the attraction of cities? First, most business and employment opportunities are found in cities, especially large cities. Second, Canadians prefer to live in an urban setting where amenities are readily available. Cities are also important for other reasons. Major urban centres are at the cutting edge of technological innovation and capital accumulation. In the new world of the knowledge economy, manufacturing does not determine a city's prosperity; rather, the determining factor lies in the creativity of its business and university communities.

Despite the remarkable growth of Canadian cities, all is not well. Urban sprawl affects all cities, forcing them to spend heavily on infrastructure in these outlying areas while their downtowns lose their raison d'être. Competition from malls and big-box stores in the suburbs has hurt downtown retail areas. In the twenty-first century, city governments face the daunting task of finding solutions to the twin challenges of urban congestion and urban sprawl by making downtowns more pedestrian- and bicycle-friendly, turning inner-city residential areas into a much denser form of residential housing, and adding more "urban parks."

On the other hand, the ever-expanding suburban nature of cities that accommodates our

TABLE 4.6 Population of Census Metropolitan Areas, 2006 and 2015

CMA	Population 2006 (000s)	Population 2015 (000s)	Change	% Change
Toronto (Ont.)	5,113.1	6,129.9	1,016.8	20.0
Montréal (Que.)	3,635.6	4,060.7	425.1	11.7
Vancouver (BC)	2,116.6	2,504.3	387.7	18.3
Calgary (Alta)	1,079.3	1,439.8	360.5	33.4
Edmonton (Alta)	1,035.0	1,331.6	296.6	28.7
Ottawa–Gatineau (Ont./Que.)	1,133.6	1,332.0	198.4	17.5
Québec (Que.)	719.2	806.4	87.2	12.1
Winnipeg (Man.)	694.7	793.4	98.7	14.2
Hamilton (Ont.)	692.9	771.7	78.8	11.4
Kitchener–Cambridge–Waterloo (Ont.)	451.2	511.3	60.1	13.3
London (Ont.)	457.7	506.4	48.7	10.6
Halifax (NS)	372.9	417.8	44.9	12.0
St Catharines–Niagara (Ont.)	390.3	408.2	17.9	4.6
Oshawa (Ont.)	330.6	389.0	58.4	17.7
Victoria (BC)	330.1	365.3	35.2	10.7
Windsor (Ont.)	323.3	335.8	12.5	3.9
Saskatoon (Sask.)	233.9	305.0	71.1	30.4
Regina (Sask.)	195.0	241.4	46.4	23.8
Sherbrooke (Que.)	191.4	214.5	23.1	12.1
St John's (NL)	181.1	214.3	33.2	18.3
Barrie (Ont.)	177.1	202.7	25.6	14.5
Kelowna (BC)	162.3	197.3	35.0	21.6
Abbotsford–Mission (BC)	159.0	183.5	24.5	15.4
Kingston (Ont.)	152.4	169.9	17.5	11.5
Greater Sudbury (Ont.)	158.3	164.8	6.5	4.1
Saguenay (Que.)	156.3	160.0	3.7	2.4
Trois-Rivières (Que.)	144.7	156.4	11.7	8.1
Guelph (Ont.)	133.7	153.0	19.3	14.4
Moncton (NB)	126.4	148.0	21.6	17.1
Brantford (Ont.)	124.6	143.9	19.3	15.5
Saint John (NB)	122.4	126.9	4.5	3.7
Thunder Bay (Ont.)	122.9	124.7	1.8	1.5
Peterborough (Ont.)	116.6	122.6	6.0	5.1
Total	21,534.2	25,132.5	3,598.3	16.7

Sources: Statistics Canada (2012c, 2016b).

automobile-oriented society is a threat in two ways. First, the costs of providing urban services to new suburbs are taxing city budgets for new roads, schools, fire halls and trucks, parks, transit services, and water/sewer systems. Second, the viability of central business districts is threatened by the loss of business to suburban stores where parking spaces are readily available.

Photo 4.5 With a population increase of 33 per cent from 2006 to 2015, Calgary is the fourth-largest and fastest-growing city in Canada (Table 4.6). Its downtown is dominated by skyscrapers, many of which are associated with the petroleum industry. Beyond the skyscrapers, Calgary, like other major cities, faces several challenges, including urban sprawl, homelessness, and inadequate revenue-sharing from provincial and federal governments.

Photo 4.6 The North Saskatchewan River frames Edmonton's downtown. Like Calgary, Edmonton is experiencing rapid population growth and this growth is pushing the residential areas further and further from the central city. For the down-town area, the challenge is to make its main street, Jasper Avenue, into a more people-friendly place. In 2015, Edmonton's population had surpassed 1.3 million, making it the fifth-largest city in Canada.

The complexity and challenges of urban Canada are compounded by their limited fiscal power in Canada's federal system whereby cities depend on provincial and federal governments for funding. Without that funding, necessary major infrastructure projects will remain on the drawing board.

Canada's Aging Population

A country where seniors outnumber children is uncharted territory for Canada. This scenario represents a serious demographic event with implications for the labour force and for the working-age taxpayers who have to foot the bill for public pensions and a variety of social costs ranging from more nursing homes to higher health-care costs. In 2011, 5 million seniors formed over 14 per cent of the population. Since this aging process is linked to the baby boomers, aging will accelerate from now until 2031 when all baby boomers will reach age 65. At that time, over 20 per cent of the population could fall into the senior citizen category (Figure 4.6). Again, the last stage of the demographic transition theory calls for an aging of the population.

The predicted trend to 20 per cent or greater is driven by three factors:

- an increase in life expectancy;
- a decline in the fertility rate;
- the movement of the baby boom generation into retirement and old age.

What are the implications of an older Canada? First, Canada's population structure will change with a smaller proportion of children (under 15 years of age), a smaller proportion of the population in the workforce (ages 15–64), and a much larger percentage over 64 years of age.

Second, Canadians are living longer, which adds economic costs in the form of greater drug and health costs, creating a larger tax burden on those in the productive age group and rising costs to the federal treasury to pay for Canada's public pensions—Old Age Security and the Canada Pension Plan. The burden for the provinces and territories may be unsustainable because health costs for the growing number of senior Canadians are projected to turn sharply upward (Gee and Gutman, 2000). Already, health costs make up the major component of

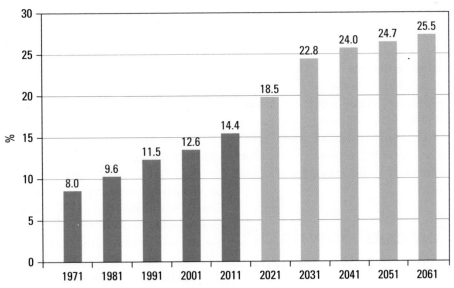

FIGURE 4.6 Population 65 years and over, 1971–2061

In 1960, 7.6 per cent of Canadians were aged 65 and over. By 2013, this figure had reached 15.3 per cent. This trend is accelerating as the baby-boom generation ages. By 2061, those in the senior age group are projected to represent 25.5 per cent of the population. The driving forces behind this increase are low fertility rates and increasing life expectancy.

Source: Human Resources and Development Canada (2015).

provincial/territorial budgets, at around 40 per cent. Could these costs reach 50 per cent, and thus squeeze funds from post-secondary education and social services budgets?

Third, the burden to pay for the growing number of seniors falls to a smaller and smaller group. The age dependency ratio provides another road marker to Canada's future demographic destination. Age dependency ratio is expressed as the number of persons in the "dependent" age groups (in the calculations of Statistics Canada, under 20 and over 64 years of age) per 100 persons in the "economically productive" age group (between 20 and 64 years). This rough measure offers an indication of the economic burden on those in the economically productive age group. According to Statistics Canada (2014c), this ratio, with some relatively minor ups and downs, has remained steady for the past several years, at about 60 persons in the combined youth and senior groups compared to 100 in the working-age population. But in the coming decades this ratio is expected to change. A Statistics Canada analysis projects that by 2056 the dependency ratio will have climbed to 84 dependants per 100 people of working age, with 50 seniors for every 100 in the "economically productive" age group (Statistics Canada, 2015e).

A social concern is linked to this aging process in that many couples are having children at older ages, so that they are responsible for young children and elderly parents at the same time. This small but growing demographic phenomenon is called the "sandwich generation." Placed within the broader social context of the unfolding twenty-first century, an intergenerational care relationship within family units appears as a new but necessary fallout from the demographic trend of seniors living well beyond their seventies.

The Ups and Downs of Indigenous Population

When Jacques Cartier sailed into Baie de Chaleur in 1541, the First Nations and Inuit population of what would become Canada may have been as high as 500,000. The exact figure will never be known.

What we have are only estimates. By reconstructing the land's capacity to support wildlife and therefore also hunting societies, anthropologist James Mooney (1928: 7) estimated that about 220,000 First Nations peoples and Inuit lived in Canada at the time of contact. More recently, scholars have revised this figure upward. Dickason (2009: 40) and Denevan (1992: 370) estimate that the number of Indigenous peoples living in Canada was closer to half a million. Whatever the exact figure, initial contact with Europeans resulted in a rapid depopulation. Factors include loss and overexploitation of hunting grounds and therefore food shortages, increased warfare, the spread of new diseases from Europe among the Indigenous peoples, and, in some instances, the intentional slaughter of Indigenous people by the European newcomers. Communicable diseases, such as smallpox, caused great suffering and many deaths. Epidemics sometimes quickly reduced the size of tribes by half. Depopulation did not take place across British North America at once but in a series of regional depopulations associated with the arrival of British settlers, although European epidemic diseases spread through Indigenous trade networks often preceded the actual appearance of Europeans. In 1857, the first comprehensive counting of the Indigenous population for British North America, undertaken by the Hudson's Bay Company at the request of the British House of Commons, totalled 139,000 (Bone, 2016: 61). By 1881, the census of Canada recorded 108,000 Indigenous people (Canada, 1884: Table 3.1). As shown in Figure 4.7, the low point was reached in 1911 when the Indigenous population was recorded as 105,611.

By the 1930s, the rebound in the Indigenous population had begun (Figure 4.7). From 1931 to 2011, the Indigenous population had increased by nearly 15 times. In 2011, the Indigenous population, as measured by ancestry, was just short of 2 million, a remarkable rate of population growth and demographic recovery from the low point of approximately 100,000 in the late nineteenth and early twentieth centuries (Statistics Canada, 2013b). In 1951, Indigenous people comprised less than 2 per cent of Canada's population and now approximates close to 6 per cent of Canada's population. By 2011, the Indigenous population as measured by ancestry totalled 1,889,400 with North American ancestry

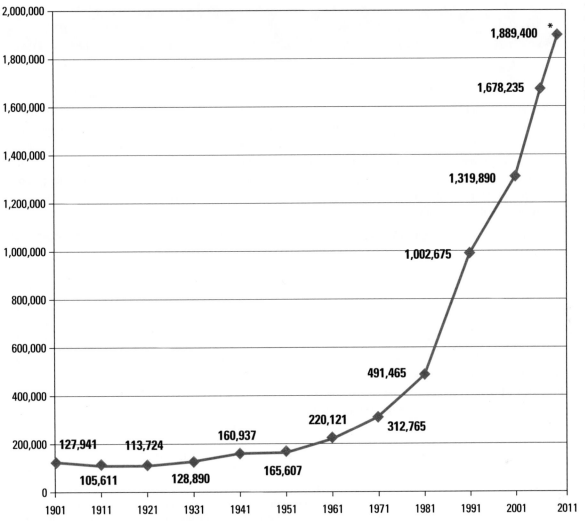

FIGURE 4.7 Indigenous population by ancestry, 1901–2011

Note: The Indigenous population by identity totalled 1.4 million in 2011. For discussion of the difference between "Indigenous identity" and "Indigenous ancestry," see Table 1.2.

*In the 2011 census, Indigenous population by identity totalled 1.4 million. many questions were no longer classified as "mandatory," including questions regarding the Indigenous population. The National Household Survey questionnaire was mailed to some 4.5 million households requesting information on social and economic subjects, including Indigenous population.

Sources: Adapted from Statistics Canada (2003b, 2013b).

THINK ABOUT IT

What is the difference, if any, between assimilation and cultural genocide?

THINK ABOUT IT

Canada's multicultural programs recognize the need for public support for newcomers to adjust to their new world. From this perspective, why shouldn't the same level of support and programs be extended to urban Indigenous people who, as new arrivals to cities, are struggling to adjust to this urban world?

accounting for 1,369,100; Métis, 447,700 and Inuit, 72,600 (Statistics Canada, 2013b). Clearly, the early twentieth-century myth of the "vanishing Indian" has been put to rest.

Indigenous people have gone through great changes since European contact. These demographic changes are classified into four phases in Table 4.7.

For a broader discussion of change affecting Indigenous peoples in their interaction with Canadian society, see "The Indigenous/Non-Indigenous Faultline" in Chapter 3, page 81.

Early contact was associated with population decline while population stabilized in late contact. The last phase shows a high rate of natural increase, though the birth rate has begun to decline. During the most recent phase, the Indigenous population has increased at a higher rate than Canada's population (see Figure 4.7). Statistics Canada, through two census questions, produces two measures of Indigenous population. One is based on identity and the other on ethnic origin (or ancestry); by ethnic origin, the figure is 1.9 million Indigenous people, forming 5.8 per cent

Vignette 4.2

The Assembly of First Nations

The Assembly of First Nations (AFN) is the national representative organization of the more than 600 First Nations in Canada. Its members consist of the chiefs of these First Nations. These chiefs vote to select their National Chief for a three-year term. The present National Chief is Perry Bellegarde. The federal government recognizes the AFN as the official body with which Ottawa interacts on the business of First Nations. The federal government funds the operations of the AFN. Some First Nations band members fear that the AFN has been co-opted by the federal government while others feel that the AFN represents the interests of the chiefs rather than their band members. Grassroots organizations, such as the Idle No More movement, appear from time to time to take the lead in espousing Indigenous concerns, rather than the AFN.

of Canada's population in 2011; the identity census question accounts for 1.4 million or 4.3 per cent.

The distribution of Indigenous people across Canada varies widely (Table 4.8). Eighty per cent reside in three regions—Western Canada, Ontario, and British Columbia. Western Canada has the highest Indigenous population, with a total 574,000 accounting for 41 per cent of Canada's Indigenous population.

Next is Ontario with 301,000 (22 per cent), followed by British Columbia with 232,290 (17 per cent). However, the percentage of Indigenous peoples to the total population in territories and provinces reveals a very different geographic pattern. In Nunavut, over 86 per cent of the population identify as Indigenous while in PEI only 1.6 per cent of the population identify as Indigenous.

TABLE 4.7 Major Phases for the Indigenous Population in Canada

Phase	Characteristics
Pre-contact	The Indigenous population in Canada in the centuries preceding European contact and settlement was at least 200,000 and possibly as large as 500,000. This population may have varied in size due to the carrying capacity of the land, which, in a hunting society, is controlled by the availability of game (food). For instance, natural conditions, especially weather, could affect the size and migration routes of animal populations.
Early contact (1500–1940)	Indigenous peoples who came into contact with Europeans were exposed to new diseases, and these new diseases often spread across the land prior to the arrival of Europeans in a particular place. Population losses were heavy. Loss of hunting lands also added to their demise. By the end of the nineteenth century, the Indigenous population was just over 100,000.
Late contact (1940–1960)	Rising fertility rates coupled with high mortality rates resulted in the stabilization of the Indigenous population. Towards the end of this phase, fertility rates were high and mortality rates declined. The result was the start of rapid population increase.
Post-contact (1960 to present)	High fertility and low mortality account for remarkable population rebound. The net result has been a population explosion. While the Indigenous population is likely to increase at a rate well above the national average in the coming decades, its natural rate of increase is expected to diminish due to a declining fertility rate. The Indigenous population now approaches 2 million with a rapidly growing number living in cities.

TABLE 4.8 Indigenous Population by Identity, Canada and Regions, 2001 and 2011

Region	Indigenous Population 2001	Indigenous Population 2011	Increase 2001–11	Increase 2001–11 (%)	% by Region
Territorial North	47,990	56,225	8,235	17.2	4.1
Atlantic Canada	54,120	94,490	40,370	74.6	6.8
Québec	79,400	141,915	62,515	78.7	10.1
British Columbia	170,025	232,290	62,265	36.6	16.6
Ontario	188,315	301,425	113,110	60.1	21.5
Western Canada	436,455	574,335	137,880	31.6	41.1
Canada	976,305	1,400,685	424,380	43.5	100

Note: For more information on Indigenous populations by identity and ancestry, see Table 1.2 and Figure 4.7. The uneven regional increases over the 10-year period probably indicate that more Canadians are identifying themselves as Indigenous, especially in regions where Métis reside.

Source: Statistics Canada (2013b).

Canada's Changing Culture

While population provides a measure of the human size of Canada, culture represents its heart and soul. Historically speaking, culture is a product of the mix of British, French, American, and Indigenous beliefs and traditions and, since the late 1960s, the addition of cultures from around the world. Canada's geographic regions reflect this diversity with Québec representing the Québécois culture based on the French language and traditions that have a different root from English-speaking Canada. The only exception to this rule is found in New Brunswick, the cultural home of the Acadians, but when grouped into all of Atlantic Canada the French fact largely disappears.

Through the process of incorporating elements of these world cultures into Canada's ever-expanding cultural mélange, the nation has grown into what, as we have seen earlier, John Ralston Saul calls a "soft" country where cultural differences are readily accepted and respected. This diversification did not appear overnight. Moving from hard to soft culture emerged from a long history where compromise won the day over racism. Racism took different forms but it has made lives miserable for Indigenous people and visible minorities, and has served to keep the English/French divide festering.

At the root of the racism that marked Canada for many years was the belief that British culture was superior to other cultures in the world. After Confederation, this superiority complex continued. Several extreme examples come to mind—the Chinese head tax of 1885, the residential schools, the "continuous passage" legislation intended to keep South Asians from coming to Canada's shores and which led to the racially charged *Komagata Maru* incident in 1914, and the internment of Japanese Canadians during World War II. The denial of entry to Jewish refugees from Nazi Germany on the eve of World War II is another historical stain on the national fabric.

As part of the march to a relatively harmonious pluralistic society, these and other negative political actions were rescinded, and prime ministers in recent years have made the appropriate (though long overdue) apologies. By the twenty-first century, this "soft" version of culture distinguishes Canada from many other nations and may well be a harbinger of what future secular societies should and will look like. Nonetheless, minorities and newcomers still experience racism in Canada. Syrian refugees were pepper-sprayed by an assailant on a bicycle outside an event in Vancouver held to welcome the newcomers; and the importation into Canada from the United States of the Black Lives Matter movement to protest mainstream police culture and its racial profiling of and occasional unjust violence towards those in urban black communities attests to the fact that racism continues to be problem.

Dynamic Nature of Culture

All cultures evolve over time. Canadian culture evolves at a very rapid rate due to the inflow of peoples from around the world. The ways of the newcomers, including their dress, languages, customs, and religions, represent both a challenge to existing Canadian culture and an opportunity for that culture to be enriched.

Canadian culture, flexible and porous as it is, includes core values that are defined by Canada's history and geography. Four core values are: (1) government is based on British parliamentary institutions and the rule of law; (2) two official languages ensure a place for French as well as English, which also means that other languages have no standing in the political and public affairs of Canadian society (except in Nunavut, where Inuktitut also is recognized as an official language); (3) Indigenous peoples, but especially status Indians, have special rights, which flow out of historic treaties, modern land claim agreements, recognition in Canada's Constitution, and numerous court cases, as we have seen in Chapter 3; and (4) tradition and law are encapsulated in the Canadian Constitution, which includes the Charter of Rights and Freedoms.

Canadian cultural rejuvenation is a remarkably peaceful feat and speaks well of Saul's concept of a soft Canada. Nevertheless, cleavages irrupt from time to time between old-timers and newcomers. Such cleavages are not a new phenomenon. In the late nineteenth century, for instance, newcomers from Central Europe and czarist Russia brought their customs, language, and religion with them. Adjusting to the existing "British" way of life that existed in Canada at that time was not always easy for the newcomers, but the vast majority of the second generation melded into the Canadian fabric and, in their own way, remade Canada's identity. The unspoken "social contract" on the Prairies at that time was that one must learn English and accept the local way of doing things. Fast-forward to the twenty-first century when Muslims from various countries are rapidly forming a significant ethnic and religious group within the Canadian mosaic. The welcoming of Syrian refugees beginning in 2015 was an unmistakable example of Canada's evolution from a hard to a soft country.

Of course, there are bumps along the road of accommodation/acculturation/integration for all newcomers. For the vast majority, these bumps, which include finding adequate shelter, finding well-paying jobs, and learning a new language, are readily or eventually overcome. For others, however, especially because of ongoing events in other parts of the world and isolated incidents within Canada such as so-called "honour killings," the process of settling in can be difficult. This has been the case for some Muslims, whose cultural trappings and ethnicities become tarred by some in the majority Canadian community. Nascent Islamophobia even found its way into the policy perspective of Stephen Harper's federal Conservative government shortly before its defeat in 2015 when it established a federal snitch line that people could phone to report "barbaric cultural practices." Many people in Europe and the United States, as well as some governments and political parties, have voiced great concern about the "threat" of unlimited floods of refugees and immigrants from war-torn Muslim-majority countries, fearing that such immigrants, with their high fertility rates, will change the fabric of society and pose threats of terrorism (Saunders, 2012; Steyn, 2006).

The constant news coverage of suicide bombings in Iraq, Afghanistan, and Pakistan, of the horrific and multi-sided civil war in Syria, of the emergence of the dystopian Islamic State in parts of Iraq and Syria, and of violent and deadly terror attacks in European countries and in the US all have created an atmosphere of fear, as did the lone-wolf terrorist attacks in Québec and on Parliament Hill in 2015. And the reported recruitment of young Canadians to join the terrorists abroad has driven this danger of extremism home to the Canadian public. For the most part, however, the public has been able to separate individual acts of terrorism from the rest of Canada's Muslim community and has embraced the Liberal government's policy of welcoming many thousands of refugees from Syria, just as the international community has applauded Prime Minister Trudeau's approach to the refugee crisis.

Culture in Québec takes on a different meaning than in English-speaking Canada. For Québec, the Québécois culture represents the survival of their way of life within a sea of English-speaking North Americans. Immigration is a key factor in Québec's demographics; but for Québec, immigration can be a double-edged sword. While immigrants add to the Québec population, some bring unfamiliar ways that, to Québécois, threaten the existing way of life. Matters came to a boil in 2007 when Hérouxville's town council announced a "code of standards" that contained Islamophobic-like rules. Immigration, highly desired to keep Québec numbers increasing, remains a "hot" cultural issue in the province that has always sought to defend its unique culture and French language. Indeed, the view in Québec has been a rejection of multiculturalism for what is called "interculturalism," that is, the necessary accommodation of many ethnic minorities to the French-Canadian majority, and the accommodation of that majority to the minorities in order to maintain cordial relations.

Ethnicity

An **ethnic group** is made up of members of a population who share a culture that is distinct from that of other groups. Each group has a common identity, shared values, and cultural/linguistic/religious bonds and symbols. Within Canada, ethnicity does not indicate a separation from Canadian culture but is simply a measure of the diversity of those members of Canadian culture. Although the 2011 National Household Survey revealed that the leading ethnic group, described as "Canadian," measured only 32 per cent, this figure likely provides a measure of old-timers whose ethnicity has softened over the centuries and who now identify as Canadians. If we add those who declared a French ethnicity, the figure for "Canadian" nearly reached 50 per cent. The argument supporting this observation is that time erases ethnicity attachment and identification with the nation-state becomes stronger.

The 2011 ranking of the next nine ethnic groups remains unchanged from the 1996 census except for North American Aboriginal origins group, which jumped from ninth to seventh (Table 4.9). The reason for this change in ranking is the rapid population growth of this group and the willingness of Métis and non-status Indians to identify as members of this group. The Chinese ethnic group added to their number through immigration, so that by 2011 this group totalled 1.5 million and occupied eighth place in ethnic rankings (Table 4.9).

As a term, "ethnicity" is preferred to "race," which refers to physical attributes such as skin colour. Ethnicity lends itself to understanding Canadian society. In its early history, Canada's population was composed of British, French, and other European peoples, as well as the Indigenous peoples, but it is now composed of many ethnic groups[2] from around the world with more than 200 different **ethnic origins** reported in the 2011 National Household Survey. By contrast, the 1901 census identified only 25 ethnic origins. Statistics Canada (2011d) relates ethnic origin to "the ethnic or cultural origins of the respondent's ancestors. An ancestor is someone from whom a person is descended and is usually more distant than a grandparent."

Ethnicity becomes complicated over time as Canadians have crossed ethnic lines to find partners and their resulting offspring are a combination of the parents' ethnicity. For that reason, the selection of "Canadian" as a person's ethnic origin makes sense to many born in Canada. Expressed differently, time erodes the ethnic connection with the country of origin. For Canadians born and raised in this country, the connection with their ethnic homeland can be tenuous at best (Beaujot, 1991: 297). Place, as cultural geographers insist, plays a critical role in the development of a regional/national identity. This phenomenon is well known. Consider, for example, the attachment of the French born in New France who had no interest in returning to France in 1763 because their lives were centred on the New World. They were no longer French but had become French Canadian. Not surprisingly, then, the ethnic selection of "Canadian" by nearly one-third of the population is attributed to the geographic notion of place overriding the concept of ethnicity, which perhaps is confirmed by the fact that the numbers for those of "English" and "French" origin dropped from 1996 to 2011. Thus, the resettlement of people in a new place causes their ethnicity to fade with time,

THINK ABOUT IT

Do you think that ethnicity, as shown in Table 4.9, is a false measure of Canadian identity?

TABLE 4.9 Ethnic Origins of Canadians, 1996 and 2011

	1996			2011	
Ethnicity	**Number**	**%**	**Ethnicity**	**Number**	**%**
Total population	28,528,125	100.0	**Total population**	32,852,320	100.0
Canadian	8,806,275	30.9	**Canadian**	10,563,805	32.2
English	6,832,095	23.9	**English**	6,509,500	19.8
French	5,597,845	19.6	**French**	5,065,690	15.4
Scottish	4,260,840	14.9	**Scottish**	4,714,970	14.4
Irish	3,767,610	13.2	**Irish**	4,544,870	13.8
German	2,757,140	9.7	**German**	3,203,330	9.8
North American Aboriginal: First Nations, Inuit, and Métis	799,010	2.8	**North American Aboriginal: First Nations, Inuit, and Métis**	1,836,035	5.6
Italian	1,207,475	4.2	**Italian**	1,489,425	4.5
Ukrainian	1,026,475	3.6	**Chinese**	1,487,580	4.5
Chinese	921,585	3.2	**Ukrainian**	1,251,170	3.8

Notes: (1) In 1996, those of Dutch origin ranked tenth, with a total of 916,215. (2) Table shows total responses. Because some respondents reported more than one ethnic origin, the sum is greater than 100 per cent. (3) Figures referring to North American Aboriginal are based on Indigenous ancestry population, i.e., those persons who reported at least one Indigenous ancestry (First Nations, Inuit, or Métis) to the ethnic origin question. "Ethnic origin" refers to the ethnic or cultural origins of a person's ancestors. (4) The rapid increase in the population of Indigenous peoples from 2.6 per cent of the Canadian population in 1996 to 5.6 per cent in 2011 can be explained only partly by Indigenous birth rates that were well above the national average. A key factor in this phenomenal jump in population is an attitudinal shift in declaring oneself as Indigenous. This trend was particularly strong among the Métis. For instance, the numbers of the Métis grew by 91 per cent from 1996 to 2006 while the other two Indigenous peoples saw a much more modest increase of under 30 per cent (Statistics Canada, 2009l).

Sources: Statistics Canada (2003a, 2009l, 2014d).

THINK
ABOUT IT

In a secular society, religion plays a secondary role—supposedly invisible in public offices and in the court of law. But, with the growing number of Muslims, is there room for shariah law or is that one "accommodating" step too far for a secular country?

and, as the roots of the second generation sink into Canadian soil, commitment to their parents' homeland fades while their new identity takes hold. This process of putting down cultural roots is normal, especially if the newcomers are welcomed into the mainstream society.

Language

In spite of Canada's multicultural society, the two official languages, English and French, represent the key cultural element leading to a successful integration into Canadian society. Yet, English language proficiency is most sought after by newcomers. While the status of the French language is guaranteed by the Constitution, outside Québec and New Brunswick the use of French is limited. Canada's two official languages, but especially English, are crucial elements in unifying Canadian society. Employment without a command of English is virtually impossible except in Québec, where proficiency in French is required.

In 2011, the overwhelming number of Canadians declared that they spoke either English or French. Among the 2 per cent who did not speak one of the two official languages, most of those newcomers spoke Punjabi, Chinese, or Spanish (Statistics Canada, 2015c). Most of them likely either had just arrived in Canada or were older parents of newcomers who entered Canada as family class immigrants. The key point is that children of newcomers, by attending schools, quickly become fluent in one or both of Canada's official languages. Of the six geographic regions, Ontario contained over half of these newcomers who did not speak one of the official languages, followed by British Columbia and Western Canada at around 20 and 18 per cent, respectively; Atlantic Canada and the Territorial North each had less than 1 per cent of the non-English/French-speakers (Statistics Canada, 2011e).

Religion

Religion is another key element of culture. In 2011, the two largest groups were Christians and those with no religious affiliation. Sixty-seven per cent or 23 million declared that Christianity was their faith while 24 per cent or 7.9 million had no religious affiliation (Statistics Canada, 2014d). Consistent with changing immigration patterns over the past several decades, four religions grew in numbers from the 2001 census: Islam (with 1.1 million members), Hinduism (498,000) Sikhism (454,965), and Buddhism (366,800). At the same time, the number

of Canadians declaring no religious affiliation grew from 4.9 million to 7.9 million (Statistics Canada, 2005, 2016c).

Canada is thought of as a Christian country. This image was certainly true until the twenty-first century. Now Canada is much more religiously diverse; plus, as noted above, a significant number claim no religious affiliation. As recently as 1971, nearly 90 per cent of Canadians declared themselves to be Christian (though some may not have been active church members). Fewer than 5 per cent declared no religious affiliation. The Jewish religion formed the second-largest religious group at that time. By 2011, the number of Christians had grown but their percentage had dropped to 67 per cent of the total population. Those following Judaism remained at just under 1 per cent. Other religions have grown in numbers and form 8 per cent of Canada's population, and their future place in Canada's religious landscape is anticipated to increase.

THINK ABOUT IT

Do you favour a strict separation of state and church? If so, where do you stand on public support for Roman Catholic schools?

Chrishowey/Dreamstime.GetStock.com

Photo 4.7 The Basilica of Notre Dame, opened in 1829, is the principal Roman Catholic Church in Montréal, and is a reminder of the Church's powerful role in the history of French-Canadian society. Today, however, the Church has lost not only its central role in Québec society but also much of its active church membership.

Vignette 4.3

Time Heals All?

Culture not only is a link to the past but also provides the institutional organizations that preserve each group's ethnicity. Religious organizations provide a powerful institutional structure that consolidates people of similar beliefs. From time to time, Canada faces challenges from cultural ideas and symbols brought by immigrants to our shores. The niqab is one such challenge—or is it? On the one hand, Canadian society rejects the idea that female public employees can cover their face with the niqab. On the other, Canadians seem to accept that an individual can choose to dress in a niqab in public. But much cultural space exists between those two views, and the devil is in the details.

Does time heal all? Certainly, Canadian society needs time to adjust to unfamiliar customs and dress. Not so many years ago, an RCMP officer of the Sikh faith requested to wear his turban instead of the standard police hat. He was refused, but eventually Ottawa ruled that the turban was acceptable headwear for an RCMP officer.[3] Now, no one questions this practice.

In 2015, the issue was the niqab. Was it a symbol of the oppression of Muslim women, or was it a preferred garment for certain Muslim women? Political sparks flew over this question in the 2015 federal election. The debate went like this. Some regarded it as a serious matter affecting core Canadian values, such as the equality of Canadian men and women, and argued that the niqab is a form of the subjugation of Muslim women and daughters by their husbands or fathers. In some people's mind, honour killings of women and young girls were linked to extremism and the wearing of the niqab was a sign of religious extremism. On the other hand, a case could be made that the niqab is simply a religious garment worn freely by a relatively small number of women. But what about the opinion of Zunera Ishaq (2015), the woman at the centre of this debate? Zunera wrote: "While I recognize that it's [niqab] not for everyone, it is for me. To me, the most important Canadian value is the freedom to be the person of my own choosing. To me, that's more indicative of what it means to be Canadian than what I wear."

Multiculturalism

Multiculturalism is the cornerstone of Canada's social policy towards newcomers. To a large degree, this policy reflects Saul's classification of Canada as a "soft" country as well as a recognition by policy-makers and the public that we are a nation of immigrants. Over the past half-century, multiculturalism has taken root in Canadian society and it is a distinctively Canadian approach to social equality in nation-building. From the federal government's perspective, multicultural policies and funding encourage respect for cultural diversity.

Ironically, this federal policy emerged as a direct result of the work of the Royal Commission on Bilingualism and Biculturalism (1970), which recommended that Ottawa recognize the multiplicity of Canada's population. The following year, in 1971, the federal Liberal government made multiculturalism official policy and in 1972 the cabinet position of Minister of State for Multiculturalism was created. Government funding to ethnic organizations soon followed. In 1988, the federal government passed the Canadian Multiculturalism Act, which is designed to encourage greater human understanding and stronger bonds among Canadians of different cultural backgrounds and ethnic origins.

For Charles Taylor, a noted Canadian philosopher, multiculturalism is a way for the Canadian government and society to recognize the worth of newcomers' distinctive cultural traditions without compromising Canada's basic political principles (Vignette 4.4). The outer boundary of multiculturalism is where it rubs against the edge of strongly held conventional values within mainstream society. But even here, subtle adjustments are

Photo 4.8 The growing Muslim population in Western Canada is reflected in Canada's largest mosque, the Baitun Nur mosque in Calgary, which serves the Ahmadiyya Muslim community. Another indicator of the rapidly growing Muslim population is the construction of the second-largest mosque, the Ahmadiyya Muslim Jama'at mosque in Saskatoon, opened in late 2016. Muslims comprised 2.7 per cent of Canada's population in 2011 and could reach 6.8 per cent by 2031 (Statistics Canada, 2010b: Table 5).

Vignette 4.4

Charles Taylor on Multiculturalism

One of Canada's leading philosophers, Charles Taylor (1994: 63), argues in *Multiculturalism: Examining the Politics of Recognition*, that:

> . . . all societies are becoming increasingly multicultural, while at the same time becoming more porous. Indeed, these two developments go together. Their porousness means that they are more open to multi-national migration; more of their members live the life of diaspora, whose centre is elsewhere. In these circumstances, there is something awkward about replying simply, "This is how we do things here." This reply must be made in cases like the Rushdie controversy, where "how we do things" covers issues such as the right to life and to freedom of speech. The awkwardness arises from the fact that there are substantial numbers of people who are citizens and also belong to the culture that calls into question our philosophical boundaries. The challenge is to deal with their sense of marginalization without compromising our basic political principles.

occurring in a wide range of areas. For example, the Toronto Stock Exchange has sought to accommodate Muslim investors by launching a Canadian stock index in May 2009 that excludes banks, pork producers, and entertainment and gambling stocks, thus allowing Islamic investors to abide by Islamic law and still participate in equity investment strategy (Boyd, 2009).

In many ways, multiculturalism is the opposite of **ethnocentricity**. While ethnocentricity aims to defend and keep the ethnic group united, multiculturalism attempts to broaden the ethnic group perspectives and interactions with those outside its circle. Tolerance and respect of others are not an automatic outcome of life in pluralistic societies. Canadian tolerance and respect were learned the hard way, going back centuries to often bitter (and sometimes violent) conflicts between French- and English-speaking Canadians. For Canada to survive as a nation, the two antagonists had no choice

but to become partners. One product of this so-called partnership was biculturalism. The other path to nation-building—a classic European-style nation-state founded on a single common ethnicity and language—was not possible in the northern half of North America. Reaching an accord (not a solution) between the two founding peoples was not a simple task and disputes continue to emerge, as discussed in Chapter 3. Since dominance is not feasible in the long term, then compromise becomes a political necessity and eventually the search for compromise becomes ingrained as a national trait.

> See the section "Faultlines within Canada" in **Chapter 1**, page 9, for more on the subject of Canada as a "soft" country.

Over time, the children and grandchildren of immigrants are more likely to find a place in mainstream Canada. Upward mobility is associated with education and perhaps inter-ethnic marriages. But the question remains: "Might multiculturalism

Vignette 4.5

Cultural Adjustment and Ethnic Neighbourhoods

Canada's regions and cities are constantly undergoing cultural adjustments resulting from new arrivals from around the world. Such adjustments, required by both newcomers and old-timers, are a product of an open immigration policy begun in the late 1960s. This policy has drawn people from a variety of world cultures, and the vast majority have relocated to major cities, with Toronto receiving the greatest number. Cultural adjustment is a particularly sensitive matter in major cities where ethnic neighbourhoods are a concern.

Why is this urban phenomenon occurring and will it last? The first part of the answer lies in limited economic opportunities for many new arrivals (especially because foreign education credentials and work experience often have not been recognized by Canadian employers) and their desire to live near members of the same ethnic group. The second part of the answer is founded on various factors. First, does the initial selection of a place of residence lead to entrapment and the solidification of that neighbourhood into a permanent ethnic ghetto? Walks and Bourne (2006) suggest that the forces of upward mobility and assimilation into Canadian society will, in time, see the dispersal of ethnic groups throughout the residential areas of Canadian cities. Stated slightly differently, in the short term, recent immigrants prefer to live in the same neighbourhoods for the affordability, comfort, and security that this sense of place provides them. In addition, one magnet for new arrivals is religious institutions. Such institutions play a key role not only in maintaining the social cohesion of ethnic groups, but also in the selection of places to live. In the long term, however, the diffusion of ethnic groups normally takes place and the neighbourhood takes on another group of low-income people.

Contested Terrain 4.2

Immigration and Multiculturalism

Immigration dictates that Canada will become an increasingly more pluralistic society and, therefore, that multiculturalism will continue to play a role not only as an adjustment mechanism for newcomers but also as a core Canadian value. On the other hand, has a rural/urban divide emerged because immigrants tend to settle in Canada's larger cities? For instance, the ethnic/racial/religious composition of Toronto's population is strikingly different from that of Timmins, where the population consists of English- and French-speaking residents and only very small numbers of Italian, Cree, and Finnish speakers (Statistics Canada, 2016f). As a consequence, socio-political events such as Pride parades and Black Lives Matter protests are commonplace in large cities but much less so or not at all in smaller centres, towns, and villages.

increase ethnic group identification at the expense of Canadian social cohesion?" Without doubt, tensions have arisen from time to time in Canada as people of different cultures, languages, and racial origins have chafed against what they perceive as barriers within Canadian society, but peaceful discord is not in itself a failure of multiculturalism but part of a process of social interplay necessary to expose and resolve differences. Canadian history is on the side of both multiculturalism and immigration because immigrants—particularly their children—have found a place within Canadian society. While this process has not always been easy, the challenge for visible minorities, and we might add, Indigenous peoples, is even greater since they are readily identifiable, and unfortunately their upward mobility is sometimes hampered by racism.

Sense of Culture and Regions: Then and Now

Canada's sense of culture and regions has changed remarkably over the last half-century. Canada reinvented itself. In the early twenty-first century, population trends and faultlines signal the direction of a future Canada with another, yet-to-be-determined sense of culture and regions. Looking back, the Canada described by Kenneth Hare in 1968—fed with newcomers from Europe and the United States—was a "white" country hardly recognizable today. Hare's Canada had just experienced an unprecedented baby boom and record-breaking economic expansion, and the country was heading into trade agreements with the United States that would effectively replace the east–west national economy with a continental one, starting with the Auto Pact of 1965. Canada was a bilingual country with a majority of English-speakers. The vast majority could trace their ancestry to British, French, and other European countries.

What followed was a shift of immigration flows from Europe to Asia, and the vast majority of these newcomers chose Toronto, Montréal, or Vancouver as their new home. These cities have undergone dramatic transformations of their cityscapes, their size and functions, and their ethnic makeup. Sense of place has changed the six regions of Canada. From 2006 to 2014, individuals and families moved to western towns and cities in response to economic opportunities, especially those in Alberta. Over this short period, all regions saw their population increase, but the greatest percentage increases took place in Western Canada, Ontario, and British Columbia (Statistics Canada, 2012a). The collapse of oil prices in 2015 followed by a decline in oil sands expansion may signal a reversal to that population shift. The unanswered question is: Will the price of oil recover, thus restarting Alberta's economy?

Key Cultural Issues

French/English Language Imbalance

Canada is a bilingual country.[4] Yet, the weight of numbers is working against French-speaking Canadians. Since Confederation, even though their population size has increased, the percentage of French-speaking Canadians has declined, from 32 per cent in 1901 to 21 per cent in 2011 (Statistics Canada, 2016g). With this decline, the place of French-speaking Canadians within Canada has weakened. Only in Québec has the French language remained strong and vibrant. In 2011, the percentage of Canadians whose mother tongue was French formed 78.1 per cent of Québec's population while, in sharp contrast, less than 4 per cent of Canadians residing in other provinces and territories spoke French (Statistics Canada, 2012i).

The language imbalance has increased over time for the simple reason of the faster rate of increase of the English-speaking population, which is largely due to the number of new Canadians arriving each year who adopt English over French. For all regions except Québec, newcomers learn English.

French/English dualism is a fundamental aspect of Canada. As Jacques Bernier (1991: 79) of Université Laval stated: "Canada's duality is intrinsic, and as long as it is not clearly recognized and dealt with, the issue of Canadian unity will remain." This duality is a political concept embedded in the historical relationship between the two cultures. The main indicator of the stability of this dualism is language; in other words, the stability of this concept depends on a relatively constant number of Canadians speaking each language. But how should we measure duality? Should mother tongue or household language hold the key? Or is the number of bilingual Canadians the most important criterion? Outside of Québec and New Brunswick, the French language is losing ground.[5] Anne Gilbert (2001: 173) points to the decision of the government of Ontario to reject the concept of recognizing both English and French as official languages as a missed opportunity to showcase Canada's serious commitment to its dual languages.

Newcomers and Canadian Culture

Everyone is a newcomer—at first. As shown in Figure 4.2, newcomers, defined as foreign-born, have always formed a significant proportion of Canada's population. This proportion is projected to increase to 22 per cent by 2011 and to 26 per cent by 2031 (Statistics Canada, 2010b: Chart 1). Within less than 20 years, then—assuming these demographic projections hold true—at least one person in four living in Canada will be foreign-born. At this level, the proportion of foreign-born will reach the highest point in the last 100 years (Figure 4.8). Clearly, the potential impact of immigration on the makeup of Canada's future population will be profound.

Immigration has shown two remarkable developments over time. First, Canadian society absorbs some of the cultural imports and multiculturalism fosters a social expression of the cultural contributions of newcomers. Second, recent immigrants, especially their children, have shown a capacity not only to integrate into Canadian society, but also to reshape it. Charles Taylor would consider such reshaping as part of the flexible and porous nature of Canadian identity (Vignette 4.4). Not all newcomers, however, escape without bumps and bruises. Simply stated, visible minorities often find acceptance into Canadian society more challenging. This challenge voices itself in different ways. The Black Lives Matter movement, emanating from the United States, has demanded that racism against black people end (see www.youtube.com/watch?v=0KNchZlt8Z8).

The cohesiveness of Canadian society depends on such integration and on an acceptance by all Canadians of cultural adaptation within the society to other cultures and religions. Such adaptation, of course, includes the ability to laugh at oneself and to appreciate the humour of other people and within other cultures. Russell Peters, an internationally known stand-up comedian who pokes fun at racism, exemplifies this positive side to immigration. Born and raised in Ontario by parents who moved to Canada from India, Peters combines his experiences of growing up "as the only brown child on the block" with insightful observations on race relations today.

Indigenous Cultural Diversity

There is a great deal of diversity among Indigenous peoples and cultures in Canada, but for all of that diversity the unifying factors among the many First Nations and the Inuit and Métis are a deep spirituality

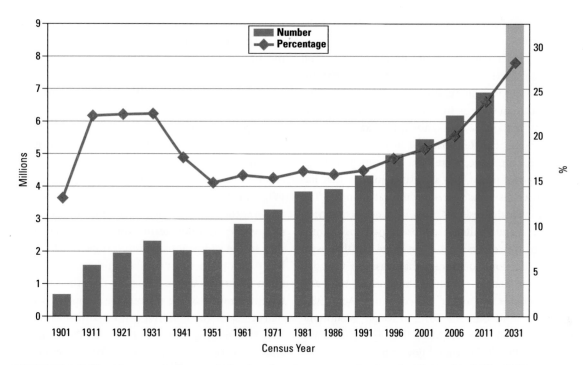

FIGURE 4.8 Number and share of the foreign-born population in Canada, 1901–2031
Sources: Chui et al. (2008); Statistics Canada (2010b).

and a desire to maintain a harmonious relationship with Mother Earth. At the time(s) of European contact and settlement, more than 50 Indigenous languages thrived in what is today Canada. Contact with Europeans took various forms at different times, and through this contact the spirituality and harmonious relationship with the land lost some of its influence within the Indigenous communities. Communities and tribes were enlisted in the European fur-trading enterprise and in European wars in North America. Some European traders and missionaries learned Indigenous languages; many more Indigenous people, out of necessity, learned French or English. Indigenous language loss is but one measure of the impact of Europeans on the first inhabitants. Christian missionaries, the Indian Act of 1876, and residential schools combined to draw—or to attempt to assimilate—Indigenous people into the settler society. The toll of these efforts was recorded in the 2015 report of the Truth and Reconciliation Commission.

In the twentieth and twenty-first centuries, resource development, at first ignorant and uncaring about the impact on the land and waters, took its toll. Perhaps no single impact of this kind has been worse than the mercury poisoning, from an upstream pulp mill, of the members of the Grassy Narrows band living along the English-Wabigoon River system in northwestern Ontario (Shkilnyk, 1985), which was first identified in the late 1960s. Since then, regulations governing industrial pollution have toughened, plus Indigenous peoples have gained more power over resource development, largely through a series of Supreme Court of Canada decisions, including the duty to consult. Indigenous peoples still have a special relationship with the land, but that relationship often takes place within the parameters of the global industrial world. Yet, a half-century later, in September 2016, Japanese researchers determined that 90 per cent of the residents of the Grassy Narrows community suffered from mercury poisoning—notably brain damage resulting in sensory impairment and lack of co-ordination—including those born long after the dumping of mercury had ceased. The causes, apart from the original pollution of the river system from the mill in Dryden, Ontario: company and government failure to clean up the pollution; unsafe storage of toxic waste; indemnity provided by government to the successive owners of the mill and timber operations; court rulings and government–business settlements that worked against the welfare of the First Nation people (McGrath, 2016).

The federal government, its institutions, and Canadian society have reshaped the original Indigenous cultures in an attempt to have them "fit" into Canadian society. In spite of these efforts, their diversity remains. First Nations, for example, consist of more than 630 bands and nearly 2,500 reserves. Each reserve, a creation of treaties with the federal government, has a distinct history that has shaped its residents' current cultural identity. The bands, even the reserves, have distinct economies, capacities, and challenges. Most Canadians are unaware of this diversity and are more familiar with the constitutional definition that classifies Canada's Indigenous peoples simply as the "Indian, Inuit and Métis peoples of Canada" (Constitution Act, 1982, s. 35[2]). And only in 2016, through a Supreme Court decision, have the Métis been recognized as a responsibility of the federal government.

Despite the cultural diversity among Indigenous peoples across Canada, other factors and events besides an abiding spirituality unite the people sociologically and experientially. Racism, dating back to the earliest missionaries and including the recommendation of British Commander-in-Chief Jeffery Amherst in the 1760s to distribute smallpox-infected blankets among tribes disobeying British authority (Dickason and Newbigging, 2015: 102), has been the experience of many Indigenous people up to the present, as have been the harms of violence and substance abuse within communities and directed at community members by non-Indigenous outsiders (Vignette 4.6 and Contested Terrain 4.3).

Another tragic outcome of Canada's colonial past is the common feature of single-parent families in the Indigenous world. Indigenous families, like African-American families in the United States, often do not include a father. As described in Contested Terrain 4.3, the reasons are complex, but the outcomes for the children can be difficult and can lead to repeating this pattern of family formation and breakdown. The residual effect of residential schools may be one factor, but the cycle of poverty, limited education, and unemployment and underemployment are contributing factors.

Vignette 4.6

Indigenous Realities: Family Instability and Murdered and Missing Women

A simple assertion that all cultures are rooted in their family structure is readily accepted. Indigenous peoples are no exception. Yet, in its early efforts to assimilate Indigenous people, the Canadian government damaged many core elements of Indigenous cultures, such as their languages and social structure; even today, its residual effect negatively affects some Indigenous families, especially males. While the federal government no longer advocates assimilation programs, such as the notorious residential schools, lingering hurts still affect the behaviour of some Indigenous peoples and their offspring. Robert Innes, writing in 2015, pointed out the need for a federal inquiry into missing and murdered Indigenous women and girls, a formal inquiry that finally was established in 2016. Innes notes that police records reveal that Indigenous males were responsible for many of these crimes against Indigenous females, but he places those facts within a colonial framework, thus providing an explanation for such crimes (Innes, 2015: 56). Simply blaming Indigenous men for the violence suffered by Indigenous women plays into many Canadians' racial and gender biases and ignores the historic role the Canadian government and Canadians have played in creating the dire situation facing many Indigenous families. The federal inquiry is expected to throw some light on why Canadian society has this black mark, expose the general public to this troubling social problem, and, it is hoped, offer some remedies. Such an approach certainly fits with Saul's concept of a "soft" Canada.

Contested Terrain 4.3

Where Are the Indigenous Fathers?

A 2012 CBC television production—*Blind Spot: What Happened to Canada's Indigenous Fathers?*—explores the subject of the "missing" fathers by interviewing a small number of Indigenous males. Some fathers, for one reason or another, have abandoned their partners and children while others are trying to make family life and parenting work. The producer of *Blind Spot*, Geoff Leo, suggests that African-American society, where fathers for one reason or another are absent—some in jail, some hooked on drugs, and others leading lives of petty crime—may provide an insight into the fatherless Indigenous families. According to the CBC documentary, many of the social problems facing Indigenous youth can be traced to dysfunctional, fatherless families. Leo looked into the literature for information on the incidence of fatherless Indigenous families. He found much literature on fatherless African-American families and the negative impact on these children, but found nothing in the academic or popular literature on fatherless Indigenous families. Why, Leo asks, have Canadian and Indigenous leaders ignored this hurtful social issue? He further questions why academics, the government, and Indigenous organizations have not recognized the problem and offered solutions. Leo challenges them to address the issue and take appropriate action. You can view the trailer at: youtube.com/watch?v=rLn1-tTVjXs.

One powerful and challenging response is provided by Indigenous scholars and activists John Swift and Lee Maracle, who state that "Men have to have a deep love, appreciation, and connection to the land and for their nation before they can love their women" (Swift and Maracle, 2016: 163). And yet, in so many instances, the land is mostly gone from Indigenous stewardship and the remains of the nation are crowded onto small reserves or live in inner cities.

SUMMARY

Canada's population continues to grow, thanks in large part to immigration. By 2016, population distribution revealed four trends:

- People remained concentrated along the southern border with the United States.
- Population had shifted to the West.
- Large cities continue to increase in size.
- Newcomers prefer to settle in large cities.

Canada relies on immigration to fuel its population growth. Multiculturalism remains a key plank in Ottawa's effort to accommodate newcomers. The search for cultural accommodation without jeopardizing Canada's traditions remains an ongoing process, though the elastic nature of Canadian culture makes the task easier. Chief Justice Beverley McLachlin (2015) expressed this ongoing search as:

the debate between tolerance and intolerance; [but tolerance] does not mean that everything must be tolerated—a civilized society has no choice but to condemn practices that cause harm to others and injure citizens or undermine the fabric of peaceful co-existence.

Tolerant as Canadians are, blemishes occurred in the past and some are with us today. That Canadian society has slowly moved from intolerance to tolerance is captured in Saul's concept of a "soft" nation. Still, inequalities exist within Canadian society do exist and they expose themselves in the four faultlines: Indigenous/non-Indigenous, core/periphery, French/English, and newcomers/old-timers. Key demographic changes are occurring along these divides, reflecting internal forces and revealing population and political shifts.

The first demographic faultline is characterized by a much higher rate of natural increase among the Indigenous population than in the general population. Digging down into the demographic situation, we find that the last colonized Indigenous people, the Inuit, show little sign of a decline in fertility rates, as is now occurring among other Indigenous peoples.

The second faultline involves changes in the sizes of Canada's regional populations. In this case, Western Canada has experienced a rapidly increasing population while Atlantic Canada has had a very slow-growing population.

The third faultline focuses on the growing imbalance in the numbers of English- and French-speaking Canadians. As the percentage of French-speaking Canadians continues to decline, their political power, especially that of Québec, is slipping away.

The fourth faultline—between new Canadians and those born in Canada—is reflected in the federal policy of multiculturalism and is played out daily in Canada's major urban centres, where the vast majority of new Canadians settle. Tensions do exist but these will likely pass in the coming generations. In the author's opinion, the phenomenon of home-grown terrorists is a temporary event and, like others before it, will fade into the mist of time.

Turning again to Chief Justice McLachlin: "Living together in the ethic of tolerance is not easy. But it is worth the effort." It is the Canadian way.

Challenge Questions

1. From 2001 to 2016, Western Canada increased its share of Canada's population while other regions did not. Is this just a short-term blip on the demographic radar screen or are the fundamentals in place for this demographic shift to continue for the foreseeable future?
2. What is the demographic basis of the argument that Canadian cities need more fiscal power to meet their growing needs?
3. Can you offer an explanation for why the Indigenous population is so diverse?
4. Under what conditions could you envisage Canada sharply increasing or reducing the number of immigrants?
5. What is the Black Lives Matter movement?
6. Why is Canadian culture changing so rapidly?

Essay Questions

1. Canada's Indigenous community is struggling to find a footing within Canadian society. This struggle lies along the Indigenous/non-Indigenous faultline. The large number of murdered and missing Indigenous women and girls is the dark side of this reality. What, in your opinion, are the root causes? Offer solutions to these root causes.

References:

Amnesty International. 2014. *Violence against indigenous Women and Girls in Canada: A Summary of Amnesty International's Concerns and Call to Action.* Ottawa: Amnesty International Canada. At: https://www.amnesty.ca/sites/amnesty/files/iwfa_submission_amnesty_international_february_2014_-_final.pdf.

Native Women's Association of Canada. 2014. *Fact Sheet: Missing and Murdered Aboriginal Women and Girls.* At: http://www.nwac.ca/wp-content/uploads/2015/05/Fact_Sheet_Missing_and_Murdered_Aboriginal_Women_and_Girls.pdf.

Royal Canadian Mounted Police. 2014. *Missing and Murdered Aboriginal Women: A National Operational Overview*. At: http://www.rcmp-grc.gc.ca/aboriginal-autochtone/mmaw-fada-eng.htm.

——. 2015. *Missing and Murdered Aboriginal Women: 2015 Update to the National Operational Overview*. At: http://www.rcmp-grc.gc.ca/aboriginal-autochtone/mmaw-fada-eng.htm.

2.   Like other advanced countries, Canada's fertility rate is below replacement level. Account for this demographic change by applying the demographic transition theory.

References:

Grover, Drew. 2014. "What Is the Demographic Transition Model?" At: https://www.populationeducation.org/content/what-demographic-transition-model.

Statistics Canada. 2016. "Fertility: Fewer Children, Older Moms." At: http://www.statcan.gc.ca/pub/11-630-x/11-630-x2014002-eng.htm.

Further Reading

Bohnert, Nora, Jonathan Chagnon, and Patrice Dion. 2014. *Population Projections for Canada (2013 to 2063)*. Statistics Canada Catalogue no. 91-529-X. 17 Oct. At: http://www.statcan.gc.ca/pub/91-520-x/91-520-x2014001-eng.htm.

Statistics Canada regularly undertakes population projections to provide insights into demographic changes that Canada probably will experience in the future. Such analyses involve low and high estimates of the components making up population increase, namely, natural rate of increase and the volume of immigration. These projections are designed to assist the federal government in shaping its demographic and economic policies.

In 2014, Bohnert, Chagnon, and Dion undertook population projections to 2063, estimating that Canada's population would fall between 40 and 63 million by 2063. These demographers predict that the growth of Canada's population will slow over the next 50 years. The reason is that as the population ages, the annual number of deaths will increase.

Within Canada's population, Bohnert, Chagnon, and Dion identified three major demographic impacts that will affect the country over the next five decades. First, birth rates are anticipated to slowly decline and death rates to increase. The net result will be a lower rate of natural increase and a greater reliance on migration to maintain the current rate of population increase. Second, as the country's population ages, the resulting economic repercussion will be a higher age dependency ratio. In short, the burden of supporting those of non-working age will fall more heavily on those remaining in the potential workforce. Third, sustained levels of immigration combined with declining rates of natural increase will accelerate the diversification of Canada's population. By 2063, their prognosis calls for a more balanced ethnic composition, which, of course, implies other cultural changes, including an increase in those belonging to non-Christian religions.

5 Canada's Economic Face

Chapter Overview

The following topics are examined in Chapter 5:

- Canada's place in the changing global economy.
- The importance of trade with the United States.
- The future of Canada's manufacturing and resource sectors.
- The possible next stages in the evolution of Canada's economic structure.
- The role of the knowledge-based economy in Canada's economic future.
- The implications of the economic issues on Canada's six geographic regions.
- The use of the core/periphery model to understand Canada's place in the global economy and each geographic region.

Introduction

In response to the twists and turns in the world economy, Canada has had to adjust its economy accordingly. Canada is particularly sensitive to world trade because of its high reliance on exports to drive its economy. For example, after several years of benefiting from high oil and commodity exports, world demand and prices dropped suddenly in 2014, ending the **super cycle**. Until then, Canada relied on its resource sector to drive the economy and to provide the bulk of exports. For Canada to prosper, many argue, oil and commodity prices must regain their former strength; otherwise, Canada's economy will remain dormant. In the meantime, Ottawa is counting on the lower Canadian dollar to drive the manufacturing sector. This federal strategy calls for an acceleration of products exported to Canada's major customer, the United States. Such an export-based strategy, to be successful, means that Canada's manufacturers must overcome stiff competition in their principal export market. In the long run, Canadian governments, both federal and provincial, believe that the future lies in a more vibrant **knowledge-based economy**.

How can we place the events that affect the Canadian economy into a global context? The economic process of globalization provides much of the explanation for the loss of manufacturing jobs in developed economies, including Canada and the United States; while Rostow's Stages of Economic Growth model offers a historic framework allowing for insights into the nature and process of industrialization by nation-states over time. In this chapter, our attention is focused on Canada's attempt to navigate through these turbulent global waters and, in doing so, chart a new direction to supplement resource extraction and processing by shifting towards a greener and more technically advanced economy.

← Workers inspect cars moving along the assembly line at the Honda manufacturing plant in Alliston, Ontario. Manufacturing is a key sector in the Canadian economy—and the heart of Canadian manufacturing lies in the automobile and auto parts industries.

REUTERS/Fred Thornhill

Canada's Economies

In reality, Canada has two economies. One focuses on manufacturing while the other concentrates on resource development. History offers an explanation for this situation. Since its founding, Canada has depended on the exploitation of its natural resources and the sale of those resources to foreign countries. The reason for this resource-based economy is simple. Geography has blessed Canada with abundant natural resources, but its relatively small population compels it to export these resources to foreign countries. At the same time, Canada's small and dispersed markets made the emergence of an industrial core difficult. Harold Innis, the first Canadian economist with a sense of geography, recognized these facts. In his writings, Innis presented his interpretation of the historic development of Canada and its regions as the **staples thesis** (Innis, 1930). In this view, regional development took place as the resources of the region were exploited. Canada's first Prime Minister, John A. Macdonald, promoted the creation of a manufacturing base, beginning in 1879, through the National Policy that saw tariffs shelter infant manufacturing operations so that they could take hold. Over the years, this manufacturing base has been rooted in Central Canada.

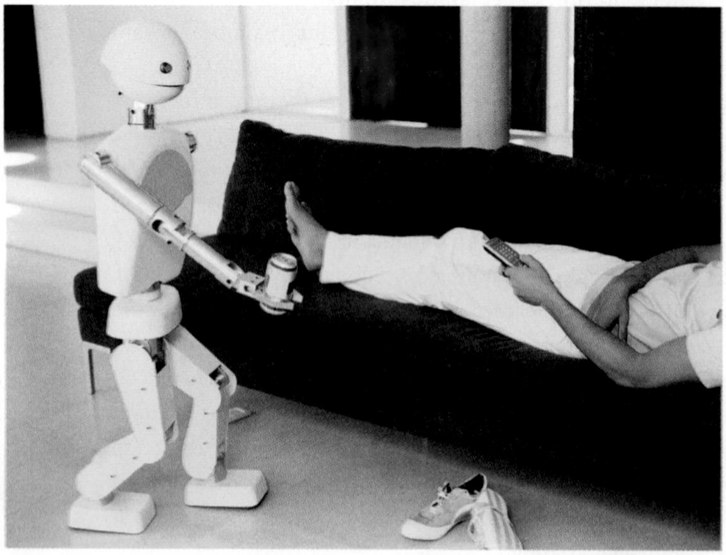

In the next section, the future direction of Canada's economy is examined. While new economic paradigms result in change, radical shifts in Canada's **industrial structure**, as well as displacements in its labour market, are expected in the lifetime of students reading this book. For example, will there be major new oil pipelines in the coming years? But the big question revolves around information technology and the knowledge-based economy. While information technology has already created amazing advances, such as cloud robotics whereby linking computers to robotics applications greatly increases computer capacity, is this the best path to the future for Canada? Ten years ago, who would have imagined that a Wi-Fi connection to cloud-based resources would allow a robotic computer to access vast sources of information for a student preparing a term essay? But are students learning more and are their essays better today? Google Maps that assist a driver to find his/her destination represent another innovative breakthrough. Yet, were we all lost a few years ago, unable to find our destinations? And these examples are only the tip of the iceberg. In his book *Rise of the Robots* Martin Ford (2015: 16–20) foresees robotics, regardless of the precise technological path, playing an ever greater role in society (Photo 5.1).

Javier Pierini/Getty Images

Photo 5.1 Robot serving beer to a young man lying on a sofa with a remote control that connects with the robot. Can you imagine having a robot to bring you your textbook for this class? And will the next step be to have the robot read the book and give you a summary?!

Canada's Future Economic Face

What will Canada's future economic face look like? Prime Minister Trudeau (Wherry, 2016a) provided his vision at the 2016 World Economic Forum in Davos, Switzerland: "My predecessor [Stephen Harper] wanted you to know Canada for its resources. I want you to know Canadians for our resourcefulness."

As the world enters what Klaus Schwab, the German founder of the World Economic Forum, has called the Fourth Industrial Revolution (Vignette 5.1), what do those words of Canada's Prime Minister mean? Most governments around

Contested Terrain 5.1

Coal, the Industrial Revolution, and Global Warming

Coal remains the principal energy source used in the industrialization process, especially in the "take-off" stage described by Rostow. However, because coal contributes heavily to global warming, world pressure is increasing for an end to coal production and to coal and other fossil fuels being used to drive industry. Ontario has already closed its coal-generated electric plants and Alberta has promised to follow. These political decisions result in higher costs for producing electricity for Ontarians, and eventually will have a similar impact for Albertans. If such a policy were extended to all countries, the opportunity for economic growth in developing countries, including China and India, would be reduced dramatically. All bets are off, however, if President Trump withdraws the US from the Paris Agreement on climate change.

the world embrace the idea of knowledge-based economies that are expected to provide robust economic growth. In applying this notion to Canada, Dan Breznitz of the University of Toronto's Munk School of Global Affairs suggests that "each region should focus on exploiting existing strengths, such as energy-related innovations in Alberta or agricultural technology in the grain belt, where strong knowledge bases already exist" (Milne, 2016: B8). But is the knowledge-based economy, with its innovative clusters, a magic elixir? Those with technological skills living in the clusters stand to benefit, but what about the bulk of Canada's workforce? And what are the consequences for Canada's weaker regions?

As Canada and other nations hurtle down the economic development path, a quick look at the historic evolution of Canada's industrial structure provides a framework for interpreting the past and hints for the future. This evolution is similar to that experienced by other industrialized countries. Economic historians, including Walter Rostow in *Stages of Economic Growth* (1960) and Klaus Schwab in *The Fourth Industrial Revolution* (2016), have charted this course.

Industrial Structure

An industrial structure, defined by the number employed in the three sectors of an economy, provides an insight into the nature of that particular economy; permits a historic view; and allows for comparisons with other economies. The three economic sectors, known as the primary, secondary, and tertiary sectors, divide the workforce by their types of employment:

- **Primary sector**: resource extraction, including minerals, farming, fishing, and logging.
- **Secondary sector**: construction and manufacturing, i.e., the processing of extracted resources for commercial sale.
- **Tertiary sector**: services, ranging from the Walmart cashier and the person who pours your first cup of the day at Tim Hortons to teachers, bankers, hairdressers, health-care workers, truckers, and computer programmers.

Thus, for example, the chair you are sitting on passed back and forth through each of the three sectors before it came to you.

Over time, employment numbers have shifted from the primary and then secondary sectors to the tertiary one. Advanced countries like Canada have over 80 per cent of their workers in the tertiary sector. Some analysts speak of a fourth sector, the **quaternary sector**, which essentially involves high-end knowledge-based workers and decision-makers, but Statistics Canada does not collect data to identify workers falling into this sector.

TABLE 5.1 Historic Shifts in Canada's Industrial Structure

Shifts	Year	Primary (%)	Secondary (%)	Tertiary (%)
Agricultural	1881	51	29	19
Early industrial	1901	44	30	26
Late industrial	1961	14	32	54
Post-industrial	2011	4	19	77
Current	2015	4	18	78

Sources: Adapted from McVey and Kalbach (1995: Table 10.3); Statistics Canada (2006, 2012a, 2016c).

In this text, our primary interest lies in the difference in the industrial structures found in the six geographic regions. Our secondary interest focuses on the evolutionary path followed by Canada's industrial structure. Canada's path provides a connection to the general theory presented in Rostow's *Stages of Economic Growth* and Schwab's *Fourth Industrial Revolution* (Vignette 5.1). For example, in 1881 just over half of Canada's workforce engaged in agriculture (Table 5.1). This dominance of agriculture fits well with Rostow's second stage, *pre-conditions for take-off*. By examining the broad historic changes in the percentage of workers in each sector, insights into the nature of Canada's economy at various historic times are possible; and historic shifts in these sectors provide a means of observing and measuring changes in the labour force over time. For instance, the primary sector formed only 4 per cent of the national labour force in 2015 (Table 5.1).

Certain major forces caused this evolution in Canada's industrial structure over time: the settling of western lands in the late nineteenth and early twentieth centuries resulted in more farm labourers; (the mechanization of agriculture by the development and use of tractors, harvesters, and combines led to the consolidation of small farms and drove farmhands and then small farmers into cities in search of factory work; automation and, more recently, the offshoring of manufacturing to developing countries pushed manufacturing employees into the service industries. Similar processes have occurred in fishing, logging, and mining, where new technologies have meant extracting more and doing so more quickly, the end result being that fewer workers are needed. At the same time, increased automation of processing and manufacturing has meant fewer jobs in the secondary sector. The broad outlines of this evolution are revealed in Table 5.1. From 1881 to the present, the percentage of workers in these three sectors of the economy has moved to the tertiary/quaternary section. By 2015, the tertiary/quaternary sector accounted for close to 80 per cent of the Canadian labour force.

The evolution of Canada's industrial world has its historic roots in the National Policy of Prime Minister John A. Macdonald in the late 1870s. His protectionist policy created the industrial core in Central Canada and set the tone for Canada's economy well into the twentieth century. At this juncture, Canada adopted more open trade policies, beginning with the Auto Pact in 1965, which ultimately led to the Canada–US Free Trade Agreement (FTA) signed by the two countries in 1988 and then the **North American Free Trade Agreement** of 1994, which superseded the FTA. The formalization in 1995 of the international General Agreement on Tariffs and Trade as the World Trade Organization solidified the role of Canada—and the rest of the world—in a neo-liberal regime of freer trade, and since that time Canada has signed and pursued bilateral and multilateral free trade agreements with other countries and blocs of countries throughout the world. Four topics—globalization, Rostow's Stages of Economic Growth model, the historic evolution of Canada's labour force, and the super cycle—offer insights into the global economic adventure and Canada's place in what Schwab has called the world's "Fourth Industrial Revolution" (Vignette 5.1).

Vignette 5.1

The Fourth Industrial Revolution

Klaus Schwab argues that the world has experienced four phases to the Industrial Revolution (Table 5.2). Each phase denotes an abrupt and radical change to the world economy; each has been driven by fossil fuels; and each has required a shorter and shorter time to reach maturity. Concerns about climate warming have given rise to green energy in Schwab's fourth phase. However, green energy remains a minor factor—and a more expensive one—in world energy production. Table 5.2 briefly summarizes Schwab's time frame for the four phases of the Industrial Revolution.

TABLE 5.2 Major Economic Revolutions over the Last 10,000 Years

Time	Event	Main Characteristic
10,000 years ago	Agrarian Revolution	Human/animal power: farming begins to replace hunting; village and urban life appears.
1750–1870	Industrial Revolution: Phase 1	Water/steam power: steam engine and rail system begin the transformation of society from an agriculturally oriented one to an industrial one.
1870–1950	Industrial Revolution: Phase 2	Coal power: industrialization accelerates with heavy industry driving the economy into a system of mass production and the division of labour.
1950–2000	Industrial Revolution: Phase 3	Coal power: automation and computers become an integral part of the economy while global energy consumption increases dramatically as developing countries undergo industrialization and demand for electricity from coal-generated plants increases.
2000–?	Industrial Revolution: Phase 4	Green power: robotics make their presence felt, but the developing world continues to rely heavily on fossil fuels while the developed world shifts to more expensive green energy.

Source: Adapted from Schwab (2016).

The National Policy and the Birth of an Industrial Core

The Prime Minister of the day, Sir John A. Macdonald, recognized the vulnerability of the newly formed state of Canada to the industrial colossus south of the border. Macdonald also recognized the importance of a manufacturing economy in a modern country. He faced the choice of economic and possible political integration with the United States or protectionism. In 1879 Macdonald chose a form of protectionism based on the protection of infant industries, whereby tariffs raised the cost of otherwise low-cost imported products, such as shoes, clothing, and farm machinery, thus allowing local firms to produce these products and thrive in the local market until they could compete in the global market. The downside of this policy was the much higher cost of manufactured goods in Canada, especially in the places distant from the newly formed industrial core in Ontario and Québec. Manufactured goods in Ontario and Québec cost

THINK ABOUT IT

In developed countries, globalization has had a negative effect on the working class. Canada is no exception in this *race to the bottom*. If the closure of the profitable Caterpillar plant in London, Ontario, in 2012 was a result of the seemingly relentless push by global companies to seek out countries with low wages and few benefits, what message does it send to Canada's manufacturing industry and its workers?

more than those produced in the United States largely because the much larger US market allowed for greater economies of scale than in Canada, plus its road and railway system served a denser population than did the transportation system in Canada.

While extremely popular in Central Canada, the rest of the country felt left out of the major benefits of the National Policy, despite their increased access to national markets with the completion of a transcontinental railway. Over time, resentment grew against what was perceived as the "entitlement" of Central Canada and Ottawa's catering to the interests of Ontario and Québec. Not until the Auto Pact of 1965 and then the Free Trade Agreement with the US, which came into effect in 1989, did this national core/periphery relationship undergo significant change to a North American trade zone and the emergence of a north–south transportation axis, i.e., the expansion of the CN railroad system into the United States (Figure 5.4).

Globalization and the Stages of Economic Growth Model

In recent decades the world has entered a new epoch whereby globalization, by widening, intensifying, and accelerating worldwide interconnectedness, has created rapidly shifting economic terrain. In this unfolding world, the grip of any nation on its economic and political levers of power weakens, giving way to the rules found in international trade arrangements and allowing for the unprecedented role for transnational industrial and financial business interests in national affairs. The consequences for developed countries like Canada are considerable, and the most identifiable results are the growing dominance of these transnational players in their economies and the decline of their manufacturing industries. Imports of Asian manufactured goods have provided Canadians with an array of low-priced consumer products; at the same time, Asian state capital has reached deep into the Canadian oil and mining sectors and private Chinese capital has flowed into real estate. The question facing Canadians is whether this is an acceptable trade-off.

The withdrawal of the United Kingdom from the European Union following a surprising 2016 referendum result and the emergence in the United States of a protectionist economic nationalism, which in some iterations verges on a populist xenophobia, are signs of discontent with globalization. For many workers, globalization has meant that their jobs have gone offshore, where workers receive much lower wages for the same work; and back home, high-paying manufacturing jobs have turned into low-wage service jobs.

In his book, Rostow (1960) presents a sweeping historical perspective on the process of industrialization. By examining the European experience, Rostow identifies five stages that developed countries have passed through to reach their current degree of economic development. Since Rostow wrote his book, the world economy has moved on and developed countries have passed through his last stage of "the Age of Mass Consumption" into another stage. This most recent stage has been marked by the spread of industrialization to developing countries; the unprecedented pace of industrialization in countries like China; the record levels of international trade; and the unrelenting advance of technological innovations. This stage may well be called "Globalization."

Rostow's five stages of economic growth, plus the current globalization stage, are outlined below.

1. *Traditional society* involved an agricultural economy consisting mainly of subsistence farming on small plots of land. The bulk of the population, perhaps as high as 80 per cent, engaged in this agricultural economy. This period of time is often referred to as the pre-industrialization stage.

2. *Pre-conditions for take-off* sees the first signs of industrialization. In this stage, agriculture turns into a more commercial endeavour with larger farms and the substitution of machinery for farm workers. Farm workers, in turn, are forced to move to the cities to seek jobs in the emerging factories. This period of time sees the start of a rural-to–urban migration along with the emergence of large cities.

3. *Take-off* occurs when industrialization clearly dominates the economy. Manufacturing surpasses agriculture in terms of economic importance, although as much as half of the population still resides

in rural areas. In contrast to the highly productive factories, productivity in agriculture remains low. In this stage, the rural-to-urban migration reaches its peak and urban growth is rapid.

4. *Drive to maturity* is associated with a more diverse economy and the diffusion of economic growth to the hinterland. The vast majority of workers are engaged in the secondary and tertiary sectors of the economy. Agriculture is highly mechanized. Large farms are necessary to maximize the efficiency of agricultural machinery.

5. *An age of mass consumption* occurs when economic output reaches record levels and high wages permit increased consumer expenditure. Growth is sustained, by the expansion of a middle class of consumers, not by exports. By now, the tertiary sector accounts for the vast majority of the labour force.

6. *Globalization* calls for the transformation of the world economy by reducing trade barriers and increasing the opportunity for industrialization to take place in developing countries. Its defining characteristics are the emergence of an international industrial and financial business structure and a weakening of the role of nation-states in their domestic economies. Technology takes centre stage, and technological advances take on a relentless pace not seen before in human history. These advances are characterized by automation, digitization, and robotics, which have dramatically transformed economic life in developed countries where blue-collar and white-collar jobs are no longer secure.

Globalization is not a smooth linear process. Workers in developed countries have felt a few bumps in the road. One bump is the relocation of jobs offshore while another is workplace automation that reduces the need for workers. But perhaps the biggest bump is the realization that the average worker is not better off than he/she was 10 years ago. The political reaction is to turn against trade agreements and, in the case of the United States under President Trump, to expect to renegotiate NAFTA. By October 2016, the International Monetary Fund (IMF) forecast a sluggish world economy (IMF, 2016).

As for the developing world, major countries like China are moving through this development process in record time. China, for instance, has passed through the take-off stage and is now entering the drive to maturity stage. Indeed, Heap (2005) even suggests that China is unlikely to return to its heretofore breakneck pace in purchasing resource materials and in seeking ownership of such resources. If the super cycle (Vignette 5.2) does not return, the implications for Canada and its resource economy are considerable.

Shortcomings in Rostow's Model

Several shortcomings can be found in Rostow's Stages of Economic Growth model. First, Rostow's thesis is based on a Western model of modernization. The question arises: can such a Western-centric model bridge cultural differences found in non-Western countries? As well, does it apply to non-capitalist economies? Without a doubt, most of the nearly 200 countries in the world have chosen

THINK ABOUT IT

If advances in technology, including robotics, significantly reduce the need for human workers, would Ottawa be forced to review its immigration policy? Could a smaller labour force and the emergence of advanced robotic workers cause Canada to reverse its immigration strategy?

Vignette 5.2

China: The Engine of a Commodities Super Cycle

When the People's Republic of China was admitted to the World Trade Organization in December 2001, global trade was radically changed as Chinese manufactured goods became able to penetrate markets around the globe. Canada and its main manufacturing provinces of Ontario and Québec felt the brunt of low-cost Chinese goods displacing the products of local manufacturers, as these Chinese goods were readily available in big-box stores and Walmart outlets across the nation. In turn, China's rapidly expanding industrial capacity required more and more imports of coal and iron to fuel its steel industry. Prices for those and other commodities rose sharply, thus creating another commodities super cycle.

the industrialization process, including command economies like China. Whether these countries will follow a linear pathway through the six stages remains unclear.

Second, Rostow based his model on the historical experience of Western countries to the 1950s. Hence, his five stages do not take into consideration more recent economic events. For example, globalization as we know it had not yet occurred. The addition of a sixth stage, as suggested above, perhaps provides a solution to this issue.

Third, the notion of stages of economic growth may not apply equally well to all countries. Not all countries, for example, have the basic resources—coal and iron ore—for the take-off stage. Also, large countries with a diverse resource base stand a better chance of successfully completing the industrialization process than small countries. Japan and South Korea, of course, provide important exceptions to both points. While coal and iron ore are in short supply in both countries, imports of lower-priced coal and iron are the basis of their iron and steel industries and these industries form the heart of their industrialization process. The success of both countries lies not in geography but in culture and history. According to Sachs (2015), small countries now starting the industrialization process have less chance of mounting the development ladder. Many are in Africa, where the forces of colonialism divided the continent into numerous small yet ethnically diverse populations.

THINK ABOUT IT

Alan Heap and Klaus Schwab have identified variations in the global **business cycle**. Why is Schwab looking at long-term shifts in the global economy while Heap is more focused on short-term variations in the commodity cycle?

The Super Cycle Theory

Economists consider super cycles to be extended periods of high global growth driven by the emergence of large, new economies that are undergoing the early stages of industrialization. One effect of this surge in demand is the unusual rise of prices for energy and raw materials within the global economy. In terms of Rostow's stages of economic growth, the demand for energy and raw materials peaked in the take-off stage. The most recent super cycle began with China's remarkable spurt of industrial growth that drove commodity and energy prices to new highs (Heap, 2005). Canada was one of the chief beneficiaries, and its resource exports to China and other Asian countries, led by coal and iron ore, soared. But in 2014, economic growth in China and the rest of the world slowed, marking the end of this super cycle (La Caixa, 2015). Since then, global growth has languished. In a provocative report, the Chief Economist of the Organisation for Economic Co-operation and Development (OECD), Catherine Mann, claimed the global economy had fallen into a "low-growth trap" (Mann, 2016). If Mann is correct, then Canada and the rest of the world have to wait for India, the second-largest country by population, to rapidly industrialize and trigger a new super cycle (Vignette 5.3).

Vignette 5.3

The Third Super Cycle

Alan Heap declared that "There have been two super cycles in the last 150 years: late 1800s–early 1900s, driving economic growth in the USA; 1945–1975, prompted by post-war construction in Europe and by Japan's later, massive economic expansion" (Heap, 2005). The current one began with the rapid industrialization of China's economy. In all three cycles, rapid economic growth created a high demand for energy, minerals, and other commodities, thus pushing their prices higher. But like all economic cycles, what goes up, eventually comes down. Accordingly, Heap roughly estimated that the present super cycle would come to an end when China's economic expansion slows. Put in terms of Rostow's Stages of Economic Growth model, as China shifts from its take-off stage to drive to mature stage, its demand for foreign sources of energy and raw materials will ease and its exports of higher-end consumer and food products will increase.

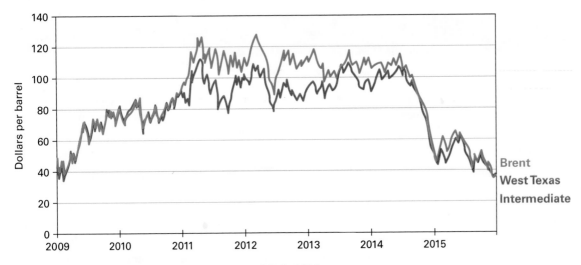

FIGURE 5.1 Daily crude oil spot prices, 2010–2015

Source: US Energy Information Administration (2016).

Oil provides one measure of the sudden collapse in commodity prices. In little more than a year, world (**Brent**) oil prices dropped from US$112/barrel in June 2014 to just below US$40/barrel at the end of 2015 (Figure 5.1). Since oil prices closely reflect the ups and downs of the global business cycle, such volatility is no surprise (EIA, 2016); what is a surprise to some is the apparent end of the Chinese-driven super cycle. By November 2016 oil had recovered a bit of ground when the price hovered at around $46/barrel, but oversupply continues to dampen oil prices (Smith, 2016).

Pipelines could change Canada's economic face. The federal government will continue to face this important political question: to approve or reject oil pipeline projects recommended by the National Energy Board. The National Energy Board (NEB) had recommended the construction of two oil pipelines, the Northern Gateway project (2014) and the Trans Mountain Pipeline Expansion (2016), and is reviewing the Energy East pipeline proposal. At the end of November 2016 the Trudeau government gave the go-ahead for Trans Mountain, put the final nail in the coffin of Enbridge's Northern Gateway, but allowed Enbridge to replace its 50-year-old Line 3 from Alberta to the US, which may also increase capacity (Wherry, 2016b). These pipelines are highly controversial and some Canadians are adamantly opposed.

The degree of opposition was demonstrated at the end of August 2016, when a group of protestors decrying the lack of objectivity on the part of the NEB forced the panel members to cancel hearings in Montréal on the Energy East proposal (Adams, 2016). Days later, the panel members stepped aside because of a possible conflict of interest. In the case of the Northern Gateway pipeline, the Federal Court of Appeal rejected the 2014 approval by the National Energy Board because the government of the time failed to properly consult with First Nations (Canadian Press, 2016).

Canada's Economy

At this juncture, the discussion turns to Canada's economy, as recorded by GDP. This measure reflects the overall health of the Canadian economy (Vignette 5.4). In this discussion, GDP represents the total dollar value of all goods and services produced over a year. In 2015, Canada's GDP totalled $1.7 trillion (Statistics Canada, 2016e). However, the annual growth rate of GDP provides a more meaningful measure.

As a rough interpretive guide, a buoyant Canadian economy occurs when annual GDP growth ranges between 2 and 3 per cent; a weak economy is marked by an annual GDP rate below 1 per cent;

THINK ABOUT IT

Which world markets use Brent oil pricing and which use West Texas Intermediate oil pricing?

Vignette 5.4

GDP: A Measure of the Economy

Gross domestic product is a measure of the size of the economy. GDP represents the total dollar value of all goods and services produced over a year or some other period of time within a country or province. However, the most critical measure of an economy's performance is found in annual percentage changes in GDP, which can be positive or negative.

and GDP figures falling between those two extremes represent a stagnant one at the low end and a slow-growing economy at the high end. To place Canada's economic performance in context, annual GDP growth rate in Canada averaged 3.1 per cent from 1962 until 2009 when the economy, caught in the global collapse, fell by −4 per cent (Trading Economics, 2016). From 2011 to 2016, annual GDP has fluctuated from a high of 3.3 per cent to a low of 0.9 per cent in 2015 (Figure 5.2).

Looking to the future, the Chief Economist at the Conference Board of Canada, Glen Hodgson (2016), sees mixed economic signals ahead, i.e., unless oil and commodity prices regain their strength there is little chance of a significant upturn in the economy. So serious is the collapse in oil and commodity prices that the Bank of Canada Governor, Stephen Poloz, "characterized the commodities price rout as a 'seismic shift' [in Canada's economy] that could last up to five years and drain $50-billion a year from the Canadian economy" (McKenna, 2016). The federal government's strategy to stimulate the economy focuses on spending in three areas: defence, infrastructure, and financial support to major manufacturers, such as the automobile companies, and to knowledge-based firms. While low interest rates make this strategy sound, the size of the debt, as of 12 November 2016, was $632 billion, which has raised alarm bells (Taxpayers.com, 2016).

Another measure of the economy takes the form of annual **unemployment** rates. Since 2014, the annual unemployment rate has stayed below 7 per cent. By comparison, the rate reached 8.3 per cent at the peak of the 2009 recession (Table 5.3).

All of Canada's geographic regions have experienced changes due to the drop in oil and commodity prices and the ensuing layoffs of workers in the resource industry. By 2015, the oil-rich provinces, Alberta, Saskatchewan, and Newfoundland

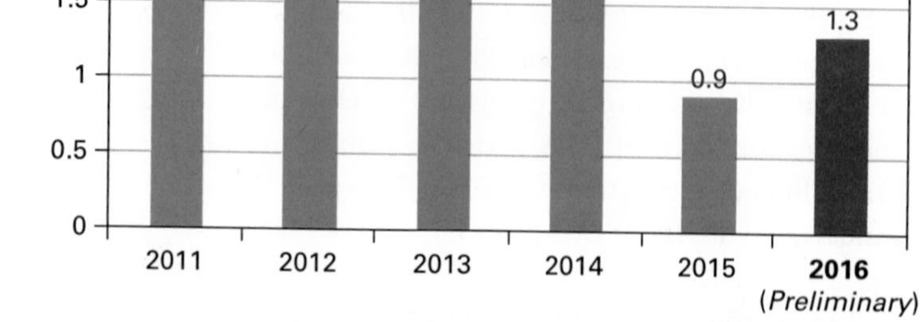

FIGURE 5.2 Annual economic growth: Year-over-year per cent change in real GDP, 2011–2016 (seasonally adjusted)
Source: Evans (2016).

TABLE 5.3 Canada's Annual Unemployment Rate, 2006–2016

Year	Rate	Year	Rate
2006	6.3	2012	7.3
2007	6.0	2013	7.1
2008	6.1	2014	6.9
2009	8.3	2015	6.9
2010	8.1	2016	7.0*
2011	7.5		

*Third quarter of 2016.
Source: Statistics Canada (2016a).

and Labrador, had felt the full and brutal impact of low oil prices. The sudden halt to the rapid regional growth for those three provinces resulted in a sharp drop in royalties and resource investment and a rise in unemployment. A measure of this economic shock is revealed in Figure 5.3: the three leading oil-producing provinces had negative provincial GDP growth from 2014 to 2015 while GDP in the other provinces increased. The much smaller territorial economies are especially vulnerable to changes in commodity prices so that, in Yukon, lower metal prices and the shutdown of a single mine had a noticeable impact on its GDP.

Key to Canada's Prosperity: Trade

Canada depends heavily on trade. Exports are especially important to Canada's economic well-being for several reasons:

- *Resources.* Canada's vast resource base ranges from agriculture to oil and gas, forestry, and minerals.
- *Global market.* Canadian production far exceeds the capacity of its domestic market, making access to foreign markets critical.
- *Economies of scale.* Production for global markets allows producers to take advantage of economies of scale (and therefore lower per-unit costs of production) than would occur if they were restricted to the domestic market.
- *Prosperity.* Exports increase employment levels, draw foreign capital, and help balance international trade.

Trade with the United States dominates Canada's economic picture. In 2015, exports to the United States reached 76 per cent of total Canadian exports; imports from the United States were considerably less, at 66 per cent of Canada's total imports (Statistics Canada, 2016d). These trade figures indicate the high degree of integration of the two economies, but they also point to Canada's dependency on trade with the United States and to a possible future irritant in Canada–US relations because Canada is exporting more than it is importing and the United

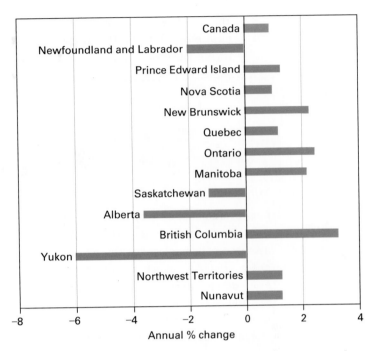

FIGURE 5.3 Annual percentage change in real gross domestic product for Canada, provinces, and territories, 2015

Source: Statistics Canada (2016f).

States currently has a significant trade deficit. Newly elected President Trump has signalled he wants to review NAFTA with the intention of making the agreement more favourable to the US.

Under the Trudeau government, special efforts are underway to increase economic ties with China. In 2015, China ranked as the second-most important export destination for Canadian products but these exports only amounted to 4 per cent of all Canadian exports (Statistics Canada, 2016d). Whether such efforts will diversify and increase Canada's international trade remains unclear, but what is clear is that China has become an economic superpower on the world stage. At the September 2016 G20 Summit in Hangzhou, when Chinese President Xi Jinping said the global economy was at a "crucial juncture" due to volatile markets and feeble trade, the rest of the world listened (BBC News, 2016).

High levels of trade between Canada and the United States are due to a number of factors:

- North America is a natural economic trade zone, expressed by the term "continentalism."

THINK ABOUT IT

China is closing the economic gap on the United States. Should Canada pay more attention to trade with China? The Liberal government thinks so, but what about potential harm to our trade agreements with the United States?

THINK ABOUT IT

With President Trump having used a plan to build a wall to keep Mexicans from illegally entering the United States as a central theme in his election campaign, do you think he would support or oppose the Gordie Howe International Trade Crossing?

- The economies of the two countries complement each other. The United States requires large quantities of Canada's resources, especially oil, and Canada requires American machinery.
- Two trade agreements greatly accelerated trade between the two countries, leading to the integration of the North American automobile and parts industry.
- A north–south transportation system facilitates such high volumes of trade (see Vignette 5.5).

Vignette 5.5

New Link in the North–South Transportation System

Canada is committed to building a new bridge over the Detroit River as the latest link in North America's transportation system. By 2020, the Gordie Howe International Trade Crossing is expected to provide a second bridge across the Detroit River, thus facilitating trade with the United States. An estimated one-quarter of the merchandise trade between the two countries travels over the privately owned Ambassador Bridge, which spans the river between Windsor and Detroit. With the increasing volume of trade, this bridge, built in 1930, has turned into a choke point. One not so minor detail has delayed the completion of this project that is important to both countries: the owner of the Ambassador Bridge, Manuel Morounis, has opposed the new bridge and is refusing to sell land needed to complete the US side of the bridge and associated highway system.

Photo 5.2 The Ambassador Bridge seen from the US side of the Detroit River. The new bridge—if it proceeds as planned—will be located roughly 3 kilometers downriver from the existing bridge.

Source: https://www.google.ca/imgres?imgurl=http://wpmedia.windsorstar.com/2012/08/1dricfinal.jpg&imgrefurl=http://windsorstar.com/tag/detroit-river-international-crossing/page/2&h=768&w=1024&tbnid=0dioYEbbI9QdtM:&tbnh=160&tbnw=213&docid=Nj5pM00KCFcbUM&itg=1&usg=__jhpVbxkGHF-MPLzJ-TNILcqdurg=#h=768&imgdii=0dioYEbbI9QdtM%3A%3B0dioYEbbI9QdtM%3A%3BF9FyjkDrkte2YM%3A&tbnh=160&tbnw=213&w=1024>

Trade Agreements

Trade agreements with the United States have had three results: (1) greater trade; (2) a more integrated North American economy; and (3) trade conflicts. For a less populous country like Canada, a **dispute settlement mechanism** in trade agreements is essential. Fortunately, the vast majority of trade in North America takes place in accordance with the rules of the **North American Free Trade Agreement** and the World Trade Organization (WTO). Nonetheless, disputes do occur between Canada and other countries, particularly with the United States. Canada has used the NAFTA dispute settlement mechanism to seek compensation from US tariffs and quotas.[1]

Raw materials and energy have always formed a major portion of Canadian exports to the United States. The free flow of these products into the United States occurs when the US experiences a shortage. In other cases, US producers have called for tariffs and quotas on Canadian products. Lumber provides one example. In this case, Ottawa decided that a bilateral agreement would prove more beneficial to Canadian producers than applying to NAFTA's dispute settlement mechanism. The two countries reached the Softwood Lumber Agreement in 2006, thus setting the conditions for Canadian exports to the United States. The means of limiting Canadian shipments to the US takes the form of an export charge when the price of lumber is at or below US$355 per thousand board feet. In this way, the profit margin for Canadian producers disappears and exporting is no longer a viable transaction. This agreement ended in October 2016, and by November of that year the US Lumber Coalition, among the most powerful lobby groups in Washington, DC, had filed a lengthy petition with the US Department of Commerce asking it, once again, to investigate unfair trade practices (McGregor, 2016).

Trade with the United States reached its peak in the years following the signing of the Canada–US Free Trade Agreement in 1988. By 2015, Canada's trade with the United States had more than tripled (Canada, 2016). Access to the US market has allowed manufacturers in Canada, especially in Ontario and Québec, to achieve **economies of scale** and thus lower per-unit costs of production. In this way,

Canada's manufacturing industries have become more competitive, and that competitive edge has encouraged exports to the United States and, to a lesser degree, other countries.

Thomas Courchene (1998) argued that the Free Trade Agreement broke Central Canada's stranglehold on Canadian markets outside of Ontario, but opened the US market to Canadian manufactured products. Since most were produced in Ontario, the principal beneficiary was Ontario. In Courchene's words, Ontario became a "North American Region State" rather than a Canadian province. The growth of Canadian National Railway (CN) from a national railway system to a North American one supports Courchene's argument (Figure 5.4).

In 1965, the political force behind the Auto Pact was founded in an economic philosophy known as **continentalism**, as have been the FTA and NAFTA. In Canada, continentalism has always lurked just below the surface of serious political thought among federal politicians and the wish of Canadian business people. The Canadian public, looking across the border at lower prices for similar goods, had no trouble understanding the advantages of that aspect of free trade but they did have concerns about the political and cultural implications of such close economic ties with the United States. Indeed, in the early 1970s, the government of Pierre Trudeau sought to move beyond Canada's reliance on trade with the US by pursuing a "Third Option" of expanding trade connections with Europe, but as political scientist Stephen Brooks remarks, this policy proved "about as effective as a statute repealing the law of gravity" (Brooks, 2012: 534). The close bilateral relationship and the geographical imperative of proximity were, and remain, too strong for major change in the direction of Canadian trade. Table 5.4 outlines some the shifts and events in Canadian trade policy from the Auto Pact to the present.

Good relationships also have played a role as Canada and the United States have been close allies for a long time. As President Kennedy remarked in his speech to Canada's Parliament in 1961: "Geography has made us neighbors. History has made us friends. Economics has made us partners. And necessity has made us allies." Derek Burney, former Canadian Ambassador to the United States, and

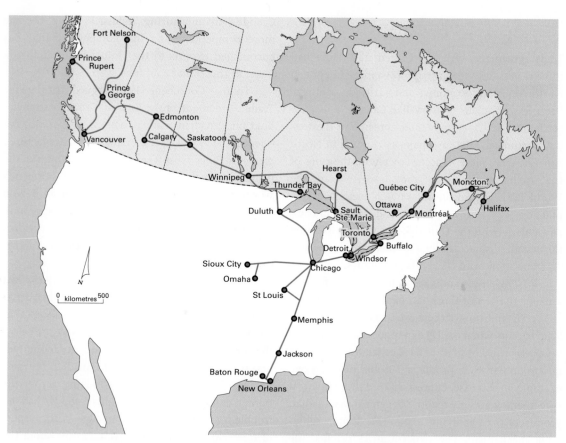

FIGURE 5.4 CN: Symbol of the integrated North American economy

With the Canada–US Free Trade Agreement, CN switched its emphasis from a predominantly Canadian east–west railway system to a North American continental system. CN now operates in eight Canadian provinces and 16 US states. Not surprisingly, the trend to expand from a Canadian base to a North American one has attracted other firms, including Canadian banks that now have substantial holdings in the US. By 2012, the Bank of Montreal's US operations were equal in size and value to those in Canada.

policy expert Fen Hampson (2012: A13) expressed the significance of the long-standing Canada–US relationship in more pragmatic terms:

> The cornerstone of Canada's foreign policy is the management of relations with the United States, not for reasons of sentiment but because that's how we preserve our most vital economic and security interests and our capacity for global influence.

Canada's trade reflects this long-standing foreign policy (Figure 5.5).

Manufacturing: Alive or Dead?

Manufacturing in Canada has suffered from a steady decline over the last decade. Global competition is central to this demise. Manufacturing employment has declined sharply, from over 900,000 workers in 2000 to 753,000 in 2016 (Dragicevic, 2014; Statistics Canada, 2016c). While contracting in the Canadian economy, manufacturing still plays an important role. For example, in 2015, manufacturers employed 1.7 million people, or 10 per cent of

TABLE 5.4 The Orientation of Canadian Trade: From North American to Global?

Date	Continental Orientation
1965	The Auto Pact between Canada and the United States creates a continental market for automobiles.
early 1970s	Failed "Third Option."
1989	The Canada–US Free Trade Agreement (FTA), designed to integrate the two economies, comes into effect.
1994	North American Free Trade Agreement (NAFTA) broadens the geographic area of the FTA to include Mexico, but to the disadvantage of Canada and the United States.
2001	Auto Pact ends because of a WTO ruling that it discriminated against foreign companies.
2006	Softwood Lumber Agreement sets the terms for lumber exports to the US.
2016	Softwood Lumber Agreement ends in October amid protectionist and anti-free trade political climate in the US.

Date	Global Orientation
1997	Free trade agreements are reached with Israel and Chile; from then to 2016, bilateral agreements are made with Peru, Columbia, Panama, and South Korea.
2002	Kyoto Protocol commits Canada and 38 other countries to cut their emissions of greenhouse gases between 2008 and 2012 to levels 5.2 per cent below 1990 levels.
2011	Canada withdraws from the Kyoto Protocol.
2014	Negotiations are completed on Comprehensive Economic and Trade Agreement (CETA) with the European Union but the complicated process of approving CETA took until November 2016.
2015	Trans-Pacific Partnership agreement is reached among 12 Pacific Rim countries—Canada, the US, Mexico, Peru, Chile, Brunei, Singapore, New Zealand, Australia, Japan, Vietnam, Malaysia— but full ratification, if accomplished, can take several years. In November 2016, President-elect Trump declared that, under his administration, the US would not sign the TPP.
Pending	Negotiations are underway for trade agreements with China and India.

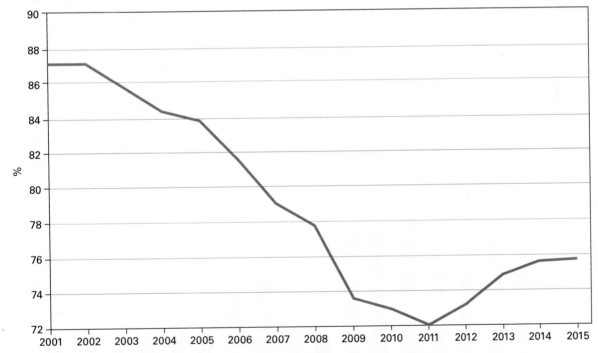

FIGURE 5.5 Share of Canadian exports to United States, 2001–2015

Trade with the United States has declined but the US remains by far the most important trading nation for Canada. Canada is anxious to sell more products to the US but Ottawa also wishes to diversify its export trade.

Sources: Statistics Canada (2011, 2016d).

Canadian workers. Canada is not unique in the retreat of manufacturing; rather, this downhill trend is common to other advanced industrial countries. The reasons vary from country to country but the common factors for Canada are:

- Canada has higher wages than most other countries.
- Automation has displaced workers.
- Outsourcing sees jobs move overseas.
- Offshore relocation moves jobs out of the country.
- A high Canadian dollar (until 2014) has made exports more expensive.

An indication of hard times for manufacturing over the last 15 years is revealed by the 9.6 per cent of Canadian workers employed in manufacturing in 2015 compared to 15.5 per cent in 2000 (Figure 5.6). Glen Hodgson, Chief Economist at the Conference Board of Canada (2015), expressed his view of the state of manufacturing in these words:

Reports of manufacturing's demise have been greatly exaggerated. . . . This decline . . . largely reflected China's emergence as an economic powerhouse and its role as the assembly workshop to the world; the rapid rise in commodity prices and the related soaring of the loonie; the 2008–09 financial crisis and recession; and the tepid global and U.S. recovery.

Hodgson added: "The future of Canadian manufacturing is like running an endless marathon to stay ahead of the competition—but running in the marathon is far better than the alternative of dropping out."

In 2014, however, the federal government believed that the lower Canadian dollar would cause manufacturers to increase production and export much of that increase to the United States. In spite of the advantage of a lower Canadian dollar, the tepid US economy has shown little capacity to absorb more products from Canada.

The heart of Canadian manufacturing lies in the automobile and auto parts industries. The Auto Pact (1965) made Canada an important manufacturing country and provided the Big Three manufacturers a decided advantage in the single market of Canada and the United States. Unfortunately for Canada, two events took that advantage away. First, NAFTA (1994) brought Mexico into the North America market. Mexico, with its much lower wage rates, soon attracted automobile manufacturers. Under these circumstances, Canada's automobile industry lost ground to Mexico. In 2000, Canada's share of the North American vehicle production was 17 per cent while Mexico's share was 11 per cent. Over the next 14 years, Canada's share dropped to 14 per cent while Mexico increased its share to 20 per cent (Figure 5.7). Second, in 2000 the World Trade Organization, in response to complaints by Japanese and European automakers, ruled that the Auto Pact—a sector-specific bilateral free trade

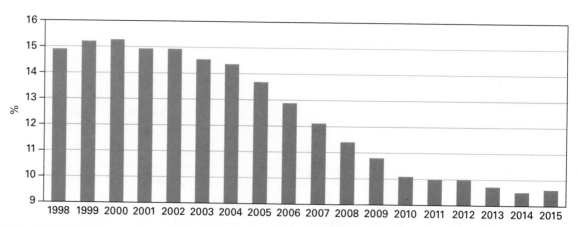

FIGURE 5.6 Manufacturing's share of total employment, 1998–2015

Sources: Bernard (2009: Chart B); Statistics Canada (2012a, 2015c, 2016c).

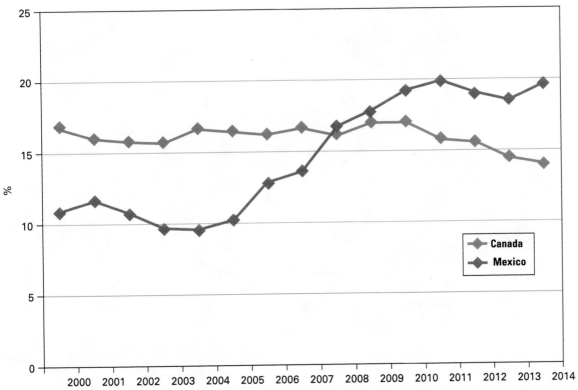

FIGURE 5.7 Canadian and Mexican percentage shares of North American vehicle production, 2000–2014 (including heavy-duty trucks)

Source: Keenan (2015).

agreement—gave Canada an unfair trade advantage with the US, and consequently the Auto Pact was terminated in early 2001.

For discussion of the auto industry in Ontario, see the section "Ontario's Economic Anchor: The Automobile Industry" in Chapter 6, page 192.

The Wave of the Future: The Knowledge-based Economy

Economists Peter Drucker (1969) and Daniel Bell (1976) and geographer David Harvey (1989) were among the first scholars to recognize a knowledge-based economy. From Bell's perspective, the **knowledge-based economy** offers hope for advanced industrial countries like Canada to offset a decline in manufacturing activities caused by globalization of trade and thus keep the unemployment

rate low. Success depends on integrating scientific knowledge, in the form of technology and innovation, into new products and services that can successfully compete internationally.

Ford (2015: xii), on the other hand, fears that this technology-driven economy and its robotic machines will not reduce but increase unemployment because human workers will be replaced by robots and androids. Already, robots are effectively completing repetitive tasks in the manufacturing sector (Photo 5.3). As Ford (2015: 7) explains, "we are, in all likelihood, at the leading edge of an explosive wave of innovations that will ultimately produce robots geared toward nearly every conceivable commercial, industrial and consumer task." Ford argues that Western society needs a *new economic paradigm* because, in the robotic age, extremely high rates of unemployment coupled with an unacceptably wide income inequality gap will be the norm; to meet this economic and social challenge, Ford calls for a guaranteed income (Ford, 2015: ch. 10).

THINK ABOUT IT

Innovations take many forms. Canada's Arctic benefits from innovations such as the multi-beam echo sounder technology that measures the depth of the ocean and creates a detailed image of the topography of the seafloor. Such collaborative technology is helping the Canadian Hydrographic Service prepare Canada's claim to the Arctic Ocean seabed. See Chapter 11 for a fuller discussion.

Photo courtesy of Robotiq

Photo 5.3 In this photo, automation engineers program a robot to tend a CNC (Computer Numerical Control) machine-tool that is used in manufacturing. Robotic machine tending frees floor workers from repetitive tasks and usually increases productivity and safety of the workers

Information Society and Innovative Clusters

An information society functions within a knowledge-based economy. Within such a society, a **creative class** exists that places a high priority on innovative and scientific research. Such research creates new products that transform society: the potential impact of an electric car on city design and greenhouse emissions; biotechnical innovations that have led to higher-yielding grains; application of green technology (e.g., green roofs) to city buildings, thus making large cities more livable places.

Innovative clusters are not spread evenly across the country. Instead, they tend to locate near major universities and in larger cities. Britton (1996: 266) stated that "Canadian urbanization is the key to understanding the location of technology-intensive activities." Marc Busch takes this idea further. His

answer is "clusters" (Atkin, 2000: C1). A cluster is a place where institutions, companies, and individuals have a commitment and enthusiasm for innovative technological research along with the capital necessary to develop and market new products. Innovative clusters often are anchored around a university or a public research agency like the National Research Council.

Richard Florida (2002b, 2012) adds to this cluster idea by contending that members of the creative class want to live in "interesting" cities. He proposes that these creative people are the drivers of urban and regional growth and the concept of "clustering," namely, that the creative class is attracted to cities with a cultural soul, where a wide variety of artistic and cultural events flourish and where ethnic diversity and tolerance of non-mainstream lifestyles are well established (Florida, 2002a, 2002b, 2005, 2008, 2012). Florida further claims that innovative firms, public research centres, and universities

Photo 5.4 Members of Black Lives Matter Toronto marching in the Pride Parade as an honoured group. At one point during the parade they staged a sit-in, bringing it to a halt for 30 minutes while their spokesperson outlined their set of demands, including barring police floats from future events.

situated in culturally rich cities have an advantage in recruiting and retaining a highly creative labour force (Florida and Jackson, 2010; Florida et al., 2010, Hracs et al., 2011).

As the centre of the Canada's music, film, and sports world, does Toronto provide such an "interesting" city? The concept of "interesting," according to Florida and his colleagues, involves world-class events such as the Toronto International Film Festival, which has rocketed Toronto onto the world stage. The Blue Jays, Raptors, Toronto FC, and Maple Leafs offer North American major league sports action, while the Toronto Caribbean Festival and Pride Parade draw tourists and participants from across Canada, the United States, and other countries. Controversy and drama fit into "interesting" cities. For instance, the 2016 Pride Parade was embroiled in controversy when members of the Toronto chapter of Black Lives Matter (Photo 5.4) stopped the parade they had been invited to participate in to demand change.

Regional Economies

Canada's economic face has a different look in each of the six geographic regions. Industrial structure by employment type provides one measure of the spatial divide. At the national level, looking at the primary, secondary, and tertiary sectors provides an overall picture of Canada's industrial structure, with the tertiary sector accounting for 78 per cent of all workers, the secondary sector 18 per cent, and the primary sector only 4 per cent (Table 5.5). The industrial structures for the six regions, on the other hand, reflect the core/periphery model with Canada's two core regions, Ontario and Québec, having higher percentages of workers in the secondary sector than the national average but the lowest in the primary sector. Western Canada, on the other hand, with its strong agriculture and resource activities, scores highest in the primary sector at 9.8 per cent of its labour force engaged in agriculture and resource extraction. The dominance of the tertiary sector is

TABLE 5.5 Industrial Structure of Canada and Regions, Percentage of Workers by Industrial Sector, 2015

Economic Sector	Ontario	Québec	British Columbia	Western Canada	Atlantic Canada	Territorial North	Canada (%)
Primary	1.7	2.2	3.3	9.8	5.2	15.0	3.7
Secondary	18.4	19.1	16.5	18.1	15.7	2.0	18.3
Tertiary	79.9	78.7	80.2	72.1	79.1	83.0	78.0
% total	100.0	100.0	100.0	100.0	100.0	100.0	100.0
Total workers (000s)	6,923	4,097	2,306	3,516	1,109	6	17,947

Source: Adapted from Statistics Canada (2016c).

found in all six regions, reflecting the evolution of Canada's economy into an advanced industrial one. As a frontier region, the Territorial North is a special case because of its lack of manufacturing jobs and its extremely high proportion of public employees, which pushes its percentage of tertiary workers to 85 per cent.

Canadian Version of the Core/Periphery Model

From a geographic perspective, the core/periphery model is adaptable to Canada's economic landscape. In this spatial version, Canada's six geographic regions are placed within the four categories: the core, the rapidly growing, the slow-growing, and the resource frontier. Within this version, regions have the possibility—at least in theory—of shifting their position within these four categories. For example, with rapid industrialization of economies of Pacific Rim countries, trade and investment with British Columbia could shift it from a rapidly growing region into a core region. With BC already leading the five provincial regions in terms of the percentage of labour force in the tertiary sector, perhaps this process is already underway.

The *core* represents the focus of economic, political, and social activity in the national economy. Most people live in the core, which is highly urbanized, diverse, and industrialized. Much of its population growth stems from in-migration rather than natural increase. Its capital city has a high capacity for innovation and economic change. Innovations and economic advances are disseminated outward from this capital city to other cities in the core and then through the national urban hierarchical system to places outside of the core. In applying this theoretic model to Canada, two geographic regions, Ontario and Québec, best represent Canada's core.

Beyond the core, the hinterland portrayed in this theoretical spatial model contains three types of areal units. The three types differ by the level of their economic development. The *rapidly growing region* has a rich resource base that is well on the road to full economic development. Of the three types of areal units, only the rapidly growing one has the potential to grow and diversify its resource base. The reason is simple. Both capital and labour flow into this area to take advantage of the rich resource base and its thriving urban centres. While initial development occurred in the primary sector, the region's economy focuses on the processing of its resource base and its service industries, including high-technology firms. In many ways, this region follows Innis's staples theory, which sees such regions evolving into diversified economies. British Columbia and Western Canada already have core-like areas and, in time, could evolve into core regions outside of Central Canada.

The economy and population growth in *a slow-growing region* are trailing behind the performances of the core and the rapidly growing region. For the slow-growing region, economic growth is stalled, unemployment is high, and out-migration is common. Often, because it is as an "older" region, resource development has passed its prime. Without sufficient diversification of its economy and with an aging population, the regional economy is treading water. Atlantic Canada is an example of a slow-growing region.

While the first two types of hinterland regions have undergone economic development, the *resource frontier* is still in the early process of such development. Far from the core, its resources are costly to develop and therefore often remain untouched. Few people live in this frontier and resource companies are just beginning to penetrate into this remote area. As energy and mineral deposits are discovered, the prospects for economic growth are enhanced. Even so, its small population and weak transportation system point to little prospects for regional diversification. The Territorial North is Canada's last resource frontier and the homeland of northern Indigenous peoples.

Provincial Unemployment Rates

Canada's unemployment rate is just under 7 per cent. Yet, some regions have higher rates and others lower rates. Unemployment rates provide additional evidence to support the contention that theoretical core/periphery regions are reflected in Canada's six geographic regions. Before 2015, western provinces exhibited lower unemployment than other provinces, with Saskatchewan and Alberta having the lowest rates (Table 5.6). The crash of oil and commodity prices let the air out of the resource

sector's balloon, resulting in an increase in the 2015 unemployment figures for oil-rich provinces—Alberta's rate rose from 4.7 per cent in 2014 to 7 per cent; Saskatchewan went from 3.8 per cent to 5.5 per cent unemployment; and Newfoundland and Labrador climbed from 11.9 per cent to 14.4 per cent. By 2015, only Ontario, British Columbia, and Western Canada had unemployment rates below the national average of 7.1 per cent. The big question down the road is whether Ontario will continue to have a strong export-based economy reliant on industrial products being shipped to the United States. If so, then Ontario could replace Alberta as the growth engine of the country and become re-established as the dominant Canadian core region. On the other hand, if oil and commodity prices rebound to their 2013 levels, then Alberta would regain its title as the growth engine of Canada.

Equalization Payments

The Canadian government has long recognized that economic opportunities vary across the country. Equalization payments to the provinces from Ottawa are designed to ensure a reasonable degree of economic equality across the country because some provinces ("have-not" provinces) are less able to meet their fiscal obligations than others ("have" provinces). The three territories have similar programs. Thus, the distribution of federal equalization payments divides the country into "have" and "have-not" regions. In this way, the equalization program should support the core/periphery model. The logical expectation would be that the two core regions, Ontario and Québec, and possibly the rapidly growing regions of Western Canada and British Columbia would qualify as "have" regions while the slow-growing region (Atlantic Canada) and the resource frontier (Territorial North) would qualify as "have-not" regions. Such is not the case for the two core regions.

Since a formal equalization program first began in 1957, Québec has benefited from equalization payments, and payments to poorer provinces were enshrined in the Constitution Act, 1982 (s. 36[2]) "to ensure that provincial governments have sufficient revenues to provide reasonably comparable levels of public services at reasonably comparable levels of

TABLE 5.6 Provincial Unemployment Rates, 2007, 2009, 2014, and 2015 (percentage of total labour force)

Province	2007	2009	2014	2015
Saskatchewan	4.2	4.8	3.8	5.5
Alberta	3.5	6.6	4.7	7.0
Manitoba	4.4	5.2	5.4	5.9
British Columbia	4.2	7.6	6.1	6.7
Ontario	6.4	9.0	7.3	6.7
Québec	7.2	8.5	7.7	7.8
New Brunswick	7.5	8.9	9.9	8.9
Nova Scotia	8.0	9.2	9.0	8.6
Prince Edward Island	10.3	12.0	10.6	7.8
Newfoundland and Labrador	13.6	15.5	11.9	14.4
Canada	6.0	8.3	6.9	7.1

Sources: Statistics Canada (2009, 2010, 2015b, 2016a).

taxation." Equalization payments today are calculated from a formula that accounts for various provincial revenue streams and provincial populations, and those provinces falling below a national average for provincial revenue per capita receive payments from Ottawa. Ontario began receiving such annual payments in the 2009–10 fiscal year. On the other hand, one province in the slow-growing region, Newfoundland and Labrador, acquired "have" status in 2009–10.

Clearly, the equalization program does not follow the core/periphery path perfectly. Or does it? Let us examine the record. Oil revenues caused Newfoundland and Labrador to move from "have-not" status to "have" status in 2009–10 while Ontario, because of the global recession and economic slowdown in the US, hit a rough patch, causing its revenues to fall. For a variety of reasons, Québec's economy has always performed just below the national average, but the province also has the advantage of low revenues from its Crown corporation, Hydro-Québec. Accordingly, Québec's total revenues used to calculate its equalization payments are low. Memorial University economics professor Jim Feehan (2014: 1) explains Québec's low electricity revenues:

A more fundamental and long-recognized problem [with the calculation of equalization payments] is the incentive for provinces receiving equalization payments to underprice the water-rental rates they charge for hydro production. Lowering water-rental rates has the effect of reducing provincial hydro revenues, which can entitle those provinces to larger equalization payments, while benefitting residents with cheaper hydro rates.

In 2016–17, the federal funds allocated for the equalization program totalled almost $17.9 billion. Much of this went to Québec ($10.0 billion), followed by Ontario ($2.3 billion), Manitoba ($1.7 billion), New Brunswick ($1.7 billion), Nova Scotia ($1.7 billion), and Prince Edward Island ($380 million) (Department of Finance, 2015). On a per capita basis, PEI received the highest allocation

TABLE 5.7 Federal Equalization Payments to Provinces, Fiscal Year 2016–2017

Province	Total Equalization Payment	Payment Per Capita
Prince Edward Island	$380 million	$2,574
New Brunswick	$1,705 million	$2,260
Nova Scotia	$1,722 million	$1,874
Manitoba	$1,736 million	$1,328
Québec	$10,030 million	$1,205
Ontario	$2,304 million	$166
Total	$17,880 million	

Notes: (1) All provinces, including the "have" provinces, apart from equalization payments, received $1,366 per capita in 2016–17 through the Canada Health Transfer and Canada Social Transfer. (2) Equalization payments to the three territories, called Territorial Formula Financing, are based on a different formula and, on a per capita basis, are much higher.

Source: Calculated from Department of Finance (2015).

of equalization funds from Ottawa (Table 5.7). Ironically, Newfoundland and Labrador, with by far the highest unemployment rate, did not receive any equalization payments.

Debt Loads in Canada

With sagging economies and the lure of low interest rates, all levels of government have increased the size of their debt. The argument for such public spending was to combat the 2008–9 recession and to boost a sluggish economy. Why not, so the argument goes, invest in much-needed infrastructure and even social programs while the interest rates are so low and unemployment is high? However, even low interest rates cannot dismiss the consequences of that debt—specifically, government spending on interest payments to service previously accumulated debt is taking a larger and larger share of current revenue. Put differently, serving the debt takes away the capacity of governments to help low-income Canadians and to improve Canada's economic competitiveness through low business taxes. In 2015–16, the net debt held by the federal government had reached a record high of nearly $619 billion; the highest provincial debts were those in Ontario ($296 billion) and Québec ($187 billion) (Royal Bank, 2016: 11). Atlantic Canada's debt was $43 billion, British Columbia's $40 billion, and Western Canada's $25 billion. In the current economic situation, these debt levels are expected to increase each year. The Royal Bank estimated that the 2016–17 net debt for Canada would approach $650 billion; Ontario would reach $308 billion and Québec $189 billion. However, the greatest percentage increase is expected to take place in Western Canada. Western Canada's debt for 2016–17 was projected at $43 billion while Atlantic Canada rises to $46 billion and British Columbia to $43 billion (Royal Bank, 2016: 11).

SUMMARY

With the global economy facing challenges on many fronts, the nation's growth is languishing. World leaders are calling for more trade to break out of the "low growth trap" (Mann, 2016). Adding fuel to the fire, the International Monetary Fund (IMF) warned it was likely to downgrade its forecast for global economic growth again this year (IMF, 2016). Prospects for Canada, then, are not bright for the foreseeable future. Canada's economic future depends on the resurgence of the global economy, a return of the super cycle, and an upsurge in its exports. The United States and, to a much lesser degree, China hold the key for Canada to again enjoy a robust economy.

Until then, Canada's economy will remain trapped in the grey zone between a recession and a rapidly growing economy. There are several challenges for the years to come:

- Can Canada chart a new direction by embracing a knowledge-based economy?
- What are the implications of such a structural change for Canada and its six geographic regions?
- Can Canada's resource economy regain its footing?

In the coming chapters, the implications for each region will be explored.

Challenge Questions

1. What is the Fourth Industrial Revolution?
2. Why does trade define Canada's economy?
3. If China's economic boom is over, what is the future for the super cycle and resource-rich regions?
4. What exactly is the knowledge-based economy and is it an attainable goal for Canada?
5. Does robotics technology present good or bad news for Canada's labour force? If bad news, would you support a guaranteed income for those unemployed even if it meant higher income taxes?
6. What impacts on Canada's economy did the Bank of Canada Governor, Stephen Poloz, outline when he "characterized the commodities price rout as a 'seismic shift'"?

Essay Questions

1. Over 40 years ago, Daniel Bell predicted a vastly different post-industrial society. Its dimensions would include the spread of a knowledge class, a shift in the economy from manufacturing to services, and an expanded role for women. Canada and other advanced societies are chasing that prediction with varying

degrees of success. Fast-forward to 2015. Are Florida and Spencer correct that "the Canadian economy is built on two distinct models with two distinct geographies. Natural resources drive the West, while knowledge and creativity propel development in the East"?

References:

Bell, Daniel. 1976. *The Coming of the Post Industrial Society*. New York: Basic Books.

Florida, Richard, and Greg Spencer. 2015. "By Ignoring the Knowledge Economy, Canada Is Taking a Step Backward." *Globe and Mail*, 7 Oct. At: http://www.theglobeandmail.com/report-on-business/rob-commentary/by-ignoring-the-knowledge-economy-canada-is-taking-a-step-backward/article26688832/.

2. Globalization has transformed Canada's economy by diminishing the country's manufacturing sector and by expanding its resource sector. Now that the global economy is slowing, economic historian Michael Bliss argues that Canada, "whose wealth is still highly dependent on the returns we can get from selling our natural resources, is very vulnerable. In a time of price depression, our wealth bleeds away." Mount an argument that defeats his thesis that our wealth bleeds away in times of price depression.

Reference:

Bliss, Michael. 2016. "Canada Beware: We Are Suffering a Great Depression in Commodity Prices." *Globe and Mail*, 15 Jan. At: http://www.theglobeandmail.com/opinion/echoes-of-the-dirty-thirties-no-quick-fix-for-commodity-prices/article28197585/.

Further Reading

Ford, Martin. 2015. *Rise of the Robots: Technology and the Threat of a Jobless Future*. New York: Basic Books.

Rose, Gideon. 2016. "Introduction: Fourth Industrial Revolution." 20 Jan. *Foreign Affairs*. At: https://www.foreignaffairs.com/articles/2016-01-20/introduction.

Schwab, Klaus. 2015. "The Fourth Industrial Revolution: What It Means and How to Respond." *Foreign Affairs*. 12 Dec. At: https://www.foreignaffairs.com/articles/2015-12-12/fourth-industrial-revolution.

According to the World Economic Forum (WEF), the world is in the throes of a new revolution, the Fourth Industrial Revolution. At the WEF's 2016 annual meeting, this subject was explored by leading social scientists and then published in a special edition of the prestigious *Foreign Affairs* journal. The contributors examine a wide range of topics, including digital fabrication, robotics, and synthetic biology, as well as the consequences for society. In the Introduction to these papers, Rose declares (2016) that the Fourth Industrial Revolution is "ripping up the rule book for people, firms, and governments alike." In this provocative collection, Klaus Schwab (2015) presents an overall view of the magnitude of this epic change by stating that:

> We stand on the brink of a technological revolution that will fundamentally alter the way we live, work, and relate to one another. In its scale, scope, and complexity, the transformation will be unlike anything humankind has experienced before.

Schwab acknowledges that its speed of change, both economic and societal, has no historical precedent. On the bright side, Schwab believes that this Fourth Industrial Revolution, like those preceding it, has the potential to raise global income levels and improve the quality of life for populations around the world as talent, more than capital, represents the critical factor. On the dark side, Schwab warns that greater inequalities within society are not only possible but likely.

Could the Fourth Industrial Revolution contain the seeds of social discontent, violent protests, and even the world rebellion that Marx predicted? Martin Ford weighs this matter of massive unemployment and social unrest by concluding that the potential for such a disruption to society is highly likely. To avoid such a catastrophe, Ford calls for national governments to provide a basic income guarantee that, in his opinion, would alleviate poverty, mitigate income inequality, and maintain social order (2015: 261).

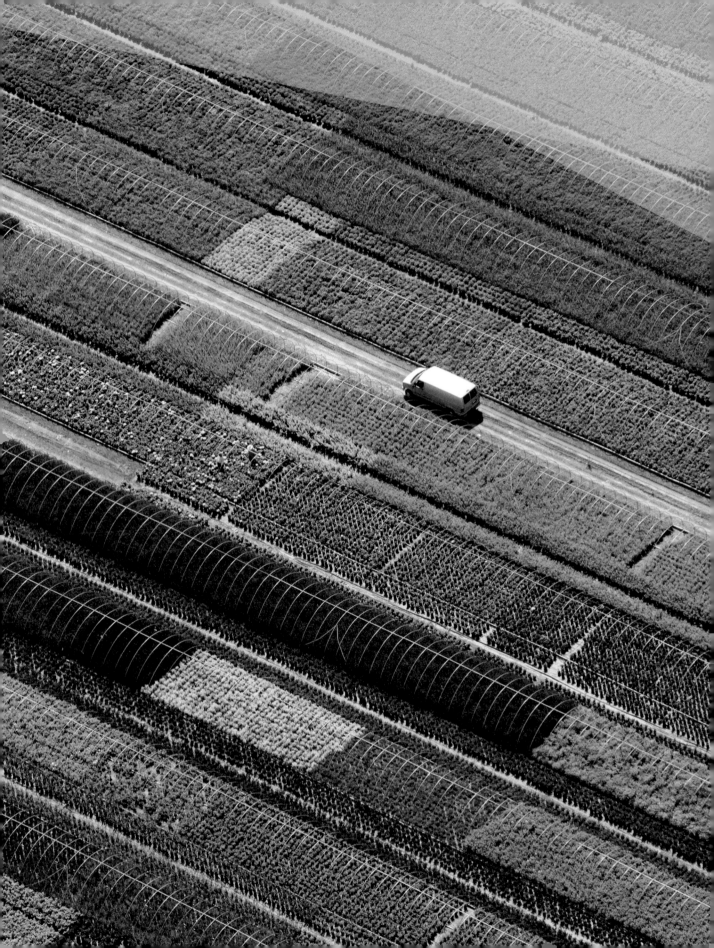

6 Ontario

Introduction

Ontario's prominent position within Canada and North America was badly shaken by the global meltdown that began in late 2008. The province's recovery has been slow and erratic. Manufacturing was hit hard and its future is still unclear. Yet, the basic factors that propelled Ontario to the leading position within Canada have not changed. In spite of all, Ontario remains the dominant region of Canada. It is, as before, the **heartland** of Canada's population, economy, and culture for English-speaking Canada. While the best days for Ontario's manufacturing-based economy are behind, the shape of the technology-driven economy is slowly coming into focus. For Ontario to prosper and progress into the next decade as well as to regain its title as the economic engine of Canada, bold and innovative measures are necessary.

← A plant nursery in Southern Ontario. Although most Ontarians are employed in service industries such as finance, tourism, and culture, southern Ontario is the second-most important agriculture area in Canada.

dan_prat/Getty Images

Ontario within Canada

Ontario remains Canada's largest province by population and economic output (Figure 6.1). As the leading industrial region of Canada, Ontario is the dominant economic force in Canada and continues its role in the North American economy, largely through the automobile industry. Besides its manufacturing sector, Ontario plays a leading role in the financial world and serves as the cultural centre for English-speaking Canada. Even so, the twenty-first century has not been kind to Ontario. In the fiercely competitive global economy, its manufacturing firms have had to compete with foreign imports—some were forced to close while others relocated offshore. The global recession of 2008–9 sent shock waves through Ontario's economy, pushing Ontario into the "have-not" group of provinces that receive equalization payments. Over the next six years, Ontario showed signs of improvement, but

not enough to stop wearing the "have-not" label. At the same time, the advanced economy employing cutting-edge technology has begun to take hold, with automation and robotics playing an ever-increasing role. However, the exact shape of that knowledge-based economy remains somewhat vague.

In the early twenty-first century, Ontario's woes sparked a debate over the future direction of the province's economy. In 2008, two of Canada's leading economists, Don Drummond and Derek Burleton (2008), declared that Ontario was at a fork in the road. In their opinion, Ontario faced two choices: it could remain committed to the manufacturing sector, or it could reinvent itself. The first option would likely result in a slow-growing economy; the second option could lead to an economy driven by high technology and associated with a high economic growth rate. Drummond and Burleton expected the provincial government to take the lead: "With much of Ontario's economic success driven by advantages that no longer exist, a new direction is required. We look to the provincial government to take leadership on this front by developing a vision on where it plans to take the economy down the road."

Since Drummond and Burleton's ominous 2008 report, Ontario has regained its footing and, according to actual and projected GDP per capita figures, the province is following the "Regain Dominance" curve rather than the "Wither" curve shown in Figure 6.2 (Ontario Ministry of Finance, 2015c). Exports from Ontario in 2015—mainly manufacturing products to the United States—reached $197 billion, up significantly from $126 billion in 2009, thus providing additional evidence for the region's recovery (Ontario Ministry of Finance, 2016b). Milke and Chassin (2016) express a less optimistic view. They argue that Ontario is falling into the trap of slow growth and high unemployment because of the province's growing debt, exacerbated by deficit spending, high taxation, and rising energy costs. Whether right or wrong, these two economists speculated that Ontario's economy is turning into a Québec-type of economy.

Ontario's Ministry of Finance (2015a) forecasts continued growth based on factors outside of the control of Ontario, i.e., a low Canadian dollar, strong US economic growth, and continued low oil prices. However, the minister gives no indication of when Ontario will cease to be a have-not

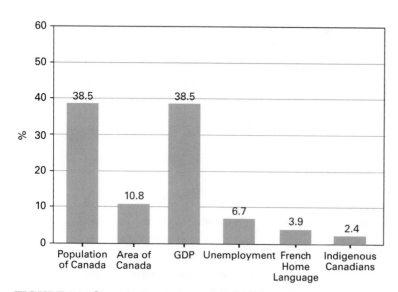

FIGURE 6.1 Ontario basic statistics, 2015

Ontario's share of the nation's GDP and population indicates the province's economic and political strength within Canada. With the lower Canadian dollar, the province's economy has regained some momentum. The good news is that its GDP rose from 36.7 in 2014 to 38.5 in 2015, while its unemployment rate dropped from 7.3 per cent to 6.7 per cent. The 2011 Census of Canada provides the most recent statistical data for French home language and Indigenous population.

Percentages of population, area, and GDP are for Canada as a whole; unemployment, French home language, and Indigenous population percentages are for Ontario. Percentages for French mother tongue and Indigenous Canadians are for 2011.

Sources: Tables 1.1, 1.2, and 5.6.

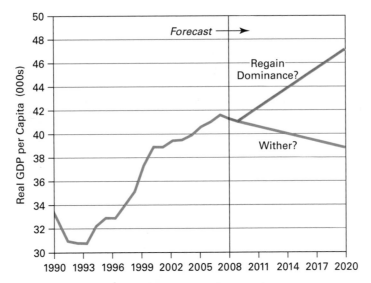

FIGURE 6.2 Ontario's economy to 2020: Which way?

Drummond and Burleton created this graph in 2008 to shock the provincial government into action. Fortunately, Ontario has fol-lowed the "Regain Dominance" curve. By calculating the real GDP/per capita figures for 2009 to 2014 from data published by the Ontario Ministry of Finance, we can see that Ontario has closely followed this line and GDP per capita has climbed from $41,000 in 2009 to nearly $44,000 in 2014. The calculated figures are: 41.0 (2009); 42.0 (2010); 42.7 (2011); 43.4 (2012); 43.6 (2013); 43.9 (2014).

Sources: Adapted from Drummond and Burleton (2008: 1); Ontario Ministry of Finance (2015c).

Photo 6.1 The Rogers Centre is the home of the Toronto Blue Jays. Such high-order cultural and sport facilities are found only in Canada's largest city. The Toronto Raptors, who play their basketball games at the Air Canada Centre, provide another example. Cultural landmarks include the Roy Thompson Hall, the Art Gallery of Ontario, and the Royal Ontario Museum.

TABLE 6.1 Equalization Payments to Ontario, 2009–10 to 2016–17 ($ millions)

2009–10	2010–11	2011–12	2012–13	2013–14	2014–15	2015–16	2016–17
347	942	2,200	3,200	3,169	1,988	2,363	2,304

Source: Department of Finance Canada (2015).

province (Table 6.1). Looking down the road to 2020, Ontario's short-term prospects hinge on four factors: a continued low Canadian dollar compared to the US dollar; a low interest rate to keep annual debt payments manageable; increased exports to the US; and finding a way through unknown waters to a knowledge-based economy.

Ontario's Physical Geography

Ontario is larger than most countries (Figure 6.3), encompassing over 1 million km². Extending over Ontario are three of Canada's physiographic regions

FIGURE 6.3 Ontario

Ontario has the largest economy and population of Canada's six regions, but this region represent a geographic paradox. The contrasts between Southern Ontario and Northern Ontario are extreme. The two sub-regions have very different physical conditions. Over time, two distinct economies have emerged, each with its own spatial pattern of population distribution. While Southern Ontario forms the industrial and population heartland, Northern Ontario is an old resource hinterland. More evidence of this paradox is that Northern Ontario occupies over 80 per cent of the land mass of Ontario but only 6 per cent of the province's population.

Source: *Atlas of Canada*, 2006, "Ontario," at: atlas.nrcan.gc.ca/site/english/maps/reference/provincesterritories/ontario.

(Great Lakes–St Lawrence Lowlands, Canadian Shield, and Hudson Bay Lowlands) and three of the country's climatic zones (Arctic, Subarctic, and Great Lakes–St Lawrence) (Figures 2.1 and 2.4). Manitoba lies to its west, Hudson and James bays to its north, while Québec, on its eastern boundary, is bordered in part by the Ottawa River. This central location within Canada and its close proximity to the industrial heartland of the US have facilitated Ontario's economic development.

Ontario is not a homogeneous natural region. For that reason, it is divided into two sub-regions (Northern and Southern Ontario). This division correlates with its physiographic regions. Accordingly, Northern Ontario consists of the Canadian Shield and Hudson Bay Lowlands while Southern Ontario matches the geographic extent of the Great Lakes–St Lawrence Lowlands that fall within Ontario (Figure 6.4). Each sub-region has a different economy. Northern Ontario has the characteristics of a resource hinterland, while Southern Ontario is the epitome of an agricultural-industrial core.

Northern Ontario stretches across 10 degrees of latitude—from 46°N to nearly 57°N. Fort Severn First Nation is located on the shores of Hudson Bay at 56° 37'N while Sudbury is at 46° 30'N. The Subarctic climate of Northern Ontario has longer and colder

THINK ABOUT IT

Why would higher interest rates hurt the provincial government's capacity to balance its budget?

FIGURE 6.4 Physiographic regions in Central Canada

Central Canada consists of Ontario and Québec. Three physiographic regions are found in Ontario and four in Québec. Canada's most productive agricultural lands, its manufacturing belt, and its core population zone all are located in one physiographic region—the Great Lakes–St Lawrence Lowlands.

winters as well as shorter and cooler summers than those occurring in Southern Ontario. Even along its southern edge at 46°N, short summers make crop agriculture vulnerable to frost damage. In addition to a difficult climate for agriculture, the rocky Canadian Shield has very little agricultural land while the Hudson Bay Lowlands has none. The rugged, rocky terrain of the Canadian Shield has only a few pockets of agriculture where former lakebeds provide the basis for soil development. Climate, soils, and physiography combine to limit agriculture in Northern Ontario.

Southern Ontario, located in the southernmost part of Canada, has Canada's longest growing season. Windsor, for example, is at latitude 42°N and Toronto is close to 44°N. Southern Ontario has a moderate continental climate. This climate is noted for long, hot, and humid summers, warm autumns, short but cold winters, and cool springs. Annual precipitation is about 1,000 mm. The greatest amounts of precipitation occur in the lee of the Great Lakes (Figure 6.5), where winter snowfall is particularly heavy (see Vignette 6.1). The Great Lakes modify temperatures and funnel winter storms into this region. During the winter, this region experiences a great variety of weather conditions. The Niagara Escarpment represents the most significant relief feature.

The section on "Physiographic Regions" in Chapter 2, page 24, especially the figures and tables, provides important background information for Ontario.

THINK
ABOUT IT

Self-driving cars and trucks are coming and their impact on cab and truck drivers will be profound.

Environmental Challenges

Ontario faces two major environmental challenges—air pollution and water pollution. Solutions are costly and require lifestyle changes. Both types of pollution represent the hidden costs of our industrial world.

In Ontario, most air pollution comes from vehicle exhaust. While the number of vehicles continues to rise, the good news is that more efficient engines and the growing number of electric cars have limited the increase in exhaust fumes. While this is a step in the right direction, until Canadians' love affair with the automobile ends, relief from automobile and truck pollution will be slow in coming. After all, the country's vast physical geography and urban sprawl make it difficult for public transit to replace the need of many for individual transportation, and electric-powered vehicles have yet to reach a mass market. Still, the number of electric cars, now just over 8,000 in Ontario, is increasing each year (Hunter, 2016).

Another step in the right direction came in April 2014 when Ontario ceased to produce electricity from coal. A little over 10 years ago, Ontario's coal-fired generating stations produced 25 per cent of the province's electricity. By 2015, nuclear-generated

Vignette 6.1

Ontario's Snowbelts

Ontario's snowbelts are legendary. On the upland slopes facing Lakes Huron and Superior and Georgian Bay, huge snowfalls totalling in the 300–400-cm range occur each winter from November to late March. The uplands on the northeast shores of Lake Superior receive the greatest total snowfall amounts of any area in Ontario, exceeding 400 cm annually. Much of the snowfall in snowbelt areas can be attributed to cold northwest to westerly winds blowing off the lakes and ascending the highlands. As the Arctic air travels across the relatively warmer Great Lakes, it is warmed and moistened. Snow clouds form over the lakes and, once onshore, intensify as the air is then forced to ascend the hills to the lee of the lakes, triggering heavy snowfalls. Areas on the downslope side of the higher ground to the lee of the lakes receive less than half the annual snow totals of the upslope snowbelt areas. For example, Toronto, Hamilton, and other places to the lee of the Niagara Escarpment are snow-shadow regions with winter amounts of 100 to 140 cm. In the snowbelt regions, snowfall accounts for about 32 per cent of the year's total precipitation; but in the snow-sparse area around Windsor and Chatham, the snow contribution is only about 13 per cent.

Contested Terrain 6.1

Cleaner Air versus Higher Electrical Costs

The good news in Ontario's plan to wean consumers away from fossil fuels is that it leads to less pollution and a healthier environment, especially in the heavily populated Golden Horseshoe of Southern Ontario that encircles the western half of Lake Ontario, including the Niagara Peninsula to the south and west of the lake and stretching to Oshawa in the east. The bad news is that the closing of its low-cost coal plants and rejection of a shift to natural gas[1] have resulted in higher electrical costs. Not only does the consumer pay more, but Ontario's already endangered manufacturing industry faces another cost challenge. As Adam White, president of the Association of Major Power Consumers of Ontario, stated: "Ontario has the highest delivered electrical prices for industry in North America, so we need to have a reality check." Industrial customers in 2013 paid about $85 per megawatt hour; this compared to around $40 in the neighbouring jurisdictions of Québec, Manitoba, and Michigan (McCarthy, 2013).

electricity (Photo 6.2) made up nearly 60 per cent of the total output, followed by hydro power at 23 per cent, natural gas at 12 per cent, and wind at 6 per cent (Ontario Energy Board, 2015). Biofuel and solar-produced electricity account for less than 1 per cent. Early in 2016, the Ontario government announced plans to subsidize the purchase of electric cars and to encourage homeowners to switch from natural gas heating to electrical and geothermal heating. The Ontario government's decision to move away from fossil fuels and into higher-cost energy has pushed some Ontarians into what can be termed energy poverty, and also has increased the cost of doing business in Ontario (Green, Jackson, and Herzog, 2016).

With the closing of the coal-burning plants and the Drive Clean program, air quality has improved, especially in the densely populated Golden Horseshoe. Smog, the most visible form of air pollution, is caused when heat and sunlight react with various pollutants emitted by industry, vehicle exhaust, pesticides, and oil-based home products. The good news is that Toronto in 2014 had its first summer free of smog alerts in 20 years, and few smog alerts have occurred since then (Chubb, 2015).

The pollution of drinking water is a serious problem in Indigenous communities across Canada, nowhere more so than in Ontario. Boil-water orders are commonplace. Patrick (2017) describes drinking water on First Nation reserves as "a geography of poor water" forcing band councils to seek water from off-reserve sources and to truck it to the individual homes where the water is stored in a cistern in each house. Unfortunately, this approach, often due to contamination of the water stored in a cistern, too often fails to provide secure drinking water. An example from the Grassy Narrows First Nation[2] in Northern Ontario provides one insight into this troubling situation, as described by Amanda Klasing (2016) of Human Rights Watch:

> The water in the well that supplies her home is contaminated with uranium; [instead,] water trucked in from a local treatment plant to fill a cistern at her house has dangerous levels of a cancer-causing by-product that comes from treating dirty source water.
>
> Exposure to the contaminants found in this water can cause illnesses ranging from gastrointestinal disorders to increased risk of cancer. Knock-on effects—like bathing less when people can't trust their water—include the proliferation or worsening of skin infections, eczema, psoriasis, and other skin conditions.

While the reasons behind such poor performance are complicated, drinking water on reserves falls under the federal government. Ottawa provides 80 per cent of the funding, but the band council is responsible for raising the remaining 20 per cent

THINK ABOUT IT

Smog, so common in larger cities, is a product of the Industrial Revolution when the burning of fossils fuels began. Now the principal source of smog comes from exhaust fumes from cars and trucks. The word "smog" is a combination of "smoke" and "fog."

Contested Terrain 6.2

Urban and Industrial Needs versus Precious Farmland

Urban and industrial Ontario is expanding. In its search for more land for people and industry, Ontario is eating into the limited stock of high-quality agricultural land. While such farm land is scarce, its market value is low compared to the same land used for housing and business. Consider the 2011 proposal by Highland Companies. Highland wanted to convert some of Ontario's most valuable farmland, with soil rated as Class I, into a quarry to extract Amabel dolostone. The farmland lies in the Township of Melancthon, just an hour northwest of Toronto. The potential value of the extracted Amabel dolostone exceeds $6 billion. Farmers in the area protested and, given the strong opposition, Highland sold its interest to Bonnefield Financial, a farmland investment and property management company. In turn, Bonnefield leased the land to local farmers who want the land to increase their economies of scale. In this case, potatoes won the day over a much more valuable mineral.

as well as for building and maintaining the drinking water system on each reserve and training the operators. Band councils, however, often do not have the financial resources and technical expertise to provide safe and reliable water systems. The bands face an additional challenge in the scattered nature of housing on reserves, making the delivery of drinking water by a pipe network from a clean water source extremely expensive. As a result, boil-water orders are widespread.

Courtesy of the Ontario Power Generation

Photo 6.2 The Pickering Nuclear Generating Station, located in Southern Ontario just east of Toronto, is one of the three active nuclear plants in the province. The facility employs nearly 4,500 people and produces about 14 per cent of Ontario's power. In January 2016, the provincial government approved a plan to continue operation of the plant until 2024.

Ontario's Historical Geography

When the American Revolution began in 1775, Ontario—except for the French settlement around Detroit (established 1701)—was a densely forested wilderness inhabited by a few fur traders and First Nations peoples. In 1760, British troops took control of Fort Detroit and the surrounding settled area. After losing the American colonies, Loyalists moved north to Nova Scotia and New Brunswick, while others re-settled in the Eastern Townships of Québec. A smaller number, perhaps as many as 10,000 Loyalists including members of the Six Nations who had fought alongside British troops, settled on land in what is today Southern Ontario, thus colonizing the wilderness area that later became known as Upper Canada. In 1784, Britain created the Haldimand Tract for its Indigenous allies and this land followed the Grand River and totalled 385,000 hectares (Darling, 2007). Over the next several decades, American, British, and European newcomers came in search of land suitable for farming. By 1812, the wilderness forest landscape of Southern Ontario had been transformed into a sparsely populated British agricultural colony. The War of 1812 effectively ended the influx of American settlers into Upper Canada, but the flow of settlers from the British Isles, especially Ireland and Scotland, continued. By 1851, Canada West (as Upper Canada

FIGURE 6.5 The Great Lakes Basin

Created 10,000 years ago at the end of the last continental glaciation, the Great Lakes form the largest freshwater system on the planet. The Great Lakes are under pressure, with declining water levels and constant pollution from human sources. The water levels of the Great Lakes have declined over the last 50 years due primarily to the warming climate (International Great Lakes Study, 2012). This decline translates into stranded cottage docks, the loss of wetlands, and receding shorelines. The Great Lakes Water Quality Agreement expresses the commitment of Canada and the United States to restore and maintain the chemical, physical, and biological integrity of the Great Lakes Basin.

Source: Based on Atlas of Canada, 2004, "Great Lakes Basin," at: atlas.nrcan.gc.ca/site/english/maps/reference/provincesterrritories/gr_lks/index.html.

had become with the Act of Union of 1841) had reached a population of 952,004, 86 per cent of whom lived in rural settings (Statistics Canada, 2007a). At the time of Confederation, the mixed forest found in the Great Lakes Lowland was gone, replaced by thousands of small farms. Some turned further north to try their luck in the few pockets of arable land within the Canadian Shield, but few were successful. Others migrated to Manitoba or to growing towns and cities in Ontario. The majority of the migrants from rural Ontario were lured to the last great American land rush, open prairie lands west of the Mississippi River.

When Canada West joined Confederation in 1867, it was renamed Ontario (Figure 3.4). At that time, the geographic extent of Ontario was about 100,000 km²—a fraction of its present size—but as Canada acquired more territory from Great Britain, Ontario and Québec obtained some of these new lands (Figures 3.5–3.7). They had little immediate value for economic development and settlement, however, because they were carved from two physiographic regions (the Canadian Shield and the Hudson Bay Lowlands) that were far from markets and had little or no agricultural potential. Since

Vignette 6.2

The Welland Canal

The Welland Canal connects Lake Ontario and Lake Erie, allowing ocean-going ships to enter the heart of North America. To avoid the Niagara River and its huge falls, the first canal-builders faced the daunting task of constructing a canal across the Niagara Peninsula, a distance of some 44 km. The first canal, opened in 1829, was dug by hand. A series of locks made from hand-hewn timbers connected a series of creeks and lakes, and horses and oxen pulled the boats along the canal by a tow line. As the size of ships increased, the original canal proved inadequate and a new canal was built in 1845. Within 40 years, even larger ships required a third renovation, which was opened in 1887. The present canal was completed in 1932. In 1973, to bypass the city of Welland, a new channel was constructed, for which a series of lift locks were needed to overcome a difference in elevation of nearly 100 m between Lake Ontario and Lake Erie. The Welland Canal has been part of the St Lawrence Seaway since 1959 and is operated by the St Lawrence Seaway Management Corporation.

Designpics/All Canada Photos

Photo 6.3 The Welland Canal is a strategic link between Lake Ontario and Lake Erie that provides a water route around Niagara Falls. To accommodate ever-increasing traffic, the lock system was divided into two at several places, as shown in this aerial photograph. In 2006, approximately 40 million tonnes of goods passed through these locks. The three leading products were grain, iron ore, and coal.

Confederation, the borders of Ontario have been extended three times, greatly increasing the geographic size of the province, but not its agricultural lands. The first expansion occurred in 1874 when Ontario's boundaries were pushed northward to about 51°N and westward towards Lake of the Woods. Ontario's second expansion, in 1889, ended the bitter contest between Manitoba and Ontario for the land around Lake of the Woods. At the same time, Ontario's northwest boundary was adjusted to the Albany River, which flows into James Bay, gaining Ontario access to James Bay. In 1912, the final boundary modification occurred when the District of Keewatin south of 60°N was assigned to Ontario and Manitoba. As a result, Ontario extended its political boundary to the northwest, stretching from Manitoba to Hudson Bay at the latitude of 56° 51'N. Through these boundary adjustments, Ontario reached its present geographic extent of 1 million km^2.

At the time of Confederation, the economic essence of Ontario was its fledgling industrial base. Transportation routes played a key role, especially the Welland Canal, which facilitated low-cost transportation (Vignette 6.2). At that time, most manufacturing activities depended on water power, so most industries were located near a stream or river. In 1879 the National Policy of Prime Minister Macdonald came into effect by imposing high tariffs on imported manufactured goods, which allowed manufacturing in Southern Ontario to flourish.

The National Policy and its impact on Ontario and the rest of Canada is discussed in Chapter 5 under the heading "The National Policy and the Birth of an Industrial Core," page 153.

Library and Archives Canada/C-034334

Photo 6.4 In 1794, York became the capital of Upper Canada. Despite its political status, this frontier village remained on the western edge of British settlement that stretched westward from Lower Canada along the north shore of Lake Ontario. By 1812, York had only 700 residents. This painting (dated 1804) illustrates a group of houses strung along the shore of Toronto Bay. Beyond this narrow strip of cleared land lies the original forest of Southern Ontario.

Library and Archives Canada/C-001669

Photo 6.5 "View of King Street [Toronto], Looking East" (1835) by Thomas Young. At the time of this painting, York had just been renamed Toronto and had a population of nearly 10,000.

Aboriginal Territory within Ontario

Ontario has 126 First Nations holding Aboriginal territory, known as reserves, determined through treaty negotiations between government and individual tribes. Most were classified as "unnumbered" and took place before 1923. Three numbered treaties—3, 5, and 9—cover portions of Northern Ontario. The first land grants to First Nations peoples took place during the days of British North America, beginning with the Haldimand Proclamation of 1784, which assigned land along the Grand River to the Iroquois who fought alongside the British in the American Revolution (Figure 6.6). In 1850, the two Robinson treaties were completed; they covered large areas east and north of Lake Huron and north of Lake Superior.

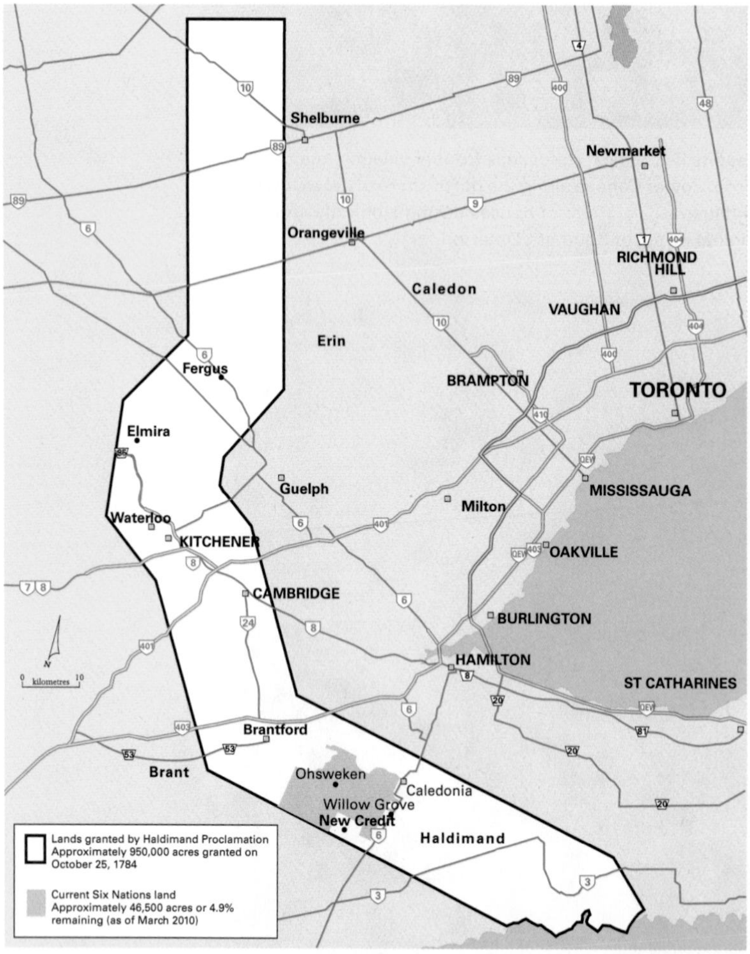

Figure 3.10, "Historic treaties," page 89, shows the location of the numbered and unnumbered treaties that blanket Ontario.

In Ontario, First Nations were granted land hundreds of years ago. When disputes arise today, reaching an agreement is challenging because the "facts" are buried in time (see Vignette 6.3). The slow pace of resolution is frustrating to Indigenous Canadians and two land disputes (Ipperwash and Caledonia) have led to violent protests by First Nations from the Kettle and Stony Point and Six Nations reserves. In the Ipperwash dispute, the facts are relatively clear: land from Stony Point was taken in 1942 to serve as a military training camp, named Camp Ipperwash. After the war, the land was supposed to have been returned but the Department of National Defence decided to keep the camp—adjoining Ipperwash Provincial Park, established in 1936—to train cadets. Promises from Ottawa to return the land were not fulfilled. By 1993, the Stony Point First Nations people were utterly frustrated with the repeated failure of Ottawa to act on its promises and in September 1995 Indigenous protestors moved into Ipperwash Provincial Park, the alleged site of sacred burial grounds, where a confrontation with the Ontario Provincial Police took place, ending in the shooting of an unarmed Kettle and Stony Point protestor, Dudley George, by an Ontario police sniper. In 2003, the Ontario government asked Justice Sidney Linden to conduct a public inquiry into the circumstances surrounding the 1995 death of Dudley George, including the role of Premier Mike Harris. In May 2007, Justice Linden issued the Ipperwash Inquiry Report, in which he concluded that Harris had not explicitly ordered the Ontario police into the Ipperwash Provincial Park to remove the Indigenous protestors. At the same time, Justice Linden called for the immediate return of Camp Ipperwash to the Kettle and Stony Point First Nation. Jim Prentice, the federal Minister for Indian Affairs and Northern Development, responded by stating that, "We'll do something immediately" (National Post, 2007). That didn't happen.

FIGURE 6.6 The Haldimand Tract

Source: Six Nations Land Resources. Based on a map at www.sixnations.ca/LandsResources/HaldProc.htm.

The provincial park was returned to the Chippewas of Kettle and Stony Point by the Ontario government at the end of 2007 with the understanding that the province and the First Nation would jointly run the park, but the Chippewas closed the 56-hectare park. At that time, the Ontario government transferred the land to the federal government, which alone has the power to add it to the reserve. Finally, under a new federal government, negotiations to return the land to the First Nation were successfully completed in April 2016 with the signing of an agreement that returned all of the land and included $95 million in compensation. The agreement "specifies that work will be done to ensure that the land . . . is safe and environmentally sound." This will mean clearing the land of unexploded devices from more than 50 years of military use of First Nation land (Mehta, 2016).

Specific land claims by Indigenous groups are not usually as "straightforward" as the Ipperwash claim. The Caledonia dispute exemplifies the complexity of some claims. An outline of the historical evolution of the Six Nations claim to a 40-hectare parcel owned by a land developer at Caledonia, Ontario, near Hamilton, suggests why, in many instances, settlements have been achieved at such a slow rate (Vignette 6.3). The basis of the Six Nations claim goes back to the original Haldimand Grant of 1784 and land surrenders in the eighteenth and nineteenth centuries. History is not clear on these issues. While the protest finally ended, negotiations between the Six Nations and the federal government are at an impasse since the federal government, in 2009, rejected the $500 million claim of the Haudenosaunee/Six Nations, leaving its offer of $125 million on the table.

THINK ABOUT IT

What is a fair price for land? Canada's offer of $125 million as a financial settlement for the four outstanding Six Nations claims falls short of the $500 million counter-offer by the Six Nations. Should the two sides simply split the difference and move on?

Vignette 6.3

Timeline of the Caledonia Dispute

Eighteenth Century

1784

The British Crown allows the Six Nations (Iroquois Confederacy) to "take possession of and settle" a strip of land nearly 20 kilometres wide along the Grand River, from its source to Lake Erie, totalling about 385,000 hectares; called the Haldimand Grant. The governor of Québec, Frederick Haldimand's intent was to provide land for settlement to loyal Iroquois who had fought beside the British in the American Revolution.

1792

Upper Canada's lieutenant-governor, John Graves Simcoe, reduces the grant to the Six Nations by two-thirds, to 111,000 hectares.

1796

The Six Nations Confederacy grants its chief, Joseph Brant, the power of attorney to sell some of the land and invest the proceeds.

Nineteenth Century

1850

The Crown passes a proclamation setting out the extent of reserve lands on both sides of the Grand River—about 19,000 hectares agreed to by the Six Nations chiefs.

(continued)

Twentieth Century

1992

Henco Industries Ltd purchases 40 hectares of land near Caledonia and names it the Douglas Creek Estates.

1995

The Six Nations disputes the ownership of this Crown land.

Twenty-First Century

2005–6

Henco Industries purchases land for its Douglas Creek Estates housing project. The following year, a group of Six Nations members occupies the housing project, erecting tents, a teepee, and a wooden building. In a search for a compromise, the Ontario government buys out Henco's interest in the disputed property for $15.7 million, thus maintaining Crown ownership of this disputed land.

2007

The federal government enters negotiations with the Six Nations to resolve the historic and current land claim disputes. Canada makes an offer of $125 million to compensate the Six Nations for four outstanding historic claims based on nineteenth-century land surrenders known as Grand River Navigation Company investment; Block 5 (Moulton Township); Welland Canal flooding; and the Burtch Tract. As well, Ottawa compensates Ontario for $26.4 million for the province's costs incurred as a result of the occupation near Caledonia and the province's purchase of the land.

2008–2014

In 2008, Canada receives a formal counter-offer of $500 million from the Six Nations. The following year, Canada rejects the claim for $500 million and restates its offer of $125 million. As a result of the inability of the two parties to breach this gap, negotiations ceased. By mid-2014, the federal government continued to refuse to seek a negotiated settlement, merely calling on the Ontario government to make sure police protect the people of Caledonia.

2016

A different developer, Empire Communities, pursues a 3,500-unit community development along the Grand River over the objections of the Haudenosaunee Confederacy (the traditional Six Nations government).

Adapted from CBC News (2006); INAC (2009); Keith (2014); Moro (2016).

Ontario Today

Canada's centre of gravity—as measured by economic performance and population size—remains in Ontario. Yet, Ontario is no longer the "strong man" of Confederation. The last 10 years have been hard, forcing Ontario to accept equalization payments.

During those years, the high Canadian dollar dampened exports, but recent data show exports increasing from a low of $126 billion in 2009 to nearly $200 billion in 2015 (Ontario Ministry of Finance, 2016b). Has Ontario turned the corner thanks to a low Canadian dollar? Along these lines of thinking, two facts stand out. First, just over 80 per cent of Ontario's 2015 exports were destined for the United States, and vehicles and parts made up nearly 35 per cent of those exports. Second, this increase in exports has been largely due to an upswing in vehicle and parts exports to the United States (Ontario Ministry of Finance, 2016b).

These mixed signals—rising exports and continued dependence on equalization payments—suggest that Ontario is "treading water." To regain its status as Canada's engine of economic growth, Ontario must confront the question posed by Drummond and Burleton in 2008: How can Ontario reinvent itself and move from an emphasis on *basic* manufacturing to *advanced* manufacturing? This path lies in the application of technology to all economic activities, and is made easier by what can be called the "Ontario advantage."

See the sections "Trade Agreements" and "Manufacturing: Alive or Dead?" in Chapter 5, pages 161 and 162.

The Ontario Advantage

Ontario, with a majority of Canada's creative wealth, as reflected in its universities and provincial/federal research facilities, is well placed to succeed in the knowledge-based economy. Indeed, if Richard Florida (2002, 2012) is correct in thinking that the creative class (which includes the so-called knowledge-based workers) want to live in "interesting" cities, then that relationship reinforces the concentration of these firms in such urban places. As the centre of the Canada's music, film, and sports industries, Toronto provides such an interesting city (Florida and Jackson, 2010; Florida et al., 2010, Hracs et al., 2011). The best example perhaps is the Toronto International Film Festival, which has become one of a handful of truly major film festivals in the world. The enthusiastic response to the Toronto Raptors hosting the National Basketball Association (NBA) All-Star Game and its many surrounding festivities in 2016 is another example of how Toronto has risen on the global popular culture stage, not least because of the Raptors' widely admired Nigerian-born president and general manager, Masai Ujiri, and the Toronto-born pop music superstar, Drake, who serves as the Raptors' "global ambassador."

Adding to the cosmopolitan nature of urban Ontario, Canada's multicultural policy and immigration record have made those cities, but especially Toronto, special on the world scene. As an open, pluralistic, and tolerant city, Toronto functions as a global city where acceptance of others, while not perfect, is a step above other places (Photo 6.6). Overall, urban Ontario underscores Ontario's advantage.

In "Information Society and Innovative Clusters," Chapter 5, page 166, Richard Florida's theory is discussed within the broader context of the information/knowledge society; his "creativity" thesis is examined in "Further Reading" in this chapter.

Photo 6.6 Less than a week after the US presidential election in November 2016, racist, white supremacist, anti-immigration "alt-right" posters appeared in public parks and on street corners in Toronto. Many citizens quickly complained and in short order the Toronto police had removed all of the signs (Siekierska, 2016).

Ontario's Industrial Structure

An industrial structure, defined by the percentages of the workforce employed in the three sectors of an economy, provides insight into the nature of that particular economy and allows for comparisons with other economies.

For discussion of the primary, secondary, and tertiary sectors of the Canadian economy, see Chapter 5, "Industrial Structure," page 151.

Most Ontario workers are employed in the tertiary sector (Table 6.2), which accounted for close to 80 per cent of all employed persons in 2016. On the other hand, Ontario's secondary sector was just short of 19 per cent, leaving the primary sector with the tiny remainder. From 2005 to 2016, the tertiary sector gained over 5 per cent while the secondary sector lost 5 per cent. These sector trends are expected to continue, with the tertiary sector perhaps reaching 85 per cent and the secondary and primary sectors dropping to 14 per cent and 1 per cent by 2021. This trend is not unique to Ontario; it is occurring in all developed countries and therefore can be interpreted as one measure of the evolving nature of national and regional economies.

The distinguishing feature for Ontario lies in its secondary or manufacturing sector. The reason is simple: the size of Ontario's secondary sector, while at just under 19 per cent of all employed persons

THINK ABOUT IT

While the future lies in the technological revolution, two questions remain unresolved. How will the advanced economy generate more jobs? How will it lead to a more equitable distribution of the wealth generated from these gains?

THINK
ABOUT IT

Is the theory valid
that wages in de-
veloping countries,
including Mexico,
will eventually
reach the level of
those in developed
countries, or is it
more likely that
wages in de-
veloped countries
will fall in the
"race-to-the-
bottom" syndrome?

in the province in 2016, forms a much larger proportion than found in the other five geographic regions. On this basis, Ontario's industrial structure confirms the province as the manufacturing heartland of Canada as well as a core region within the Canadian version of the core/periphery model.

But all is not well in the manufacturing world. Ontario is caught in a global shift as manufacturing activities move to other countries with lower wages. In Chapter 5, the process of industrialization, as described by Rostow and Schwab, provides a detailed account of this historic process and Canada's place within that process. An analysis of Ontario's current economic situation points to the need for a cutting-edge knowledge-based economy with a highly trained workforce, supported by innovative companies and the state, to produce more sophisticated products and export them to other countries.

Ontario remains Canada's heartland of manufacturing. With just over 750,000 employed in manufacturing in 2016, Ontario accounts for almost 45 per cent of all manufacturing jobs in Canada and 11 per cent of the jobs in Ontario (Statistics Canada, 2016c). Yet, employment in this industry has declined sharply from over 900,000 workers in 2000. At the same time, the percentage of workers in manufacturing jobs as a part of Ontario's total employment has dropped from 15.8 per cent in 2000 to 10.8 per cent in 2016 (Dragicevic, 2014; Statistics Canada, 2016c). This downward trend in manufacturing employment, as noted above, is common to other advanced industrial countries. The reasons vary from country to country but globalization's dark side leads to job loss and dampens wages in the manufacturing industry. Factors common to Ontario are:

- automation;
- outsourcing;
- offshore relocation;
- high Canadian dollar (to 2014) relative to other national currencies, especially that of the United States.

Until 2014, globalization brought a double whammy to Ontario. Manufacturing companies left Ontario to set up their operations in countries with lower costs of doing business, leaving their highly paid Canadian workers out of work. One example was the 2012 closure of the Caterpillar assembly plant in London, Ontario. The closure of this plant was a result of the seemingly relentless "race to the bottom" by global companies to move manufacturing jobs to those countries with low wages, few benefits, weak labour laws, tax concessions, and weaker environmental protections.

In Ontario, both the primary and secondary sectors are losing ground to the tertiary sector. One explanation for this trend is that machines are replacing more workers in these sectors than in the tertiary sector. Take agriculture as an example. Classified as a primary activity, highly mechanized agriculture has relatively few employees compared to the value of its output. Placed in a national context, Southern Ontario is the second-most important agriculture area in Canada, after Western Canada, but its impact on employment is slight. Even so, temporary workers from foreign countries are widely employed in the more labour-intensive forms of agriculture, such as garden crops and fruit.

TABLE 6.2 Ontario Industrial Sectors by Number of Workers, 2005 and 2016

Industrial Sector	Workers 2005	Per cent 2005	Workers 2016	Per cent 2016	Percentage Difference
Primary	128,000	2.0	114,000	1.6	-0.4
Secondary	1,509,000	23.6	1,313,000	18.7	-4.9
Tertiary	4,761,000	74.4	5,581,000	79.7	5.3
Total	6,398,000	100.0	7,008,000	100.0	

Notes: (1) Each sector is composed of a series of industrial activities. For instance, in June 2016 the secondary sector consists of three industries and employees: utilities (51,200 employees), construction (515,700), and manufacturing (746,100). (2) Statistics Canada revises these figures each month: the total number of workers in October 2016 was 7,018,700. (3) The percentage increase from 2005 to 2016 was 9.5%.

Adapted from Statistics Canada (2006, 2016c).

See Chapter 5, "Industrial Structure," page 151, for discussion of how technology has been central to each historic shift in Canada's industrial structure.

Technical Spearheads

Each region has its technical spearheads. These spearheads represent major economic thrusts for the region and also illustrate the unique character of the region as it moves into the knowledge-based economy. For Ontario, automobile manufacturing has been an economic anchor for more than a half-century, along with Canadian banks. Automobile manufacturing continues to play a key role in Ontario's economy, though in a diminished capacity. Robotic welding, for instance, has lessened the need for welders in the manufacturing process for automobiles, while the introduction of digital banking systems has lessened the need for bank tellers and financial planners in the financial sector. Along the entire economic front, advances in technology are pushing firms into the knowledge-based economy. No sector is excluded. In the primary sector, for instance, agriculture, forestry, and mining all have seized on the opportunities for greater efficiency derived from employing various forms of advanced technology. Consequently, the need for workers in these fields is reduced and productivity has increased. In a sense, it is the old story of industrialization where capital, in the form of investment in mechanization, replaces labour. Now, that capital takes the form of various types of advanced technology. In the case of the banking industry, the major banks have invested several billion dollars in digital technology to make this transformation. On the other hand, the federal and Ontario governments provide capital to the automobile companies in the form of grants for two reasons:

- as an incentive to expand operations or to remain in Ontario;
- in an effort to promote automotive research[3] in Ontario.

A Digital Future for Banks

Canadian banks have chosen a digital future, and signs of that future exist already. For instance, the Bank of Montreal is experimenting with operating small branch banks without human tellers (Shecter, 2015). Brian Porter, the CEO of Scotiabank, described this paradigm shift in banking: "We're in the technology business. Our product happens to be banking, but largely that's delivered through technology" (Berman and Kiladze, 2016). Leading the charge into the digital world of banking in Canada, the CEO of Laurentian Bank, François Desjardins, called the traditional banking model "obsolete." In late September 2016, Laurentian Bank, based in Montréal, announced plans "to close dozens of branches and cut about 300 staff" (Berman, 2016b).

Two things are clear. First, banks are on the path to become more efficient and more profitable. Second, this path means fewer bank branches and employees.

Where does that digital banking system appear on the Canadian landscape? One place is Toronto. As the financial capital of Canada, Toronto is home to the five largest banks—Royal Bank of Canada, Toronto-Dominion, Canadian Imperial Bank of Commerce, Bank of Montreal, and Bank of Nova Scotia. (The sixth-largest bank, the National Bank of Canada, is headquartered in Montréal, where the Bank of Montreal (BMO) maintains its official legal headquarters although the BMO chairman, its president, and many senior executives are located in Toronto.)

Automation has hit the bank employees and branch banks hard. As more and more customers find online banking convenient, the need for branch banks and their tellers decreases. For example, Royal Bank of Canada reduced its workforce by an average of 1,200 employees a year from 2010 to 2015. Most cuts occurred with tellers, whose numbers fell over this five-year period from 11,000 to 6,000 (Berman, 2016a). For banks and their bottom line, a digital banking system is more profitable than the traditional banking model.

The Global Reach of Financial Institutions

Canadian banks ceased to serve just the Canadian market some 40 years ago. The Bank of Nova Scotia is the most international of the Big Five, with an extensive presence in the Caribbean and Latin America. By 2015, Scotiabank operated in 56 countries. The Bank of Montreal and Toronto-Dominion have

THINK ABOUT IT

If advanced technology displaces workers in the tertiary sector, where will they go? Note that McDonald's has automated its ordering system, thus reducing the number of its employees taking orders.

THINK ABOUT IT

Workers are also consumers, and they rely on their wages to purchase products and services. If workers are replaced by robots, who will buy the goods?

a strong foothold in the US. This international strategy parallels the move by CN back in the 1980s.[4] At that time, CN jumped at the opportunity to become a North American railway system (Figure 5.4). Canadian banks move into the global economy for three reasons. First, the Canadian banks are strengthened by their presence in a larger market. Second, the rapid growth of the middle classes in developing countries provides an opportunity for banks to expand their customer base at a more rapid pace than in Canada. Third, the digital banking system, once defined in Canada, can be transferred to other countries at a very low cost.

Table 5.5, "Industrial Structure of Canada and Regions, Percentage of Workers by Industrial Sector, 2015," page 168, provides an overview of each region's employment pattern.

Ontario's Economic Anchor: The Automobile Industry

The automobile industry was the heart and soul of manufacturing activity in developed countries (Dicken, 1992). This is no longer the case, as developing countries have taken over that role. Consequently, Ontario faces the question: does this industry have a future in Canada?

The answer is complicated and the future, while seeming to be heading in one direction, can change course. However, we do know that:

- Robotics technology and government support have kept assembly and parts firms alive, though with a smaller workforce.
- Expansion is highly unlikely because investment for new plants gravitates to low-wage countries such as Mexico (Figure 6.7).

Moreover, the experts do not see a bright future for automobile manufacturing in Canada. One automobile analyst predicts a bleak future for Ontario's automobile industry:

"The bad news is behind us but there's no good news in front of us," reckons Dennis

DesRosiers, an industry analyst. He predicts that Canada will continue gradually to lose its production base until "somewhere between 2030 and 2040 we'll be Australia," where the last carmaker with a factory in [that] country is scheduled to close its gates by 2018. (*The Economist*, 2015)

But what are the chances for transforming the Ontario industry into a high-tech automobile research hub that constantly improves the assembly-line production model? As it turns out, not bad. General Motors got the ball rolling in June 2016 when it announced plans for up to 750 new research jobs in Ontario for the development of systems related to driverless vehicles (Flavelle, 2016). Now, if other companies follow GM's lead to invest in high-tech automobile research, a revitalized form of advanced manufacture could emerge. Yet, how can we attribute so much to a revitalized industry based on one high-tech hub? The answer lies in economic momentum where spinoff effects squeeze more out of the original investment, which can lead to additional jobs and global status.

While the auto industry has moved into robotic forms of manufacturing, it is feeling the cold chill generated by the dark side of globalization. Canada's automobile manufacturing industry was sheltered by the Auto Pact and the Canada–US Free Trade Agreement, but first NAFTA and then a 2001 WTO ruling[5] unravelled this protection. The application of modern technology, such as robotic welding,[6] and substantial federal and Ontario grants and loans have stemmed the tide in the short run, but questions remain regarding the longer run.

Without a doubt, the automobile industry that once drove the Ontario economy has dwindled (Table 6.3), and, consequently, Ontario is hurting. One sign is the loss of nearly one-third of those employed in this industry over the last decade, due partly to lower production and partly to replacement of workers by robotic machines (Figure 6.8). The low Canadian dollar has offered a short-term ray of hope, but the long-term prognostication for Canada's automobile industry, as well as for the auto industries of the European Union and the United States, is grim. The global shift of this industry, like

THINK ABOUT IT

Can industries such as the automobile and airplane manufacturers survive without government support?

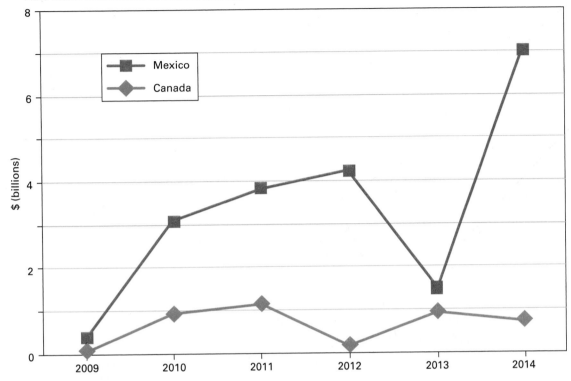

Auto maker investments in Canada and Mexico

FIGURE 6.7 **The heart of the problem: Mexico attracts more investment than Canada**

Keenan (2015).

the textile industry in previous decades, is moving inevitably to low-wage industrializing countries. For example, Mexico is now the favourite place for automobile investments (Figure 6.7). With Toyota's 2015 decision to relocate its Corolla production to Mexico, Ontario's automobile industry was back on

its heels, but, as noted above, GM's decision in 2016 to pursue innovative research may have set Ontario's auto industry on a new course.

See Table 5.4, "The Orientation of Canadian Trade: From North American to Global?" page 163, for more on the Auto Pact and the FTA.

THINK
ABOUT IT

What are the
implications of
driverless vehicles
by 2020?

Contested Terrain 6.3

The Bailout of Chrysler and GM: Sound Public Policy?

At the time of the major recession of 2008–9, Canada and Ontario were loath to see the core of the Canadian manufacturing sector—motor vehicles—die. In 2009, Canada and Ontario intervened in the marketplace to provide financial assistance to Chrysler Canada (US$3.8 billion) and General Motors Canada (US$10.6 billion).

Was this sound public policy by the federal and Ontario governments, which are now calling for a knowledge-based economy? Public investments might have been better placed with the technology industry, such as Nortel (which filed for bankruptcy protection in January 2009 and subsequently was wound down) and Blackberry (originally Research In Motion, which was unable to compete successfully against Apple's iPhone and has foundered since 2009).

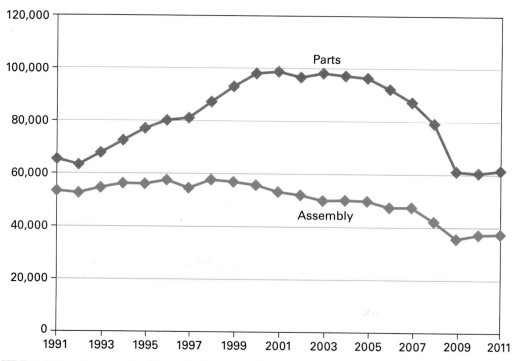

FIGURE 6.8 Employment in Canada's automobile industry

In the 1990s, employment in the automobile industry reached its peak. Its decline in the first decade of the twenty-first century is a remarkable reversal of good fortune for auto workers and their industry. In the next decade, further contractions are likely—unless, of course, workers' wages adjust to the global reality—but who wants wages at the level of Mexico and other developing countries?

Sources: Canadian Auto Workers Union (2012: Figure 1), from Statistics Canada, CANSIM Table 281-0024, reprinted with permission from Canadian Auto Workers Union (CAS-Canada); Industry Canada (2015b, 2015c).

Breakthrough?

The first solid sign of progress towards the advanced economy in Ontario's automobile industry came from General Motors (GM). In an unexpected announcement in June 2016 by GM, Ontario was selected as the innovation hub for innovative research on the automobile of the future. Attracted to the cosmopolitan environment of Greater Toronto, GM will design, engineer, and conduct innovation studies at Oshawa's Innovation Hub and at Markham's Automotive Software Development Centre (Keenan, 2016a). GM Executive Vice-President Mark Reuss described Ontario's advantages: "We selected Canada [Greater Toronto] for this expansion because of its clear capacity for innovation, proven talent and strong ecosystem of great universities, startups, and innovative suppliers" (Wingrove, 2016).

This decision by GM, encouraged by Ottawa, is definitely a step in the right direction. As an additional bonus, GM has signed a four-year agreement with its union workers and committed just over a half-billion dollars to its Oshawa and St Catharines assembly plants (Macaluso, 2016). As discussed in Chapter 5, the Auto Pact greatly benefited Ontario, but much was lost when NAFTA gave Mexico access to the North American market. GM's investment marks a turning point that could turn Greater Toronto into a global research centre for the automobile of the future and, at the same time, keep Ontario's assembly factories operating.

A second sign of progress for workers came from the September 2016 agreement reached with General Motors. More union workers were hired; wages went up; and benefits expanded. Unifor President Jerry Dias said: "The gains made in this agreement are historic and more than what has been achieved in the past ten years" (Canadian Press, 2016). Not to be outdone, GM of Canada President Steve Carlisle issued a statement that the agreement will position

TABLE 6.3 Ontario Motor Vehicle Production, 1999–2014

Year	Small Cars	Large Cars and Trucks*	Total
1999	1,626,316	1,432,497	3,058,813
2000	1,550,500	1,411,136	2,961,636
2001	1,274,853	1,257,889	2,532,742
2002	1,369,042	1,260,395	2,629,437
2003	1,340,175	1,212,687	2,552,862
2004	1,335,516	1,376,020	2,711,536
2005	1,356,197	1,332,165	2,688,362
2006	1,389,536	1,182,756	2,572,292
2007	1,342,133	1,236,657	2,578,790
2008	1,195,426	882,153	2,077,579
2009	822,267	668,215	1,490,482
2010	967,077	1,101,112	2,068,189
2011	990,482	1,144,639	2,135,121
2012	1,040,298	1,423,066	2,463,364
2013	965,191	1,414,615	2,379,806
2014	913,533	1,480,357	2,393,890
2015	888,565	1,394,909	2,283,474

*This category consists of light-duty vehicles, including large sedans, mini-vans, and pickup trucks, and heavy-duty vehicles such as buses, cargo vans, and armoured vehicles.

Source: OICA (2016).

the automaker's Canadian operations at the "forefront of an industry that is experiencing dramatic transformation and change" (Canadian Press, 2016).

Suddenly, the gloom surrounding the Canadian automobile industry and their workers lifted. While the industry is still under stress, the GM agreement is likely to be duplicated by Fiat and Ford.

Automobile Assembly Plants

Eight automobile assembly plants are concentrated in Southern Ontario where transportation links to the major markets of Canada and the United States are readily available and driving distances are short (Figure 6.9 and Table 6.4). Since the globalization of automobile trade, Canada's competitive advantage has slipped and two plants have closed—the GM plant at Sainte-Thérèse near Montréal (2002) and the Ford plant in St Thomas, Ontario (2011). Other shifts have taken place or are pending—such as GM moving its Camaro assembly operation from Oshawa to Michigan in late 2015 and Toyota's decision to move its Corolla production from Cambridge to Mexico by 2019. Not surprisingly, employment dropped from nearly 60,000 in the 1990s to less than 40,000 by 2010. By 2014, assembly employment was just over 40,000 (Figure 6.8). If this hollowing-out of Ontario's automobile manufacturing continues unabated, then perhaps DesRosiers's dire prediction of the end of such manufacturing in Ontario will take place within the next 20 years (The Economist, 2015).

Automobile Parts Firms

The automobile industry consists of two separate operations: the assembly of automobiles and trucks and the production of their parts. In addition, some manufacturing firms supply semi-processed materials. In Southern Ontario, fabricating firms produce steel, rubber, plastics, aluminum, and glass parts for automobile assembly and parts plants in Canada and the United States. Finally, service firms, ranging from the advertisers and designers to the sales and service staff, manage the finished product. In short, the auto industry is a final-product type of manufacturing, and as such, its added value reaches a maximum.

The automobile parts industry employed almost 100,000 workers from 1999 to 2005 but by 2009 this number fell to 60,000. By 2014, employment in the parts industry had edged upward to 68,078 (Figure 6.8).

By being highly efficient and strategically located, automobile parts firms can operate on a just-in-time principle—auto components are produced in small batches and quickly delivered as needed to their customers. This allows the assembly plants to achieve considerable savings by reducing their inventories, warehousing space, and labour costs.

As well, subcontracting or outsourcing parts had two advantages for automobile companies. First, it allowed manufacturers to concentrate on assembling automobiles, thereby reducing their costs and improving the quality of their product. Second, parts companies were not unionized and therefore had lower wages. This wage differential—and the

THINK ABOUT IT

President Trump could play a wild card that favours Canada. If the US reopens NAFTA, Washington is likely to focus its attention on Mexican automobile exports to the US. If the auto gods are on Canada's side, those restrictions will not affect Canada.

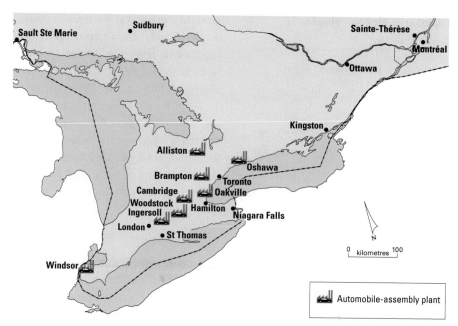

FIGURE 6.9 Automobile assembly centres in Ontario

Asian automakers are capturing more and more of the North American market. Honda and Toyota expanded their Ontario manufacturing primarily because of strong demand for their automobiles in the US. Ontario is an attractive production site in North America for the Japanese manufacturers as a consequence of support from both the federal and provincial governments, easy access to the US market, and a productive, "small-town" labour force.

TABLE 6.4 Ontario Automobile Assembly Plants, 2015

Location	Products
Fiat Chrysler Canada Inc.	
Brampton, Ontario	Chrysler 300; Dodge Challenger; Dodge Charger
Windsor, Ontario	Dodge Grand Caravan; Chrysler Town & Country; Cargo Van
Ford of Canada Ltd	
Oakville, Ontario	Ford Edge; Ford Flex; Lincoln MKT; Lincoln MKX
General Motors of Canada Ltd	
Oshawa, Ontario	Chevrolet Equinox; Chevrolet Impala
Oshawa, Ontario	Buick Regal; Chevrolet Impala; Cadillac XTS
Ingersoll, Ontario	Chevrolet Equinox; GMC Terrain;
Honda Canada Manufacturing Inc.	
Alliston, Ontario	Honda Civic
Alliston, Ontario	Honda CR-V
Toyota, Canada	
Cambridge, Ontario	Toyota Corolla; Lexus RX350; Lexus RX450h
Woodstock, Ontario	Toyota RAV4; RAV4 EV

Note: Windsor's assembly plant will cease producing the Chrysler Town & Country sedan and replace it with the Chrysler Pacifica; Oshawa will lose the Chevrolet Camaro to Lansing, Michigan, while Ingersoll will see the GMC Terrain move to Mexico; Cambridge will see the Toyota Corolla moved to Mexico and replaced with RAV4.

Sources: Industry Canada (2015a). Reproduced with the permission of the Minister of Public Works and Government Services Canada.

savings it provides—is the main reason why General Motors, Ford, and DaimlerChrysler continue to divert work from assembly plants to parts firms. In Ontario, the Canadian-based Magna International has grown into the third-largest auto parts company in North America.

Ontario's Core

Southern Ontario is the most highly industrialized and urbanized area in Canada. By 2016, nearly 13 million people—over 93 per cent of the province's total population—lived in Southern Ontario. The vast majority resided in 13 major cities known as census metropolitan areas (CMAs). Most importantly, Toronto, with a population of just over 6.1 million in 2016, is by far the largest city in Canada and, as a result of its size, contains many higher-order businesses, cultural attractions, and services not found in other cities.

Since urban centres are where innovative firms can take root, they are the future of the Canadian economy. Southern Ontario's urban geography provides an enormous economic advantage and signals its significance within Ontario and Canada. In comparison with the other five geographic regions, Ontario has 15 CMAs (13 of which are located in Southern Ontario); Québec and Western Canada have five each while BC and Atlantic Canada have four each.

Urban growth has varied considerably for these CMAs, and this variation mimics economic growth (Table 6.5). From 2001 to 2016, the fastest-growing cities in Ontario were Oshawa (31.3 per cent) Toronto (30.9 per cent), Guelph (30.4 per cent), Ottawa–Gatineau (24.7 per cent) (although some of its residents live across the Ottawa River in Québec), and Kitchener–Cambridge–Waterloo (23.4 per cent). In contrast, the four slowest-growing cities were Thunder Bay (2.2 per cent) and Sudbury (5.9 per cent) in Northern Ontario, as well as St Catharines–Niagara (8 per cent) and Windsor (9.1 per cent).

Southern Ontario consists of three sub-regions: the Golden Horseshoe, the Ottawa Valley, and southwestern Ontario.

TABLE 6.5 Population of Census Metropolitan Areas in Southern Ontario, 2001 and 2015

Census Metropolitan Area	Population 2001 (000s)	Population 2015 (000s)	Change (%)
Peterborough	110.9	122.6	10.6
Thunder Bay	122.0	124.7	2.2
Brantford	118.1	143.9	21.9
Guelph	117.3	153.0	30.4
Sudbury	155.6	164.8	5.9
Kingston	146.8	169.9	13.6
Windsor	307.9	335.8	9.1
Oshawa	296.3	389.0	31.3
St Catharines–Niagara	377.9	408.2	8.0
London	432.5	506.4	17.1
Kitchener–Cambridge–Waterloo	414.3	511.3	23.4
Hamilton	662.4	771.7	16.5
Ottawa–Gatineau*	1,067.8	1,332.0	24.7
Toronto	4,682.9	6,129.9	30.9
Total	9,012.7	11,263.2	25.0

*Statistics Canada has combined Ottawa, Ontario, and Gatineau, Québec, as a single CMA although these cities exist in different political jurisdictions.

Source: Adapted from Statistics Canada (2007b, 2016b).

The Golden Horseshoe

The Golden Horseshoe obtained its name because of its horseshoe-like shape around the western end of Lake Ontario and its outstanding economic performance over the years. This tiny area of the Great Lakes Lowland forms the most densely populated area of Canada. The Golden Horseshoe is anchored by Toronto and it extends from the US border at Niagara Falls westward to Hamilton (Vignette 6.4), northward to Toronto, and then on to Oshawa to the east. Well over 8 million Canadians live, work, and play in Canada's largest population cluster, and many visitors come either as tourists or on business trips. Accounting for nearly one-quarter of Canada's population, the Golden Horseshoe contains numerous towns and cities, including Toronto, Hamilton, Oshawa, St Catharines, Niagara Falls, Burlington, Oakville, Pickering, Ajax, and Whitby. Toronto is its urban anchor, while Hamilton has been the focus of heavy industry and Oshawa is Canada's leading automobile-manufacturing city.

Vignette 6.4

Hamilton: Steel City or Rust Town?

Hamilton, situated at the west end of Lake Ontario only 50 km from Toronto, is known as Steel City. Unfortunately, the North American steel industry has fallen on hard times and Hamilton is hurting. Only one of Canada's largest steel firms (Dofasco) still exists, as ArcelorMittal Canada, a business unit of the Luxembourg-based steel and mining giant. The defunct Stelco steel mill (Photo 6.7) casts a dark shadow over Hamilton, and in late 2016 US Steel continued to seek an acceptable buyer for the vast plant. Perhaps Trevor Cole's gloomy future for Hamilton may still hit the mark: "As prosperity plumped nearby rivals such as Burlington, Oakville, Mississauga, Kitchener–Waterloo and—especially—Toronto, it skipped Hamilton completely, cruelly, until most of its big-name companies were gone, the stores along Barton Street deteriorated into dark and crumbling shells, downtown became a kind of forbidden zone, and even the Mafia couldn't make any money" (Cole, 2009). Fast-forward to 2016. What are the facts? According to the Conference Board of Canada, Hamilton took advantage of a weaker Canadian dollar and a strengthening US economy in 2015 to boost manufactured exports to the United States (Arcand et al., 2015). But what happens when the Canadian dollar regains its strength?

Photo 6.7 The Stelco steel mill in Hamilton, Ontario.

John Rennison, The Hamilton Spectator

Agriculture plays an important role. Ontario has over half of the highest-quality agricultural land (known as Class I) in Canada. Leading crops by value are corn and soybeans (Ontario Ministry of Agriculture, 2016). The Niagara Fruit Belt is a particularly rich farming area on the narrow Ontario Plain that extends from Hamilton to Niagara-on-the-Lake.

This small agricultural zone contains the best grape and soft-fruit growing lands in Canada, and is home to vineyards that account for most of Canada's quality wines, including the unique ice wine, made from grapes left on the vine (Photo 6.8) and not harvested until sustained temperatures of −8°C or lower are reached, normally sometime from December to February (Wine Country Ontario, n.d.). While the Niagara Fruit Belt occupies a northerly location for grapevines and soft-fruit trees, local factors have more than offset the threat of frost at 43°N latitude:

- **Air drainage** from the Niagara Escarpment to Lake Ontario reduces the danger of both spring and fall frosts.
- The water of Lake Ontario is warm in autumn and its proximity to the Niagara Fruit Belt helps to moderate advancing cold air masses.
- In early spring, the cool waters of Lake Ontario keep air temperatures low, thereby delaying the opening of the fruit blossoms until late spring when the risk of frost is much lower.

While natural factors can adversely affect fruit and grape harvests, urban sprawl is a much more dangerous threat to this unique corner of Ontario. The Greenbelt Act of 2004 protected about 1.8 million acres of forest and agricultural and wetlands around the perimeter of the Golden Horseshoe, but municipal exceptions can occur and the amount of productive farmland continues to be under threat.

Toronto

Toronto is Canada's largest city. As defined as the Greater Toronto Area (GTA), Toronto includes the four regional municipalities that surround it: Durham, Halton, Peel, and York. Falling within Greater Toronto are 16 cities and towns: Pickering, Ajax, Whitby, Oshawa, Clarington, Markham, Richmond Hill,

THINK ABOUT IT

If you were a successful farmer on prime agricultural land, had no children interested in continuing to farm, and were offered millions of dollars by a developer to sell your farm (and the developer had worked out the legal details for making a sale possible), what would you do: Sell your farm and take an early retirement? Continue to farm because you enjoy it and believe this is the ethical thing to do? Look to sell the property at a lower price to someone who will continue to farm?

Photo 6.8 The Niagara Fruit Belt extends about 65 km between Hamilton and Niagara-on-the-Lake, and is one of the major soft-fruit and grape-producing areas in Canada. Most vineyards are located on the slopes of, or below, the Niagara Escarpment. For many years, hardy vines that produced low-quality grapes resulted in poor-quality, inexpensive wine. With the Free Trade Agreement, Canada had to remove its tariffs, making it difficult to compete with foreign wines. Since that time, farmers in the Niagara Fruit Belt have been successful in growing the finest varieties of grapes and have been able to make some of the finest wines in the world.

Vaughan, Aurora, Stouffville, Newmarket, Bradford, Brampton, Burlington, Mississauga, and Oakville.

Toronto is the focus of the province's cultural, demographic, and economic growth. It continues to draw many newcomers, who, in turn, enrich Toronto's culture. Located on the shore of Lake Ontario, Toronto has a spectacular skyline dominated by the CN Tower, which is the third-tallest tower in the world (Photo 6.9). A cluster of universities, including the University of Toronto, York University, and Ryerson University, plus a host of technical colleges, offers the widest variety of programs in Canada.

Within Canada, Toronto sits at the top of Canada's urban hierarchy. One sign of its dominance is the number of corporate headquarters, including the main offices of national and international banks and investment firms. A more conventional sign is that the city offers a range of urban services to residents in the GTA, plus "high-end" ones to those within and beyond the GTA. High-end services include opera presented at the famous Roy Thomson Hall

concert venue; a lively theatre and concert scene; financial transactions at Canada's primary stock exchange, the Toronto Stock Exchange; and top-level North American professional sport teams not found elsewhere in Canada. National and international events add another unique aspect to Toronto.

Toronto is known as a city of neighbourhoods, partly because immigrant groups have clustered in certain areas. Little Italy and Little Portugal are older, well-established ethnic neighbourhoods. More recently, Asian, African, and Caribbean neighbourhoods have emerged. Immigration has had an impact on Toronto's cityscape, including architecturally and in commercial activities designed to meet the demands of these new Canadians. Asian theme malls are common in Canada's largest cities where Asian populations congregate. Toronto's Pacific Mall is the largest Chinese mall in North America.

Toronto Island is a unique neighbourhood that has survived confrontation with city planners who had decided to transform the area, accessible

Photo 6.9 The CN Tower at 553 m high dominates Toronto's skyline on an early summer evening, as seen from Toronto Island. The illuminated structure on the left is the Rogers Centre (originally named the SkyDome), home of the Blue Jays baseball team.

AndresGarciaM/Thinkstock.com

by a short ferry ride from downtown, into public open space. Its geography—essentially a sandbar extending into Lake Ontario that at one time was attached to the mainland—consists of a series of islands, most of which now is dedicated to parkland. However, residential communities exist on two islands (Ward's Island and Algonquin Island).

Ottawa Valley

The national capital is located in the Ottawa Valley and federal government operations are found on both sides of the Ottawa River. The major city in the valley, Ottawa–Gatineau, is not only a major population cluster in Canada, but this politically hybrid city lies on both sides of the Ottawa River in two different provinces. Taken together, Ottawa–Gatineau is the fourth-largest metropolitan area in Canada, and in 2015 its population totalled 1.3 million (Table 6.5). Carleton University and the University of Ottawa are two of the province's major centres of higher education.

Migration from other parts of Canada and immigrants from abroad account for much of Ottawa–Gatineau's population growth. Many are attracted by the employment opportunities offered by the federal government and the business community.

In its early days, the Ottawa–Gatineau region along the Ottawa River was an important juncture for fur brigades—French traders and their Algonquin and Huron partners—that travelled between Montréal and Huronia in the first half of the seventeenth century, but by the mid-1640s Iroquois blockades of the river often stopped the passage of fur traders (Dickason with McNab, 2009: 104–5). By the early nineteenth century, logging and saw-milling were important activities in the Ottawa Valley, but those days, too, are gone. The land used for milling in the Ottawa River by the paper giant Domtar is now proposed for a new urban use, as Chaudière and Albert islands are the focal points of the billion-dollar Domtar Lands Redevelopment project known as Zibi (Photo 6.10). This mixed-use

Courtesy of Windmill Development Group and Dream Unlimited Corp.

Photo 6.10 This artist's rendition shows the bold plan of the Domtar Lands Redevelopment that would transform derelict and contaminated land in the Chaudière area into a world-class sustainable community. The project, called Zibi (meaning "river" in Algonkian) after the Kitigan Zibi First Nation in Québec, straddles both Ottawa and Gatineau. While the two cities are separated only by the Ottawa River, different provincial jurisdictions have resulted in a historic cultural divide. The intent of the plan is to create a community that respects the unique history and culture of both sides of the river while providing a cohesive connection point that draws the two sides of the National Capital Region together.

project entails residential, retail, recreational, and commercial components.

In today's Ottawa–Gatineau, the federal government is the major employer, followed by the high-technology sector. The federal government requires a wide variety of goods and services in its daily operations. This demand provides an opportunity for many small and medium-sized firms in the Ottawa Valley. By locating its departments and agencies in both Ottawa and Gatineau, the federal government has ensured that Ottawa's economic orbit extends to a number of small towns on both the Ontario and Québec sides of the Ottawa River.

Southwestern Ontario

Southwestern Ontario is further south than anyplace else in Canada. The geographic extent of this prosperous agriculture area reaches south to Windsor, the Detroit River, and Lake Erie; Lake Huron forms its western and northern boundary, while the Golden Horseshoe defines its eastern limits. Southwestern Ontario contains the third major urban cluster in the province. The Kitchener CMA (Cambridge, Kitchener, and Waterloo), with a 2015 population of 511,300, and London (population 506,400) are the largest cities. With several major universities, including Waterloo, Wilfrid Laurier, Western (the University of Western Ontario), and the University of Windsor, southwestern Ontario has a strong knowledge-based economy. In particularly, Kitchener, Waterloo, and Cambridge form Canada's "Technology Triangle" where innovative research benefits from exchanges between universities and technology firms.

London provides administrative, commercial, and cultural services for the larger region. It is also the headquarters of several insurance companies, including London Life. Among its economic activities, London is noted for manufacturing, including the production of armoured personnel carriers and diesel locomotives by General Dynamics Land Systems, and, in recent years, its controversial sale of military hardware to Saudi Arabia.[7] London, therefore, has a sound and growing industrial foundation based on insurance, manufacturing, and high-tech

industries. Such manufacturing firms pay relatively high wages to their employees, and consumer spending by these employees supports a strong retail sector.

Automobile assembly plants are located in Cambridge, Ingersoll, Alliston, Woodstock, and Windsor (Table 6.4 and Figure 6.9). Hitachi produces Euclid-Hitachi trucks at its plant near Guelph. Auto parts plants play an important role in the economy of southwestern Ontario while a number of high-tech firms, particularly in the Kitchener CMA, add to the region's economic diversity.

Ontario's Hinterland: Northern Ontario

Ontario's hinterland is the forgotten north of Ontario. Many Northern Ontarians are dissatisfied with their lot. Such grumbling is common in resource hinterlands. Claiming to be isolated and ignored by the provincial government based in Toronto, some of its citizens have called for a new province called Mantario (Di Matteo, 2006). But would that solve this hinterland's problem of slow economic and population growth? Geographers will note that the resource potential of Northern Ontario's physiographic region of the Canadian Shield pales in comparison to the St Lawrence and Great Lakes Lowlands, where the agricultural lands of Southern Ontario are situated. Besides a currently limited resource economy, this northern hinterland has a small but aging population and is distant from major markets. In 2011, Northern Ontario had a population of 775,178—around 6 per cent of Ontario's total population. Looking to the future, Northern Ontario's population will likely remain around 800,000 but its share of the total Ontario population is expected to drop, perhaps to 4 per cent (Figure 6.10).

While the size of its land base is considerable, its two physiographic regions—the Hudson Bay Lowlands and the Canadian Shield—contain little or no agricultural land and offer few opportunities for the industrial development found in Southern Ontario. Its fewer than 800,000 people mostly reside in towns along the two major transportation routes:

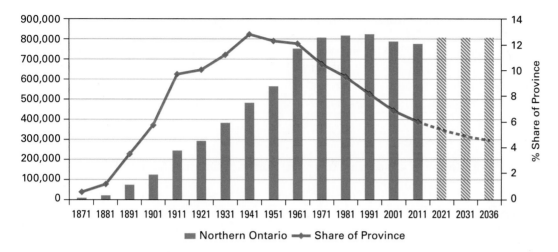

FIGURE 6.10 Historical and projected population in Northern Ontario, 1871–2036

Cuddy (2015: 7).

- The southern route, defined by the CP rail line and the Trans-Canada Highway, connects North Bay with Sudbury, Sault Ste Marie, Nipigon, Thunder Bay, Dryden, and Kenora.
- The northern route, defined by the CN line and a major highway, connects North Bay, Timmins, Kirkland Lake, Cochrane, Kapuskasing, and Nipigon to Thunder Bay.

In addition, this resource hinterland has experienced business closures and population losses over the last decade. The problem is simple: the region is suffering from an economic decline and its aging population reflects that economic demise. Added to that demographic situation, few immigrants settle in Northern Ontario and many of its young people leave for other regions.

Like other slow-growing regions, Northern Ontario's resource base is losing its economic strength for two reasons:

1. The most accessible mineral and timber resources have been exploited, so new resource production is more costly. The rich and varied deposits in the Ring of Fire are a case in point. Its development is stalled for several reasons, including the absence of a transportation link.

2. Resource companies are under pressure to modernize by employing more advanced technology; and this process results in a reduced labour force. Those firms that cannot afford to modernize are often driven from the market by costs or by failing to meet higher environmental standards.

The urban population of Northern Ontario reveals the plight facing this hinterland. Its two largest cities, Sudbury and Thunder Bay, have experienced slow population growth over the past 15 years—and their combined population increase over this span of time accounts for most of the small population gain in Northern Ontario. For example, from 2001 to 2015, these two centres accounted for a population increase of nearly 12,000 (Table 6.6). While population estimates for the smaller centres are not available for 2015, the dismal resource economy has hit these smaller communities and their current population levels likely reflect a continuance of the declines or very slight increases seen between 2001 and 2011 (Table 6.7).

Figure 2.1, "Physiographic regions and continental shelves in Canada," page 25, and Figure 6.4, "Physiographic regions in Central Canada," page 179, delineate Ontario's physiographic regions. Also see "Physiographic Regions" in Chapter 2, page 24.

TABLE 6.6 Population of Northern Ontario CMAs, 2001–2015

CMA	Population 2001	Population 2015	% Change 2001–15
Sudbury	155,601	164,800	5.9
Thunder Bay	121,986	124,700	2.2
Total	277,587	289,500	4.3

Source: Statistics Canada (2012g, 2016b).

TABLE 6.7 Population of Cities and Towns in Northern Ontario, 2001–2011

Centre	Population 2001	Population 2011	% Change 2001–11
Sault Ste Marie	78,908	79,800	1.1
North Bay	62,303	64,043	2.8
Timmins	43,686	43,165	−1.2
Kenora	15,838	15,348	−3.1
Temiskaming Shores*	12,904	13,566	5.1
Elliot Lake	11,956	11,348	−5.1
Kapuskasing	9,238	8,196	−11.3
Kirkland Lake	8,616	7,334	−14.8
Total	243,449	242,800	−0.3

*Temiskaming Shores is the restructured area comprising the three former municipalities of New Liskeard, Haileybury, and Dymond Township.

Sources: Adapted from Statistics Canada (2007b, 2012g).

Northern Ontario's resource economy is based on forests and minerals. Forest enterprises have fared poorly over the last decade due to the changing demand for its products; the very competitive US market where the bulk of forest exports are sent; and the Softwood Lumber Agreement. The mining industry, on the other hand, had a series of very prosperous years until the price for commodities dropped sharply in 2014. Thus, the forest industry is troubled by a declining demand for its products while the mining industry is subject to boom-and-bust conditions. A short review of each industry follows.

Forest Industry

The boreal forest stretches across Northern Ontario, providing the province with most of its 57 million hectares of productive forest area, most of which is classified as softwood. The main species are black spruce, poplar, and Jack pine. From this resource, the forest industry of Ontario produces approximately $10.6

billion of products each year, with most exported to the US. Access to the American market is critical and is controlled by agreements between Canada and the US (Natural Resources Canada, 2015a). The 2006 Softwood Lumber Agreement (SLA) ended in October 2016. Under the 2006 SLA, Canadian lumber firms were allocated 34 per cent of softwood lumber sales in the US market. Each province was allocated a share of those exports based on 2004–5 exports, so Ontario was allotted about 9 per cent of the total Canadian softwood lumber exports to the US (CTV News, 2006). Because of strong opposition from US lumber interests, as reflected by the US lumber lobby filing a complaint in November 2016, it is likely that the next agreement will further limit Canadian softwood lumber exports to the United States.

For a fuller discussion of the Softwood Lumber Agreement, see Chapter 9, "Dependency on the US Market," page 308.

From an economic perspective, the forestry industry remains by far the most important primary industry in Northern Ontario. At least a dozen communities depend on the forest industry, including Kenora, Red Rock, Dryden, Thunder Bay, Terrace Bay, and Kapuskasing. Within Canada, Ontario ranks just behind British Columbia and Québec in forestry employment and production. Ontario's mills produce pulp and paper, lumber, fence posts, and plywood. The pulp and paper industry in Northern Ontario accounts for about 16 per cent of the national production, and Ontario, along with Québec and BC, is a leading exporter of newsprint and pulpwood to the US (Natural Resources Canada, 2015a). In 2013, Canadian forest exports were valued at $28.4 billion with Ontario accounting for 12.6 per cent (Natural Resources Canada, 2015a).

While mill closures have taken place across the country, the Ontario forestry industry faces three issues. First, many mills were built before World War II and continue to use old technology, which results in much higher discharges of toxic wastes into the environment. At considerable cost, most forestry mills have updated their operations to ensure a cleaner and safer natural environment, but some have not. A second problem is the dependency on the US market. The end of the SLA in 2016 and the "America First" trade position of incoming US President Trump have sent shivers through the Canadian softwood lumber industry. The third issue is the rising cost of electrical energy. For many companies, energy has become the make-or-break number on the balance sheet.

Mining Industry

The mining industry is Northern Ontario's second economic anchor. Based on non-renewable resources, the major drawback of such development is its limited lifespan. The exception to that rule is the Sudbury nickel deposit, which has lasted for more than 100 years. Most have a much shorter lifespan, often less than 20 years.

The global economic cycle represents another challenge to the mining industry by creating boom-and-bust conditions. By 2012, high demand and prices resulted in Canada's mineral production soaring to over $50 billion, with Ontario accounting for the largest share of this total at $10.7 billion

or 21.4 per cent (Natural Resources Canada, 2012). By 2014, China's economy was slowing, dragging the demand for commodities down. In 2014, value of production in Ontario was slightly higher ($11 billion) than in 2011 ($10.7 billion) due to gold and nickel (Natural Resources Canada, 2012, 2015c). In 2015, Ontario accounted for 46 per cent of Canadian gold production (Figure 6.11). Other commodity prices dropped, resulting in the value of Canada's mineral production in 2014 slipping to $44.8 billion, with the greatest losses occurring in coal and iron ore.

The Canadian Shield provided ideal geological conditions for the formation of hard-rock minerals such as diamonds, gold, nickel, and copper. In 2014, metallic mineral production in the Canadian Shield in Ontario had a value of $8 billion, with gold, nickel, and copper leading the way. Non-metallic minerals, many of which come from the sedimentary strata in Southern Ontario, added another $3 billion, making the total value of mineral production $11 billion (Natural Resources Canada, 2015c). Among a dozen gold mines, Red Lake near the Manitoba border remains the leading producer. Ontario's first diamond mine (the Victor Mine, Photo 6.11), located in the Hudson Bay Lowlands some 500 km north of Timmins, came into production in 2008 and in 2019 is expected to close (Talaga, 2015). At that point, De Beers will be responsible for decommissioning

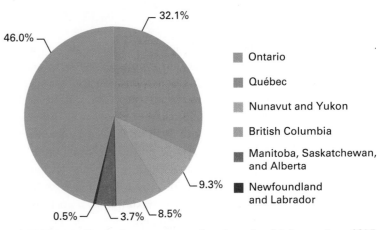

FIGURE 6.11 Canadian mine production of gold, by region, 2015

Preliminary percentages.

Source: Natural Resources Canada (2016).

Photo Courtesy of De Beers Canada

Photo 6.11 Panoramic view of the Victor Diamond Mine.

the mine site; currently, the company is searching elsewhere in the region for a new diamond deposit (Figure 6.12).

The future of mining in Northern Ontario depends on higher commodity prices and the development of the mineralized belt in Northern Ontario known as the "Ring of Fire." This belt contains an estimated $60 billion worth of minerals, including base metals, platinum, and palladium, along with North America's largest deposit of chromite (Figure 6.13). Development in the Ring of Fire has been delayed for several reasons, including the vast size of the required capital investment, lack of accessibility to the site, environmental concerns, and negotiations with First Nations. Ontario has pledged $1 billion towards infrastructure and has called on Ottawa to match this pledge. The All-Season Community Road Study conducted by SNC-Lavalin included four remote northern communities: Webequie First Nation, Eabametoong First Nation, Neskantaga First Nation, and Nibinamik First Nation. Chief Bruce Achneepineskum of Marten Falls First Nation, a fly-in community south of the Ring of Fire, wants to be connected to this proposed road system (Curry, 2016):

The road would bring down the cost of living in remote communities. It would free up money to further construction, build more houses, people could buy more food and it would allow a little bit of freedom for those residents to come in and out of the community and mingle with the outside world.

Bolstering his argument is the fact that, at present, it costs about 52 cents per pound for goods to be transported into his community. On the other hand, some local members of these First Nations have expressed concern about two negative features of the road: the possibility of southern hunters using the road to hunt in the local area; and more drugs and alcohol flooding into their communities.

But resource developments move slowly. Ontario's Mines Minister Michael Gravelle explained that "developing the Ring of Fire is a long-term venture, not a quick fix. . . . the interests of First Nations communities in the region, environmental concerns and the needs of developers all have to be balanced off" (Brennan, 2015). However, the key is much higher commodity prices.

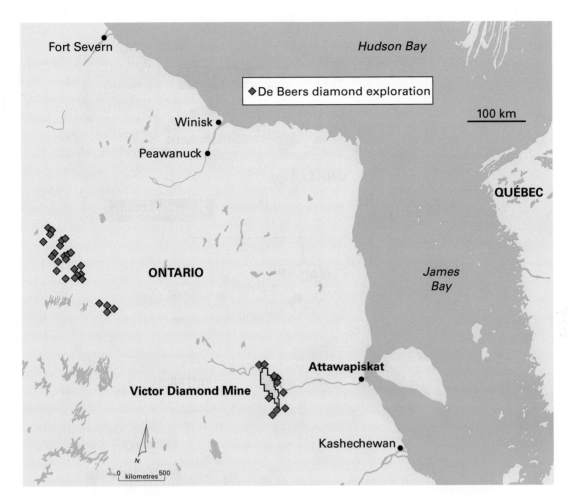

FIGURE 6.12 De Beers diamond explorations in the Hudson Bay Lowlands

Source: Talaga (2015).

Indigenous Communities in Northern Ontario

Many First Nations members reside in Northern Ontario. Most live in the cities and towns found in the more developed area close to the railway and highway routes. For example, Thunder Bay's population consists of 11,670 Aboriginal people, who form 9.8 per cent of the total population (Statistics Canada, 2014). The northern extents of Northern Ontario include approximately 20,000 First Nations people who live in 31 First Nation communities north of the CN rail line. Another 4,000 Ontarians reside in the Far North, most at the gold mining

town of Red Lake. In these Treaty No. 9 lands, First Nation communities are both small and isolated (Treaty No. 9 is shown in Figure 3.10). Only Mishkeegogamang First Nation (located near Savant Lake in Figure 6.13) has a highway connection to the south, via Highway 599.

Current resource development in Ontario's Far North involves two mines—the gold mine at Red Lake and the Victor Diamond Mine—as well as explorations by De Beers for further diamond deposits (Figure 6.12). De Beers, the owner of the Victor Mine located on the traditional lands of the Attawapiskat First Nation, negotiated impact and benefit agreements (IBAs) with that band and two other First Nations, Moose Cree First Nation and

FIGURE 6.13 Northern Ontario's Ring of Fire

The Ring of Fire mineral region in Northern Ontario was allegedly so named by a prospector and former chairman of a Toronto-based mining company, Noront Resources, who was a Johnny Cash fan—one of Cash's best-known songs is titled "Ring of Fire." The exploitation of these resources will require careful planning and co-operation among the major players: the provincial government, the mining companies, and more than a dozen First Nations whose traditional homelands are in this region of Ontario's north.

Taykwa Tagamou Nation. While the IBAs with De Beers cannot solve their dire economic and social situations, De Beers agreed to hire local workers for both construction and production operations (Bone, 2012: 245). According to a CBC report (Porter, 2013), Attawapiskat receives about $2 million annually from De Beers as a royalty payment. But is it enough? With the annual revenue of De Beers's diamond production at about $400 million, Attawapiskat's royalty amounts to only about 0.5 per cent of revenues, well below that obtained by other First Nations and the Inuit for resource projects on their lands. Resource development in the future, such as the Ring of Fire, will bring about another set of negotiations under the rubric of the **duty to consult** and the signing of IBAs.

SUMMARY

In 2008, Ontario faced a fork in the road. By 2016, its economy had improved—GDP was up and unemployment down, and exports to the US had increased. Still, Ontario is not out of the woods. The stimulus of a lower Canadian dollar did not provide the expected jump in manufacturing and exports to the United States, though figures for 2015 did show a modest increase. Another negative factor is that the bellwether of Ontario's economy, its automobile industry, continues to lose ground to Mexico. Then, too, the most telling point is that the province must be struggling because it still qualifies for equalization payments.

For Ontario to prosper and progress into the next decade and to retain its title as the economic engine of Canada, this core region must combine its "old" resource/manufacturing economy with a good dose of high technology. However, such medicine, as revealed in the digitization model for banks, creates more profits but with fewer workers. Fortunately, the application of advanced technology to the automobile industry is a win-win situation—more jobs and high-paying jobs, plus a chance to spark the advanced economy more broadly. While the path forward does not always result in more employment and high-paying jobs, Ontario has no choice but to follow this path.

Challenge Questions

1. For much of its recent history, Ontario has fashioned its prosperity on trade with the United States. Is this "all eggs in one basket" strategy still valid?

2. Is Mexico's growing automobile industry spelling the end of Ontario's automobile manufacturing era?

3. Why does GM's investment in automobile research open the door to an advanced economy?

4. Does the shift of workers to the tertiary sector fit with Florida's thesis about the rise of the creative class and the knowledge-based economy, or does it say more about the slide into low-wage service jobs found in this sector?

5. Hobson's choice: If the knowledge-based economy represents the future of Ontario, would you have "saved" Nortel rather than General Motors and Chrysler?

6. Ontario is divided into two sub-regions. Would you consider this an unexplainable paradox or an inevitable geographic outcome?

Essay Questions

1. Manufacturing forms the heart of Ontario's economy, yet these industries are stagnant. Will manufacturing simply fade away in Ontario or can it be rejuvenated by knowledge-based innovations?

    References:
    Blizzard, Christina. 2015. "Ontario's Manufacturing Slump Draws Fire." *Toronto Sun*, 18 July. At: http://www.torontosun.com/2015/07/18/ontarios-shrinking-manufacturing-sector—300000-jobs-lost-in-15-years.
    Boothe, Paul. 2015. "The Future of Canadian Manufacturing: Searching for Competitive Advantage." Ivey–Lawrence National Centre for Policy and Management. At: http://www.ivey.uwo.ca/cmsmedia/1775585/fom-searching-for-competitive-advantage.pdf.
    Mordue, Greig. 2016. "The Future of Manufacturing, Revealed in an Ontario Budget Line Item." *Globe and Mail*, 1 Mar. At: http://www.theglobeandmail.com/report-on-business/rob-commentary/the-future-of-manufacturing-revealed-in-an-ontario-budget-line-item/article28949846/.

2. Why are electricity prices so high in Ontario compared to Québec?

References:

Hydro-Québec. At: http://www.hydroquebec.com/publications/en/corporate-documents/comparaison-electricity-prices.html.

Kitts, Daniel. 2015. "What Ontarians Don't Know about Rising Hydro Rates." TVO, 6 Nov. At: http://tvo.org/article/current-affairs/the-next-ontario/what-ontarians-dont-know-about-rising-hydro-rates.

Further Reading

Florida, Richard. 2012. *The Rise of the Creative Class—Revisited*. New York: Basic Books.

Without a doubt, Richard Florida has turned the academic world on its head with his creative class thesis whereby urban economic development is driven by urban amenities. The creative class includes those engaged in the knowledge-based economy.

For Toronto and other major cities in Canada, Florida sees the emergence of a new social class based on creativity transforming the very nature of city life. His argument is that creativity is the driving force behind the emerging urban society, where more and more emphasis is placed on cultural amenities such as the arts and sports. As Florida (xxiii) puts it, "the role of creativity as the fundamental source of economic growth and the rise of the new Creative Class" represent the common thread underlying the broad social changes taking place in major cities. Knowledge-based companies, including high-tech firms, need talented people, and talented people want urban amenities.

Yet, Florida presents a puzzle, claiming that unlike past emerging classes of people with common traits and concerns who steered the direction of their society, the creative class is unaware of its own existence and thus is unable to consciously influence the course of the society it leads. Even Statistics Canada does not record those employed in the knowledge-based economy. Perhaps the answer lies in applying the biological notion of osmosis whereby social change gradually seeps into the urban society—and institutions like Statistics Canada—thus modifying society without a direct plan of action.

7 Québec

Introduction

By virtue of its geography, language, and history, Québec occupies a unique place in Canada and North America. As a French-speaking region making up 23 per cent of Canada's population and 2 per cent of the population in North America, the province for many years has viewed the preservation of the French language and, therefore, the culture of the province as a fundamental political challenge.

Geography has blessed Québec's Canadian Shield with an exceptional combination of water and topography uniquely suitable for producing hydroelectric power. The harnessing of these rivers by Hydro-Québec represents both an economic and a political strategy employed by the Québec government to keep the province's economy strong.

For over a hundred years, Québec and Ontario served as the heartland of Canada's manufacturing industry. In the twenty-first century, however, its grip on its historical share of the economy and population of Canada has weakened. While the province retains its place as the second-ranked region in terms of population size, its economy, as measured by GDP, trails the resource-based economy found in Western Canada. Québec has taken the first steps towards a knowledge-based economy, and two economic spearheads—Bombardier and SNC-Lavalin—demonstrate advances in this area. A third spearhead and economic anchor—since the "Quiet Revolution" of more than a half-century ago—has been Hydro-Québec, the gift that keeps on giving through relatively low-cost energy rates for homes, business, and industry and through pride in a French-Canadian success story and know-how.

← Québec City is one of the oldest European settlements in North America. An intersection in Old Québec City captures the essence of the area in the city that has been designated a UNESCO World Heritage Site.

Zoonar GmbH/Alamy Stock Photo

Québec's Place within Canada

Québec's economic and demographic position continues to grow. However, its growth is less than the national average and well below that found in Ontario, Western Canada, and British Columbia. In this sense, Québec's economy and population are losing ground and its place within Canada is diminishing. Already Western Canada's economy, as measured by its share of national GDP, outranks Québec's economy. Although Québec is still the second-most populous region, the Québec share of Canada's population has slipped from 29 per cent in 1966 to 23 per cent in 2015 (Figure 7.1) (Statistics Canada, 2011). Worse yet for Québec, this downward trend is likely to continue. The economic and population gains taking place in Western Canada outstrip those in Québec (Figure 7.3). For example, the 1966 population of Québec (5.8 million) exceeded Western Canada (3.4 million) by 2.4 million (Statistics

Canada, 2011). By 2015, this gap had narrowed to 1.6 million. **Demography** has political implications, for Québec's political clout diminishes as the faster-growing regions obtain more seats in the federal House of Commons than Québec.

The fact that Québec's population growth rate has become more dependent on immigration means a more diverse population (Vignette 7.1). On the one hand, immigration brings an influx of talented people so necessary for a knowledge-based economy. On the other hand, the impact of a more diverse population on Québec culture, language, and ethnic nationalism is a pivotal political challenge.

Québec's Culture, Identity, and Language

Following the founding in 1608 of the first European settlement at Québec by Samuel de Champlain, settlers came from France to the St Lawrence Valley. Over the centuries, by clinging tenaciously to the land through many adversities, their ancestors made this corner of North America a homeland for the French-speaking people. La Fête nationale du Québec (Saint-Jean Baptiste Day, the national holiday of Québec) celebrates this accomplishment on 24 June each year. However, the road has not always been easy or pleasant, and the collective memory often recalls humiliations and resistance as well as hard-fought victories. Flowing through this collective memory is the fear of a loss of Québec's culture, identity, and language. Separatism is one response to that fear while another is Confederation, which allocates selective powers to provinces and, in a few cases, a special role to Québec normally reserved for the federal government. One example is membership in La Francophonie Summit, normally restricted to national governments; also, immigration to Québec is controlled and managed by the province.

The French language, Québécois culture, and a francophone identity have generated a strong sense of belonging among the majority of Québec citizens, forming the basis of ethnic pride, loyalty, and nationalism, which from time to time fuels the desire for an independent political state. Such feelings are

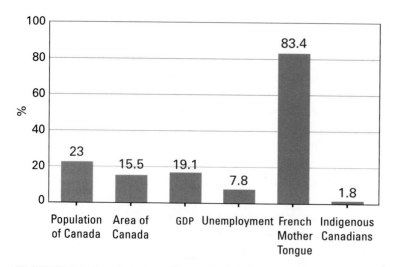

FIGURE 7.1 Québec basic statistics, 2015

By population size, Québec remains the second-ranking geographic region in Canada, though Western Canada and British Columbia are narrowing the demographic gap. Its economy now ranks third behind those of Ontario and Western Canada. A comparatively high unemployment rate is a sign of its sluggish economy.

Percentages of population, area, and GDP are for Canada as a whole; unemployment, French home language, and Indigenous population percentages are for Québec. Percentages for French mother tongue and Indigenous Canadians are for 2011.

Sources: Tables 1.1, 1.2, and 5.6.

Vignette 7.1

The Quiet Revolution and Natural Rate of Population Increase

Québec's natural rate of population increase dropped dramatically following the Quiet Revolution. At that time, the Québécois began the transformation into a more urban and liberal society. No longer in the grip of the Roman Catholic Church, birth control measures became widespread, causing the birth rate to drop. For example, prior to 1960, Québec had the highest birth rates in Canada, sometimes referred to as "the revenge of the cradles" (*la revanche des berceaux*). Since then, the birth rate has fallen below the national average. In 2014, the fertility rate of 1.62 was well below the replacement level of 2.1 (Institut de la statistique du Québec, 2016: 12). This demographic reality and a relatively high immigration rate are creating a more diverse population, especially in Montréal.

particularly strong among the "old stock"—the descendants of some 10,000 settlers who migrated from France in the seventeenth and eighteenth centuries—but are less strong among anglophones and allophones. While their first loyalty is often to Québec, most Québécois also have a strong attachment to Canada.

For a more complete discussion of the historic origins of the concept of a political partnership, see "One Country, Two Visions" in Chapter 3, page 107.

Québec's culture is largely derived from the historical experience of **francophones** living in North America for over 400 years and of their being part of Canada for more than 150 years. Clearly, Québec's

FIGURE 7.2 Pastagate: Language inspector rejects "pasta" on Italian restaurant menu

The maelstrom that erupted over Pastagate in 2013 may have reduced the chances of Bill 14 passing in the National Assembly (see "Further Reading"). In any case, the bill was withdrawn and Louise Marchand, head of the Office québécois de la langue française, was forced to resign because one of her language inspectors told a Montréal Italian restaurant owner that words on the menu such as "botiglia," "pasta," and "antipasto" must have French translations. Several months later, the government announced changes to how its "language police" would monitor the use of other languages in public places.

Source: Brian Gable/The Globe and Mail

Contested Terrain 7.1

Maîtres Chez Nous

Since the Quiet Revolution, the Québec government has passed legislation to take control of the economy and, in doing so, strengthen the role of the Québécois. The creation of the Hydro-Québec monopoly was one such step while another was Bill 101, the Charter of the French Language. Bill 101, passed in 1977, limited the use of English in order to preserve the French language. Since then, the government has continued to revise and tighten the legislation. One example is the Office québécois de la langue française, whose role is to identify and eliminate commercial signs using English (Figure 7.2). Even so, Québec nationalists want more restrictions on the use of English (Lemay, 2010). On the other hand, the business community fears that the language policy has already turned Québec into a "hermit state," isolating Québec but particularly Montréal from Canada and the rest of the world (Jarislowsky, 2012: A19; Aubin, 2013). An immediate example was the decision of Sun Life, one of the largest insurance and financial firms in the world, to move its operations from Montréal to Toronto in January 1978, just after Bill 101 was passed. Without a doubt, balancing the two perspectives, that is, protecting the French language without alienating business, represents a formidable challenge for the Québec government. In the ideal world described by Richard Florida, talented people would move to Montréal and other urban centres to stimulate the knowledge-based economy, but at the same time accommodate themselves to the French language and Québec culture.

sense of place and identity is based on its struggle to survive within an English-speaking North America. The decision to join Confederation has had both

For a brief account of John Ralston Saul's concept of Canada, see "Faultlines within Canada" in Chapter 1, page 9. For a broader historic discussion of two competing visions of Canada, see "The French/English Faultline" in Chapter 3, page 103, and "French/English Language Imbalance" in Chapter 4, page 142.

benefits and costs. Confederation provides a safe place within North America, though relations between French- and English-speaking Québecers have been strained from time to time. The resolution of these occasional disagreements has led to a type of federation built on compromise. This complex concept of compromise—as identified by Saul in his book *Reflections of a Siamese Twin*—helps defuse tensions between French- and English-speaking Québecers. As a living, dynamic concept, "compromising" federalism continues to evolve and survive.

"La Belle Province," while home to the largest francophone population outside of France, contains a minority composed of **anglophones**, whose mother tongue is English, and **allophones**, immigrants whose mother tongue is neither English nor French. This minority is concentrated in the Montréal

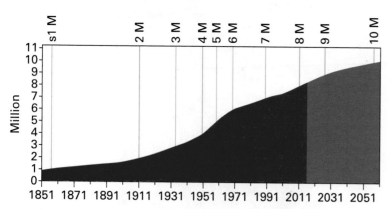

FIGURE 7.3 Population of Québec, 1851–2011, and projected population, 2021–2061

In 2015, the population of Québec had reached 8.3 million and its population is projected to reach 10 million by 2061. From 2015 to 2061, the projected population growth is low, a consequence of two important demographic features: (1) the annual natural increase is expected to decline or, at most, remain stable; (2) the annual number of immigrants is unlikely to exceed 40,000. In 2014, for instance, the natural increase was 24,700 while the net immigration totalled 31,600.

Source: Institut de la statistique du Québec (2016: 10–12).

Vignette 7.2

Demography Has Political Consequences

As Canada's population increases, the number of Canadians in each of the six regions has increased—but at different rates. In the twenty-first century, Québec has had a low rate of population increase compared to the national average. Only Atlantic Canada has had lower rates. The political consequence for Québec has been twofold: more seats but a lower proportion of the total seats in the House of Commons.[1] By comparing the number of seats in the House of Commons in 2000 and 2015, the degree of erosion of its political power is revealed. In 2000, Québec had 75 seats that formed 24.9 per cent of the 301 seats in the House of Commons. By the 2015 federal election, Québec had more three more seats for a total of 78 seats. Yet, its percentage of seats fell to 23.1 per cent of the 338 seats in the House of Commons.

Arerial Archives/Alamy

Photo 7.1 The Port of Montréal is a major container port. In 2015, 27 per cent of its container traffic came from the European Union. With the prospect of a trade agreement with the EU, container traffic is expected to increase significantly. Montréal has two geographical advantages over competing ports. First, it is close to major markets in Ontario and the US Midwest. Second, container traffic can reach Chicago and other cities on the Great Lakes by lower-cost lake transport. However, as container ships have increased in size, docking in Montréal's relatively shallow harbour has made this port less competitive with Atlantic ports, including Halifax.

Vignette 7.3

The St Lawrence River

The St Lawrence River provides a natural waterway into the interior of North America and, consequently, played a key role in the history of New France. After the construction of the St Lawrence Seaway in 1959, ocean ships could sail into the Great Lakes by making use of a series of locks, such as the eight locks on the Welland Canal that are managed by the St Lawrence Seaway Management Corporation. In a nutshell, the St Lawrence Seaway is an essential part of North America's transportation system and links Québec to North America's manufacturing belt. Cities along its shores from Sept-Îles to Montréal have benefited greatly from the waterway's role as a major shipping route. Montréal's favourable location on the St Lawrence (Photo 7.1 and Figure 7.4) gives it an economic advantage and fuels the city's growth.

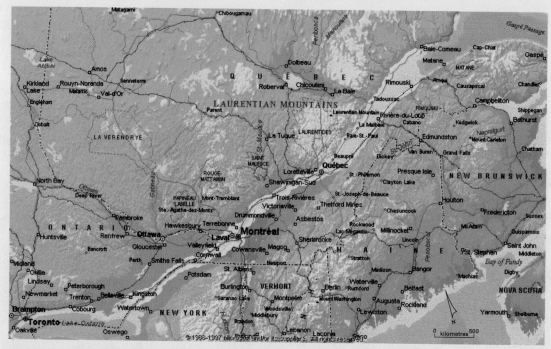

FIGURE 7.4 The St Lawrence River and Lake Ontario

Source: Paul Hebert, Biodiversity Institute of Ontario. At: www.aquatic.uoguelph.ca/rivers/stlawmap.htm.

In "Information Society and Innovative Clusters," Chapter 5, page 166, Florida's theory is discussed within the broader context of the information/knowledge society and his "creativity" thesis is examined in "Further Reading" in Chapter 6.

and Gatineau. The Québécois whose first language is French represent the dominant demographic force in the province. The remaining Québecers include Indigenous peoples, whose mother tongues include Cree, Inuktitut, and Innu-aimun. In northern Québec, Cree, Inuit, and Innu (Naskapi) form the majority in most communities, where they tend to speak their native language, English, and French in that order. From time to time, social tensions surface between the French-speaking majority and the province's minority groups as the Québécois continue to assert their desire to be "maîtres chez nous."

Québec's Physical Geography

Québec, the largest province in Canada, has a wide range of natural conditions and physiographic regions. Its climate varies from the mild continental climate in the St Lawrence Valley to the cold Arctic climate found in Nunavik (Inuit lands lying north of the fifty-fifth parallel). Four of Canada's physiographic regions extend over the province's territory—the Hudson Bay Lowlands, the Canadian Shield, the Appalachian Uplands (Photo 7.2), and the Great Lakes–St Lawrence Lowlands—and each has a different resource base and settlement pattern (Figure 6.4). The Canadian Shield extends over most of Québec—close to 90 per cent—while the Appalachian Uplands and Great Lakes–St Lawrence Lowlands together form nearly 10 per cent. By far the smallest physiographic region is the Hudson Bay Lowlands, which constitutes less than 1 per cent of Québec's land mass and where very few people live.

The heartland of Québec is the St Lawrence Lowland. Formed from the Champlain Sea some 10,000 years ago, this physiographic region provides the best agricultural land in Québec. Settlers from France began farming along the edge of the St Lawrence River some 400 years ago. New France was established within this region and, by means of the St Lawrence, spread into the interior of North America. It remains the cultural and economic core of Québec.

The Appalachian Uplands physiographic region is an extension of the Appalachian Mountains, which stretch northward from the state of Georgia. While this ancient geological feature reaches into Québec and Atlantic Canada, its topography is much subdued and consists more of rugged hills and rolling plains. Most arable land in this region is in Estrie, where dairy farming prevails. Tourism has become an important source of income during summer on the Gaspé Peninsula. Mining and forestry are other economic activities in the region. With the exception of the Lake Champlain gap in the Appalachian Uplands, easy road access to the populous parts of New England is blocked by these rugged uplands. The Lake Champlain gap has therefore become a very important north–south transportation link between Montréal and points south in the US, especially New York City.

As the largest physiographic region in Québec, the Canadian Shield is noted for its forest products and hydroelectric production—it has most of the hydroelectric sites in Canada because of a combination of heavy precipitation, large rivers, and significant changes in elevation. Beyond the commercial forest zone lie the lands of the Cree and Inuit, where the Cree must coexist with the massive La Grande hydro project. The Québec government supports a hunting-and-trapping program, thus encouraging many Cree families to stay on the land. This program has important cultural and social values. In Arctic Québec, a number of Inuit settlements are found along the coasts of Hudson Bay and Hudson Strait. Further to the east, near the Québec–Labrador border, upward of 15,000 Innu live in several communities.

The geographic extent of Québec's four climatic zones are shown in Figure 2.4, page 41.

Photo 7.2 Estrie, formerly called the Eastern Townships, lies in the Appalachian Uplands physiographic region. Dairy farms are found in the rolling countryside, which is surrounded by wooded uplands. Hay is the principal crop and is used as feed for dairy cows.

Clara Parsons/Valan Photos

With four climatic zones in Québec, weather varies greatly. The four zones are Arctic, Subarctic, Atlantic, and Great Lakes–St Lawrence. The Subarctic climate zone extends over 60 per cent of Québec, followed in extent by the Arctic, Great Lakes–St Lawrence, and Atlantic zones. The weather across Québec falls within a predictable range for each climatic zone, but, like other regions of Canada, Québec has had its share of extreme weather events: in recent memory a devastating 1996 flood in the Saguenay region and, in 1998, the worst ice storm in Canadian history, which struck southern Québec and eastern Ontario.

Environmental Challenges

Québec, as an old industrial region, is confronted with a series of environmental problems, most of which stem from the discharge of agricultural, industrial, and mining wastes into the atmosphere and water bodies or from the construction of huge hydroelectric dams. Asbestos mining represented a major health concern to the workers and those using

Vignette 11.4, "The Arctic Council and the Circumpolar World," page 379, discusses transnational issues related to the Far North.

the product, and this extractive activity finally ended in 2012. Even Québec's so-called pristine North has been affected as mineral exploration companies have failed to clean up their sites, leaving the landscape littered with abandoned machinery, chemicals, and oil barrels (Duhaime, Bernard, and Comtois, 2005: 262). The sudden closure of the Nunavik nickel mine in 2014 has raised similar environmental concerns. Public attention is now focused on the National Energy Board hearings for the proposed Energy East pipeline. Many are concerned about a pipeline leak causing a bitumen spill into the St Lawrence River. This river holds a special place for Québecers, and efforts to restore waters of the St Lawrence River began in earnest in 1988 when Québec and Canada joined forces to tackle the pollution problems facing this river. In 2011, the two governments launched a long-term effort, *The St. Lawrence Action Plan: 2011–2026* (Québec and Canada, 2012, 2015).

Québec's Historical Geography

Relative to some other parts of North America, the history of European settlement in Québec is long, rich, and complicated by the period of British rule and then the search for a place within Confederation (see

Vignette 7.4

Does Geography Draw Québec into the Circumpolar World?

Mining development in Nunavik has international implications for Québec. China's quest for raw materials to feed its fast-growing industries has extended to Nunavik, but this nickel mine venture has not turned out well. While the Chinese firm Jilin Jien, through its subsidiary Jien Canada Mining Ltd (formerly Canadian Royalties), had long-term plans for this mine, the operators of Nunavik Nickel Mine filed for bankruptcy shortly after the price of nickel, like the price of other commodities, collapsed from $15/lb in 2010 to $5 in 2014. This bankruptcy raised two as yet unanswered questions. First, in the case of bankruptcy, is the company still responsible for the environmental cleanup? Second, does Québec have a responsibility to ensure safe passage through the Northwest Passage when ore from Arctic Québec is shipped to China? For example, in September 2014, the Nunavik Nickel Mine sent an unescorted ship loaded with nickel from Deception Bay through the Northwest Passage to Bayuquan, China. Failed venture or not, this mining operation set a precedent by shipping its product across the Northwest Passage, thus drawing Québec more closely into the Circumpolar World and perhaps a seat at the Arctic Council.

TABLE 7.1 Timeline: Historical Milestones in New France

Year	Geographic Significance
1534	Jacques Cartier sails into the Bay of Chaleur and claims the land for France. The following year, Cartier discovers the mouth of the St Lawrence River, which provides access to the interior of North America.
1608	Samuel de Champlain, described as the "Father of New France," founds a fur-trading post near the site of Québec City. Champlain was instrumental in the development of the fur economy, which provided the initial economic basis for New France.
1642	Paul de Chomedey de Maisonneuve establishes Ville-Marie on Île de Montréal, which is strategically situated at the confluence of the Ottawa and St Lawrence rivers. Later, Ville-Marie was renamed Montréal.
1701	La grande paix de Montréal is proclaimed between New France and 40 First Nations surrounding the colony of New France.
1759	The struggle between France and England over North America sees the British defeat the French army on the Plains of Abraham at Québec. The final battle between French and English forces ends with the capture of Montréal by the British. In 1763, the formal surrender of New France to England takes place with the Treaty of Paris.

Tables 7.1–7.3). Beneath the surface of this search lies the deeply fractured French/English faultline. Québec's historical geography can be divided into three periods: New France, British occupation, and Confederation.

New France, 1608–1760

The introduction of North America to the French began in 1534 when Jacques Cartier sailed into the Bay of Chaleur and set foot on the shores of the Gaspé Peninsula. The first permanent French settlement in Québec was established in 1608, when Samuel de Champlain founded a fur-trading post at the site of Québec City, thus establishing a French colony in North America. Over three decades, on foot and by ship and canoe, Champlain explored in the unknown heart of the continent through what are now six Canadian provinces and five American states, and by doing so he created the territorial basis for the French Empire in North America. Although France eventually lost its North American colony, it left a cultural legacy in the form of the French language and the Catholic religion, and a French stamp on the landscape with its unique settlement pattern and arrangement of farms into long lots. Notably, the vision of Champlain to strive for a French settlement in the New World founded on harmony with and respect for the Huron and, when possible, other Indigenous groups differed sharply from English

and Spanish settlements and attitudes towards the First Peoples. David Fischer (2008) argues that the "humanist" values of Champlain and the respect for the values and traditions of the "other" have been important in marking Canada as different from other "New World" countries. La grande paix de Montréal of 1701 provides an example of a respectful and peaceful relationship between the First Nations peoples and the French settlers.

During the seventeenth and eighteenth centuries, France had control over vast areas of North America. Its core, however, was the St Lawrence Valley, from which New France developed a vast fur-trading empire. The wealth from the fur trade was enormous and was the reason for France's interest in the New World. Almost every male French settler wanted to participate in the fur trade, which left only a few to clear the forest and till the land. Indeed, several canoes full of beaver pelts could make a man extremely wealthy compared with the meagre returns obtained from the back-breaking toil of clearing land and breaking the soil. Frenchmen who were coureurs de bois (fur traders; literally, "runners of the woods") often lived with the Indigenous people. A few were extremely successful and returned to France to enjoy their good fortune. Others remained in the fur trade or settled in New France.

Geography played a part in New France's success both as a fur-trading empire and as an agricultural colony. The St Lawrence River provided a route to the interior, which gave the French explorers and fur traders an advantage over their English rivals, who had to contend with crossing the Appalachian Mountains or, in Canada after 1670, ply the trade further north through Hudson Bay. The famous French explorer, René-Robert Cavelier, Sieur de La Salle, reached the mouth of the Mississippi River at New Orleans in 1682. Early in the eighteenth century, French fur traders, led by Pierre Gaultier de Varennes, Sieur de La Vérendrye, established a series of fur-trading posts in Manitoba.

New France also established a successful agricultural society based on the seigneurial system. Once the land was cleared, the fertile soils in the St Lawrence Lowland provided a solid basis for essentially agricultural settlement. Farming took hold in New France, particularly following the efforts of

Jean Talon (1626–94), the greatest administrator of New France.

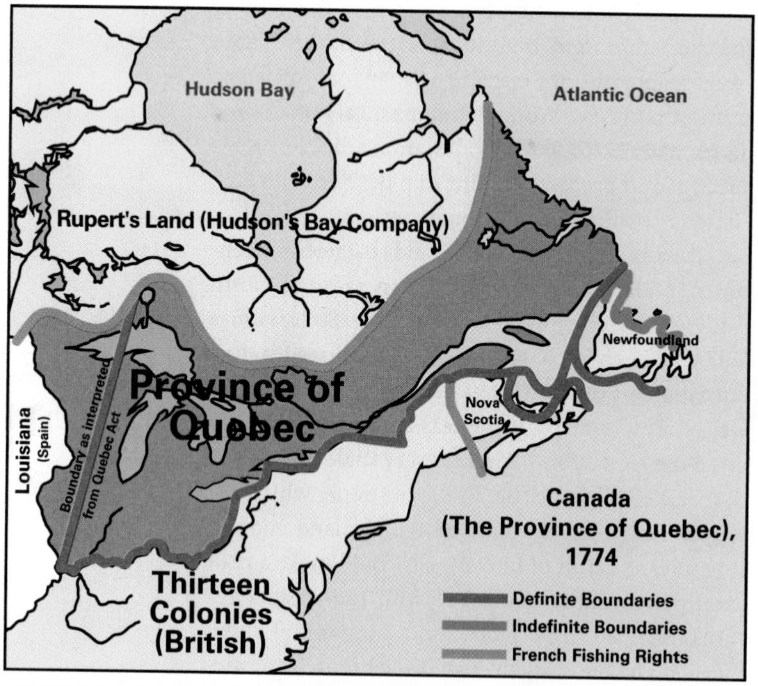

The Seigneurial System

When the first Intendant of New France, Jean Talon, arrived in New France in 1665, he encountered a population of only 3,000 inhabitants, most of whom were men engaged in the fur trade. Talon had been instructed by Louis XIV to create a feudal agricultural society resembling that of rural France in the seventeenth century. Talon undertook three measures to achieve this goal. First, he recruited peasants from France. Second, he sent for young women—orphaned girls and daughters of poor families in France—to provide wives for the men of the colony. Third, he imposed the French feudal system of land-ownership, known as the seigneurial system. In the seigneurial system, huge tracts of land were granted to those favoured by the king, namely, the nobility, religious institutions of the Roman Catholic Church, military officers, and high-ranking government officials. The seigneur was obliged to swear allegiance to the king and to have his tenants cultivate the lands on his estate. In exchange for use of the land, the tenants owed certain obligations to their seigneur: paying yearly dues (cens et rentes) to their seigneur; working the seigneur's land, especially in regard to road maintenance (corvée); and paying rent for using the seigneur's grinding mill and bake ovens (droit de banalité).

By 1760, there were approximately 200 seigneuries. Seigneuries, which were usually 1 by 3 leagues (5 by 15 km) in size, were generally divided into river lots (rangs). These long, rectangular lots were well adapted to the St Lawrence Valley for several reasons, the most important of which was that each habitant had access to a river, either a tributary of the St Lawrence or the river itself. At that time, most people and goods were transported along the river system in New France. For that reason, river access was vital for each habitant family. The seigneurial system was abolished in 1854 by the legislature of the Province of Canada.

FIGURE 7.5 Map of British North America, 1774

The Quebec Act (1774) defined the lands of the Province of Québec, which approximated the drainage basin of most of the St Lawrence River. What is now northern Québec was part of Rupert's Land, a territory granted by the British Crown to the Hudson's Bay Company and defined by the watershed of the rivers flowing into Hudson Bay. At that time (1774), the Louisiana Territory (land west of the Mississippi River to the Rocky Mountains) was claimed by Spain.

Source: https://en.wikipedia.org/wiki/Constitutional_history_of_Canada.

British Colony, 1760–1867

Following the defeat of the French, the British ruled Québec for over 100 years. The British governor

TABLE 7.2 Timeline: Historical Milestones in the British Colony of Lower Canada

Year	Geographic Significance
1763	The Treaty of Paris awards New France to Great Britain.
1774	The British Parliament passes the Québec Act, which recognizes that Québec, as a British colony, has special rights, including use of the French language, the Catholic religion, and French civil law (see Figure 7.5).
1791	The British Parliament approves the Constitutional Act that creates two colonies in British North America called Upper Canada and Lower Canada.
1841	Based on the report of Lord Durham following the failed rebellions in Lower and Upper Canada of 1837 and 1838, the British Parliament passes the Act of Union that reunites the Canadas into a single colony and makes English the official language of the newly formed Province of Canada.

was installed at Québec City along with a regiment of British troops, while the fur trade continued to flourish and the agricultural economy went unchanged. Most French Canadians were peasant farmers. After the Conquest of New France by the British, their life on the land remained much the same. Their social and economic lives revolved around the parish church and a landholding system centred on the seigneuries. Life in the towns and cities, however, changed radically due to a massive influx of British immigrants, the powerful political position of English Canadians, and their control of the commercial and industrial sectors of urban places. By 1851, French Canadians accounted for only about half of the population of Montréal. From 1851 to 1951, enormous demographic changes took place. The saving grace for the Canadiens was their high fertility rate (*la revanche des berceaux*).

Land hunger forced many French Canadians to migrate. By the middle of the nineteenth century, many had left the St Lawrence Lowland due to a land shortage. French Canadians migrated in three directions: to the Appalachian Uplands east and south of Montréal (the Eastern Townships, now known as Estrie), where they either purchased farms from English-speaking farmers or found jobs in textile mills; to the Canadian Shield, where they tried to exist on extremely marginal agricultural land; or to New England's industrial towns, where most were employed in textile factories. By the early twentieth century large numbers of French Canadians, perhaps as many as 1 million, had left Québec for the United States, while only a small number settled in the Canadian West, which was calling out for homesteaders.

By the 1830s, political unrest was growing in both Upper and Lower Canada. A British governor appointed in England ruled each colony with the assistance of wealthy members of the community. This cozy arrangement not only concentrated power in the hands of a few but also led to blatant abuse by powerful elites. In Upper Canada, the political elite was known as the Family Compact; in Lower Canada it was the Château Clique. In 1837, rebellions broke out in each colony (Vignette 7.5). The British army crushed both rebellions.

Following the rebellions, the British government sent Lord Durham to British North America to seek a political solution. Durham recommended an elected rather than an appointed government, where power was dispersed among elected representatives rather than concentrated within an appointed elite. Durham also observed the French/English faultline, which he described as "two nations warring in the bosom of a single state." In Durham's report he recommended responsible (elected) government and the union of English-speaking people in Upper Canada with the French-speaking settlers of Lower Canada.[2] Lord Durham believed that assimilation of the French was desirable and possible, claiming that the French Canadians were "a people with no literature and no history" (Mills, 1988: 637). He recommended that English be the sole language of the new Province of Canada, and that a massive immigration of English-speaking settlers be launched to create an English majority in Lower Canada. In response to

Photo 7.3 Roman Catholic churches are found in most communities across Québec, signifying the dominant role the Roman Catholic Church once played in the social life and political affairs of the province. Faith was a key pillar of French-Canadian identity, the other being the French language. The popular novel *Jean Rivard* (1874) reflects the central role of the Church in shaping the thinking and lives of the people. A young French Canadian is advised by his *curé* on the advantages of becoming a farmer rather than a lawyer. The novel promotes the virtue of living a subsistence rural lifestyle in a remote area of Québec's Clay Belt, far from Montréal with its large English-speaking population and worldly temptations. Here, in the remote Clay Belt, the French language, religion, and heritage could flourish. By the time of the Quiet Revolution in the 1960s, however, the Church's influence in Québec affairs had greatly diminished and many churches had lost many of their parishioners.

Durham's recommendations, the British Parliament passed the Act of Union in 1841, uniting the two colonies into the Province of Canada and creating a single elected assembly.

Confederation to the Quiet Revolution

Confederation, achieved in 1867, sought to unite two cultures—English and French—within a British parliamentary system. For Québec, Confederation provided a political framework offering three benefits: an economic union with Ontario, Nova Scotia, and New Brunswick; a political environment where Roman Catholicism and, to a lesser degree, the French language were guaranteed protection by Ottawa; and provincial control over education and language. George-Étienne Cartier, one of the Fathers of Confederation and a French-Canadian leader, viewed these provincial powers as a way for Québec to shape its own destiny within Confederation. Cartier may have identified a fourth benefit—since Québec and Ontario often had mutual economic interests, they could, by working together, influence federal policies and thereby shape the future of Canada.

Confederation also led to the expansion of the geographic size of Québec (Figures 3.4 and 3.6). Since Confederation, Québec's geographic size has increased greatly. It is now 1.5 million km². As Canada acquired more territory from the British government, Ottawa assigned to Québec parts of Rupert's Land lying north of the St Lawrence drainage basin. In 1898, the Québec government received the first block of Rupert's Land. The second was obtained in 1912.[3] Some of this land, however, was claimed by the British colony of Newfoundland. In its argument, Newfoundland demanded all of Québec's territory that drained into the Atlantic Ocean. Though the British Privy Council awarded this land, known as Labrador, to Newfoundland in 1927 (Figure 3.7), to this day the Québec government does not recognize the decision. As former Premier Jean Charest said in September 2008, "This is a traditional position that all governments have reiterated. There is a boundary line on which there is no agreement" (Robitaille, 2008).

Beyond the political benefits of Confederation, Canada provided the economic environment for the rapid growth of manufacturing in Québec, but especially in Montréal. The key federal legislation was based on Prime Minister Macdonald's National Policy. In the early days, most manufacturing took place in Montréal and involved clothing and textiles. These firms were largely owned and operated by English-speaking Canadians. At Confederation, Montréal was the major metropolis of Canada. Many of the country's largest companies and banks were headquartered in Montréal: the Canadian Pacific

Vignette 7.5

The Rebellions of 1837–8

In Lower Canada, Louis-Joseph Papineau, a lawyer, seigneur, and politician, was the leader of the French-speaking majority in the Assembly of Lower Canada. Papineau had fought with the British forces against the invading American army at Chateauguay in 1812. A strong supporter of the Church and the seigneurial system, Papineau was a leading political figure of the Patriotes. In 1834, Papineau issued a list of grievances known as "The Ninety-Two Resolutions." At this time, the economy was depressed and tensions between the French-Canadian majority and the British minority were growing. Papineau sought to shift political power from the British authorities to the elected Assembly of Lower Canada. He planned to use his majority in the Assembly to pass legislation, including tax bills. The British government rejected his resolutions, and it was just a matter of time before an armed uprising broke out. When it did, the British reacted with force. Even with the strong support of rural areas, Papineau and his Patriotes were soundly defeated. Nearly 300 rebels were killed in six battles. Papineau fled to the United States, but in 1845 he was granted amnesty and returned to Québec. Following a second uprising in Lower Canada in November 1838, the British captured hundreds of rebels and ultimately 12 men were sentenced and executed and another 58 were exiled to Australia (Bumsted, 2007: 169). A rebellion based on the same popular objections to elite rule also took place in Upper Canada in 1837, and it, too, was crushed. The British government sought to remedy the unrest in both of its colonies. It began this process with a fact-finding mission headed by Lord Durham. The result and Britain's solution was the Act of Union in 1841.

Railway, the Grand Trunk Railway, the Molson Bank, the Bank of Montréal, the Merchants' Bank, and the Bank of British North America. Montréal served as the primary port for trade with Britain and the United States.

In 1960, the Quiet Revolution unleashed the forces of change that drove Québec into a modern industrial state. As with other social revolutions, its origins began earlier. Yet, the election of the Liberal government of Jean Lesage marked a dramatic transformation in government, French-Canadian society, and the place of French within Québec. His government initiated major political innovations that accelerated the process of social and economic change. In effect, the provincial government replaced the Catholic Church as the leader and protector of French culture

TABLE 7.3 Timeline: Historical Milestones for Québec in Confederation

Year	Geographic Significance
1867	The Dominion of Canada is formed, the new state consisting of Québec, Ontario, New Brunswick, and Nova Scotia.
1898	Ottawa extends Québec's northern boundary to the Eastmain River, thus expanding Québec's territory well beyond its core area of the St Lawrence Lowland into the Cree lands of James Bay in the Canadian Shield.
1912	Ottawa adds the Territory of Ungava to Québec, thus extending Québec to the Inuit lands of Nunavik. With the addition of these two northern areas in 1898 and 1912, Québec's territory more than doubles.
1927	In settling a dispute between Canada and Newfoundland, Britain rejects Canada's claim that the boundary should be placed just inland from the shore. Instead, Britain declares that the boundary is to follow the Hudson Bay and Atlantic Ocean watersheds. Québec does not recognize this boundary.
1960	The Quiet Revolution begins.

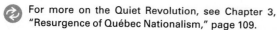

For more on the Quiet Revolution, see Chapter 3, "Resurgence of Québec Nationalism," page 109.

and language in Québec. The Quiet Revolution instilled a sense of pride and accomplishment among Québecers. The main reforms of the Lesage government were hinged on state intervention in the Québec economy through Crown corporations, and on the expansion of a French-speaking provincial civil service. The government's principal achievements were:

Discussion of the "French/English Faultline" in Chapter 3, page 103, includes more information on the historic twists and turns to Québec's place within British North America and then within Confederation.

- nationalization of private electrical companies under Hydro-Québec;
- modernization and secularization of the education system, making it accessible to all;
- investment of Québec Pension Plan funds in Québec firms, thereby stimulating the francophone business sector;
- establishment of Maisons du Québec (quasi-embassies) in Paris, London, and New York, thus signalling to Ottawa that the Québec government wanted to represent Québec interests to the rest of the world.

With these accomplishments behind them, Québecers felt confident about their future. Lesage's 1963 campaign slogan, "*Maîtres chez nous*" (Masters in our own house), became a reality. For federalists in Québec, these achievements proved that a strong Québec could function within Canada, but for separatists they were not enough. The rise of separatism in Québec signalled that some Québécois felt only an independent Québec could adequately represent French-Canadian interests. For them the slogan became "*Le Québec aux Québécois*" (Québec for the Québécois). After two referendums, Québecers have, for the time being, turned away from pursuing political separation and are focusing more on economic and social concerns. Then, too, Québec nationalism, which is at the core of the separatist movement, has shifted somewhat from the goals and values of the "old stock" francophones and has become more inclusive, i.e., embracing all French-speaking Québecers, including immigrants (allophones) and bilingual anglophones. Even the federal government has referred to Québec as a "nation" within Canada. Nonetheless, philosophical

and jurisdictional disagreements are never far from the surface in the relationship between Québec and Ottawa.

Québec Today

Québec, a modern industrial society operating within a francophone environment, lies in Canada's heartland. While Québec and Ontario have long served as a manufacturing core within Canada, both are striving to gain a secure foothold in the knowledge-based economy where technology is transforming traditional economic activities into a much more automated and digitized system. In the meantime, the province has seen its place within Canada diminished mainly because its economic and population growth rates have fallen below the national average. In addition, globalization of trade squeezed its manufacturing sector, resulting in the loss of many jobs. Indeed, Québec's clothing and textiles industry, which historically has accounted for well over half of all Canadian production, felt the pinch early on as freer trade over the past several decades involved "the gradual elimination of import quotas and tariffs" (Finances Québec, 2005), especially after 1995 with the establishment of the World Trade Organization. When China joined the WTO in 2001 many thousands of low value-added and low-wage jobs fled to China and other low-wage countries. Further signs of its weak economic state are identified by the following: Québec receives the largest share of equalization payments; its unemployment rate is above the national average; and its per capita debt is the highest in the country (Lamman et al., 2016).

Yet, culture might trump the economy—or at least add to its vibrancy. Without a doubt, the francophone cultural world is one of Québec's economic strengths. Following Richard Florida's thesis that creative people crave a vibrant arts community,

See the section "Debt Loads in Canada" in Chapter 5, page 170, for a fuller discussion of provincial debt.

THINK ABOUT IT

Why do Québec governments, regardless of political affiliation, advocate a vision of Canada as a "partnership" between founding peoples?

Québec's film industry has a worldwide reputation and its music community, ranging from popular to classical music, ranks highly within Canada and North America (Photo 7.4). Montréal and Québec City provide the cultural cluster and are vital to the province's cultural renaissance.

What does the future hold for Québec? Can it reinvent itself as a knowledge-based economy? Its industrial structure helps to answer these questions, while the leading businesses provide another lens for understanding Québec's present and future.

Québec's Economy

Québec's economy ranks third in the country, comprising 23 per cent of the national GDP. The St Lawrence River provides low-cost water access to the heart of North America (Photos 7.1 and 7.10). Its economic growth has lagged behind other regions of the country, and in 2016 the provincial economy remained in the slow lane. Robert Hogue, senior economist with the Royal Bank of Canada, predicts a continuation of the weak annual economic growth that averaged only 1.4 per cent over the past five years (Hogue, 2016: 7). While the province is benefiting from the lower value of the Canadian dollar, its principal market, the United States, has yet to attain robust growth, which, in turn, has dampened Québec exports to the US. Québec's exports account for a substantial share of Canada's high-tech exports in aerospace production, biotechnology, information technologies, pharmaceuticals, and rail transportation. The province has its share of start-up businesses, largely in Greater Montréal. Stingray Digital, for example, is now a global player in the digital music services field.

Industrial Structure

In 2015, Québec had a population of 8.3 million, with 4 million workers who made up 23 per cent of Canada's labour force (Table 7.4). In this core region, the percentages of workers in the three sectors comprising Québec's industrial structure are, as would be expected, very similar to those found in Ontario (see Table 6.2). In 2016, Québec's primary sector accounted for just over 2 per cent of workers (mostly

Photo 7.4 Montréal has many fine facilities for the arts. The Maison Symphonique, situated in the Place-des-Arts cultural hub in the city's east downtown, is one such facility. The Maison Symphonique has many special features; most importantly, the music hall, with its exceptional acoustics, represents a feat of sound engineering (Dick-Agnew, 2011). Its urban access is outstanding as it is just metres from a subway line and ample underground parking exists for those travelling by car.

Courtesy of Diamond Schmitt Architects, photo by Peter Legris. www.dsai.ca

in agriculture), 18.5 per cent were in the secondary sector (mostly in manufacturing), and close to 80 per cent were in tertiary activities. Québec's economy has shifted more and more into an advanced economy where information, research, and service activities are widespread. At the same time, Québec's tertiary sector has increased its share of the total labour force at the expense of the primary (forestry) and secondary (manufacturing) sectors (Statistics Canada, 2012a). In addition, as elsewhere, the application of technology to primary and secondary activities has dampened the percentages in these categories from 2005 to 2016 by replacing workers with machines, including robotics.

The secondary sector, which consists of utilities, construction, and manufacturing, distinguishes the Québec and Ontario industrial structures from those of the other geographic regions. As core regions, both Québec and Ontario employ close to 19 per cent of the total labour force in the secondary sector (Tables 6.2 and 7.4). Significantly, manufacturing

TABLE 7.4 Québec Industrial Sectors by Number of Workers, 2005 and 2016

Industrial Sector	Workers 2005	Percent 2005	Workers 2016	Percent 2016	Percentage Difference
Primary	99,000	2.7	89,000	2.2	−0.5
Secondary	827,000	22.2	762,000	18.5	−3.7
Tertiary	2,791,000	75.1	3,271,000	79.7	4.6
Total	3,717,000	100.0	4,122,000	100.0	10.9

Source: Adapted from Statistics Canada (2006, 2016d).

is the leading activity (Statistics Canada, 2016c). In comparison, the four other geographic regions, the so-called hinterlands, have smaller secondary sectors and construction, not manufacturing, is the leading activity in that sector. In 2015, both British Columbia and Western Canada had around 17 per cent of their labour force in the secondary sector, while Atlantic Canada had 15 per cent and the Territorial North approximately 2 per cent.

Knowledge-based Economy

The next step in securing an advanced economy in Québec goes beyond a few "spearhead" firms that employ robotic techniques. These firms are at the cutting edge of technology and, as such, are global leaders in modern technology applied to manufacturing. How other firms can gain a place in the global export business depends heavily on applying modern technology to the production process to create global product demand. The existing spearhead firms demonstrate that approach. The reality for Québec is that the decline in its "traditional" manufacturing is likely to continue because of global trade that permits products from low-wage countries to enter Canada and thus displace local producers, as has happened, for example, in the clothing and textiles industries.

Montréal, like Toronto, has the advantage of a creative class that Florida argues is essential for an innovative society so necessary for a knowledge-based economy. Unlike Toronto, Montréal may have difficulties in recruiting non-French speakers from the global pool of creative people. The shift in the labour market to high-tech industries has two consequences for Montréal's labour force. First, the demand for highly skilled workers is increasing, creating labour shortages and a search for skilled immigrants. Second, the demand for highly skilled workers from the international labour pool who have a command of both French and English narrows the selection process.

Spearhead industries provide hope for the future. In fact, many economic gains in Québec have come from the knowledge-based sector and its advanced manufacturing techniques that improve efficiency and reduce labour costs. Such high-tech firms require a global reach, something that a select number of Québec companies have already achieved. Because Montréal has a critical mass of high-tech companies, several universities, and strong provincial support, it is the most important centre for the new economy in Canada. Leading components are found in aerospace, biotechnology, fibre optics, and computers (both hardware and software). Québec also excels in engineering/construction on the international stage.

The knowledge economy is closely linked to research and development (R&D), a general term for activities in connection with corporate or governmental innovation. The investment costs are high and the prospects of success are not guaranteed. Except for large corporations, R&D is too risky. On the other hand, without R&D, the prospects for long-term success in the global market are diminished. The public sector has recognized this dilemma. Governments, both federal and provincial, have invested heavily in R&D at universities and public research institutes and also provide tax incentives for private research firms. Most funds come from the federal government, with minor support from provinces. For the period 2004 to 2013, Québec's financial support to provincial-based firms ranks second,

THE CANADIAN PRESS/Ryan Remiorz

Photo 7.5 Bombardier's CS100 assembly line at Dorval in Greater Montréal. With its corporate headquarters in downtown Montréal, Bombardier is a global player in aerospace. World competition in this field makes success for a relatively small private firm difficult.

just behind the three western provinces (Institut de la statistique du Québec, 2016). Beyond funding research, the Québec government often intervenes in the marketplace to support local firms.

Technical Spearheads

Each region has its technical spearheads. For Québec, aerospace (Bombardier) and engineering (SNC-Lavalin) serve as global spearheads, while Hydro-Québec dominates the provincial economy as an economic anchor. Each has its corporate headquarters in Montréal.

Bombardier

Bombardier, founded in 1942 in Valcourt, Québec, by Joseph-Armand Bombardier, a mechanic, began as a manufacturer of snowmobiles (Ski-Doo) and later developed all-terrain vehicles and personal watercraft (Sea-Doo). Through acquisitions of existing firms, the company by the 1970s had expanded into train manufacturing and in the 1980s extended its corporate reach to include aircraft. Today, aircraft and aircraft parts are Québec's leading export (Figure 7.6).

The commercial jet aircraft market remains extremely competitive with a crowded field of manufacturers, including Boeing (US), Airbus (Europe), and Embraer (Brazil), plus new players from Russia (Irkut—United Aircraft Corporation), China (COMAC), and Japan (Honda Aircraft and Mitsubishi Aircraft). Boeing leads the field but, unlike Bombardier, much of its business comes from the US Defense Department. Bombardier, like its competitors, has to invest heavily in new products and, since not all such investments are profitable, the risk level is high. Both the federal and provincial governments have provided assistance to Bombardier in the past. In 1966, Ottawa provided the first assistance.

Since then, the total aid package may have reached $2 billion (Owram, 2016). The good news is that these innovations fall into the area of high technology and design engineering, both aspects of the new economy.

Bombardier produces three types of aircraft—jet aircraft with the capacity for over 100 passengers; smaller business jet aircraft; and turbo aircraft. In a highly competitive field, new product development is essential. Two such projects, the C Series commercial aircraft (Photo 7.5) and the Learjet 85 business jet, exemplify the risk. In the case of the Learjet 85, sufficient sales did not materialize and this venture was cancelled in 2015. The C Series aircraft has run into a series of production delays and cost overruns. Its long-anticipated maiden commercial flight from Zurich to Paris took place in 2016. By September of that year, four airlines had placed orders: Swiss Air, Air Canada, Air Baltic, and Delta Air Lines. Will the C Series aircraft attract customers? The jury is still out on that question but Bombardier has bet its future on this aircraft.

In 2016, the company received US$1 billion financial support from the Québec government in exchange for part interest in the C Series. These public funds were committed to the C Series commercial aircraft. A request for support from Ottawa remains under consideration. The records show that Ottawa first provided funding to Bombardier in 1966. Most assistance came under the "refundable when profitable" category. The total federal assistance from 1966 to 2016, including those funds aimed at the C Series, has exceeded $2 billion (Owram, 2016).

Bombardier has another side to its business. Known as Bombardier Transportation, this company is based in Berlin. The rail component provides a more stable business operation because the global demand for rail products is much greater than that for aircraft. As well, its high-quality rail systems have made a mark in the industry; in addition, its strategy has been to locate manufacturing plants in countries whose rail systems use Bombardier Transportation products, which range from high-speed trains to commuter trains and streetcars.

Photo 7.6 Flexity streetcars operating on Toronto's light rail system. By September 2016, Toronto Transit had 22 units in operation. Bombardier Rail has fallen behind in supplying these streetcars, much to the annoyance of Toronto Transit.

william87/ Thinkstock.com

Bombardier's rail manufacturing sales and sites around the world provide evidence of the company's global reach. Bombardier Transportation employs around 40,000 people and its products and services operate in over 60 countries. Its solid foothold in India is a result of the strategy to locate manufacturing in countries that provide sizable orders. For example, in 2016 Bombardier Transportation delivered the first metro car from an order for 162 cars by Delhi Metro. The new trains will increase the existing fleet from 614 to 776, making it one of the largest Bombardier metro fleets in the world. Production is centred in Savli in the state of Gujarat in western India.

Bombardier rail systems are found around the world, including in Montréal and Toronto. The Toronto Transit Commission has placed large orders for 204 new streetcars and 420 commuter rail cars. Production takes place at its Rail Vehicles Production Site at Thunder Bay. Unfortunately, the company has struggled to deliver the Toronto orders on time because of start-up issues associated with the intricate nature of manufacturing a new product (Smee, 2016). In the case of the streetcars, Toronto Transit had received 22 cars by September 2016 (Photo 7.6). The delivery schedule calls for an additional eight cars for a total of 30 by the end of 2016; 40 in 2017; 76 in 2018; and 58 in 2019. Bombardier understands the concerns of Toronto Transit and is establishing a second production line at its Thunder Bay plant to ensure production increase.

SNC-Lavalin

SNC-Lavalin, one of the leading engineering and construction groups in the world, has its headquarters in Montréal as well as offices in over 50 countries. The company specializes in engineering assignments in four key sectors: oil and gas, mining and metallurgy, infrastructure, and hydro power. The company has undertaken both large and small assignments in each province and territory. In 2015, almost half of its $10 billion business took place in Canada while 15 per cent was in the Middle East and 14 per cent in Australia, with total revenues reaching $10 billion (SNC-Lavalin, 2016). For

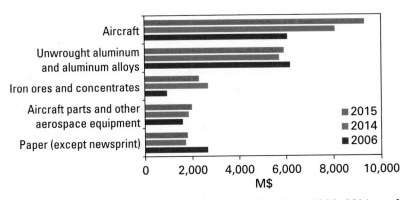

FIGURE 7.6 Major export products from Québec, 2006, 2014, and 2015 (millions of $)

Aircraft and aircraft parts represent the leading export by value, making up 15 per cent of 2015 Québec exports, which totalled $81.7 billion. The next largest exports by value are aluminum and iron ore. In 2015, the United States once again received the bulk (72 per cent) of Québec's exports while China was the second-most important destination, at 3 per cent. In 2006, China was the fourth-most important destination for Québec exports.

Source: Institut de la statistique du Québec (2016: 42).

Photo 7.7 Keeyask hydroelectric generating station, Manitoba.

example, the company is providing engineering services to Manitoba Hydro in its Keeyask generating station on the Nelson River (Photo 7.7). This project is a collaborative effort between Manitoba Hydro and four partner First Nations—Tataskweyak Cree Nation, York Factory First Nation, Fox Lake Cree Nation, and War Lake First Nation—known collectively as the Keeyask Cree Nations.

However, SNC-Lavalin is best known for its engineering projects in foreign countries. For instance, in August 2016 the company was awarded a contract worth $21.7 million to build mechanical and piping systems for a graphite mine in Mozambique (Canadian Manufacturing, 2016). More importantly, during Premier Li Keqiang's visit to Canada, SNC-Lavalin signed an agreement-in-principle for a new joint venture with China National Nuclear Corporation and Shanghai Electric Group to form a new company to develop, market, and build advanced-fuel CANDU reactors (Marotte, 2016). This agreement furthers the 2014 understanding between SNC-Lavalin and China National Nuclear Corporation to collaborate on nuclear energy projects in China by applying the advanced-fuel CANDU reactor technique, thus reducing fuel costs for Chinese electrical utilities.

In the past, the company has landed spectacular contracts, such as a massive urban planning project in Algeria to build a new city to be called Hassi Messaoud near Algeria's largest oil field. This project did not proceed, indicating the risky nature of global operations. Another risk involves the challenges of securing contracts. Export-dependent firms run the risk of bending the rules, i.e., offering bribes to officials, to obtain contracts. The "Gaddafi disaster" ranks as one of the worst cases of bending the rules. Ben Aissa, a former SNC-Lavalin executive for the Middle East, asserted that kickbacks to the regime of Mu'ammer Gaddafi were necessary to obtain contracts in Libya. Be that as it may, in October 2014 a Swiss court formally declared Aissa guilty of foreign corruption, money laundering, and fraud, all related to activities in Libya (Hutchinson, 2015). Such firms as SNC-Lavalin and other multinationals—especially in the extractive industries—always run a risk of being tainted by or drawn into corrupt practices when they operate in non-democratic or politically corrupt states.

Québec's Economic Anchor: Hydro-Québec

Unlike the two global-oriented businesses considered technical spearheads, Hydro-Québec focuses its attention on the province and adjacent jurisdictions. For example, Churchill Falls[4] in Labrador produces close to 14 per cent of its power while sale of electricity to New England and New York State generates around $2 billion annually, and half of those funds flow back to the provincial government (Cousineau, 2012). In 2015, for instance, profits from exports to the United States totalled $900 million (Hydro-Québec, 2016b).

From these revenues, Hydro-Québec is able to conduct research and to improve its performance at its research centre, IREQ (Institut de recherche d'Hydro-Québec). IREQ seeks ways to improve power system reliability and long-term operability, energy efficiency, ground transportation electrification, and emerging renewables, often in collaboration with universities, public research agencies, and industrial firms. This research centre consists of a broad range of scientists, technicians, engineers, and specialists. IREQ's activities are carried out in two facilities at Shawinigan and Varennes (just east of Montréal; Photo 7.8). Not surprisingly, robotics research plays a role in developing new technologies for inspecting and assessing production, transmission, and distribution facilities. IREQ has developed robots to inspect live transmission lines, de-ice ground wires and conductors, and inspect underwater structures at the many dams. Not so well known, researchers at IREQ are contributing to the development of all-electric and plug-in hybrid vehicles by developing high-performance lithium-ion batteries. In fact, Hydro-Québec holds 15 licences and 100 patents on battery materials, and companies using these materials include Sony, Merck, BASF, Phostech, PHET, and Solvionic (Hydro-Québec, 2016a).

For discussion of the difficult relationship between Hydro-Québec and Newfoundland and Labrador, see Contested Terrain 10.2 "Churchill Falls: Bonanza for Quebec", page 342.

Photo Hydro-Québec

Photo 7.8 IREQ's research facility at Varennes, just east of Montréal.

The James Bay Project

This massive hydroelectric project, announced in 1971 by Premier Robert Bourassa, targeted three separate river basins (La Grande, Great Whale, and the Nottaway-Broadback-Eastmain-Rupert basins). The scope of the project is huge. It involves an area one-fifth the size of Québec, but that area also serves as the homeland for the Cree. Construction of the first phase of the James Bay Project, La Grande, began in 1972 and was completed 13 years later at a cost of $13.7 billion (Bone, 2016: 174).

Phase 1: Located in the Hudson Bay drainage basin, the first phase of this massive construction undertaking began in 1972 with La Grande river basin. In order to increase the flow of water through the turbines, waters from three rivers (Eastmain, Opinaca, and Caniapiscau) were diverted into La Grande Rivière. The power is sent to southern markets in Québec and the US via high-voltage transmission lines suspended from large steel towers. At that time, these "Crown" lands belonged to the province. The Cree and Inuit who inhabited these lands saw them as their homelands. Legal conflict was resolved at the negotiation table and the result was twofold. First, construction could proceed. Second, the 1975 James Bay and Northern Québec

Agreement (JBNQA) ensured the Cree and Inuit of certain benefits and land rights.

Phase 2: In 1985, the second phase, known as the Great Whale River Project, was announced. Little was accomplished as the key to proceeding depended on long-term contracts with utilities in New England and New York. A combination of fierce opposition from the Québec Cree and environmental organizations and the arrival of a natural gas pipeline to New England in the early 1990s caused the government to cancel the Great Whale River segment of the James Bay Project. The arguments against Phase 2 were:

- From the Cree perspective, this hydroelectric project would create an industrial landscape where their traditional way of life would be threatened.
- From the perspective of the Sierra Club, the potential damage to the northern environment was unacceptable.
- From the perspective of US utility companies, the lower price for natural gas tipped the scales against signing a contract with Québec.

Phase 3: In 2001, the Paix des Braves (Peace of the Braves) agreement allowed the third phase of the

FIGURE 7.7 Cree communities of Québec

In a relatively short time (several decades), the Québec Cree have moved from the land to settlements. As of 2015, virtually all of the 17,500 Cree resided in eight communities that comprise Eeyou Istchee, the Cree name for their homeland. The largest Cree community is Chisasibi, with nearly 5,000 inhabitants in 2015. The other communities are Eastmain, Mistissini, Nemaska, Waskaganish, Waswanipi, Wemindji, and Whapmagoostui.

James Bay Project—involving diversion of waters from the Nottaway, Broadback, Eastmain, and Rupert river basins to La Grande Rivière—to proceed. In exchange for their permission, the Cree obtained economic benefits and guarantees of jobs in this $2 billion industrial project. The acceptance of such

an agreement was an astonishing reversal for the Québec Cree, who had bitterly opposed the project and who had mounted numerous national and international protests against further hydroelectric developments in their traditional lands. Some argue that the Cree now recognize that their participation in such economic developments is their only option. But feelings run high because efforts to protect the land for a hunting and trapping lifestyle have faltered. Paul Dixon, the Cree trapper representative, put it this way: "They [Québec] promised the traditional way of life would continue undisturbed. Today, the whole territory has been slated for development" (Roslin, 2001: FP7).

By this time, however, most Cree had become settlement dwellers and their attachment to living on the land had weakened (Figure 7.7). Some, especially younger Cree, have chosen an urban lifestyle. For them, living on the land is no longer a viable option. Some say that the Cree leaders had to make a deal. Faced with a rapidly growing population, high unemployment rates, a critical shortage of public housing, and a desperate need for sewer and water systems, the Cree leaders had to seek an agreement with the Québec provincial government. Québec wanted to develop the northern resources and the Cree needed revenue to operate their communities and to find work for their people. Under the terms of the Paix des Braves, the Cree are to receive $3.6 billion over 50 years (roughly $70 million a year), but these funds released Québec from its obligations for economic and community development associated with the James Bay and Northern Québec Agreement. Whether the Cree will benefit from this model of economic development remains to be seen. What is clear, however, is that similar agreements are taking place across the country, indicating that Indigenous peoples want to participate in economic development taking place on their traditional lands.

The James Bay and Northern Québec Agreement

The James Bay hydro project was a watershed event for the evolution of Indigenous land claims in Canada. Such lands, until Supreme Court of Canada decisions in later years, were Crown lands under the authority of provincial governments. When construction began in 1972, the Cree asked the Inuit to join them in taking legal action to halt the construction until the Cree and Inuit land claims were addressed. The resulting compromise was the JBNQA. Under this agreement, both the federal and Québec governments became responsible for providing the "treaty" benefits. As the first modern land claim agreement in Canada, this 1975 agreement provided land, cash, and self-administrative power over socio-cultural matters (education, health, and social services) to these two Indigenous peoples. In exchange, the Cree and Inuit surrendered their claims to northern Québec and allowed construction of Phase 1 (La Grande) to proceed.

Québec's Core

Québec's population and economic activities are concentrated in the densely populated St Lawrence Lowland. Québec's core, extending from Montréal to Québec City, represents the Québec section of the North America manufacturing belt. Transportation plays a key role because many firms rely on just-in-time deliveries. While rail and road transportation are essential elements in the just-in-time system that connects parts firms with manufacturers, the St Lawrence River provides an additional advantage to Québec by affording easy access for bulk and container products to the interior of North America and its manufacturing heartland.

Québec's hinterland lies to the north. It consists primarily of sparsely populated northern lands where the main economic pursuits involve forestry and mining. The relationship between the two regions is similar to the spatial divide between Southern Ontario and Northern Ontario. Both demonstrate a regional version of the core/periphery model. In the Québec version the core's population is largely francophone while the sparsely populated North is substantially Indigenous.

Within Québec, three demographic features stand out. First, most population growth occurs in the larger cities found in the core. Second, most newcomers migrate to Montréal. Third, the majority of anglophones and allophones who reside in Québec live in Montréal (Figure 7.8). For that reason, the language faultline is most visible in this city and much of the work of the Office québécois de la langue française takes place in Montréal (Figure 7.2).

THINK ABOUT IT

Outside of northern Québec, the legal status of lands occupied in the past by Indigenous peoples remained unchanged after the 1975 signing of the JBNQA, i.e., they were defined as Crown lands. Aboriginal title, which involves communal or group rights, was recognized in the 1997 ruling by the Supreme Court of Canada in *Delgamuukw v. British Columbia*.

THINK ABOUT IT

If you were the Premier of Québec, why would you prefer to supply New England with electricity rather than Ontario?

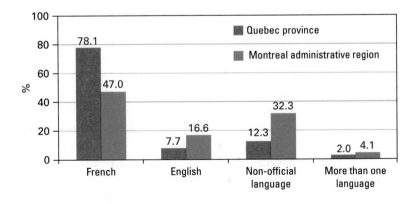

FIGURE 7.8 Population by mother tongue, 2011: Québec and Montréal

The 2011 Canadian census revealed a large language gap between the province of Québec and its largest city, Montréal. In the province as a whole, including Montréal, 78 per cent of the residents spoke French as their mother tongue. In Montréal, only 47 per cent had French as their mother tongue.

Source: Institut de la statistique du Québec (2016: 14).

Photo 7.9 The International Civil Aviation Organization Building in Montréal. A UN agency, the ICAO manages the administration and governance of the Convention on International Civil Aviation and works with member states and industry to reach consensus on international civil aviation standards. Conveniently, the ICAO Building also houses the International Business Aviation Council.

The Manufacturing Core: Montréal to Québec City

Manufacturing is concentrated in the Montréal/Laval area but extends eastward to Sherbrooke and northeast to Québec City. Unlike Ontario with its heavy concentration of manufacturing in the automobile industry, Québec leans heavily on the aerospace industry and, to a lesser degree, on biotechnology, information technology, and pharmaceutical firms. A strong cluster of biotechnology and pharmaceutical firms is found in Laval. To stay ahead of competitors, these international firms have spent heavily in research, making Montréal a leading research centre in Canada. In addition, a number of international agencies are based in Montréal, such as the International

Air Transport Association (IATA), the International Business Aviation Council (IBAC), and the International Civil Aviation Organization (ICAO) (Photo 7.9).

Québec's core contains the majority of the province's major cities. The population increase associated with these cities provides a measure of their economic well-being. From 2001 to 2015, the population of the major cities, with the exception of Saguenay, grew, led by Gatineau (formerly Hull), with a 28 per cent increase, followed by Sherbrooke, Montréal, and Québec City (Table 7.5). The population growth in Gatineau, across the Ottawa River from the nation's capital, was largely due to the expansion of employment and business opportunities generated by the federal government. The population of Saguenay (formerly Chicoutimi–Jonquière) increased by only 3.3 per cent over this 14-year period. Located in the resource hinterland of the Lac Saint-Jean region, this city has suffered as employment in its two main economic activities, the aluminum plants and the forestry mills, has declined.

Montréal

Montréal, the metropolis of the province, is the industrial, commercial, and cultural focus of Québec. Yet the city is a paradox. On the one hand, *The Economist* ranked Montréal as the twelfth-most livable city in the world (*The Economist*, 2016). On the other, Vancouver (third), Toronto (fourth), and Calgary (fifth) were ranked higher, and the Conference Board of Canada has estimated the city's GDP growth rate for 2016 at 1.6 per cent, placing it tenth in Canada, well behind Vancouver at 4 per cent and Toronto at 3.4 per cent and just ahead of Regina at 1.3 per cent (Arcand et al., 2016). The complexity of Montréal, a paradoxically vibrant yet struggling city, is presented in "Further Readings."

Montréal is the largest census metropolitan area in the province with an estimated 2015 population of over 4 million. Nearly half of Québec's population lives in the Montréal CMA, which includes the cities of Laval and Longueuil as well as the municipalities of Beaconsfield, Baie-D'Urfé, Côte-Saint-Luc, Dollard-Des-Ormeaux, Dorval, Hampstead, Kirkland, L'Île-Dorval, Montréal-Est, Montréal-Ouest, Mont-Royal, Pointe-Claire, Sainte-Anne-de-Bellevue, Senneville, and Westmount. Like Toronto, Montréal has developed

TABLE 7.5 Population of Census Metropolitan Areas in Québec, 2001 and 2015

City	Population 2001 (000s)	Population 2015 (000s)	% Change 2001–15
Montréal	3,451.0	4,060.7	17.7
Québec City	686.6	806.4	17.5
Gatineau	257.6	330.8	28.4
Saguenay	154.9	160.0	3.3
Sherbrooke	176.0	214.5	21.9
Trois-Rivières	137.5	156.4	13.8

Source: Statistics Canada (2007, 2016b).

an effective combination of metro lines and surface bus transportation that provides quick and inexpensive city transportation. Montréal is the growth engine for Québec and also is the fourth-largest French-speaking city in the world. In that sense, Montréal is pulled into the global economic world, but at the same time the province tries to protect the French language. The most recent attempt to ensure the prominence of French in Montréal occurred in 2012 with Bill 14, but that proposed legislation did not see the light of day (De Courcy, 2012).

Montréal is one of Canada's oldest cities. Historically rich but infrastructurally poor, the city (perhaps more than other Canadian cities) needs huge investment in its infrastructure. One sign of its plight took place in 2015 when Montréal discharged 5 billion litres of untreated sewage into the St Lawrence River over four days while repairs to the sewerage system were undertaken (Gerbel, 2015). Situated on an island, Montréal has a dozen bridges and overpasses that are well past their best years. Like other cities, the cost of improving its infrastructure is well beyond its means. Fortunately for Montréal, the federal government is responsible for two bridges crossing the St Lawrence River, the Jacques Cartier and Champlain bridges. City mayors have challenged Ottawa to provide more tax dollars to cities for infrastructure. Ottawa has responded by sharing a portion of the federal gas tax.

Following the Canada–US Free Trade Agreement in 1989 and, especially, the establishment of the rules-based World Trade Organization in 1995, Montréal's manufacturing sector had to respond to strong foreign competition. Labour-intensive manufacturing firms experienced great difficulty in competing with foreign firms that had substantially lower labour costs. Montréal's

manufacturing firms made two major changes: labour-intensive plants substituted machinery for workers to increase productivity, and high-technology firms expanded. By the late 1990s, Montréal's economy had become much more specialized in aerospace, computers, fibre optics, multilingual software, telecommunications, and other areas of industrial research and development. The provincial government has taken a leading role by providing subsidies for high-tech firms that relocate to Montréal and other Québec cities. Universities, such as Université de Montréal and McGill University, serve as a critical link to the high-tech industry.

Montréal and Toronto

From the founding of Canada, Montréal was the leading city. In the 1970s, Toronto caught up to Montréal and gradually surpassed it. Beginning in the 1970s, especially with the election of the first PQ government in 1976, Montréal lost it place as the premier city in Canada. Sun Life's move from Montréal to Toronto in 1978 was a shift of symbolic importance. The principal reason for this shift in metropolitan power was the strong economic growth in Southern Ontario powered by the Auto Pact and the resulting expansion of the automobile industry. A secondary factor was the economic and demographic fallout from the political unrest in Québec and the very real possibility of Québec separating from Canada. At that time, many anglophones and some corporations moved to Toronto. While the francophone business community and the provincial government kept the Montréal economy growing, by 1981 Toronto had a population of 3.0 million compared to Montréal's 2.8 million (Table 7.6). Since then, the momentum of Toronto's growth has caused the population gap to widen.

TABLE 7.6 Population Change: Montréal and Toronto, 1951–2015 (000s)

Year	Montréal	Toronto	Difference
1951	1,539	1,262	277
1961	2,216	1,919	297
1971	2,743	2,628	115
1981	2,828	2,999	−171
1991	3,127	3,893	−766
2001	3,426	4,683	−1,257
2006	3,636	5,113	−1,477
2011	3,824	5,583	−1,759
2015	4,061	6,130	−2,069

Sources: Statistics Canada (2002, 2007, 2012b, 2016b).

Québec City

Founded in 1608 by Samuel de Champlain, Québec City is one of the oldest cities in North America. Québec City, the historic capital of French Canada and the capital of modern-day Québec, has the second-largest urban concentration in the province, totalling over 800,000 people in 2015. Québec City has a magnificent physical setting on high banks along the St Lawrence River with the rugged terrain of the Canadian Shield lying only a short distance to the north posing a sharp contrast to the more gentle landscape of the St Lawrence Lowland. As the only walled city in North America and with buildings over 300 years old, the city has a vibrant tourist industry with many international visitors (Photo 7.10). In 1985, UNESCO selected Québec City as a World Heritage Site.

The economic base of Québec City revolves around three functions. First, it is an administrative centre. As the provincial seat of government, Québec City employs a large number of civil servants. Université Laval, one of the largest universities in Canada, ranks highly among universities in North America. Second, Québec City has a substantial manufacturing base that is benefiting from increased exports to the United States, largely because of a softer Canadian dollar. Third, the city is a world-class tourist centre. The Old World charm of Québec City draws tourists from around the world, while special events such as its Winter Carnival are very popular. Then, too, Québec City is only minutes away from excellent seasonal recreation areas—from skiing in the winter to water sports in the summer.

Québec's Northern Hinterland

Northern Québec lies in the permafrost lands that extend well beyond the rich farmland and industrial zone of the St Lawrence Valley (Vignette 7.6). This hinterland, situated in the physiographic regions of the Canadian Shield and the Hudson Bay Lowland, has three principal economic activities, forestry,

Photo 7.10 A cruise ship moored at Québec City, in the St Lawrence River.

Rolf Hicker Photography/Alamy Stock Photo

Vignette 7.6

Administrative Regions in Québec's North

L'Institut de la statistique du Québec divides the province into 16 regions for the purpose of providing regional statistics. The four regions most closely aligned with the North are: Nord-du-Québec (10), Côte-Nord (09), Abitibi-Témiscamingue (08), and Saguenay-Lac-Saint-Jean (02). While Nord-du-Québec lies well within the North, the southern extents of these "statistical" regions do not correspond with the southern boundary of the North used in this text, i.e., the southern edge of permafrost. To view the map of these regions and to connect to a variety of statistical data for these regions, see: www.stat.gouv.qc.ca/statistiques/profils/region_00/region_00_an.htm.

hydroelectric generation, and mining. These lands in the boreal forest and tundra remain the homelands of the Cree, Innu, and Inuit where hunting and fishing play a prominent role in securing country food for the Indigenous economy. Its resource-based economy—mining and forestry—depends on foreign markets. With commodity prices depressed, mines have either closed or cut back production. Forest companies, on the other hand, have enjoyed a resurgence of exports to the United States.

As an old resource hinterland, long-term prospects are not bright and employment is falling, partly due to market conditions and the automation taking place in the forest and mining industries. Surprisingly, the vast hydroelectric system that has placed its industrial stamp on the landscape requires few employees in its post-construction phase. Consequently, like Northern Ontario, the resource-based economy is not generating jobs and the number of people residing in Québec's North continues to drift downward. On the other hand, the Inuit and Cree populations are increasing rapidly. By 2015, the Cree numbered 17,468 while the Inuit, known as Nunavimmiut, totalled 13,204; together, their population growth over the last five years in the Nord-du-Québec region exceeded 10 per cent while the other three northern regions comprising the Québec North had negative growth rates (Institut de la statistique du Québec, 2016). Nord-du-Québec most closely matches the geographic area of the James Bay hydroelectric projects while the other three administrative regions are heavily involved in forestry and mining (Vignette 7.6).

New Political Realities

The Cree and Inuit represent the majority of the population in Nord-du-Québec. Both are seeking a new relationship with the province that provides more independence, but within Québec. Such an arrangement does not exist—a semi-autonomous region within a province. What form that political relationship(s) will take is unclear. The attempt of the Inuit, as represented by Makivik, to gain a measure of autonomy along the lines of Nunavut remains a work in progress. **Makivik Corporation** and **Kativik Regional Government** came into existence as a result of the James Bay and Northern Québec Agreement. Makivik is the business arm that manages the Inuit compensation funds from the JBNQA and other revenues generated by their investments and companies. As well, Makivik represents the Inuit in political and economic matters, such as negotiating the Nunavik Inuit Offshore Land Claim (resolved in 2008) and in seeking self-government. On the other hand, Kativik Regional Government provides the various public services to residents of Nunavik, including education and security.

These two organizations have allowed the Inuit to manage their own affairs and thus gain administrative experience in different areas for over 30 years. In the process, the dream of a regional government emerged within Makivik. The breakthrough for this radical political goal came in 1983 when Premier René Lévesque stated unequivocally that an Inuit regional government within Québec was possible.

Such a government, controlled by the Inuit, would respond to their needs, desires, and aspirations. To achieve that goal, three formidable challenges had to be resolved. First, how can a regional government function within a province? This calls into question the division of powers between the province of Québec and the soon-to-be-formed government of Nunavik. Second, how can Nunavik (a non-ethnic government) treat all its residents equally and still promote Inuit culture? Lastly, how can 11,000 people living in 14 communities scattered over 500,000 km² govern themselves and also generate sufficient revenue to pay for their government?

The road to Nunavik is long and difficult. Somehow the structure, operations, powers, and design of this new form of government within a Canadian province can be achieved. The process began with the JBNQA that created Indigenous organizations to administer and manage the funds associated with that Agreement. The federal and provincial governments negotiated the details of an autonomous political region with Makivik. In 2011, a referendum was held on the proposed Inuit self-government proposal. The rank-and-file Inuit rejected the proposed political system, indicating that they could not see the advantage of this version of self-government over the existing governance conducted by the Kativik Regional Government. If the leadership of Makivik wishes to bring a revised proposal on self-government to the Inuit, the corporation must gain the confidence of the people.

Forest Industry

Forests cover nearly half of Québec. In total, Québec accounts for nearly 760,000 km² of forest lands. This valuable natural resource consists of mixed forest in the St Lawrence Lowland and the Appalachian Uplands (Figure 2.1). Here, commercial forests play a small role in logging operations but a key role in maple syrup production and in harvesting hardwoods for furniture-making. Most logging operations that produce softwood lumber and wood for pulp and paper mills are in the boreal forest found in the Canadian Shield.

Québec has 22 per cent of Canada's productive forest lands. Québec ranks first among Canada's geographic regions in terms of area of productive forest lands but it ranks second behind British Columbia in total volume of wood cut. Québec's strength lies in pulp and paper production. Québec's advantage is its close proximity to major US cities, especially New York, where, historically, the demand for pulp and paper has been extremely high. Pulp and paper represent the most important forest export product. In 2015, the value of forest exports was $9.2 billion, with pulp and paper making up nearly 70 per cent. Unfortunately for the pulp and paper industry, the demand for their products has been declining as more and more readers are turning to the Internet for their news rather than buying "hard"-copy newspapers and to e-readers for books. For that reason, the future appears gloomy. Evidence of difficult times is reflected in employment in the forest industry. The Québec forest industry generated more than 68,000 direct jobs as recently as 2009, but since then the number has decline. In 2015, the number of forestry workers was 59,000 (Natural Resources Canada, 2016b).

Mining Industry

Mining has always been important in northern Québec. In 2015, the value of Québec's metallic mineral production was close to $7.7 billion, but the estimate for 2016 dropped to $7.2 billion (Institut de la statistique du Québec, 2016: 33). For both years, the province ranked third in Canada in mineral production. In 2015, gold production led the way, making up 31 per cent of the total value, followed by iron ore at 11 per cent. However, the previous year, iron ore was the leading mineral by value (Institut de la statistique du Québec, 2016). The drastic drop in commodity prices, save for gold, exemplifies the boom-and-bust cycle.

Geology has favoured this part of the world. For instance, the Labrador Trough contains large iron and nickel deposits. This unique geological structure extends for about 1,100 km southeast from Ungava Bay through both Québec and Labrador. Further south, it turns southwest past the Wabush and Mont Wright areas to within 300 km of the St Lawrence River. Deposits of iron were first reported in 1895 by A.P. Low of the Geological Survey of Canada, the first geologist to investigate the region's mineral potential. At that time, however, these deposits had no commercial value because more accessible mines could supply the needs of the iron and steel companies. After World

War II, the United States was no longer self-sufficient in iron ore. Its steel mills called for more ore and that ore came from the Labrador Trough. Today, all of the iron ore production in Canada comes from this region, and in 2015 Québec accounted for 56 per cent of this production (Figure 7.9).

Through a process of market integration initiated by US steel companies, Québec's resource hinterland became dependent on a particular group of steel companies in the industrial heartland of the United States for its economic well-being. Two mining companies, Québec Cartier Mining Company and the Iron Ore Company of Canada, developed iron mines in isolated areas of northern Québec and Labrador. By 1947, plans were laid for an open-pit mine in northern Québec near the border with Labrador. The Iron Ore Company built a town (Schefferville) for miners and their families; transmitted power from Churchill Falls to operate the mine and the town; and built a railway (the Québec North Shore and Labrador Railway) to deliver the iron ore to the port at Sept-Îles, from where the ore was transported to supply US steel mills in Ohio and Pennsylvania.

The demand for iron ore rose in the 1960s, resulting in the establishment of three more mining towns—Wabush and Labrador City in Labrador and Fermont, Québec. At the same time, Québec Cartier Mining Company built a similar iron-mining

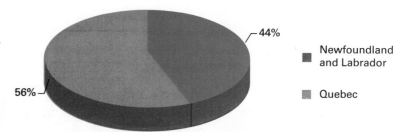

FIGURE 7.9 Canadian mine production of iron ore, by province, 2015

Preliminary percentages. Production from Nunavut was not included for 2015.

Source: Natural Resources Canada (2016a).

operation by constructing the Cartier Railway from Port-Cartier on the St Lawrence River to the resource town of Gagnon. But by the 1980s world steel production had surpassed the demand, causing a severe slump in the demand for iron ore. To add to this economic problem, US steel plants were now less efficient than the new steel mills in Brazil, Canada, Korea, and Japan, and lower-cost iron mines had opened in Australia and Brazil. As lower-priced steel from these countries undercut the price of US steel, American steel companies had to reduce their output, close plants, and sell their shares in the two mining companies. The mining companies were forced to restructure their operations to reduce costs. The repercussions for workers were severe.

Vignette 7.7

Indigenous Peoples Benefit from Resource Profit-Sharing Agreements

Indigenous peoples across Canada remain divided on participating in resource development projects. Those opposed are largely concerned about the potential environmental damage to the land and wildlife—both of which are key elements in their culture and economy. Those in favour see the benefits that flow from impact and benefit agreements as a positive element. As Stephen Buffalo, the president of Indian Resource Council, put it, "From a First Nations standpoint, we're really trying to not be poor. Oil and gas, and energy, is one way to advance, and build our communities, and build houses and rec centres and hockey rinks" (Cryderman and McCarthy, 2016: B3). The Raglan nickel mine in Arctic Québec illustrates this point. Makivik signed the Raglan Impact Benefit Agreement in 1995 with Falconbridge Ltd, thus allowing the Inuit to share in the profits. By 2015, this agreement had generated over $100 million for Nunavik residents (Rogers, 2015). Most benefits go to residents of Salluit and Kangiqsujjuaq (Photo 7.11), the two Inuit communities closest to the nickel mine at Raglan. Salluit receives the greatest share because it is closest to the mine and the port at Deception Bay. In 2014, after $14 million was shared among Salluit's 1,100 beneficiaries, each adult got $15,000 and every child received $3,500.

Maarten Udema / Alamy Stock Photo

Photo 7.11 The settlement of Kangiqsujjuaq in Arctic Québec on Hudson Strait had a population in 2011 of 696.

The mining workforce was reduced and two mines, at Schefferville and Gagnon, were closed.

As the world business cycle improved in the twenty-first century, demand from iron and steel plants around the world, especially in China, increased. In 2000 Rio Tinto, a British-Australian multinational, became the principal shareholder of the Iron Ore Company of Canada, and eight years later the Luxembourg-based ArcelorMittal purchased the Québec Cartier Mining Company. The two companies increased their production accordingly. Rio Tinto's Iron Ore Company of Canada operates a pellet plant and mine at Labrador City and at Wabush Mines. The concentrated ore is shipped by rail to Sept-Îles for transshipment to world markets. ArcelorMittal Mines Canada has two mines, Mont-Wright and Fire Lake, plus a pellet plant at Port-Cartier.

Mine (and town) closures are not unusual events. Several northern Québec communities are single-industry towns and rely on mining for their existence. Extraordinary measures are taken to survive. Residents of Malartic, for example, are relocating outside of town because one of the largest gold deposits in North America exists under the town. As in other resource towns, times can be tough. In 2008, half of Malartic's workers were either on unemployment insurance or on welfare. But this $1 billion project, located in the famous Abitibi gold belt, breathed new life into the community by creating nearly 500 permanent jobs and some 800 construction jobs (Séguin, 2009). Since 2011, Malartic gold mine (Photo 7.12) has outpaced other mines to become the largest gold mine in Canada.

As noted earlier, the cyclical nature of the mining industry, due to its dependence on world markets, poses a problem for resource communities. Global companies operate to make profits and have no commitment to local communities, so community prosperity and employment are tied to global demand. Low demand means layoffs and even the closure of mines and ore-processing mills. This boom-and-bust cycle is particularly hurtful to the narrowly based economies of resource hinterlands. The world demand for mineral products has gone through several cycles since World War II. In 2014, another drop in commodity prices triggered the most recent cycle. Such price fluctuations have had a profound impact on Québec's iron-mining communities and their workers.

Photo 7.12 Mining operations at Malartic gold mine.

© Mathieu Dupuis www.mathieudupuis.com

SUMMARY

Culture remains the fundamental distinguishing feature of this region of Canada. Québec's francophone culture and French language remain strong. As the heartland of francophones in Canada and North America, Québec has a special role to play. Cultural events like La Fête nationale du Québec evoke a sense of ethnic nationalism and a love of the land and its people, which is popularly expressed as *"J'ai le goût du Québec."* Within this cultural context, the French language serves as a linchpin.

Québec's position within Confederation is weakening as its share of Canada's population and economic output declines. The reason is simple: while Québec's economy and population have expanded, other regions of Canada—Ontario, British Columbia, and Western Canada—have expanded at a more rapid rate. If this trend continues, Québec's place will be seriously eroded. Yet two bright lights suggest a turnaround. First, Québec has recognized the importance of the knowledge-based economy and is devoting more public funds for scientific research initiatives than any of the other five regions. Its leading firms are spearheading research into advanced technology and applying that technology to their manufacturing processes. Already, Québec has a few internationally established companies that can compete on the world stage; the challenge is to expand in this vital economic sector. Second, Hydro-Québec is flexing its economic muscle by building more hydroelectric dams, producing more electricity, and seeking to sell more power to the lucrative New England energy market. Most important, Hydro-Québec is playing a key role in research and using the results, often robotic, to improve its operations.

Challenge Questions

1. What are the political implications for Québec if its share of Canada's population and GDP continues to decline?

2. Why is Montréal the focal point of the language faultline in Québec?

3. Is the Paix des Braves fundamental to continued development of the James Bay Project and why did the Cree accept this agreement?

4. A fork in the road: if Canada had accepted Henri Bourassa's concept of cultural dualism over the model of 10 equal provinces, would Québec have a more secure place in Canada? Furthermore, under those circumstances, would multiculturalism exist? See the section "Partnership Vision" in Chapter 3.

5. What is meant by "advanced manufacturing"? How does it fit into the knowledge-based economy? Do the spearhead firms practise advanced manufacturing?

Essay Questions

1. Bombardier is Canada's major aircraft manufacturer. Global competition is fierce. Bombardier gambled on building a larger aircraft known as the C Series program. By 2015, the firm was in trouble because this gamble did not work. Bombardier had to ask the Québec government for financial support—a US$1 billion bailout of the troubled C Series. Québec did support the Montreal-based company but Bombardier has asked Ottawa to match Québec's contribution. If you were the Prime Minister, would you support or reject this request? Provide details to support your argument.

   References:

   Bombardier. 2016. "C-Series." At: http://commercialaircraft.bombardier.com/en/cseries.html.

   Innovation, Science and Economic Development Canada. 2015. "Evaluation of the Bombardier CSeries Program." 4 Aug. At: https://www.ic.gc.ca/eic/site/ae-ve.nsf/eng/03651.html.

   Sinclair, Benjamin. 2015. "Why Airbus Is Determined to Crush Bombardier Inc." *The Motley Fool*, 6 May. At: http://www.fool.ca/2015/05/05/why-airbus-is-determined-to-crush-bombardier-inc/.

   Van Praet, Nicolas. 2016. "Bombardier, Ottawa at Odds over Bailout Conditions." *Globe and Mail*, 15 Apr. At: http://www.theglobeandmail.com/report-on-business/bombardier-ottawa-at-odds-over-bailout-conditions/article29643628/.

2. In Québec, comedian Sugar Sammy tackles Québec's language rules with his bilingual shows and a popular rap group, the Dead Obies, uses bilingual lyrics. In what ways might such alternative popular culture expression serve as a thin edge of the wedge in getting the provincial government to recognize that its language law does not reflect the reality in urban Québec? Can or should such cultural expression affect public policy?

   References:

   Behiels, M.D., and R. Hudon. 2013. "Bill 101 (Charte de la langue française)." *The Canadian Encyclopedia*. At: http://www.thecanadianencyclopedia.ca/en/article/bill-101/.

   Hamilton, Graeme. 2016. "How a Comedian, a Rap Group and a Separatist Critic Are Slaying a Sacred Cow: Québec's Language Rules." *National Post*, 17 Mar. At: http://news.nationalpost.com/news/canada/how-a-comedian-a-rap-group-and-a-separatist-critic-are-slaying-a-sacred-cow-quebecs-language-rules.

Further Reading

Hadekel, Peter. 2015. "Stagnation City: Exploring Montreal's Economic Decline." *Montreal Gazette*, 31 Jan. At: http://montrealgazette.com/news/local-news/montreals-economic-stagnation.

Peter Hadekel begins his article with a statement that frames his argument:

> The Montreal skyline is dotted with construction cranes as an unprecedented building boom continues to unfold in condo and office construction. On the surface, at least, signs of prosperity abound. But look a little deeper and you'll see a city that's slipping behind the rest of the country.

As Hadekel points out, at its peak in the 1950s, Montréal was Canada's business capital. Many major companies, both financial and resource firms, had their headquarters in Montréal. In addition, Montréal was the centre of Canada's light manufacturing industries, led by clothing, textile, leather, and shoe firms. Well into the 1970s, Montréal held on to its position as the largest city in Canada based on its thriving financial and manufacturing industries. By the 1980s Toronto had taken over the lead both as Canada's business capital and as the largest city (Table 7.6).

Hadekel argues that Montréal's downward demographic and economic slide began when the idea of an independent Québec took hold. In the minds of Québec nationalists, French President Charles de Gaulle signalled France's support for an independent Québec in 1967 when he addressed a large Montréal crowd with the words "Vive le Québec libre."

Within a year, René Lévesque formed the Parti Québécois (PQ), and after the PQ gained power in 1976 some English-speaking Montrealers felt uneasy and joined the flight of companies, led by Sun Life, to Toronto and other cities. This loss continues: between 1998 and 2012 Hadekel notes that almost 30 per cent of company head offices in Montréal moved elsewhere. Besides this ongoing exodus, Montréal received another blow. Low-cost Asian imports began to replace Québec-manufactured consumer products and thousands of workers lost their jobs. By the twenty-first century, the negative impacts of globalization—imports plus offshoring, outsourcing, and contracting out—had decimated Montréal's old manufacturing base.

Montréal was caught in a dilemma. City tax revenue was unable to keep up with the infrastructure needs, causing its physical structure to fall into disarray while the province put funding and efforts into its Plan Nord to develop northern Québec's resources. An economist, Mario Lefebvre of the Institut de Développement Urbain du Québec, has recognized this shortcoming and called for a Plan Sud that would see the province invest in Montréal's knowledge-based economy as well as prepare the city to take full advantage of CETA.

Today, according to Hadekel, Montréal finds itself in a weak position within the global economy because other global cities are outpacing Montréal in the race to attract capital, talent, and ideas to form a knowledge-based economy. The leader of the Coalition Avenir Québec, Henry Aubin (2013), puts it more forcefully:

> The problem is not just that anglos are leaving Québec—they've been leaving for years and years. The problem is also that we've built a great big fence around Québec that effectively keeps outside talent out. Any dynamic economy has to cross-fertilize with other cities and bring in new talent.

In 2014, Boston Consulting Group (BCG) came to the same conclusion. After interviewing 50 top executives, BCG concluded that the single greatest challenge facing Montréal is the provincial selection process for immigrants, which places too heavy an emphasis on the candidate's French language skills. In BCG's opinion, the pool of international talent so necessary for the knowledge-based economy is hardly tapped because of the province's selection rules. Of course, the preference for French-speaking immigrants is understandable and fits nicely within the political goal of keeping Montréal, and the province, a bastion of French speakers. The quandary is to balance these two goals. Montréal wants to participate more fully in the global economy by attracting more members of the creative class who are so necessary for a successful advanced modern economy. Yet, the risk of relaxing language requirements for immigrants could fly in the face of the province's language goal.

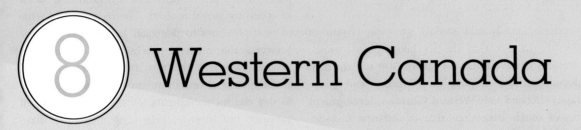

⑧ Western Canada

Introduction

Western Canada, rich in natural resources, lies in the heart of North America. Consequently, geography dictates its need for access to tidewater to allow its exports to reach world markets. Over the past decade, global demand for its resources, especially oil and potash, allowed Western Canada but particularly Alberta to experience record economic and population growth, thereby transforming the region into the economic engine for Canada. With the end of the resource boom in 2014, Alberta and Saskatchewan faced hard economic times while Manitoba, lying outside of the oil bubble, continued its slow but steady growth. Fort McMurray, the epicentre of Alberta's oil sands, suffered from a collapse in oil prices, a shortage of pipelines to tidewater, and a catastrophic wildfire. At the same time, Western Canada's agriculture has been an economic anchor for more than a century and in recent years has adjusted to world markets with record acreages sown in canola, pulses, and other specialty crops, coupled with increasing exports of meat products to the United States.

← At a latitude of just over 53°N, Edmonton is North America's most northerly city with a population over 1 million.

Michael Wheatley/Getty Images

Western Canada within Canada

Western Canada is a rapidly growing region of Canada. In terms of the six geographic regions, Western Canada ranks second in GDP and third in population size (Figure 8.1). History and geography dictated that Western Canada's development began much later than that of Atlantic Canada, Québec, and Ontario, but due to its fertile soils and vast energy deposits the region now accounts for a larger share of the national GDP than Québec and, given the continuance of current population growth rates, it will overtake Québec in population in the coming years.

Geography presents unique advantages and challenges to Western Canada. Enormous energy resources and fertile agricultural lands form the basis of its rapidly expanding economy and population. Challenges exist, too. First, the region's continental position makes transportation a central cost factor in accessing global markets. The controversial issue of new pipelines to tidewater has created a divide between the oil-rich provinces of Alberta and Saskatchewan and other provinces that are concerned about potential environmental impacts. Second, its dry continental climate affects the variability of harvests, but innovative farming techniques have greatly reduced that risk. At the same time, concerns about global warming increasing crop failure due to dry conditions so far have not been realized.

Access to the US market is constrained from time to time by US tariffs, particularly for cattle and softwood lumber. Attempts to diversify export markets, especially to Asia, have had mixed results, though the September 2016 state visit to China by Prime Minister Trudeau had an immediate positive

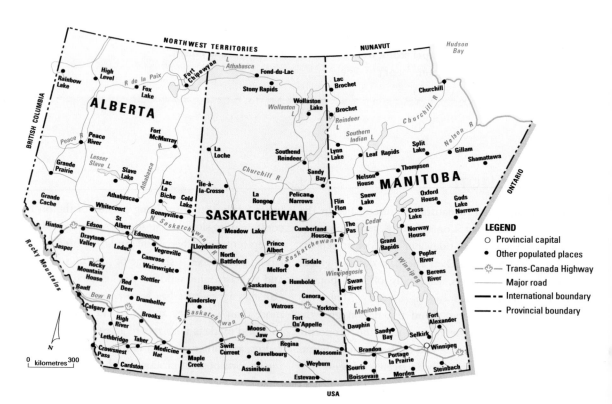

FIGURE 8.1 Western Canada

The two highways, the Yellowhead and the Trans Canada, follow the earlier rail routes of the CNR and CPR, respectively. The proposed Trans Mountain Expansion pipeline route closely follows the CPR line.

Source: Reference map of the Prairie Provinces, at: atlas.nrcan.gc.ca/data/english/maps/reference/provincesterritories/prairie_provinces/map.pdf, Natural Resources Canada, 2000. Reproduced with the permission of the Minister of Public Works and Government Services Canada, 2013.

effect on sales of canola and new opportunities for uranium transactions. Third, and perhaps the most pressing issue, the shift away from fossil fuels driven by concerns about global warming has troubling implications for Western Canada's energy sector. The immediate shock wave takes the form of a carbon tax imposed by the Alberta government and, in the coming years, by the federal government on all provinces. Lastly, water, especially drinking water, is limited. Demands from industry are rising, creating a potential conflict between consumer and industrial water demands. Cities like Regina are particularly vulnerable to future shortages of drinking water (Vignette 8.1). The search for solutions to these challenges is necessarily ongoing.

As an exporting region, Western Canada trades mainly with the United States, Pacific Rim countries, and the European Union. Prices for its resource products follow a cyclical pattern. In the last decade, for example, high prices for oil and other commodities stimulated the economy, especially the economies of Alberta and Saskatchewan. On the other hand, low prices for grains, livestock, and forest products have hampered these resource activities while high prices for canola and pulses have had the opposite effect. Canola and pulse crops now exceed spring wheat in returns to farmers and in sown acres.

Western Canada's Population

Western Canada's population reached 6.7 million by 2016 (Table 1.1). In terms of the six geographic regions, Western Canada ranked third with over 18 per cent of Canada's population. Its major cities contain most of its population, led by Calgary (1.4 million), Edmonton (1.3 million), and Winnipeg (nearly 800,000). Saskatoon and Regina add to this urban mix with nearly 540,000 residents.

Western Canada's sizable Indigenous population is a significant demographic element. By 2016, just over half a million Indigenous people lived in Western Canada, forming nearly 10 per cent of Western Canada's population. Since the population growth of Indigenous people outpaces the rest of the population, their proportion of the total population seems assured of increasing. As well, this demographic fact explains why First Nation reserves are increasing their population size at the same time that some First Nations members are moving to cities, causing the urban Indigenous population to expand.

THINK ABOUT IT

Given the past boom-and-bust economic pattern associated with agriculture and resource development, is the author overly optimistic about Western Canada's economic prospects?

Vignette 8.1

Water Deficit and Evapotranspiration

Precipitation is both limited and highly variable on the Canadian Prairies. Some years result in drought conditions and crop failures. In those years, the Prairies have a "water deficit." This deficit is measured in terms of potential evapotranspiration, which is the amount of water vapour that can potentially be released from an area of the earth's surface through evaporation and transpiration (the loss of moisture through the leaves of plants). There is a water deficit if the evapotranspiration rate is greater than the average annual precipitation. For example, most of the grassland natural vegetation zone receives less than 400 mm annually, while its evapotranspiration rate exceeds 500 mm. The difference indicates a water deficit of over 100 mm. At that time, crops draw on the water reserves in the soil. When those reserves are exhausted, crop failure occurs. Urban centres not located on rivers or lakes secure their water from wells or, in the case of Regina and Moose Jaw, from Buffalo Pound Lake, a shallow reservoir in the Qu'Appelle Valley. The water level of this reservoir is maintained by diverting water from Lake Diefenbaker on the South Saskatchewan River. The map of precipitation in Chapter 2 (Figure 2.7) indicates the geographic location of this water deficit area.

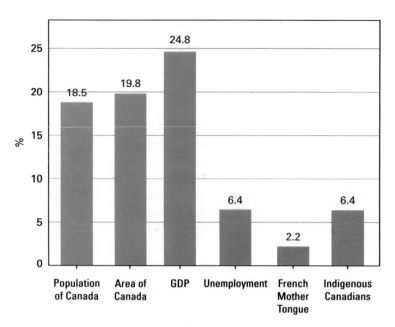

FIGURE 8.2 **Western Canada basic statistics, 2015**

Western Canada contains nearly 20 per cent of Canada's land mass and 19 per cent of its population. Its economic strength, as measured by its share of the national GDP, is almost 25 per cent (although by December 2016 the Alberta unemployment rate had climbed to 9 per cent). For comparison, Québec has 19 per cent of Canada's GDP but accounts for 23 per cent of its population. Significantly, except for the Territorial North, the population of Western Canada has the highest percentage of Indigenous Canadians.

Percentages of population, area, and GDP are for Canada as a whole; unemployment, French home language, and Indigenous population percentages are for Western Canada. Percentages for French mother tongue and Indigenous Canadians are for 2011.

Sources: Tables 1.1, 1.2, and 5.6.

Western Canada's Physical Geography

Western Canada has two major physiographic regions—the Interior Plains and the Canadian Shield—as well as small portions of two others— the Hudson Bay Lowlands and the Cordillera (Figure 2.1). A thin portion of the Cordillera, the Rocky Mountains, forms a natural and political border between southern Alberta and British Columbia. Each physiographic region has a particular set of geological conditions, physical landscapes, and natural resources.

The four physiographic regions found in Western Canada are discussed in Chapter 2.

The tiny slice of the Cordillera, along the eastern flank of the Rocky Mountains in Alberta, provides logging and mining opportunities. Its spectacular mountain landscape attracts thousands of visitors each year. This region has two internationally acclaimed parks, Banff National Park (Photo 8.1) and Jasper National Park, which attract visitors from around the world. Calgarians are especially fortunate in having easy access to the Kananaskis Country Provincial Park, where a number of mountain recreational activities— camping, hiking, and skiing—are available.

In the Interior Plains are three physiographic sub-regions that indicate the elevation of the land rising towards the Rocky Mountains: the Manitoba Lowland (250 m elevation); the Saskatchewan Plain (550 m); and the Alberta Plateau (900 m). The sedimentary rocks found in the Interior Plain contain valuable deposits of fossil fuels. By value, the four leading mineral resources are oil, gas, coal, and potash. Most petroleum production occurs in a geological structure known as the Western Sedimentary Basin, which underlies most of Alberta and portions of British Columbia, Saskatchewan, and Manitoba. While potash and coal mining take place deep in the earth's crust, some minerals are close to the surface, thus permitting open-pit mining. In southeast Saskatchewan, brown coal is extracted through open-pit mining and then burned to produce thermal electricity. In northeast Alberta, the huge petroleum reserves in the Athabasca tar sands are exploited by both open-pit mining and sub-surface mining techniques that involve injecting steam deep underground to "liquefy" the bitumen and then pumping the slurry liquid to the surface.

The Canadian Shield, consisting mainly of bare rocks exposed at the surface, extends over one-third of northern Manitoba and Saskatchewan as well as a small part of Alberta. While logging takes place along the southern edge of the Canadian Shield, most economic activity is associated with mining and hydroelectricity. In northern Saskatchewan, uranium companies produce most of Canada's uranium from open-pit and underground mines. Manitoba's northern rivers, particularly the Nelson River, have huge dams and power stations.

A continental climate controls weather conditions. Far from moderating ocean influences,

Photo 8.1 Lake Louise, one of Banff National Park's most stunning natural features, lies within the alpine recreation zone of Calgary. The lake's famous turquoise colour is caused by fine rock particles, called "glacial flour," in the stream water from alpine glaciers. The steep-sided U-shaped valley behind the lake, known as a glacial trough, indicates the erosional effect of an alpine glacier.

this climate is characterized by cold, dry winters and hot, dry summers. The resulting range of temperatures is extreme—from lows of −30°C in January to +30°C in July. During the winter, Arctic air masses often dominate weather conditions in the Prairies, placing the region in an Arctic "deep freeze" (Figure 2.5). The hot, dry summer weather, on the other hand, results from the northward migration of hot, dry air masses from the Southwest US (Figure 2.6).

Annual precipitation, whether in the form of snow or rain, is among the lowest in all regions except the Territorial North (Figure 2.7). The region is dry for two main reasons. First, distance from the Pacific Ocean reduces the opportunity of moist Pacific air masses to reach Western Canada. Second, orographic uplift of these Pacific air masses over the Rocky Mountains causes them to lose most of their moisture, leaving little precipitation for Western Canada. A combination of strong winds and sub-zero temperatures can produce blizzard-like weather. In southern Alberta, strong winds that become warm and dry as they flow down a mountain slope are known as chinooks. On the other hand, the Alberta clippers with their strong, frigid winds produce true blizzard conditions, due to severe blowing and drifting snow.

In general, annual precipitation is low, especially in Alberta and Saskatchewan. A most significant feature of precipitation in Western Canada is the irregularity of summer precipitation. Natural Resources Canada (2010) has described this weather feature:

> All regions of Canada can experience seasonal [summer] dry spells, but only in the Prairie provinces can precipitation cease for a month, surface water disappear for entire seasons, and drought persist for a decade or more.

The amount of precipitation tends to decrease across Alberta and Saskatchewan as both depend heavily on moisture from Pacific air masses. On average, Calgary receives 413 mm annually; Saskatoon's figure falls to 350 mm; Peace River 386 mm. Further east, precipitation increases, with Winnipeg recording an average annual amount of 514 mm. While Saskatoon depends heavily on precipitation from Pacific air masses, southern Manitoba (including Winnipeg) receives heavy summer rainfall from the moist Gulf of Mexico air masses. As a result, southern Manitoba is rarely troubled by drought compared to the prairie lands in southern Saskatchewan and Alberta. The driest lands are found in Palliser's Triangle[1] where, on average, less than 400 mm falls each year. One exception are the Cypress Hills located in Palliser's Triangle. Average annual precipitation reaches 460 mm because of its high elevation (Photo 8.2). Evapotranspiration provides one measure of water deficit/surplus by measuring transpiration and evaporation, thus providing an indication of dryness/drought (Vignette 8.1).

In Western Canada, the Prairies are the agricultural heartland. Lying within the Interior Plains physiographic region, two natural vegetation zones (parkland and grassland) and three chernozemic soil zones (black, dark brown, and brown) exist (Figure 8.3). The parkland is a transition zone between the boreal forest and the grassland natural vegetation zone (Photo 8.3). Within the grassland, the dry climate becomes more prevalent as the

©pictureguy66/123RF

Photo 8.2 The Cypress Hills, located along the Alberta–Saskatchewan border, here tower above the wheat fields of Saskatchewan. At 600 m above the surrounding Interior Plains, the Cypress Hills stand out as a physiographic, climatic, and vegetation anomaly. As an isolated island of lodgepole pine and white spruce surrounded by the semi-arid Prairies, few thought that the pine beetle could reach this remote area. But that assumption was incorrect and efforts to stem the attack of this beetle on the forest of the Cypress Hills began in the summer of 2012. See Vignette 2.4, "Cypress Hills," for more on this unique area of Western Canada.

Photo 8.3 Within the Fertile Belt, black and dark brown chernozemic soils have formed under tall-grass natural vegetation and they now provide farmers with one of the most fertile soils in Canada. In this photograph taken near Biggar, Saskatchewan, three types of rotations systems are illustrated. The dark brown field represents summer fallow where chemicals are used to control weeds, known as chem fallow; the yellow field contains a spring wheat crop; and the green field consists of grassland used for pasture.

evaporation rate increases towards the American border. The result is a change in natural vegetation from tall grass to short grass. Beneath the two types of grasslands, chernozemic soils were formed; black chernozemic soils are associated with tall-grass natural vegetation and dark brown and brown soils with short-grass natural vegetation. Figure 8.3 illustrates the spatial expanse of these soils, while Figure 8.4 shows that the Fertile and Dry Belts closely parallel the location of these soil types.

Environmental Challenges

Nature provides Western Canada with its major environmental challenge—droughts. In a dry continental climate, dry spells and droughts are a common feature, but their occurrence is unpredictable. While normal precipitation is low, its variation from year to year is the critical factor. Dry spells and even droughts occur after several years of below normal precipitation. For that reason, adequate rainfall in a dry continental world is a highly valued commodity.

Two factors, one natural and the other human, are placing more and more pressure on this water resource. First, climate warming results in slightly higher average monthly temperatures and these higher temperatures are increasing the evapotranspiration rate. Second, as the population and industry of Western Canada grow, so does the demand for its scarce water supplies (Vignette 8.1).

Within Western Canada, the Dry Belt—Palliser's Triangle—is the most vulnerable area for drought (Figure 8.4). While average annual precipitation in the Dry Belt is the lowest in Western Canada— from place to place, precipitation varies from 250 to 300 mm per year—below-average precipitation results in so-called "dry years." A series of dry years in the 1930s resulted in the disastrous Dust Bowl, with the longest-lasting drought conditions occurring in the Dry Belt, driving thousands of homesteaders off the land. The most recent dry spell extended from 1999 to 2002. By the summer of 2002, the cumulative effect of several dry years left reserves of soil moisture extremely low. With insufficient precipitation and low soil moisture, farmers in Saskatchewan, Manitoba, and Alberta saw their hay crops fail,

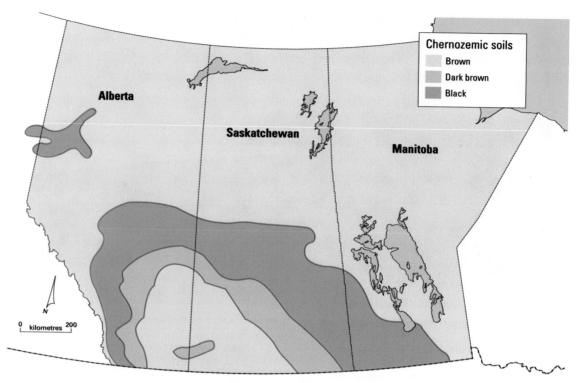

FIGURE 8.3 Chernozemic soils in Western Canada

Three types of chernozemic soils are found in the Canadian Prairies: black, dark brown, and brown. The differences in colour are due to the varying amount of humus in the soil, which, in turn, is a factor in the natural vegetation cover—short grass, tall grass, and parkland vegetation. The soil of the Peace River country, formed in a moister environment than the Prairies and under an aspen forest in the parkland natural vegetation zone rather than in the grassland zone, is "degraded" black soil. For more on the natural difference between the Peace River and the Prairies, see Figure 2.7 "Annual precipitation in millimetres."

leaving livestock without feed or water. From 2003 to 2012, annual precipitation has rebounded, creating a decade of "wet years." When arid conditions will return is unknown, but in a dry continental climate, a spell of adequate precipitation for 10 years or so is often followed by several years of below-average precipitation. From a historical perspective, map-makers in the late nineteenth century still labelled the Great Plains of the United States as the Great American Desert. American settlers following the Oregon Trail had no thoughts of stopping in the Great Plains but pushed across the Rocky Mountains to a more favourable climate for agriculture along the Pacific coast. The Palliser Expedition was charged with determining if the Canadian Prairies had the potential for agricultural settlement. Palliser's conclusion was mixed—short-grass lands were not suitable for farming but long-grass lands could sustain the tilling and support agriculture (Vignette 8.1). In 1858, another expedition, organized in Canada West (Ontario) and led by Henry Hind, confirmed that the long-grass area and parkland (the natural vegetation zone between the grasslands and the boreal forest) offered the best land for agricultural settlement.

One of the major threats to the environment is posed by the extraction of bitumen from the Alberta oil sands. With one of the world's largest bitumen deposits, Alberta currently is benefiting from the oil sands. Yet, this mining operation poses three major environmental challenges to Alberta, Canada, and the world. First, the release of greenhouse gases to the atmosphere through the upgrading process is among the largest in Canada. Second, open-pit mining has created a scarred industrial landscape and the reclamation process, if successful, will take time and money. Third, separating the oil from the bitumen requires large amounts of water—drawn from the Athabasca River—and heat. The resulting

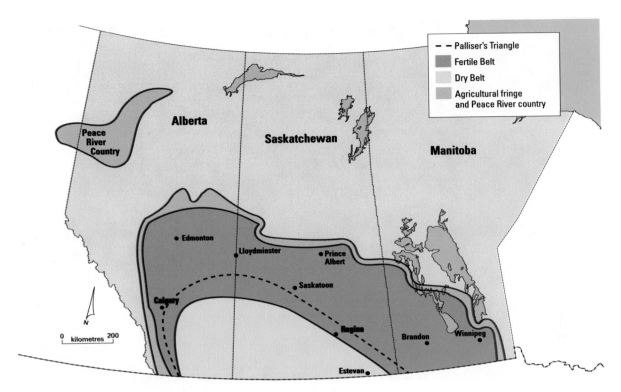

FIGURE 8.4 Agricultural regions in Western Canada

Farming in the Prairies can be divided into three areas: the Fertile Belt, the Dry Belt, and the agricultural fringe and Peace River country. Each region has a distinct type of agriculture because of variations in physical geography. A key differential factor is the length of the growing season.

toxic waste is drained into huge tailing ponds. While each challenge has serious consequences for Alberta and Canada, tailing ponds deserve special attention.

Alberta's oil sands industry produces 1.8 billion litres of toxic water each day. The issue facing industry is what to do with this vast quantity of non-renewable water. Industry's solution is tailing ponds, but these are not without problems. First, since the toxic waters cannot be released into the local rivers and lakes, they must be stored in large ponds for an indefinite time. Second, the amount of toxic water is increasing every day, thus forcing companies to either increase the size of existing tailing ponds or create new ones. Third, leakage from these ponds has a negative effect on the landscape, groundwater, and surface waters, including the Athabasca River. Native communities downstream from the tar sands development, notably at Fort Chipewyan, have experienced health consequences, including unusually high rates of cancer. Since 1967 when tailing ponds were first established, no pond has been reclaimed. Over 50 years later, the geographic extent of these lake-sized ponds is enormous and they pose an obvious example of "dirty oil."

Towards the end of the twenty-first century, when the first open-pit mines close, the oil companies are required to turn these tailing ponds back to their "natural" state. Since the companies have considerable scope in terms of "natural" state, two approaches are favoured. One option is to cover the depression with soil and then plant trees, bushes, and native grasses. Another and a less expensive option is to convert the tailing ponds into large "natural" lakes by burying the toxic sludge into deep pits and covering it with layers of earth, topped off with fresh water that will form a lake. These reclamation schemes for the toxic tailing ponds are experimental and pilot projects are pushing the oil companies into uncharted (and messy) waters.

Western Canada faces other environmental challenges. Concern about climate change tops the list, with the warmer climate affecting the boreal forest and causing more wildfires. The disastrous

THINK ABOUT IT

Oil from Alberta has been a critical element in US geopolitical strategy, which calls for reducing oil imports, especially from the Middle East. Yet, US environmentalists do not want imports of "dirty oil" from Alberta. Do you think the environmentalists or the strategists will win the day?

Photo 8.4 Pincher Creek, located near the foothills of the Rockies in southwest Alberta, is famous for its livestock industry. More recently, Pincher Creek has become the site of wind energy production, helping to make Western Canada the leading region for wind-produced electricity in Canada. Powerful chinook winds from the Rocky Mountains make southwest Alberta a particularly attractive site for wind turbines.

wildfire at Fort McMurray illustrates this point—an unstoppable wildfire in the boreal forest near Fort McMurray swept into the town in early May 2016, forcing a massive evacuation (Photo 8.5).

A second concern is drinking water. With the ever-increasing drawing of water from the South and North Saskatchewan rivers for agricultural, industrial, and urban uses, what does the future hold? With the glaciers in the Rocky Mountains retreating, future supplies may be in jeopardy. Oddly, Manitoba faces the opposite problem—the annual threat of spring floods from the north-flowing Red River. Spring thaw comes earlier in North Dakota and, as the rising waters of the Red River reach Manitoba, river ice dams often form, causing the rising waters to overflow their banks into the extremely flat terrain of the Manitoba lowland. The Red River Floodway, completed in 1969, has kept floodwaters from reaching Winnipeg by diverting the northward-flowing river around the city, but other communities and farmland in the Red River Valley remain vulnerable. The extent of the April 2011 Red River flood is

shown in photo 2.14. Notably, spring flooding in this area may be occurring more frequently.

In Chapter 2, "Extreme Weather Events," page 46, the Red River Valley, spring floods, and the diversion of water around Winnipeg by the Red River Floodway are discussed.

Another challenge is the need to remove the radioactive wastes from abandoned uranium mines near Lake Athabasca before the radioactive waste seeps into the lake and eventually spreads throughout the Mackenzie River system. For years, these dangerous wastes were recognized as a serious hazard to the environment but a decommissioning agreement between the federal and Saskatchewan governments was stalled over the sharing of the cost of cleanup. In fact, estimating cleanup costs was difficult and actual costs may exceed the estimate. In 2007, the federal and provincial governments announced an agreement to share equally the estimated cost of $24.6 million. The Saskatchewan Research Council (SRC) is responsible for this multi-million dollar reclamation project,

Fort McMurray Wildfire
Terry Reith/CBC Licensing

Photo 8.5 On 1 May 2016 the fire known as "the Beast" was first sighted about 15 km southwest of Fort McMurray. High winds and dry conditions allowed the fire to spread rapidly. Within two days, the fire had jumped about a kilometre across the Athabasca River—what normally would have been a reliable fire break—and reached the town, forcing more than 80,000 residents to flee. Oil camps nearby were also threatened and oil production was virtually halted in May. Such mammoth fires do not die readily, but smoulder underground in tree roots, peat, and nutrient-rich soil, surviving heavy rains and winter snows. In late 2016 "the Beast" was deep underground along the Alberta–Saskatchewan border, where in the spring of 2017 firefighters were expected to locate its extent and seek to extinguish it.

which involves assessing and reclaiming the Gunnar Uranium Mine and Mill site, the Lorado Uranium Mill site, and 36 satellite mine sites in northern Saskatchewan. By 2011, the assessment was completed and reclamation work began, but with no end to the cleanup in sight (SRC, 2012, 2016).

Western Canada's Historical Geography

Western Canada's recorded history goes back to the fur-trading days. Beginning in 1670, the Hudson's Bay Company (HBC) administered for 200 years much of Canada's western interior. This area was part of Rupert's Land (all the land draining into Hudson Bay). In 1821, when the company merged with its rival, the North West Company, the HBC acquired control over more land, known as the North-Western Territory

(lands draining into the Arctic Ocean). Before 1870, when Canada was ceded these lands by the British government (Figure 3.4), the HBC used this vast territory exclusively for the fur trade.

The land in Western Canada began to be used by Europeans for purposes other than fur trading at the beginning of the nineteenth century. In 1810, Lord Selkirk, a Scots nobleman who was concerned with the plight of poor Scottish crofters (tenants) evicted from their small holdings, acquired land in the Red River Valley from the Hudson's Bay Company. The first Scottish settlers arrived in 1812 to form an agricultural settlement near Fort Garry, the principal HBC trading post in the region. This became known as the Red River Settlement. Selkirk's settlers, however, faced an unfamiliar and harsh environment and had great trouble establishing an agricultural colony. Over the years, many gave up and left for Upper Canada and the United States.

THINK ABOUT IT

If NAFTA is re-negotiated, do you think the US will press Canada for access to our water?

At the same time, many former officers and servants of the Hudson's Bay Company, along with their Indigenous wives and children, settled at Fort Garry. In addition to these English-speaking people were the French-speaking Métis who had worked for the North West Company. Because the Métis were Catholic and spoke French, they formed a separate cultural group within the settlement. After the consolidation of the Hudson's Bay Company and the North West Company, former North West Company employees were let go. Many were Métis who settled at Red River, where they turned their attention to subsistence farming, freighting, and buffalo hunting.

During the negotiations with Britain over Confederation, the subject of the annexation of Rupert's Land into the Dominion of Canada arose, and provision was made in the British North America Act for its admission into Canada. In 1869, the Hudson's Bay Company signed the deed of transfer, surrendering to Great Britain its chartered territory for £300,000—with the notable exception of the lands surrounding its posts and about 1,133,160 ha of farmland. In 1870, Great Britain transferred Rupert's Land to Canada.

But What about the Original Inhabitants?

In the nineteenth century, Plains people and Métis formed the population of Western Canada. Both depended on the buffalo and the fur trade. In the last half of the century, commercial hunting of buffalo in the United States and Canada ended with the destruction of the great buffalo herds. With the virtual extinction of the buffalo, the Plains peoples (Sarcee, Blood, Peigan, Stoney, Plains Cree, Nakota, Lakota, Blackfoot, and Saulteaux) could no longer support themselves. The transfer of Hudson's Bay lands to Canada, coupled with Ottawa's plan to settle the arable lands of Western Canada, meant that the only option for Plains peoples was to sign treaties and live on reserves (Figure 3.10).[2] The Métis were also confronted by the impact of these historic changes on their way of life. Yet, because they were not semi-nomadic like the Plains peoples and, instead, formed an organized settlement at Red River that was remote from Canada, the Métis were more able to resist Canada's desire to settle the Prairies with farmers.

 The rebellions of 1869–70 and 1885 are examined in Chapter 3; see page 96 and page 98.

In 1867, the population at Red River was nearly 12,000, mostly Métis. The arrival of land surveyors and settlers led the Métis, under the leadership of Louis Riel, to mount the Red River Rebellion in 1869. The Métis wanted to negotiate the terms of entry into Canada from a position of strength—that is, as a government—and they obtained major concessions from Ottawa: guaranteed ownership of land, recognition of the French language, and permission to maintain Roman Catholic schools. In 1870, the fur-trading district of Assiniboia became the province of Manitoba. But the rebels' victory was hollow. First, Ottawa sent troops to exert Canada's control over the new province, forcing Riel and his followers to flee. Second, settlers began to pour into Manitoba, changing the demographic balance of power and overwhelming the Métis community.

Many Métis left the colony to search for a new place to settle in the Canadian West. Such a place was Batoche, just north of the site where Saskatoon now is situated. Within 15 years, however, settlers would again encroach on the Métis agricultural settlement. In 1885, as before, the Métis, led by Louis Riel, rebelled. This time, the Canadian militia defeated the Métis at the Battle of Batoche and Riel was captured, found guilty of treason, and hanged.

The experiences of First Nations tribes during the early period of western settlement were somewhat different. Tribes such as the Blackfoot had roamed across the Canadian Prairies and the northern Great Plains of the United States long before the arrival of European explorers, fur traders, and settlers. The tribes were semi-nomadic and hunted buffalo. By the 1870s, the buffalo had virtually disappeared from the Prairies, leaving the Plains peoples destitute. They had little choice but to sign treaties with the federal government. Between 1873 and 1876, all the tribes (except for three Cree chiefs—Big Bear, Little Pine, and Lucky Man—and their followers) signed numbered treaties in exchange for reserves, cash gratuities, annual payments in perpetuity, the promise of educational and agricultural assistance, and the right to hunt and fish on Crown land until such land was required for other purposes. In 1882, impending starvation for his people also forced Big Bear to accept Treaty No. 6. Over the next few years, however, the

Cree sought other concessions from the federal government. When these efforts failed, Cree warriors supported the doomed Métis rebellion in 1885 by attacking several settlements, including Fort Pitt, the Hudson's Bay post on the North Saskatchewan River near the present-day Alberta–Saskatchewan border.[3]

Treaties with Ottawa offered the First Nations peoples prospects for survival and time to find a place in a new economy, but the treaties also made them wards of the Crown. Confined to reserves, First Nations were isolated from the evolving Canadian society and became increasingly dependent on the federal government. Further north, the Woodland Cree and Dene (Chipewyan) tribes who lived in the boreal forest were not as affected by the encroachment of western settlers. Although they, too, signed treaties, these northern peoples continued their migratory hunting and trapping lifestyle well into the next century. In 1930, the federal government transferred to the provinces the jurisdiction it had exercised over the Crown lands and natural resources of the region since its purchase from the Hudson's Bay Company in 1870. This transfer did not mention Indigenous rights, and nearly a century later the omission remains a bone of contention within the Indigenous world. By the 1950s, life on the land had its hardships, ranging from food shortages to virtually no medical services for those still on the land. Consequently, many Indigenous people in the northern reaches of the Prairie provinces moved to settlements.

Settlement of the Land

Settlement of the Prairies by Europeans required transportation infrastructure. In 1881, Ottawa announced generous terms: the Canadian Pacific Railway Company was awarded a charter, whereby the company received $25 million from the federal government, 1,000 km of existing railway lines in eastern Canada owned by the federal government, and over 10 million ha of prairie land in alternate square-mile sections on both sides of the railway to a maximum depth of 39 km. The terms were successful—the CPR line was completed in 1885, with mostly foreign workers having overcome the difficult and dangerous labour involved in pushing the rail line across the Cordillera. As a result, the new Dominion achieved four important nation-forming goals:

Photo 8.6 Louis Riel. The Métis search for a place within Confederation began with armed resistance in 1869–70 and 1885. Louis Riel was the political and spiritual leader of both rebellions. After the Métis insurgents lost the Battle of Batoche in 1885, Riel surrendered to the Canadian forces. He was tried and convicted of high treason, and on 16 November 1885 Riel was hanged as a traitor. He remains a hero to the Métis to this day.

- An east–west transportation link united Canada from coast to coast.
- The vast territory west of the Red River Valley was secured for Canada.
- The Canadian Prairies could be settled.
- A rail-based transportation system to eastern ports could be used to ship farm products to the world's major grain market in Great Britain and other European countries.

The settling of Western Canada by Europeans marks one of the world's great migrations and the transformation of the Prairies into an agricultural resource frontier. Under the Dominion Land Act that Ottawa had passed in 1872, homesteaders were promised "cheap" land in Manitoba—by building a house and cultivating some of the land, they could obtain 65 ha of land for only $10. Following 1872, an influx of prospective homesteaders began arriving, most coming from Ontario and, to a lesser degree, from the Maritimes, Québec, and the United States. However, settlement did not occur west of the Red River Valley until the Canadian Pacific Railway was completed. Then, homesteaders began to occupy lands in Saskatchewan and Alberta. The first wave of homesteaders came from Ontario, Great Britain, and the United States. The second wave came from Continental Europe.

By 1896, the federal government sought to increase immigration by promoting Western Canada in Great Britain and Europe as the last agricultural frontier in North America. The Canadian government initiated an aggressive campaign, administered by Clifford Sifton, Minister of the Interior, to lure more settlers to the Canadian West. Thousands of posters, pamphlets, and advertisements were sent to and distributed in Europe and the United States to promote free homesteads and assisted passages. Prior to 1896, most immigrants came from the British Isles or the United States—these were "desirable" immigrants. Sifton's campaign, however, cast a wider net to areas of Central and Eastern Europe that were not English-speaking and therefore provided "less desirable" immigrants. The strategy generated considerable controversy among some English-speaking Canadians who believed in the racial superiority of British people.

Nevertheless, Clifford Sifton's efforts paid off. At the end of the 1880s, the Canadian Prairies had few settlers beyond Manitoba, and most of them had taken land near the Canadian Pacific Railway line. Following the recruitment campaign, a flood of settlers arrived and the land was quickly occupied. Thus began the great migration to Western Canada. After 1896, the majority of settlers—about 2 million—were Central or Eastern Europeans from Germany, Russia, and Ukraine. This large influx of primarily non-English-speaking immigrants led to a quite different cultural makeup in Western Canada from that in Central Canada, where the French and English dominated. Within a remarkably short span of time, cultural and linguistic assimilation had forged a non-British but English-speaking society

from the sons and daughters of these immigrants. Some, however, kept separate. For instance, Doukhobor settlers were Russian-speaking peasants whose adherence to communal living made adjustment and acceptance difficult if not impossible. By 1905, Alberta and Saskatchewan had sufficient populations to warrant provincial status. By the outbreak of World War I, the region of Western Canada was settled.

See Chapter 3, "Sifton Widens the Net," page 101, for discussion of Sifton's immigration policy and of the plight of the pacifist Doukhobor sect.

The decision to build the CPR along a southern route (from Winnipeg to Regina to Calgary) had two repercussions for farms. First, the railway provided them with a means of getting their crop to market. Second, crop failure was high because one-quarter of the land opened to homesteaders was in the driest part of Western Canada known as Palliser's Triangle. Dissatisfaction with the monopoly held by the CPR prompted farmers to seek an alternative rail route, known as the Hudson Bay Railway.

Western Canada Today

Western Canada consists of the three Prairie Provinces. Alberta, the economic giant of the three provinces, has 63 per cent of the population in Western Canada and accounts for 72 per cent of the region's GDP (Table 8.1). Each province has much natural wealth. Saskatchewan, for example, has most of the cropland and is the leading producer of potash and uranium. In addition to having the richest agricultural land in the West, Manitoba produces vast amounts of hydroelectric power from the Nelson River. Even so, Alberta holds the trump resource card—oil and gas. Indeed, Alberta's oil production in 2015 allowed Canada to rank as the fifth-largest producer in the world (*Forbes*, 2016).

Industrial Structure

In 2015, Western Canada had a population of 6.7 million with a labour force of 3.7 million workers who made up 19 per cent of Canada's labour force (Table 8.2). With a strong resource-based economy, the percentage of workers in the three categories

TABLE 8.1 Western Canada: Population and GDP, 2015

Province	Population	Per cent of Western Canada	Per cent of Canada	GDP ($ billions)	Per cent of Western Canada	Per cent of Canada
Alberta	4,216,875	63.4	11.7	294.7	72.2	17.9
Saskatchewan	1,138,879	17.1	3.2	58.5	14.4	3.6
Manitoba	1,298,591	19.5	3.6	54.8	13.4	3.3
Western Canada	6,654,345	100.0	18.5	408.0	100.0	24.8
Canada	35,985,751		100.0	1,642.8		100.0

Sources: Adapted from Statistics Canada (2016d, 2016e).

comprising Western Canada's industrial structure is, as would be expected, very similar to other resource-oriented regions. In 2016, Western Canada's primary sector accounted for 8 per cent of workers (mostly in oil/gas activities), 17.2 per cent were in the secondary sector (mostly in manufacturing), and close to 80 per cent were in the tertiary sector. Western Canada's economy has shifted more into an advanced economy where information and research are widespread. At the same time, the tertiary sector in Western Canada has increased its share of the total labour force at the expense of the primary and secondary sectors (Table 8.2). In addition, the application of technology to primary and secondary activities has dampened the percentages in these categories from 2005 to 2016 by replacing workers with machines.

Given the importance of agriculture and natural resources, it is not surprising that employment by industrial sector in Western Canada reveals the relative prominence of primary activities. While Table 8.2 presents only a generalized picture of the western economy, the importance of the primary sector is undeniable. For instance, the percentage of people employed in this sector is five times that of the 1.6 per cent employed in the primary sector in Ontario, Canada's principal industrial core region. Yet, the percentage of primary workers has

decreased both absolutely and relatively from 2005 to 2016 (Table 8.2). This trend follows that found in the other regions, namely, that the total percentage of workers in and relative importance of the primary sector continue to decline due to improved technology. The tertiary sector showed the greatest absolute growth with the addition of nearly 75,000 workers and its percentage of the labour force reached a high of 74.8 per cent. The oil sands and potash industries support a robust mining-oriented manufacturing sector in Edmonton, Calgary, and Saskatoon as well as in industrial centres in Ontario and Québec. This expansion results in a strong construction industry and, together with the highly specialized manufacturing for that industry, accounts for the relatively high performance of the secondary sector.

Knowledge-based Economy

The knowledge-based economy is closely linked to research and development (R&D). Governments, both federal and provincial, have invested heavily in R&D at universities and public research institutes as well as providing tax incentives for private research firms. While applied research takes place in a variety of fields, the focus is on agriculture, energy, and potash. The push for advancing technology into these sectors of

TABLE 8.2 Western Canada Industrial Sectors by Number of Workers, 2005 and 2016 (000s)

Industrial Sector	Workers 2005	Per cent 2005	Workers 2016	Per cent 2016	Percentage Difference
Primary	284.3	10.0	276.7	8.0	–2.0
Secondary	468.6	16.5	595.8	17.2	–0.7
Tertiary	2,095.3	73.5	2,584.1	74.8	+1.3
Total	2,848.2	100.0	3,456.6	100.0	+21.4

Sources: Adapted from Statistics Canada (2006, 2016c).

the economy is largely generated by the need to export these products to foreign markets. The key is to apply modern technology to create economic advances. In the case of plant breeding, two examples are Marquis spring wheat and canola. Energy research looks into carbon sequestration in Alberta and Saskatchewan.

Technical Spearheads

The spearheads of Western Canada, as might be expected, focus on primary sector activities: agriculture, oil, and mining. In all three fields, technological advances have made them more efficient and, in the case of agriculture, more suitable for prairie growing conditions. Technology in agriculture has played and continues to play a critical role by ensuring greater yields, improving farming practices, and creating more efficient farm implements.

Plant Breeding and Biotechnology

The first variety of spring wheat grown in the Prairies was known as Red Fife. Farmers from Southern Ontario brought these seeds to Manitoba in the late nineteenth century. Unfortunately, the Prairies have a much shorter growing season than Southern Ontario. Frost often damaged the Red Fife wheat crop, thus threatening agriculture in the Prairies. By 1910, this problem was resolved when federal plant breeders developed Marquis wheat, which has a shorter maturation period and therefore was more suitable for the West. Farmers quickly accepted Marquis wheat and harvests became more reliable and profitable.

Today, Western Canada is the global centre for biotechnology with the major research facilities located in Saskatoon, where research conducted by private seed developers, federal researchers, and university plant breeders improves a wide variety of plants and seeds. Their combined efforts have increased yields, reduced plant diseases, and improved the quality of the final product.

In the 1970s, plant breeders at the University of Saskatchewan were able to alter rapeseed into a commercial product called canola. Since then, plant breeders have improved the quality of canola. The ultimate goal was achieved—a high-quality edible oilseed that would thrive on the Canadian Prairies.

THINK ABOUT IT

While Monsanto was legally correct to take Percy Schmeiser to court, did Monsanto step over a moral boundary?

Canola oil has very little saturated fat—just 7 per cent, the lowest level of any vegetable oil. With consumers accepting canola oil, the area seeded to this crop grew substantially and soon exceeded spring wheat. The main reason for its popularity among farmers is its high price and the option to haul the seeds to local crushing plants, thus reducing transportation cost to tidewater and foreign markets.

One of the private seed developers, the global giant Monsanto, developed and patented a canola plant that is resistant to its Roundup herbicide (Monsanto, 2012). With these seeds, farmers are able to control weed competition and obtain high yields, but, besides the cost of the seed, farmers must sign a formal agreement with Monsanto that specifies that new seed must be purchased from the company every year. This is to prevent farmers from collecting seeds from last year's crop to save the cost of purchasing new seed. The company monitors the cropland to seek out such farmers and then take those farmers to court, arguing that seeds with its modified plant cells belong to Monsanto. The most famous case in Saskatchewan, *Monsanto Canada Inc. v. Schmeiser*, went to the Supreme Court of Canada. In 2004 the Court ruled in favour of Monsanto (Photo 8.7).

Technological Breakthrough: Horizontal Drilling in Oil Shale

Horizontal drilling, often called directional drilling, has revolutionized how oil and gas wells are drilled. Most importantly, horizontal drilling technique has greatly improved the capacity of the drilling system to reach previously inaccessible oil and gas deposits. While slanted drilling was first used in the 1930s, technical advances have pushed this type of drilling to the forefront. This form of drilling has several advantages. First, horizontal drilling will produce many times more oil and gas than a vertical well. A vertical well only penetrates a few feet of the oil or gas zone, but a well drilled horizontally may penetrate several thousand feet into this zone. Second, unproductive rock formations, such as the Bakken oil shale located primarily in southern Saskatchewan and North Dakota, have become productive due to horizontal drilling. But the story does not end here. Since the Bakken formation has poor porosity,

CP Photo/Saskatoon Star Phoenix--Richard Marja

Photo 8.7 Farmer Percy Schmeiser leaves a press conference after the Supreme Court of Canada, in the 2004 case of *Monsanto Canada Inc. v. Schmeiser*, ruled that Monsanto has the right to collect fees for canola seeds Schmeiser collected. The Court determined that Monsanto's patented invention of genetically modified plant cells applies to all seeds with those cell characteristics. To many ecologists and environmentalists, global companies like Monsanto and the modified crops they produce pose a serious threat to the environment.

oil could not flow along these horizontal drill holes. The solution is hydraulic fracturing, which involves pumping fluid and rounded beads into it to break the shale and keep open the fissures thus created, which allows oil to flow. One downside to this technology is that the toxic fluid used in the process can enter the water table and underground aquifers, making the water unfit for drinking. Another environmental issue that has arisen with hydraulic fracturing or "fracking" is the instability it creates in the earth's crust, which is believed to lead to earthquakes, as has happened repeatedly in the state of Oklahoma.

Technological Gamble: Carbon Capture and Storage

Carbon capture and storage (CCS) is a technology that can be used to help reduce the impact of greenhouse gas emissions by capturing CO_2 and storing it underground (Figure 8.5). This technology is pushing into uncharted territory where capital costs are high and the outcome uncertain. Like most technological gambles, the first-time construction process is a "learning one," as is the theoretical goal of capturing 90 per cent of the carbon contained in the fumes from burning coal. Valuable lessons are learned that might assure lower construction costs and a higher percentage of carbon capture in future plants. Alberta (with bitumen processing) and Saskatchewan (with lignite thermal coal burning) have large carbon emissions, and they have led the way in carbon capture and storage efforts. Both provinces and the federal government have provided funds to large coal and oil sands companies to develop carbon capture and storage technology.

Quest Project

In Alberta, the Quest Project, a joint venture among Shell Canada (60 per cent), Chevron Canada Limited (20 per cent), and Marathon Canadian Oil Sands

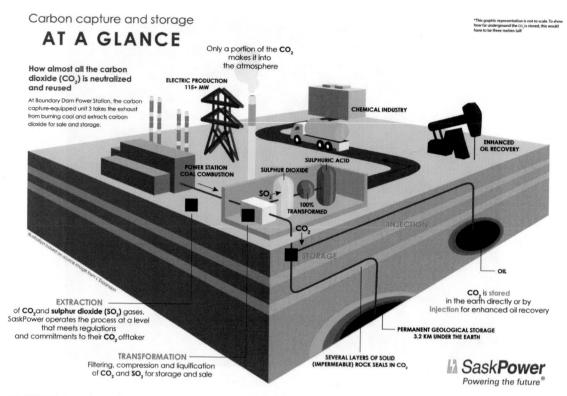

FIGURE 8.5 Carbon capture and storage at Boundary Dam Power Station

Carbon capture involves trapping the carbon dioxide at the Boundary Dam Power Station and shipping the carbon dioxide gas by pipeline to the Weyburn-Midale oil field where the gas is pumped underground to enhance the extraction of oil.

Source: SaskPower, 2016, at: http://www.saskpower.com/our-power-future/innovating-today-to-power-tomorrow/capturing-carbon-and-the-worlds-attention/.

Holding Limited (20 per cent), came into commercial production in 2015. It reduces carbon dioxide emissions from Shell's Scotford bitumen upgrader at Fort Saskatchewan (just east of Edmonton) by one-third. However, in 2012 Shell was not prepared to proceed with the construction phase because of its high cost—some $1.35 billion. The Alberta and the federal governments responded by providing 65 per cent of the construction cost ($745 million and $120 million respectively), thus allowing Shell to launch the project (VanderKlippe, 2012).

Saskatchewan Carbon Sequestration Project

Almost half of the electric power produced in Saskatchewan comes from lignite coal. Worse yet, 70 per cent of greenhouse emissions come from coal-fired thermal plants. Saskatchewan's carbon sequestration experiments at its Weyburn oil field have greatly reduced those emissions. Since 2014, SaskPower's coal-fired power plant carbon sequestration facility near Estevan, Saskatchewan, began operations, but a number of technical issues halted operations. The cost of this facility was high, at $1.4 billion, but the goal to reduce greenhouse gas emissions by 90 per cent from this power plant certainly would be a huge step in the right direction. As a first-time construction effort, the plan fell short of expectations. According to Mike Monea of SaskPower (Wilt, 2016), "Nobody's ever put all this equipment together before. Now [that] it has [been done], engineers are saying, 'We'd change this, or we wouldn't do this next time.'" The sale of the carbon dioxide gas to enhance the extraction of oil at the Weyburn-Midale field more than compensates SaskPower for the operating cost of the carbon extraction process.

Western Canada's Economic Anchor: Agriculture

Agriculture was the economic spearhead that led to European settlement of the Prairies, and it remains a key anchor of Western Canada's economy. In the twenty-first century, while still important, agriculture is no longer the principal engine of economic growth. Natural resource extraction, led by the oil and gas industry, has taken over that role.

The critical trends in agriculture in Western Canada are:

- larger farms, fewer farmers, and older farmers;
- technology that allows for less fallow land and more cropland;
- adoption of advanced technology, i.e., biotechnology;
- depopulation of rural Western Canada and the demise of rural towns;
- growth of foreign markets for pulse and specialty crops.

Larger Farms, Fewer Farmers, and Older Farmers

The irreversible trend of larger farms, fewer farmers, and older farmers continued into the twenty-first century. By 2011, Statistics Canada's *Census of Agriculture* reported fewer than 100,000 farms in Western Canada, with the average farm size over 1,000 acres (Statistics Canada, 2012c: Table 1). Of the three provinces, Saskatchewan's farm size was the largest, at nearly 1,700 acres. Over the last 30 years, the average size of farms in the province has nearly doubled and the number of farms has declined by 45 per cent—from 175,000 farms to 96,000 farms. As the number of farms declined, so did the number of farmers. Another critical factor is the average age of farmers—over 50 years of age—which raises the question: "Who will farm the land 20 years from now?" The average age of Alberta and Saskatchewan farmers was 54.2 years, while Manitoba was not far behind at 53.1 years (Statistics Canada, 2012b).

Agricultural Regions

Western Canada is blessed with a rich agricultural land base made up of rich chernozemic soils. Within the physiographic region of the Interior Plains, two distinct agricultural regions can be identified: (1) the Fertile Belt (black soil associated with parkland and long-grass natural vegetation; and (2) the Dry Belt (brown soils with short-grass natural vegetation). As well, the agricultural fringe and Peace River Country are on the northern edge of agriculture in the West with degraded black soils (Figure 8.3). These sub-regions have very different growing conditions from the two principal agricultural regions. The major factors controlling those conditions are the number of frost-free days and the soil moisture. The Fertile Belt provides the best environment for crop agriculture. The Dry Belt is a grain/livestock area. In the agricultural fringe and Peace River Country, the short growing season associated with threat of early frost in the late summer encourages farmers to grow feed grains and raise livestock.

The Fertile Belt extends from southern Manitoba to the foothills of the Rocky Mountains west of Edmonton (Figure 8.4). The higher levels of soil moisture, an adequate frost-free period, and rich soils make this belt ideal for a variety of crops and livestock. For over a hundred years, farmers planted

Photo 8.8 Canadian production of pulses and specialty crops, such as peas, lentils (three types of which are shown here), chickpeas, and beans, rose from about 1 million tonnes in the early 1990s to nearly 6 million tonnes in 2015. Saskatchewan farmers grow most of Canada's lentils. The province exported $2.5 billion worth of lentils in 2015 with most sent to India and Turkey (Bakx, 2016a). Lentils form a key ingredient in many curry dishes.

Vignette 8.2

The Great Sand Hills

The Great Sand Hills are situated in a semi-arid climatic zone of short-grass vegetation. Located in the centre of Palliser's Triangle, some sand dunes in the Great Sand Hills remain void of natural vegetation, making them subject to wind erosion, while others have stabilized with a covering of native prairie grasses. Cacti, creeping juniper, and small shrubs like wild rose, saskatoon, chokecherry, and silver sagebrush grow in the Great Sand Hills. Some 12,000 years ago, these hills were formed from wind action causing beach deposits of former glacial lakes to form desert-like sand dunes.

grain seeds, especially spring wheat. By the twenty-first century, the acreage in grain had declined, while the planting of canola, pulse crops (peas and lentils; Photo 8.8), and specialty crops (buckwheat, canary seed, ginseng, herbs, spices, industrial hemp, mustard seed, safflower seed, and sunflower seed) had increased. This change was fuelled by global markets and by consistently low prices for wheat and higher prices for canola, pulse crops, and specialty crops.

The Dry Belt contains both cattle ranches and large grain farms. It extends from the Saskatchewan–Manitoba boundary to the southern foothills of the Rockies and north nearly to Saskatoon (Figure 8.4). However, the driest area, or heart of the Dry Belt, occupies a much smaller area, stretching southward from the South Saskatchewan River to the US border (Vignette 8.2). The arid nature of the Dry Belt is due to a combination of low annual precipitation and to longer, hotter summers resulting in high evapotranspiration rates. Within the Dry Belt, feed grain and hay crops are grown to supply winter feed for the cattle ranching that

Ron Erwin/All Canada photos

Photo 8.9 The Great Sand Hills of southwest Saskatchewan.

dominates in this area; chickpeas, which have a long tap root, represent a new crop. Cattle ranches are large because of the lower productivity of the dry land and the need for huge grazing areas to support a rotational grazing system.

The Dry Belt is often referred to as "Next Year Country," and dry summer weather often can lead to crop failure. However, farmers face a whole range of other natural hazards: summer frosts, hail, grasshoppers, and plant diseases such as stem rust. All these hazards make farming much more difficult than farming in Southern Ontario. In 2016, for example, early snowfall in the first week of October prevented some farmers from completing their harvest and those crops are now classified as feed grain.

Irrigation on these semi-arid lands has provided another solution to dry conditions (Photo 8.10). The most extensive irrigation systems are in southern Alberta. In fact, nearly two-thirds of the 750,000 ha of irrigated land in Canada are located in Alberta. In the 1950s and 1960s, two major irrigation projects were developed in the dry lands of Alberta and Saskatchewan: the St Mary River Irrigation District is based on the internal storage reservoirs of the St Mary and Waterton dams in southern Alberta, and Lake Diefenbaker serves as a massive reservoir on the South Saskatchewan River. Alberta irrigators have two advantages over their Saskatchewan counterparts. First and most important, southern Alberta has a longer growing season than Saskatchewan. Consequently, the selection of crops is wider, including corn, sugar beets, and other specialty crops that provide a high return per acre. Second, with most processing plants situated in southern Alberta, farmers have a shorter distance to market than do those in Saskatchewan.

Peace River Country

On the northern edge of agricultural lands, Peace River Country is situated between 55°N and 57°N on the Alberta Plateau. This sub-region has relatively high elevations and its rivers have deeply cut into the landscape (Photo 8.11). Except for the area surrounding Grande Prairie, the growing season is much shorter than that of the Prairies, but the longer length of daylight in the summer somewhat offsets that disadvantage. Grain, hay, and pasture dominate the land-use pattern, with livestock central to agricultural practices. Agricultural land is often surrounded by aspen forest.

Canola: The Prairie Staple?

Grain production, particularly spring wheat, has been the prairie staple for over 100 years. Grains do well in dry conditions where other crops would fail. But two factors turned prairie farmers against spring wheat—low world prices and high rail transportation costs. Until 1995, the federal government subsidized grain exports. The cancellation of that subsidy, known as the Crow Rate, led grain farmers to seek alternative crops. From 1971 to 1995, the acreage seeded in spring wheat in Saskatchewan never fell below 10 million acres and exceeded 14 million acres 18 times (Saskatchewan Ministry of Agriculture, 2009: Tables 2.3, 2.9). Without a doubt, wheat was the prairie staple.

Russ Heinl/All Canada Photos

Photo 8.10 In the dry lands of southern Alberta, water is king. Irrigation waters from the Oldman River reservoir allow some farmers to specialize in growing corn, sugar beets, potatoes, and other vegetables.

Photo 8.11 The town of Peace River and nearby farms in the valley of the Peace River. Beyond the deeply entrenched river lies the Alberta Plateau, a sub-region of the Interior Plains. See "The Interior Plains" in Chapter 2, page 29, for more information.

Since 1986, canola acreage in Saskatchewan jumped from 2.5 million acres to 11.1 million acres in 2015 (Canola Council of Canada, 2016). A similar shift from wheat to canola took place in Alberta and Manitoba. As shown in Table 8.3, canola is the new prairie staple (Photos 8.12 and 8.13).

Canola's popularity with prairie farmers lies in its profitability. Not only does canola command a higher price than wheat, but also farmers have the option to truck their crop to one of the many canola refineries. Yorkton has two canola refineries, but the largest canola crushing facility in North America is located just east of Saskatoon at the small town of Clavet. The Clavet facility was opened in 1996 and has undergone two expansions; with its current capacity the plant processes 1.5 million metric tonnes of canola each year. The Clavet plant and other canola crushing plants in Western Canada produce canola oil and specialty canola oils, as well as canola feed for livestock. The products are in high demand in North American and world markets. For Western Canada's economy, the processing of canola represents an important value-added industry.

TABLE 8.3 Leading Crops by Acreage in Western Canada, 2016

Province	Canola	Spring Wheat	Durum Wheat	Lentils
Manitoba	3.1	2.8	—	—
Saskatchewan	10.9	6.9	5.0	5.3
Alberta	5.8	5.4	1.1	0.6
Western Canada	19.8	15.1	6.1	5.9

Source: Statistics Canada (2016j).

Fred and Myrna Budgeon

Photo 8.12 Weather is a constant challenge facing prairie farmers. Just when a farmer thinks a bumper crop is on the way, nature throws a curveball—or a snowball. In this case, the swathed canola field near Crossfield, Alberta, looked great in August 2012 (left) but along came strong winds and the canola was tangled into a mess (right), resulting in a drop in yields and profits.

© Robert Berdan

Photo 8.13 Along with pulse crops, canola (shown here) has replaced spring wheat as the principal crop in Western Canada because it is more profitable. Still, spring wheat remains a popular crop for two reasons. First, spring wheat is used in most farmers' crop rotation scheme for canola. Second, wheat is a reliable crop in a dry climate. Canola is nitrogen deficient, meaning that the plant requires additional inputs of nitrogen fertilizers. Farmers are switching to pulse crops in a rotation with canola because pulses add nitrogen to the soil.

Livestock Industry

The beef livestock industry is concentrated in southern Alberta. The main export market is the United States. In 2015, beef exports totalled $2.2 billion (Agriculture and Agri-Food Canada, 2016). The hog industry, on the other hand, is found mainly in Québec, Ontario, and Manitoba. Hog exports reached $3.4 billion (Agriculture and Agri-Food Canada, 2016).

The Free Trade Agreement (1989) and the dismantlement of the Crow Benefit that subsidized the rail shipment of feed grains from Western Canada to Ontario set the tone for the current geographic shape of the beef livestock industry in Canada. Competition within the North American market forced Canadian operators to build larger processing plants, to specialize in a single product in each plant, and to demand lower wages from employees.

Western Canada's Resource Base

Western Canada has a vast and rich resource base. Besides its agriculture, the region has a variety of natural assets. Alberta's oil sands are at the top of the list (Figure 8.6) followed by the vast oil and potash reserves found in Saskatchewan. Both depend on export markets. The required capital investments for additional production are huge. With the commodity and oil bubbles breaking in 2014, foreign investments have ground to a halt and those approved remain on the drawing board. For example, in 2016 Alberta Energy approved three proposals for steam-injection wells in the oil sands at a combined construction cost of $4 billion, but the companies require an oil price of $60/barrel to consider proceeding (Healing, 2016). With investment stalled and prices below profit-making levels for new

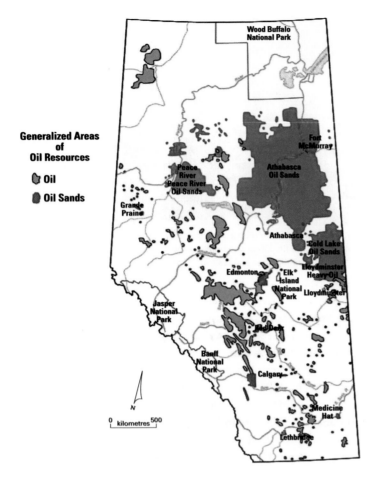

FIGURE 8.6 Alberta's hydrocarbon resources: Oil sands and oil fields

Alberta ranks third in the world in oil reserves. Alberta's total oil reserves are 170.8 billion barrels, of which crude bitumen reserves account for 169.3 billion barrels and conventional crude oil reserves for 1.5 billion barrels. Clearly, the oil sands formed the basis of former Prime Minister Stephen Harper's claim in 2006 that Canada was an emerging "energy superpower." A decade later, does Prime Minister Justin Trudeau's vision of a sharp reduction in fossil fuel production, with the imposition of a carbon tax, threaten the future of the oil sands and put to rest the "energy superpower" claim?

Source: Alberta (2007), from Energy Resources Conservation Board/Alberta Geological Survey.

projects, the oil sands and, to a lesser degree, potash are no longer the driving forces behind Canada's economy. In the case of the oil sands, production has increased but the value of production and exports has dropped sharply. On the other hand, potash producers have reduced output in an effort to allow supply and demand to again push prices up. The loss of their economic contribution is one reason why Canada fell into the post-2014 economic quagmire and carried an international trade deficit in 2015.

For Alberta and Saskatchewan, the question is whether world oil prices, as measured by West Texas Intermediate (WTI), will again exceed $60/barrel and perhaps $100/barrel. To obtain the Brent price, Alberta oil must reach tidewater. The pricing gap is nearly US$14. In August 2016, the West Texas Intermediate (WTI) price of oil averaged US$44.80/barrel while Western Canada Select (WCS) was around US$30/barrel (Alberta Energy, 2016). Landlocked Alberta oil is priced by the Western Canada Select (WCS) pricing system. Until world energy and commodity prices rebound from their present low prices and/or new pipelines reach tidewater, the economies of Alberta and Saskatchewan will remain in the doldrums. One barrier to shipping diluted bitumen (dilbit) by pipelines, as discussed below, is the fear of spills into rivers or harbours because the bitumen is much more difficult to remove than conventional oil because of its tendency to sink rather than float on or near the water surface.

Manitoba, on the other hand, has little oil and potash production and therefore avoided this sharp decline caused by low oil prices. A more detailed examination of Manitoba's industrial structure reveals that its manufacturing sector forms a much larger proportion of its economy than in the other two provinces. For that reason, plus very limited oil and potash production, Manitoba's real GDP grew 1.6 per cent in 2015, third among provinces and above the national average of 1.1 per cent (Manitoba Finance, 2016).

If foreign investors return to the oil sands and expand oil extraction, the Canadian Association of Petroleum Producers predicts that Alberta oil sands will account for a larger and larger share of Canadian oil production, reaching 81 per cent by 2030. In 2015, 80 per cent of oil production came from Alberta; Saskatchewan contributed 15 per cent and Newfoundland and Labrador 5 per cent (National Energy Board, 2016).

The three oil sands fields are known as Athabasca (Fort McMurray), Peace River, and Cold Lake. With most oil sands deposits too deep to mine, an in-situ system is employed, which is similar to conventional oil production. Operations began with open-pit mining because of its low cost per unit of output; more recent operations have had to

Contested Terrain 8.1

Drawers of Bitumen?

Canada and Canadians have long been considered hewers of wood and drawers of water. Alberta, for example, processes only 60 per cent of its crude bitumen production. To break away from this theme, more bitumen should be processed at home, thereby accomplishing three goals—more jobs in Alberta, a stronger manufacturing sector, and avoidance of shipping diluted bitumen (dilbit) that spells environmental disaster when unexpected but inevitable spills occur. Yet, from a business point of view, oil companies prefer to ship crude bitumen to existing refineries rather than build new plants in Alberta.

extract bitumen from much deeper deposits, necessitating the employment of the more expensive in-situ methods. The Cold Lake field, while the largest single oil sands deposit, is 400 m below the surface. In 1966, when Imperial Oil purchased the leases to this deposit, the technology to extract the oil was not in place. Imperial Oil's research unit devised new recovery technologies known as cyclic steam stimulation and gravity drainage (Figure 8.7).

Suncor Energy, the largest oil sands company, operates open-pit mines at Millennium and Steepbank and in-situ production at MacKay River and Firebag. The in-situ operations employ steam-assisted gravity drainage, where parallel pairs of horizontal wells are drilled: one for steam injection and one for oil recovery. The bitumen is then sent by pipeline to Suncor's upgrading facility at Fort McMurray. The other major open-pit mines are Syncrude Aurora and Mildred Lake.

Pipelines, Promises, and Pollution

Alberta's oil sands projects symbolize all that is right and wrong with resource development. Vast profits drive the economy, create high-paying jobs, and generate a demand for Canadian manufactured products. The Canadian Association of Petroleum Producers (CAPP) forecast 3.7 million barrels/day for 2030, up from 2015 production of 2.4 million barrels/day (Figure 8.8). Yet, these developments scar the landscape, pollute the waters, and emit carbon dioxide and other greenhouse gases into the atmosphere (Hodson, 2013).

As *New York Times* reporter Coral Davenport (2015) put it:

> The once-obscure Keystone project became a political symbol amid broader clashes over energy, climate change and the economy.

| Stage 1:
Steam Injection | Stage 2:
Soak | Stage 3:
Melted Bitumen Production |

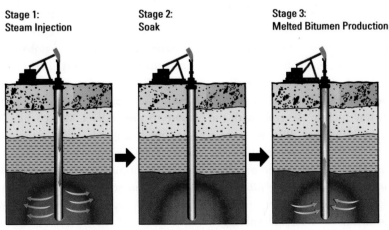

FIGURE 8.7 **Cyclic steam stimulation (CSS)**

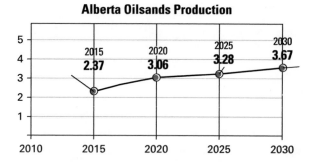

FIGURE 8.8 Projected Alberta oil production to 2030

Source: Bakx (2016b).

The rejection of a single oil infrastructure project will have little impact on efforts to reduce greenhouse gas pollution, but the pipeline plan gained an outsize profile after environmental activists spent four years marching and rallying against it in front of the White House and across the country.

For better or worse, US President Barack Obama's November 2015 rejection of the Keystone XL pipeline, which was to transport oil sands bitumen from Alberta to the US Gulf coast for refining, forced Canada to look to other markets and to other pipelines. To do otherwise—an option that many environmentalists claim is imperative—would leave a valuable fossil fuel in the ground at the cost of slowing the national economy and damaging Alberta's economy.

At the moment, Ottawa is trying to balance the country's economic needs with its commitment to the Paris Agreement to reduce carbon emissions (Minsky, 2016; Mas and Cullen, 2016). Opposition to each of the proposed pipelines has been unrelenting and will continue. Besides Keystone XL—which in fact may find its way back to the table with the surprising election in November 2016 of Donald Trump as US President—pipeline approval by the Prime Minister was given in late November 2016 to the Kinder Morgan Expansion from Alberta to Vancouver; Enbridge's Northern Gateway pipeline to Kitimat, BC, was firmly rejected; and Enbridge's Line 3 replacement from Alberta to the US, with

a possibility of increased capacity, was approved. The fate of the Energy East pipeline from Alberta to Saint John, New Brunswick, is yet to be determined (Figure 8.9).

But what about the damage already inflicted on the environment? The Kurek report (Kurek et al., 2013) revealed that oil sands production is polluting air and water at greater rates and over a larger geographic area than previously thought. The findings of these researchers, published in the highly regarded *Proceedings of the National Academy of Sciences*, clearly refute industry's argument that pollution is caused largely by natural seepage rather than by their industrial operations. Given the higher levels of pollution expected from what at that time was the expanding oil sands industry, the authors call on industry to take immediate action to reduce the pollution as well as for governments to implement stronger regulations to ensure such reductions occur. The Alberta Conservative government's response was to create an independent agency, Alberta Environmental Monitoring, Evaluation and Reporting Agency (Shrivastava and Stefanick, 2015). This agency, however, was criticized as being "an unnecessary, expensive, and industry-friendly bureaucracy" and a "'failed experiment in outsourcing'" and subsequently was scrapped by the new provincial NDP government (Gerein, 2016), to be replaced with more stringent internal government monitoring.

Besides atmospheric pollution and pollution of lands and waters near the oil sands projects, pipelines also are a concern and the oil sands are far from large markets. President Obama's rejection of the Keystone proposal was based in part on the impact—actual and symbolic—of increased Alberta oil sands development on global warming and climate change (Davenport, 2015). It was also related to America's increasing energy self-sufficiency, a result of extensive fracking in the States. With the route to the Gulf of Mexico blocked, at least for the time being, other proposals have moved ahead (Figure 8.9 and Table 8.4). The most recent pipeline applicant, TransCanada, has proposed the Energy East pipeline to connect Hardisty, Alberta, to Saint John, New Brunswick. This proposal calls for the conversion of 3,000 km of existing natural gas pipeline to crude oil service plus the construction

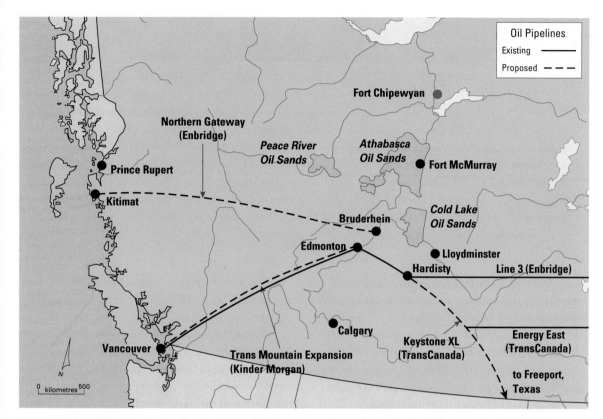

FIGURE 8.9 Oil sands deposits, with proposed and approved pipelines and expansion

Proposed and approved pipelines from Alberta to other areas in North America indicate that the oil will continue to flow. The Energy East line, if approved, would involve conversion of an existing TransCanada line from the Alberta–Saskatchewan border to near Montréal and a new line to the east coast; Enbridge's Line 3, approved for replacement, crosses the border at Gretna, Manitoba/Pembina, North Dakota; Kinder Morgan's Trans Mountain has been approved; Northern Gateway has been rejected; and Keystone XL may yet rise from the dead.

of 1,600 km of new pipeline from near Montréal to Saint John.

Even with National Energy Board (NEB) and federal government approval, pipeline construction may not occur, as turned out to be the case with Northern Gateway. And the unexpected can affect the outcome. For instance, in September 2016 the leak from a Husky Oil pipeline into the North

TABLE 8.4 Recently Proposed Oil Pipelines to Tidewater

Proponent and Pipeline	Point of Origin	Destination	NEB Status	Capacity (thousand bbl/d)
Kinder Morgan/Trans Mountain Expansion*	Edmonton	Burnaby, BC	Approved 2016	590
Enbridge/Northern Gateway*	Bruderheim, Alberta	Kitimat, BC	Approved 2014**	525
TransCanada/Energy East	Hardisty, Alberta	Saint John, NB	Proposed 2016	1,100

*Kinder Morgan proposed to twin its existing pipeline and use the new pipeline to bring more bitumen to its ocean vessel loading facility on Burrard Inlet. Enbridge planned two pipelines, one to transport diluted bitumen to Kitimat and the other one to bring diluent to the oil sands.
**In June 2016 the Federal Court of Appeal ruled against federal approval of Enbridge's $7.9 billion Northern Gateway project because of Ottawa's failure to properly consult First Nations post-approval.

Sources: Canadian Association of Petroleum Producers (2012a: 27); Proctor (2016); TransCanada (2016).

Contested Terrain 8.2

Pipeline Ruptures: Rare Events?

The risk of pipeline ruptures is low, but they do happen. An Enbridge pipeline rupture that spilled diluted bitumen into Talmadge Creek, which flows into the Kalamazoo River, falls into the horrendous category and ranks as the largest inland spill in the United States. In 2016, an oil spill into the North Saskatchewan River came less than three years after the catastrophic pipeline rupture in the US, illustrating that ruptures in pipelines are far from rare. Husky Oil's argument that the spill into the North Saskatchewan River was a "one-time event" resulting from ground movement (Bickis, 2016) was incorrect, according to Grant Ferguson, a geological engineer at the University of Saskatchewan, who argues that slope instability leading to slope failures is common along Saskatchewan riverbanks (Biber, 2016).

Saskatchewan River affected the drinking water of a number of downstream communities and provided ammunition to Montréal opponents of the Energy East line who fear a similar leak into the St Lawrence River. On the other hand, the federal government's September 2016 approval of the Northwest LNG pipeline to Prince Rupert could send a positive signal to the proponents of other pipeline proposals.

Mining in Western Canada

The mining industry has helped to diversify the economy of Western Canada. Like the oil and gas industry, mining depends on exports to foreign markets. The variety and value of mineral production in Western Canada are significant, with coal, gold, nickel, potash, and uranium leading the way. In 2015, the value of mineral production, including coal, was $12.5 billion, down nearly $1 billion from the previous year with the biggest drop in the value of potash, declining nearly $1.5 billion from the previous year (Natural Resources Canada, 2016a).

The geology of each province differs sufficiently to produce three distinct types of mining. Alberta contains rich bituminous coal reserves along the eastern slopes of the Rocky Mountains while Saskatchewan has large lignite deposits. Both provinces use coal for thermal-electric power generation. Manitoba, on the other hand, produces its electricity from hydroelectric power stations. Only Alberta exports coal, mainly to Japanese and South Korean steel plants. Alberta metallurgical coal is mined in the East Kootenay and Peace River coalfields, then shipped by rail to BC ports for export to Asia (Natural Resources Canada, 2016a).

Potash, uranium, and diamonds are the major mineral deposits in Saskatchewan, though only potash and uranium have producing mines. The **potash** deposit lies approximately 1 km below the surface of the earth, reaching its thickest extent around Saskatoon. Royalties from potash make up a surprisingly small portion of the revenues of the Saskatchewan government. In 2015–16, potash contributed $557 million while oil companies paid $555 million (Saskatchewan Ministry of Energy and Resources, 2016). Both royalty payments were well below the previous year, oil by nearly $350 million and potash by $240 million. The drop in royalties from oil and potash is due to sharp oil and potash price declines over that 12-month period.

Canada (which, in effect, means Saskatchewan) is the world's largest producer and exporter of potash. Canadian Potash Exporters (Canpotex), based in Saskatoon, manages the entire Saskatchewan potash exports outside of North America. It is the world's largest exporter of potash, with its main customers being China, India, and Japan, as well as the US. The province has the largest and highest-quality deposit in the world, and with the closure in 2015 of the potash mine in New Brunswick, all of Canada's potash production—which is used to produce potassium-based fertilizers—comes from Saskatchewan (Vignette 8.3). World demand varies, but Canadian potash producers adjust production

Vignette 8.3

Potash: Saskatchewan's Underground Wealth

Potash is a general term for potassium salts. Potassium (K), a nutrient essential for plant growth, is derived from these salts. Roughly 95 per cent of world potash production goes into fertilizer, while the remainder is used in a wide variety of commercial and industrial products, ranging from soap to explosives.

In Saskatchewan, potassium salts are found in the Prairie Evaporite, which extends over much of southern Saskatchewan at varying depths. The potash mines near Saskatoon operate at just over 1,000 m below the surface while Belle Plain mine near Regina operates at the 1,600 m level. The deposit at each mine has a maximum thickness of 210 m. Since the Prairie Evaporite slopes downward towards the border with the United States, this potash formation reaches its greatest depth in Montana and North Dakota—depths that are not economical to mine. The more accessible potash deposits are found near Saskatoon, where six of the nine mines are located. In fact, Saskatoon claims to be the "Potash Capital of the World."

volume (Figure 8.10) to maintain price—at the expense of their workers, who are laid off, and farmers, who must pay high prices.

Uranium mining also takes place in Saskatchewan (Table 8.5). Production began in 1953 on the northern shores of Lake Athabasca near Uranium City. Since the late 1970s uranium mining has shifted south to the geological area of the Canadian Shield known as the Athabasca Basin. Currently, three mines are operating—Cigar Lake, McArthur River, and McClean Lake. Rabbit Lake mine, the least

profitable, was closed in 2015 because of the decline in world demand. A mill at Key Lake processes the ore into a uranium concentrate (U_3O_8) known as yellow cake. The product is either exported to foreign countries, like China, or trucked to Ontario refineries at Blind River and Port Hope and to undisclosed refineries in the United States.

Manitoba has two major mineral deposits—copper-zinc and nickel—both located in the Canadian Shield. Mining for copper and nickel in Manitoba is relatively expensive. As well, the

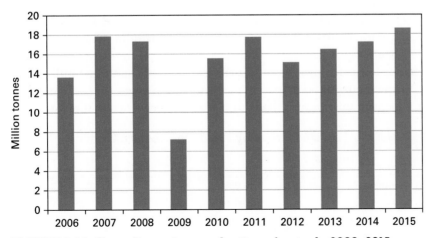

FIGURE 8.10 Canadian mine production of potash, 2006–2015

Note: Production total for 2015 is a preliminary figure.

Source: Natural Resources Canada (2016b).

TABLE 8.5 Uranium Mines and Mills in Northern Saskatchewan

Facility	Licensee	Licence	Type
Cigar Lake Mine*	Cameco Corporation	Operation	Licensed to mine up to an average of 8,200,000 kg of uranium per year
Key Lake Mill	Cameco Corporation	Operation	Licensed to mill up to an average of 7,200,000 kg of uranium per year
McArthur River Mine	Cameco Corporation	Operation	Licensed to mine up to an average of 7,200,000 kg of uranium per year
McClean Lake Mill	AREVA Resources Canada Inc.	Operation	Licensed to mine and mill up to 3,629,300 kg of uranium per year
Rabbit Lake Mine and Mill**	Cameco Corporation	Operation	Licensed to mine and mill up to 4,250,000 kg of uranium per year

*Richest ore body in the world at nearly 16% grade of U_3O_8. Most ore bodies are under 5% grade.
**Mining Suspended in 2016 due to low global demand.

Source: Canadian Nuclear Safety Commission (2017).

high cost of shipping the processed product to distant markets adds to their economic disadvantage. Copper and zinc ore bodies are found near Flin Flon, a mining and smelter town in northern Manitoba that began production in 1930, shortly after a rail link to The Pas was completed in 1928. At one time, Flin Flon produced most of Canada's copper and zinc, but today it is an aging resource town with a declining population. Thompson, located some 740 km north of Winnipeg, is a nickel-mining town. In 1957, after a rail link to the Hudson Bay Railway was completed, the mine facility, smelter, and town were constructed. Unlike Flin Flon, Thompson was a specially designed resource town with a complete array of urban amenities. The first nickel was produced in 1961. During the 1960s, Thompson's population soared to 20,000. Since then, the population of Thompson and of many other resource towns has dwindled: greater mechanization in the mining process results in a smaller labour force, and this, in turn, leads to a contracting service sector. In 1991, Thompson had a population of 14,977, but by 2011 it had fallen to 12,839.

Forest Industry: Is a Revival in Sight?

The boreal forest stretches across the northern part of Western Canada and along the foothills on the eastern slopes of the Rocky Mountains. The bulk of the forested area lies in Alberta (Table 8.6). The forest industry depends on exports to the United States. As with other regions, Western Canada's forest industry hit the skids with the US housing crisis. Plants closed and little logging took place. Indigenous workers and businesses have been particularly hard hit because they depend heavily on this industry for their livelihood. In an attempt to support pulp and paper mills, the federal government, under its Green Transformation Program, has provided financial assistance for investments

TABLE 8.6 Forested Areas by Province, Western Canada

Province	Area (ha)	% of Western Canada Forest
Manitoba	18,968	28.4
Saskatchewan	20,043	30.0
Alberta	27,718	41.5
Western Canada	66,729	100.0
Percentage Canada		21.5*

"*Canada's total forested area is 310,134 ha"

Source: Statistics Canada (2011).

in capital projects that improve environmental performance and economic efficiency. But the key to production depends on exports to the United States, with Canadian softwood lumber maintaining around 30 per cent of the US market prior to the ending of Softwood Lumber Agreement in October 2016. The US Lumber Coalition—the American lobby group—wants that figure lower. Judging by the intensity of the current situation and the protectionist position of the incoming American President, any new agreement could greatly reduce exports to the US.

For discussion of forestry exports to the US, see Chapter 9, "Dependency on the US Market," page 308.

Western Canada's Urban Core

In this fast-growing region, the economic and demographic advances are taking place in the major urban areas. From 2001 to 2015, the total population of the five census metropolitan areas of Regina, Saskatoon, Winnipeg (Vignette 8.4), Edmonton, and Calgary increased by 21 per cent, but three cities greatly exceeded this average. Calgary had a population increase of 51 per cent; Edmonton, 45 per cent; and Saskatoon, 35 per cent (Table 8.7). In 2015, these five cities accounted for 62 per cent of Western Canada's population.

A second order of urban centres includes Airdrie, Lethbridge, Red Deer, Grande Prairie, Medicine Hat, Wood Buffalo (Fort McMurray), Brandon, Prince Albert, Moose Jaw, and Lloydminster (Table 8.8). From 2001 to 2011, the rate of urban growth varied considerably for the towns and cities of Western Canada. This variation reflects differences in local economic growth and in the pace of consolidating populations into regional centres. From 2001 to 2011, the fastest-growing cities in Western Canada were in Alberta: Wood Buffalo at 57 per cent, Grande Prairie at 49 per cent, and Red Deer at 34 per cent. Lloydminster, which straddles the Alberta–Saskatchewan border, came in at 47 per cent.

Al Harvey/Slide Farm

Photo 8.14 Saskatoon, situated on the South Saskatchewan River, is Saskatchewan's largest city with a population of 305,000 (2015). Known as the "Bridge City," Saskatoon has witnessed rapid population growth over the last 10 years, outpacing its southern rival, Regina. As with most Canadian cities, Indigenous people have relocated to Saskatoon. By 2011, the Indigenous population comprised over 10 per cent of Saskatoon's residents and by 2016 that figure could have been close to 15 per cent.

Calgary–Edmonton Corridor

The Calgary–Edmonton Corridor has emerged as the most urbanized region in the Western Canada region and one of the densest in Canada. With major universities and colleges in its cities, it is a hub for the knowledge-based activities where high-tech industries thrive and cutting-edge research takes place. Over the past decade, this urban corridor has had a high rate of population growth, exceeding 25 per cent.

Anchored by Calgary and Edmonton, the 400-km corridor includes the cities of Airdrie and Red Deer and a host of smaller centres. Calgary has become one of Canada's key corporation headquarters, especially for the oil and gas industry. British Petroleum, Encana, Imperial Oil, Suncor Energy, Shell Canada, and TransCanada are headquartered in Calgary, as is Canadian Pacific Railway. With its proximity to Banff, the Rocky Mountains, and Kananaskis Country, Calgary offers easy access to

Vignette 8.4

Winnipeg

Winnipeg, the capital and the largest city in Manitoba, is located at the confluence of the Red River and the Assiniboine River—the location of Lord Selkirk's early nineteenth-century settlement for Scottish crofters that became the predominantly Métis Red River Settlement. At the time of the building of the Canadian Pacific Railway, Winnipeg was the largest city in the West. As the "Gateway to the West," Winnipeg controlled the grain trade and served as the wholesale hub for Western Canada. After World War II, the oil boom in Alberta stimulated urban growth in Calgary and Edmonton, causing Winnipeg's grip on commercial trade in Alberta to shrink. Even so, by 1951 Winnipeg remained the largest city in Western Canada, with a population of 357,000 compared to 177,000 for Edmonton and 142,000 for Calgary. Thirty years later, Winnipeg had slipped behind both Edmonton and Calgary in population. By 2015, the populations of Calgary and Edmonton had jumped to well over 1 million. Winnipeg's population expanded more slowly, nearly reaching 800,000 by 2015. Still, Winnipeg, with one of the most diverse economies of any major city in Canada, has a solid advanced economy base consisting of aerospace, finance, and agribusiness, as well as other manufacturing industries.

As the birthplace of the Métis Nation and home of the largest Métis community in Canada, Winnipeg is unique among Canadian cities. Since the census began recording Indigenous people, Winnipeg has always had the largest number of Indigenous people of any city in Canada. Between 2006 and 2011, the number of Indigenous people increased from 68,380 to 72,335, indicating a growth rate of 5.8 per cent (Winnipeg, 2016). By 2016, the figure could reach 75,000. The most likely reasons are (1) Manitoba has a large Indigenous population (Table 8.9); (2) access by road to Winnipeg facilitates migration to the city; (3) the Métis have deep historic roots in the Red River area, and they comprise nearly 60 per cent of the Indigenous population in Winnipeg (Winnipeg, 2016). Struggling to find a place in the North End of Winnipeg is not easy and some young people drift into street gangs. The good news is that a growing number of Indigenous people have found their urban footing, forming an ever-increasing number of middle-class Winnipeggers, and have left the North End for better housing and other services in more affluent areas of the city.

TABLE 8.7 Census Metropolitan Areas in Western Canada, 2001–2015

CMAs	Population 2001	Population 2015	% Change
Regina	192,800	241,422	25.2
Saskatoon	225,927	304,975	35.0
Winnipeg	676,594	793,428	17.3
Edmonton	937,845	1,363,277	45.4
Calgary	951,494	1,439,756	51.3
Total	2,984,660	4,142,858	33.8
Western Canada	5,073,323	6,678,425	31.6

Source: Adapted from Statistics Canada (2007, 2016g).

TABLE 8.8 Population of Small Cities, 2001–2011

Centre	Population 2001	Population 2011	% Change
Lloydminster	20,988	30,798	46.7
Moose Jaw	33,519	34,421	2.7
Prince Albert	41,460	42,673	2.9
Airdrie	20,382	43,155	111.7
Brandon	46,273	53,229	15.0
Grande Prairie	36,983	55,032	48.8
Wood Buffalo	42,581	66,896	57.1
Medicine Hat	61,735	72,807	17.9
Red Deer	67,829	90,564	33.5
Lethbridge	87,388	105,999	21.3

Note: Except for Airdrie, all urban places in this table were classified by Statistics Canada as "census agglomerations." Airdrie falls under the category of a city within the Census Subdivision of Rocky View County.

Sources: Adapted from Statistics Canada (2007, 2012d, 2016k, 2016l).

TABLE 8.9 Indigenous Population* by Province, Western Canada

Province	Population 2001	Population 2011	Change (%)	% of 2011 Provincial Population
Alberta	156,225	220,695	41.3	6.2
Manitoba	150,045	195,900	30.6	16.7
Saskatchewan	130,185	157,740	17.5	15.6
Western Canada	436,455	574,335	31.6	
Canada	976,305	1,400,685	41.0	

*Population based on responses to the identity (not ancestry) question in the 2011 National Household Survey.

Source: Statistics Canada (2013b).

mountain recreation. Edmonton, besides being the provincial capital, is a petrochemical industrial node. Known as the "Gateway to the North," Edmonton serves as a staging centre for the oil sands and for diamond mining in the Northwest Territories.

Further discussion of Indigenous demography is found in Chapter 4, "The Ups and Downs of Indigenous Population", page 130.

Table 1.2, page 13, explains the Statistics Canada distinction between Indigenous identity and Indigenous ancestry.

THINK ABOUT IT

Do urban places offer a solution to the economic and social issues facing First Nations peoples?

SUMMARY

Geography has dealt Western Canada a full hand of resources, but also two deuces—distance and climate. Locked in the heart of North America, its export products are more expensive because of the long haul to ocean ports, while its interior location generates a dry, continental climate with low precipitation and therefore uncertainty for crop agriculture. For Alberta oil, the need for an expanded pipeline capacity to tidewater is essential and constitutes a controversial political topic. Price plays a critical role. For example, low prices for energy, potash, and forest products have stalled these economic activities while high prices for canola and pulses have had the opposite effect. In the last decade, canola and pulses have exceeded spring wheat in returns to farmers and canola has surpassed spring wheat in sown acres.

The transformation of Western Canada's economy is clear—more processing of agricultural products, a larger service sector, and growing urban centres where knowledge-based research clusters focus on technological innovations in agriculture, oil sands extraction, and mining. In spite of a few dips, if the upward-moving trend line for global prices continues for the region's underground wealth and agricultural products, a robust economy is secure for the short and middle terms. These positive signs raise the question: Has Western Canada reached a turning point where the promise of Next Year Country finally arrived?

Challenge Questions

1. Nature plays a critical role in prairie agriculture, especially in the area known as Palliser's Triangle. Besides a dry summer, what other natural factors affect the size and quality of the harvest?

2. For Western Canada, long distance to ports and then global markets translates into high transportation costs. In the 1920s, farmers called for an "on to the Bay" rail line based on the old Hudson's Bay Company route to its major market in England. Nearly a hundred years later, oil sands companies are calling for access to the Chinese market via the Trans Mountain Expansion pipeline. Yet, opposition to this now-approved project is fierce among many individuals and groups in BC. Who are the main opponents and what are their reasons for opposing the project?

3. Wheat is no longer king. Why are more and more farmers switching from wheat to canola?

4. Why doesn't Alberta insist that all bitumen produced in its oil sands be refined in the province, thus reversing the image of Canada as a nation of "hewers of wood and drawers of water"?

5. Why is carbon capture and storage a technological gamble?

Essay Questions

1. The Alberta oil sands region is one of the largest petroleum deposits in the world. Unfortunately, the resource is trapped in the heart of North America. Are the solutions additional pipelines, increased rail capacity, or, as Leap Manifesto advocates argue, no new pipelines?

References:

Hislop, Markham. 2016. "Neatbit by Rail: An Alternative to Oil Sands' Pipeline Problems to USA, Asia Markets." *North American Energy News*, 18 Jan. At: http://theamericanenergynews.com/markham-on-energy/7076.

Lameman, Crystal. 2016. "The Leap Manifesto Is a Path to Jobs and Justice." *Globe and Mail*, 22 Apr. At: http://www.theglobeandmail.com/opinion/the-leap-manifesto-is-a-path-to-jobs-and-justice/article29739425/.

Lemphers, Nathan. 2013. "Moving Oil Sands to Market—by Pipeline or Rail?" Pembina Institute. 23 May. At: http://www.pembina.org/blog/732.

Myhr, Peder, and Rebecca Joseph. 2016. "What Is the Leap Manifesto?" Global News, 9 Apr. At: http://globalnews.ca/news/2628968/what-is-the-leap-manifesto-talk-of-the-ndp-convention-explained/.

2. Are impact and benefit agreements succeeding in providing Indigenous people with benefits from resource development that end fiscal dependency?

References:

Cameco Corporation. 2014. "Aboriginal Peoples Engagement." At: https://www.cameco.com/sustainable_development/2014/supportive-communities/aboriginal-peoples-engagement/.

Cameco Corporation. 2014. "Case Study—Collaboration Agreement in Pinehouse: One Year Anniversary." At: https://www.cameco.com/sustainable_development/2014/supportive-communities/aboriginal-peoples-engagement/.

Fraser Institute. 2012. "What Are Impact and Benefit Agreements (IBAs)?" Mining facts.org. At: http://www.miningfacts.org/Communities/What-are-Impact-and-Benefit-Agreements-(IBAs)/.

Hursh, Nathan. 2015. "An Equal Agreement." *SaskBusiness Magazine* (June): 7–12. At: http://www.sunrisepublish.com/common/pdfs/publications/SaskBusiness_Magazine/SB_June_2015_web.pdf.

Van der Linde, Damon. 2016. "How a $900-Million Lawsuit Is Shaping the Future of Canada's Natural Resource Landscape." *National Post*, 15 Apr. At: http://business.financialpost.com/news/mining/how-a-900-million-lawsuit-is-shaping-the-future-of-canadas-natural-resource-landscape.

Further Reading

Casséus, Luc. 2009. "Canola: A Canadian Success Story." *Canadian Agriculture at a Glance*. Ottawa: Statistics Canada Catalogue no. 96-325-X.

In the 1970s, plant breeders at the University of Saskatchewan modified rapeseed to create the hybrid crop canola, which produces food-grade oil. Canola is often grown in rotation with Canada's traditional cereal crops of wheat, oats, and barley. The area seeded with canola was originally spring wheat but now pulse crops are more common. Global prices favour canola over wheat. Increasing yields, improved marketing, higher-quality crops, and increases in both canola prices and quantity sold have helped boost Canada's cash receipts for canola. By 2005 the crop had surpassed wheat to become the most valuable field crop in Canada.

⑨ British Columbia

Introduction

At the crossroads between Asia and North America, international trade plays a key role in the economy of British Columbia. With its growing economy and population, this Pacific province maintains its distinctive place and independent spirit on the western edge of Canada. The promise of its vast natural gas deposits satisfying the need for cleaner energy in Asian countries augers well for the future of the province and for the smog-affected cities of Asia. A major trade deal to send natural gas from BC to Asian markets would no doubt cement trade ties with that continent.

British Columbia's position in Canada represents a paradox. On the one hand, its orientation to Ottawa and Central Canada has never been easy. On the other hand, its natural inclination is for closer relations with the US Pacific Northwest and, more recently, with countries on the Pacific Rim. This paradox underscores British Columbia's often-strained relations with Ottawa, as reflected in the political concept of Cascadia and in BC opposition to oil pipelines from Alberta to the BC coast. British Columbia, a rapidly growing region, has turned into a west coast powerhouse with Vancouver leading the way with its shipbuilding and filmmaking as economic spearheads. In the northern reaches of the province, natural gas production is a potential spearhead, while the forest industry has been an economic anchor for many years.

← Saturna Island (right) and Samuel Island (left) are two mountainous islands that form part of the Southern Gulf Island chain in the Salish Sea near Victoria. The spectacular physical geography of British Columbia is perhaps the region's greatest natural asset.

Josef Hanus/ 123RF

British Columbia within Canada

With its rapidly expanding economy, British Columbia's strength flows from its resource sector, its advanced economy, and its geographically favourable location on the Pacific Rim. This combination has propelled BC into the Fourth Industrial Revolution, as described by Klaus Schwab (see Chapter 5). From that perspective, BC is well on its way to modernizing its economy by applying new technology to a variety of enterprises.

For additional information on the Fourth Industrial Revolution, see Vignette 5.1, "The Fourth Industrial Revolution," page 153.

FIGURE 9.1 British Columbia

Vancouver's isolation from Central Canada and its close link to Washington, Oregon, and California are revealed in the following driving distances: Montréal, Ottawa, and Toronto are over 4,300 km east of Vancouver. Los Angles is less than half the distance, at 1,735 km, while Bellingham, Washington, is just 85 km away, making it the most popular US shopping destination for Vancouverites. BC opposition to oil pipelines is stirring the national unity pot, creating a new dimension to the centralist faultline. Not surprisingly, BC has a closer association with the Pacific Northwest than with the rest of Canada. Academics refer to this sense of political place as Cascadia.

Source: Atlas of Canada, at: atlas.nrcan.gc.ca/site/english/maps/reference/provinceterritories/british_columbia, Natural Resources Canada, 2007. Reproduced with the permission of the Minister of Public Works and Government Services Canada, 2013.

This Pacific region, by persistently outpacing the national average for economic and population growth, is consolidating its position within Canada. At the time of entry into Confederation, BC was a minor player in the affairs of Canada. Today, BC is an economic and political force rivalling the two core regions of Ontario and Québec, and with its anticipated natural gas developments the province could well pass Western Canada, which is so heavily reliant on oil sands projects. Greater Vancouver, as the third-largest city in Canada, symbolizes this remarkable pace of economic and population growth.

Geography has placed British Columbia at the western edge of Canada, far from the economic/political heart of the country. Often feeling forgotten by Ottawa, this geographic fact underscores the basis for tensions between BC and Central Canada. For most British Columbians, however, the dramatic interface between the sea and the mountains defines the province. The love affair with its Pacific coast dominates its sense of place. As Premier Christy Clark said, "You can't understand British Columbians unless you can grasp the emotion that people feel about our coast. It's what makes us so different from Alberta and Ontario and other parts of the country" (Hunter, 2016).

From a physiographic perspective, the province is divided into two parts. The Cordillera accounts for the bulk of the area of the province, including the spectacular interface between the Pacific Ocean and the Coast Mountains. Lying beyond the Rocky Mountains, the Interior Plains occupies a small but energy-rich portion of its northeast corner. British Columbia has access to the Pacific Ocean except for its far north, where the Alaska Panhandle blocks access to the ocean.

British Columbia is an emerging giant within Canada's economic system. This west coast region's economy is heavily based on its natural resources and the export of those resources and those produced in Western Canada, namely coal, grain, oil, and potash.

Four countries—the US, China, Japan, and South Korea—account for over 85 per cent of exports and imports moving through BC ports (Table 9.1). In 2015, the value of exports reached an all-time high of $36 billion. British Columbia has diversified its foreign trade over the last 15 years. Prior to the global recession in 2009, the United States accounted for over 60 per cent of all exports, but now it is closer to 50 per cent. The economic crisis that began in late 2008 changed the very nature of BC's global exports.

The potential of natural gas shipments to Asia would only strength the growing ties to Asia. Pipelines may add more natural gas to its export list, but the possibility of additional bitumen pipelines from the Alberta oil sands is a charged political issue. Ironically, the Trans Mountain pipeline has carried crude oil to Greater Vancouver for over 60 years, and more recently it has transported bitumen from the oil sands.

British Columbia's scenic beauty supports a vibrant tourist industry, and its expanding knowledge-based industries, including the film and high-technology industries, help drive economic growth in new directions. Trade is crucial. Lumber, pulp, natural gas, and coal are the province's four main exports. Imports, especially from China, Japan, and South Korea, flow through Vancouver to markets across Canada. The expansion of CN and CP rail lines and the twinning of sections of the Trans-Canada Highway are facilitating access to the Port of Vancouver and exports to Asian countries (Photo 9.1). While Prince Rupert remains in the shadow of Vancouver, new facilities at the Port of Prince Rupert signal its arrival as a potential major player in international shipping. Prince Rupert may serve as a liquid natural gas port for the huge natural gas deposits in northeast British Columbia, while Kitimat's chances to export bitumen from the Alberta oil sands were quashed by a federal moratorium on oil tankers using Dixon Entrance, Hecate Strait, and Queen Charlotte Sound and the Federal Court of Appeal decision in 2016 to rescind approval of the Northern Gateway pipeline because of Ottawa's failure to consult properly with First Nations along the proposed route. Vancouverites may not be so pleased, however, because Ottawa approved Kinder Morgan's proposed bitumen pipeline (the Trans Mountain Expansion) to Burrard Inlet in late November 2016.

For more information on proposed pipelines from the Alberta oil sands, see the section "Pipelines, Promises, and Pollution" in Chapter 8, page 271.

Photo 9.1 The seven-lane Pitt River Bridge just east of Vancouver was completed in late 2009. As part of the Asia-Pacific Gateway and Corridor Initiative, this bridge serves to improve access to Vancouver along the north shore of the Fraser River, with easier and quicker flow for trucks carrying exports to ports in the Lower Mainland for shipment to Pacific Rim countries. Supported by both the provincial and federal governments, the Pitt River Bridge represents one phase of joint government efforts to create a superhighway corridor from Calgary to Vancouver.

Population

British Columbia contains nearly 5 million people, comprising just over 13 per cent of Canada's population. Population size provides a measure of BC's importance within Confederation. Its population growth, which has consistently outperformed the national increases, reflects its potential future within Canada's six geographic regions (Figure 9.2).

Yet, BC's population distribution is uneven. This skewed characteristic takes on a core/hinterland pattern as most residents reside in the Lower Mainland and in Victoria and Kelowna. Population distribution, therefore, represents a critical economic and social divide. Along the BC northern coast and in much of the Interior, population densities are low and towns like Prince Rupert, Terrace, and Quesnel have suffered population losses while the major urban centres continue to grow rapidly.

Greater Vancouver best illustrates this divide. The city, with its natural beauty, mild climate, and diverse population, is an ideal place for Richard Florida's "cultural class." Here, the performing arts, filmmaking, and the rest of the entertainment industry centred in Vancouver add to BC magic, making Vancouver one of the three most "livable" cities in the world (Economist Intelligence Unit, 2012). Unfortunately, Vancouver is one of the most expensive cities in which to establish roots because of high housing prices, caused in part by newcomers migrating to Greater Vancouver. With ever-increasing immigration, especially from China and Hong Kong, the Lower Mainland's population has become much more diverse than the rest of the province (Photo 9.2). In 2011, over half of its residents were classified by Statistics Canada (2016l) as belonging to visible minority groups, with Chinese forming the largest single group. Visible minorities in the rest of the province composed less that 10 per cent of that population. In fact, outside of Asia, Metro Vancouver has the largest portion of its residents with Asian backgrounds: 43 per cent of Metro Vancouver residents are of Asian heritage. The only major cities outside Asia that come close to Metro Vancouver for their portion of residents with Asian backgrounds are San Francisco (33 per cent Asian), London, England (21 per cent), Toronto (35 per cent), Calgary

THINK ABOUT IT

Oil spills are very difficult to remove from marine environments. Why is bitumen more difficult to clean up than oil?

Photo 9.2 Immigration plays a key role in the growth of Greater Vancouver. Chinese immigrants form the largest single group and the urban landscape of Greater Vancouver reflects this demographic fact in the form of Chinese-Canadian "ethnoburbs" as well as ethnic shopping centres and restaurants. One example of the vibrant Chinese community is the Vancouver Chinatown Night Market, which is open on weekends throughout the summer.

(23 per cent), and Sydney, Australia (19 per cent) (Todd, 2014).

Following the old adage that the larger the population, the more political clout a region has in Ottawa, BC influence in the affairs of state has increased. In part, this old adage fuels political friction between BC and the federal government. The struggle for political power and respect is ongoing and underscores the centralist/decentralist faultline. From time to time, various signs of disenchantment with Ottawa emerge. To those living in British Columbia, the province fits comfortably into the Pacific Northwest. In a sense, the Rocky Mountains are both a physical and political divide. The concept of Cascadia, consisting of Idaho, Oregon, Washington, and British Columbia provides a populist expression of regionalism. Cascadia is an expression both of regional ties that cross the international border and of a disconnect towards Ottawa and Central Canada.

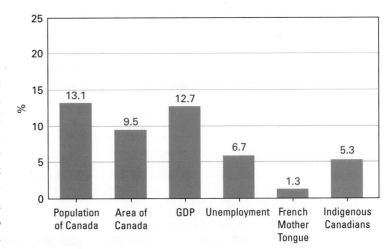

FIGURE 9.2 British Columbia basic statistics, 2015

BC's share of Canada's GDP and population continues to outpace the national average, but its small number of French-speaking Canadians is markedly different from some other regions in Canada.

Percentages of population, area, and GDP are for Canada as a whole; unemployment, French home language, and Indigenous population percentages are for British Columbia. Percentages for French mother tongue and Indigenous Canadians are for 2011.

Sources: Tables 1.1, 1.2, and 5.6.

British Columbia's Physical Geography

The spectacular physical geography of British Columbia is perhaps the region's greatest natural asset. The variety of its natural features is unprecedented. Then, too, British Columbia is famous for its mild west coast climate. The combination of two contrasting climates (west coast and interior) with mountainous terrain has resulted in a wide variety of natural environments or ecosystems. Three examples of natural diversity are rain forests along the coast, desert-like conditions in the Interior Plateau, and alpine tundra found at high elevations in many BC mountains. As well, its fjorded coastline provides many deep harbours surrounded by the Coast Mountains. Burrard Inlet is one such fjord. Yet, the growth of ocean shipping activities, especially the proposed jump in the number of Suezmax supertankers carrying Alberta bitumen, increases the risk of a spill into Burrard Inlet (Figure 9.3).

The physical contrast between the wet BC coast and the dry Interior is largely due to the effect of the Coast Mountains on precipitation. Easterly flowing air masses laden with moisture from the Pacific Ocean are forced to rise sharply over this high mountain chain, and consequently most moisture falls as orographic precipitation on the western slopes while little precipitation reaches the eastern slopes.

The climate of the west coast is unique in Canada. Winters are extremely mild and freezing temperatures are uncommon. Summer temperatures, while warm, are rarely as high as temperatures common in the more continental and dry climate of the Interior Plateau of British Columbia. Moderate temperatures, high rainfall, and mild but cloudy winters make the west coast of British Columbia an ideal place to live and a popular retirement centre for those Canadians wanting to escape long cold winters.

The Pacific Ocean has a powerful impact on BC's climate, resource base, and transportation system. Unlike in Atlantic Canada, the continental shelf in BC extends only a short distance from the coast. Within this narrow zone are many islands, the largest being Vancouver Island, followed by Haida Gwaii.[1] The riches of the sea include salmon, which return to the rivers, such as the Fraser and the Skeena, to complete their life cycle. Most of BC's

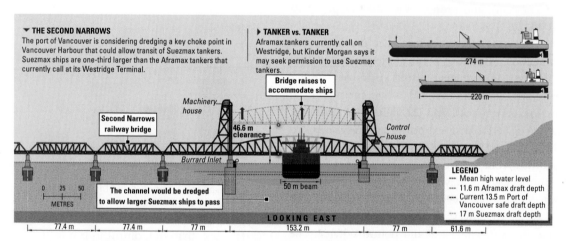

FIGURE 9.3 The Second Narrows Bridge: Getting supertankers to port

Burrard Inlet serves as the Greater Vancouver harbour. Its safe depth for tankers is 13.5 m. The Aframax tankers that now come to the Kinder Morgan oil terminal in Burnaby to load bitumen from the Alberta oil sands require 11.6 m draft depth. Kinder Morgan prefers the larger Suezmax supertanker, but its draft depth is considerably greater than 13.5 m and will require dredging at the Second Narrows Bridge.

Source: Kheraj (2015); *Globe and Mail*, 4 Aug. 2012, at: www.theglobeandmail.com/report-on-business/inudstry-news/energy-and-resources/sizing-up=bcs-pipelines/article4461986/. Illustration by John Sopinski and Michael Bird.

natural wealth, however, is not in the sea but in the province's diversified physical geography, which provides valuable resources, particularly forests, minerals, and hydroelectric power.

British Columbia's narrow and sometimes deep continental shelf is, in fact, a submerged mountain range. Vancouver Island and Haida Gwaii form the Pacific edge of the Cordillera, and the boundary between the Pacific and North American tectonic plates extends underwater along the west coast of these islands. Not surprisingly, then, Canada's largest

measured earthquake (magnitude 8.1) occurred in 1949 off the coast of the Haida Gwaii archipelago, and in August 2012 another major quake (magnitude 7.7) struck the same area. In 2015, one 4.0 and another 4.1 magnitude were recorded in the southern tip of Haida Gwaii.

A small portion of northeast British Columbia, including the Peace River Country, is part of the Interior Plains (Figure 2.1). Here, the geological structure is part of the petroleum-rich Western Sedimentary Basin. Significantly, a massive natural gas

THINK ABOUT IT

From studying Figure 9.4, would you conclude that the mountain chain found on Vancouver Island and on Haida Gwaii is geologically related and that a submerged portion of this mountain chain lies under the waters separating these two islands?

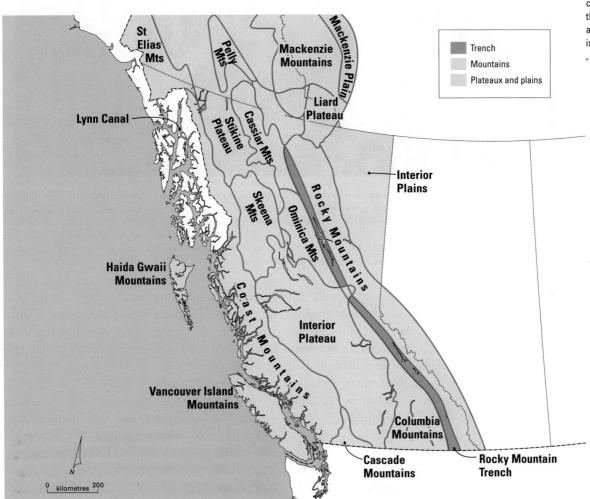

FIGURE 9.4 Physiography of British Columbia

British Columbia's complex topography is evident in the Cordillera, while the Interior Plains demonstrates a much less severe topography. With the grain of the land running north and south, BC's transportation system runs north and south much more easily than east and west. Imagine the difficulty of highway and railway construction across the Columbia Mountains. These mountains actually contain four mountain ranges, and each presented problems for surveyors in finding a pass in order to construct the Canadian Pacific Railway. These north/south trending mountains included the Cariboo, Monashee, Selkirk, and Purcell mountains. Add the Rocky Mountains to the list and challenge of an east–west transportation system is revealed.

Photo 9.3 Hell's Gate, located near Boston Bar, is confined by high canyon walls of the Coast Mountains that rise 1,000 m above the rapids. The Fraser River found a way through the Coast Mountains to the Pacific Ocean at Hell's Gate. Here, an Airtram carries tourists down to the visitors' centre by the river, and fishways enable salmon to head upstream to their spawning grounds. The Canadian Pacific Railway has its tracks on the lower reaches of the canyon while the Trans-Canada Highway is located in the upper reaches. In 1914, blasting through these mountains to improve the original route for the Canadian Pacific Railway caused a rockslide that blocked the salmon migration.

THINK ABOUT IT

How have investors and speculators slipped around BC's Provincial Agricultural Land Commission to convert prime agricultural land into residential properties in BC's Fraser Valley? (See Tomlinson, 2016).

deposit was discovered near the border with the Northwest Territories, and with the federal government's approval in September 2016 of the Pacific NorthWest liquefied natural gas project the next step is for Petronas, the Malaysian state-owned oil and gas giant, to proceed. The problem facing Petronas is low natural gas prices, not to mention 190 conditions that must be met and court challenges from First Nations along the proposed pipeline route.

Because of the rugged nature of the Cordillera, little arable land exists. Only about 2 per cent of the province's land is classified as arable. British Columbia's largest area of cropland lies outside of the Cordillera physiographic region in the Peace River Country. Within the Cordillera, most arable land is in the Fraser Valley, while a smaller amount can be found in the Interior, especially the Okanagan and Thompson valleys. This shortage of arable land poses a serious problem for British Columbia. With urban

development spreading onto agricultural land, British Columbia lost some of its most productive farmland. From the end of World War II to the 1970s nearly 6,000 hectares of prime agricultural land were lost each year to urban and other uses. With only 5 per cent of BC's land mass classified as cropland, the provincial government responded to the serious erosion of its agricultural land base by introducing BC's Land Commission Act in 1973. This Act formed the **Provincial Agricultural Land Commission**, which is charged with preserving agricultural land from urban encroachment and encouraging farm businesses (Provincial Agricultural Land Commission, 2014). With continuing pressure from urban land developers, this legislation remains under fire from market economy–oriented groups such as the Vancouver-based Fraser Institute, the central argument being that more "value" can be derived from non-agricultural use of the land (Katz, 2010).

Vignette 9.1

BC's Precipitation: Too Much or Too Little?

British Columbia receives the greatest amount of precipitation along its Pacific coast. In simple terms, two precipitation areas exist in British Columbia—one in the Pacific climatic zone, where heavy precipitation occurs, reaching 3,000 mm of precipitation per year at Prince Rupert. Vancouver, on the other hand, receives just under 1,500 mm per year while Victoria gets only half that amount. In the Cordillera, precipitation figures are well below those of the Pacific Coast. The figure for Kamloops, for example, is less than 300 mm per year while Kelowna's precipitation is around 350 mm per year.

Climatic Zones

British Columbia has two climatic zones, the Pacific and the Cordillera. Because of the extremely high elevations in the Coast Mountains, few moist Pacific air masses reach the Interior Plateau. The spatial variation in precipitation is remarkable. Heavy orographic precipitation occurs along the western slopes of the Insular and Coast mountains, where 3,000 mm of precipitation fall annually in some locations (Vignette 9.1). In sharp contrast, the Interior Plateau receives less than 350 mm per year. In the Thompson Valley and Okanagan Valley of the Interior Plateau, hot, dry conditions result in an arid climate with sagebrush in the valleys and ponderosa pines on the valley slopes. Most rain falls in the winter. For those along the Pacific coast, the so-called **Pineapple Express**, which originates over the warm waters around Hawaii, brings torrential rains but also relatively warm weather in the winter months, while those inland receive heavy snowfalls.

The three types of precipitation are described in Vignette 2.12, page 44.

Environmental Challenges

British Columbia's coast, the interface between the ocean and the land, represents one of Canada's most dramatic landscapes. The challenge is to preserve this landscape for future generations. Its old-growth forests symbolize this unique ecosystem.

Environmentalists made strong efforts to protect and preserve areas of this land of giant trees, but too little avail—until 1983, when environmentalists clashed with logging companies by chaining themselves to ancient Douglas fir trees to prevent the logging of old-growth forests in **Clayoquot Sound** on Vancouver Island. The search for a compromise was long and bitter because logging companies saw old-growth forests as prime logging areas. More than 30 years later, the creation of the **Great Bear Rainforest** (Figure 9.5) as a UNESCO **biosphere reserve** may have provided a solution where selective logging can take place; where core areas of the ancient forest can be preserved; and where the First Nations can find a place in both worlds—their traditional world and the Western market economy. As Dallas Smith, who represented the 26 First Nations in the establishment of conditions for any economic activity in the Great Bear Rainforest, has explained:

> Now it's necessary to take steps to ensure that our communities are able to share in the economic success [resulting from sustainable logging], in the balance that we have achieved in the Great Bear. If that [meaning Third World conditions] is still the case 10 years from now, the Great Bear has failed. (Hunter, 2016)

Logging is just one form of pressure on the environment. Mining takes on a different form of pressure. While mining is an important economic activity, it carries with it a variety of threats to land

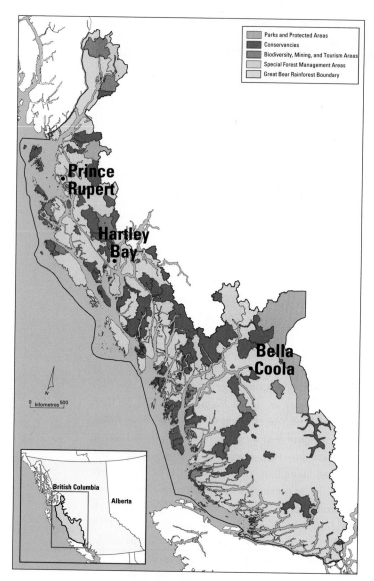

FIGURE 9.5 Great Bear Rainforest Land Use Zones

Source: BC Ministry of Forests, Lands and Natural Resource Operations (2016).

nearby lakes and rivers, leaving behind debris that clogged salmon-bearing streams (Meissner, 2016). Fortunately, no one was injured, but the landscape and streams were badly polluted.

Pipelines, while the most economic method for transporting oil and gas, have lost favour with the public because of a number of leaks into rivers and streams. In 2010, an Enbridge pipeline in Michigan leaked bitumen into the Kalamazoo River with some sinking to the bottom of the river in oily globs. After two years, the cost of the cleanup totalled US$1.2 million (Hasemyer, 2016). On 21 June 2016, a much smaller oil spill occurred near Lloydminster, Saskatchewan. The Husky Oil pipeline ruptured and approximately 200,000 litres of heavy oil and diluents entered the North Saskatchewan River. Downstream, three communities (North Battleford, Prince Albert, and Melford) had their drinking water systems closed, but by mid-September the river water was again suitable for their water treatment plants. However, oil globs that sank to the bottom of the river remain and will take years to dissipate.

BC residents have every right to worry about bitumen pipelines that would cross their province to reach tidewater. While the risk of a leak or spill is low, they do happen. Everyone on the Pacific coast recalls the disastrous oil spill in 1989 from the tanker *Exxon Valdez*. The cleanup of the gooey mess on the marine landscape around Prince William Sound, Alaska, was next to impossible. On the other hand, for the landlocked Prairies, access to tidewater on the Pacific coast is essential for the export of their agricultural, mineral, and oil products. For many BC residents, oil pipelines carrying bitumen across BC to the coast represent a threat to their coast and lands. A spill from a tanker could foul the coastline, while a leak from the pipeline could pollute both land and rivers. From the perspective of the oil sands producers, access to tidewater is needed to obtain the Brent price for their product and thus increase their profits. Out of this pipeline squabble comes another challenge to national unity (see Contested Terrain 9.1). In 2012, Premier Christy Clark (BC

and water. Tailing ponds are a common feature of mining operations where the waste products are stored. But such storage is like a time bomb because eventually one pond will spring a leak. Indeed, one of the worst catastrophes was the collapse of a massive tailing dam at the Mount Polley copper/gold mine (Photo 9.4). On 4 August 2014, 24 million m³ of toxic mine waste and contaminated water gushed from the tailing pond into

THE CANADIAN PRESS/Jonathan Hayward

Photo 9.4 On 4 August 2014, the tailing dam burst at the Mount Polley mine, sending toxic contents downstream into Hazeltine Creek and Quesnel Lake near the town of Likely.

Government, 2012) staked out her position with five demands:

1. Successful completion of the environmental review process.
2. World-leading marine oil spill response, prevention, and recovery systems for BC's coastline and ocean to manage and mitigate the risks and costs of heavy oil pipelines and shipments.
3. World-leading practices for land oil spill prevention, response, and recovery systems to manage and mitigate the risks and costs of heavy oil pipelines.
4. Legal requirements regarding Aboriginal and treaty rights to be addressed, and First Nations to be provided with the opportunities, information, and resources necessary to participate in and benefit from a heavy-oil project.
5. That British Columbia receives a fair share of the benefits of any proposed heavy oil projects to reflect the risk incurred by the province, its taxpayers, and the BC environment.

As we have seen, the Northern Gateway project will not proceed in the foreseeable future. The Trans Mountain Expansion, on the other hand, has gained approval and will move ahead. This Kinder Morgan project consists of twinning its existing line from Edmonton to Vancouver, increasing its storage capacity at its terminal in Burnaby, and bringing supertankers to transport the bitumen to various markets

Contested Terrain 9.1

Piping Oil across British Columbia

The centralist/decentralist faultline in British Columbia originates in the province's perceived lack of support for its interests, which are often seen to be ignored in favour of so-called national interests. This perception poses an irritant in BC's relations with Ottawa and reinforces other grievances that tend to increase political tensions. The squabble between BC and Alberta over proposed bitumen pipelines that would cross BC to reach tidewater has created a new political divide. The Premier of British Columbia, Christy Clark, has insisted that BC receive its fair share from such proposed projects, arguing that most risk falls on BC lands, waters, and people. Accordingly, British Columbia should receive "a fair share of the fiscal and economic benefits of a proposed heavy oil project that reflects that level and nature of the risk borne by the province, the environment and taxpayers" (Clark, 2012).

(see Figures 9.6 and 9.7 and Photo 9.5). In May 2016, the National Energy Board approved its application, subject to 157 conditions that must be met, with the comment that the project would deliver several "important benefits" to Canada, including "increased access to diverse markets for Canadian oil" and "considerable government revenues from the project" (Morgan, 2016). The pipeline expansion has incited fierce opposition, and even with government approval this opposition will continue.

Rafal Gerszak for The Globe and Mail

Photo 9.5 Tugboats escort the tanker *Aqualegend* to Kinder Morgan's Westridge marine terminal in Burnaby, BC. *Aqualegend* is classed as an Aframax tanker, the largest type permitted to dock at Westridge terminal. Despite increasing opposition from city governments and environmental groups, among others, Kinder Morgan plans to twin its Trans Mountain pipeline to increase its bitumen shipments, and hopes also to increase the size of tankers used for transport.

Many fear a spill from one of the anticipated 400 oil tankers per year travelling through Vancouver's harbour. Twenty-one municipalities, including Vancouver, Burnaby, Port Moody, and Victoria, have vehemently opposed the expansion project, along with 17 First Nations, from the Squamish in BC to the Lummi Nation in the state of Washington.

Waiting for the "Big One"?

Indiscriminate logging practices and oil pipelines pose human-made risks to British Columbia's natural environment. Another significant risk comes from nature itself—just off the coast of BC the Pacific and North American tectonic plates overlap. The Pacific Ring of Fire of volcanic and earthquake activity encircles the Pacific basin, and Vancouver and Victoria lie within the Ring of Fire. Just south of Vancouver Island, the threat of the "Big One" comes from the smaller Juan de Fuca plate inching underneath the North American plate. As shown in Figure 9.8, the likelihood of earthquakes, and especially of a

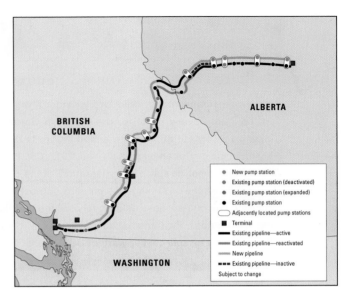

FIGURE 9.6 Map of the proposed twinning of the Trans Mountain pipeline

The National Energy Board and federal government approved Kinder Morgan's Trans Mountain Expansion, although opposition has been strong and included both the Vancouver and Burnaby city councils.

Source: Kinder Morgan (2015).

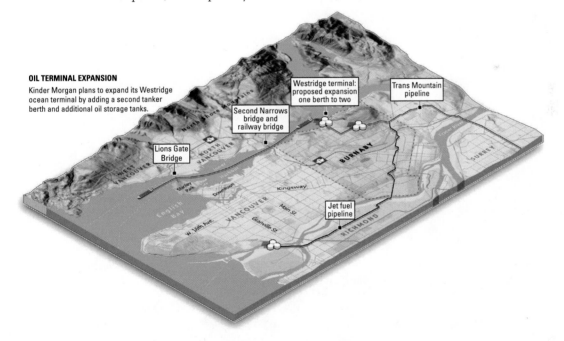

FIGURE 9.7 Westridge oil terminal expansion, Burnaby, BC

Part of Kinder Morgan's planned expansion of its shipping capacity of bitumen involves adding a second tanker berth and additional oil storage tanks at its Westridge terminal. Situated on Burnaby Mountain, local residents are concerned about the expansion plans. While Kinder Morgan tries to assure the population that the risks of an oil leak from its storage tanks are extremely low, residents remember the 2007 oil leak.

Source: "Sizing Up BC's Pipelines," Globe and Mail, 4 Aug. 2012, at: www.theglobeandmail.com/report-on-business/industry-news/energy-and-resources/sizing-up-bcs-pipelines/article4461986/. Illustration by John Sopinski and Michael Bird/The Globe and Mail; Sources: Port Metro Vancouver; Kinder Morgan; Enbridge; Google Maps; ESRI.

Vignette 9.2

Polluter Pays—Or Can a Company Dodge the Bullet?

Does an insurance policy paid for by Kinder Morgan sound like a good idea for the Canadian taxpayer? At the Joint Review Panel for the Northern Gateway pipeline project, Robin Allan, the former CEO of Insurance Corp. of BC, recommended that Enbridge purchase an insurance policy that would cover $1 billion in claims for an oil spill (O'Neil, 2012: C5). But Allan's proposal did not deal with the liability for a catastrophic marine spill of the magnitude of the *Exxon Valdez* accident. Of course, since Kinder Morgan does not own the oil tankers, the pipeline company is not liable for marine spills. Since the *Exxon Valdez* disaster, shipowners have deliberately limited their liability to one asset—the ship (Boulton, 2010). Under those conditions, the Canadian taxpayers are on the hook for cleanup costs. Back in 1989, cleanup of the *Exxon Valdez* oil spill cost upward of US$3.5 billion.

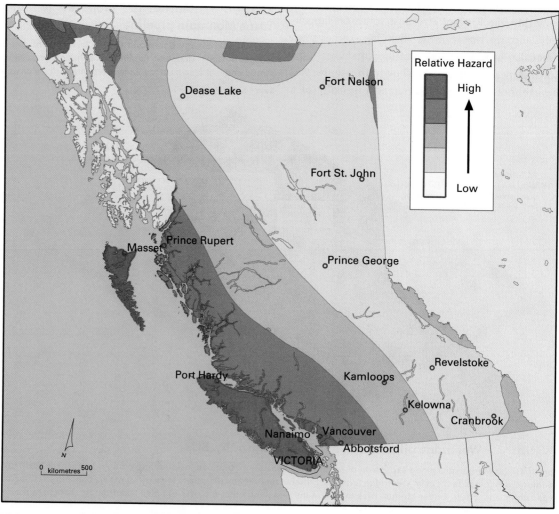

FIGURE 9.8 2015 simplified seismic hazard map for British Columbia

Source: Adapted with the permission of Natural Resources Canada.

megathrust earthquake, is especially great in this region. While the "Big One" may not happen soon, the Vancouver/Victoria area is subjected to minor earthquakes on a regular basis. According to seismologist Alison Bird, who works for the Geological Survey of Canada in Victoria, every 14 months a period of around two weeks takes on a higher probability of an earthquake. During those two weeks, she will not park underground (Wagstaffe, 2016).

A devastating earthquake could occur tomorrow, or not for many decades. Regardless of when, seismologists are convinced that a megathrust earthquake—"the Big One"—will strike this heavily populated region (Wagstaffe, 2016).

British Columbia's Historical Geography

Indigenous peoples lived along the Pacific coast of British Columbia for over 10,000 years before European explorers reached the northern Pacific coast in the mid-eighteenth century. The Spanish had already sailed northward from Mexico to California, but the Russians were the first to reach Alaska and establish fur-trading posts along its coast. In 1778, Captain James Cook established Britain's interest in this region by sailing into Vancouver Island's Nootka Sound (Photo 9.6), where he and his sailors found the Nootka village of Yuquot. The Nootka, now known as Nuu-chah-nulth, fished for salmon and hunted the sea otter. Upon landing, Cook engaged in trade for sea otter pelts, which opened up a profitable trade with China, although Cook, among the greatest of nautical explorers, did not live to see this trade flourish—he was killed in a skirmish with natives in the Hawaiian Islands on the return voyage. After the Royal Navy published Cook's record of his voyage, British and American traders came to the Pacific Northwest to seek the highly valued sea otters. Russian fur traders, based in Alaska, also harvested sea otters. Spain, which considered the lands Spanish territory, was disturbed by these interlopers and sent a fleet northward from Mexico in 1789. At Nootka Sound on the west coast of Vancouver Island, the Spanish seized several ships and built a fort to defend their claim. In 1792, Captain George Vancouver of Britain's Royal Navy sailed around Vancouver Island. In the following year, Alexander Mackenzie of the North West Company travelled overland from Fort Chipewyan to just south of Prince George and then to the Pacific coast near Bella Coola, which is just over 400 km north of Vancouver. Under the Nootka Convention (1794), the Spanish surrendered their claim to the Pacific coast north of 42°N, leaving the British and Russians in control.

In the early nineteenth century, the North West Company established a series of fur-trading

THINK ABOUT IT

If Canada had obtained the power to make international treaties in 1867, why would it seek to have the boundary at the Lynn Canal?

Photo 9.6 Captain James Cook's ships moored in Nootka Sound in 1778, as depicted in a watercolour by M.B. Messer. Four years earlier, the Spanish explorer Juan Hernandez sailed along the BC coast. However, there is the possibility that Francis Drake, while on a secret mission to find a western entrance to the Northwest Passage, reached these waters in 1579 (Hume, 2000: B1).

Library and Archives Canada/C-011201

posts along the Columbia River. From 1805 to 1808, Simon Fraser, a fur trader and explorer, explored the Interior of British Columbia on behalf of the North West Company. He travelled by canoe from the Peace River to the mouth of the Fraser River. As elsewhere, the strategy of the North West Company was to develop a working relationship with local Indian tribes based on bartering manufactured goods for furs. After 1821, when the North West Company merged with its rival, the Hudson's Bay Company, the HBC took charge of the Oregon Territory, which extended from the mouth of the Columbia River, at the present-day border between Oregon and Washington, to Russia's Alaska. In the late nineteenth century, a bitter dispute arose over the boundary of the Alaska Panhandle and access to Dawson City and the Klondike gold rush. The boundary dispute was settled in 1903 by a six-man tribunal, composed of American, Canadian, and British representatives. The settlement totally favoured the United States, suggesting that Canada's interests may have been sacrificed by Great Britain, which sought better relations with the United States.

In 1843, American settlers began to arrive on the coast from the eastern part of the United States. In the same year, the HBC relocated its main trading post from Fort Vancouver at the mouth of the Columbia River to Fort Victoria at the southern tip of Vancouver Island. The increasing number of American settlers who came west along the Oregon Trail represented a challenge to the authority of the Hudson's Bay Company. A few years later, the United States claimed the Pacific coast northward to Alaska, where Russian fur-trading posts existed. In 1846, Britain and the United States agreed to place the boundary between the two nations at 49°N and then to follow the channel that separates Vancouver Island from the mainland of the United States. While the loss of the Oregon Territory in present-day Washington and Oregon was substantial, Britain was fortunate to hold onto the remaining lands administered by the Hudson's Bay Company. Britain recognized that its hold on these lands through the HBC was tenuous and could not withstand the political weight of the growing number of American settlers. Indeed, without the presence of the HBC and Britain's negotiating skills, Canada might well have lost its entire Pacific coastline.

The gold rush of 1858 brought about 25,000 prospectors from California to the Fraser River. The major finds were made in the BC Interior, where the town of Barkerville was built near Quesnel. By 1863, Barkerville had a population of about 10,000, making it the largest town in British Columbia. To ensure British sovereignty over territory north of 49°N, the British government established

Vignette 9.3

Indigenous Title: Who Owns BC?

How much of BC belongs to First Nations? Up to 1993, only the 14 pre-Confederation Douglas treaties signed between 1850 and 1854 with the Coast Salish on Vancouver Island, as well as those bands belonging to Treaty No. 8 of 1899 in the northeast corner of the province, had acquired Indigenous title to a portion of their lands. For the rest, BC claimed that Indigenous title was extinguished upon BC entering Confederation. The 1973 Supreme Court of Canada ruling in the *Calder* case challenged BC's legal position of extinguishment. While the Supreme Court rejected the Nisga'a claim to Aboriginal title, the justices' split decision opened the door for land claims. According to Frank Cassidy (1992: 11), this 1973 Supreme Court decision represented "a centrepiece in the historical development of the province of British Columbia." Yet, progress has been slow as only four final agreements had been reached by 2016 under the BC Treaty Process: the Tsawwassen First Nation (2009); the Maa-nulth Treaty (2011); and the Yale First Nation and the Tla'amin First Nation agreements (2016). The Final Agreement with the Nisga'a in 2000 took place outside of the BC Treaty Process.

the mainland colony of British Columbia in 1858 under the authority of Sir James Douglas, who was also governor of Vancouver Island. In 1866, the two colonies were united. During Douglas's time as governor, land claims were settled on Vancouver Island but not on the mainland (see Vignette 9.3).

For further discussion of Aboriginal rights and the modern treaty process, see Chapter 3, "Modern Treaties," page 90, and Vignette 3.7, "From a Colonial Straitjacket to Indigenous Power," page 94.

Confederation

By the 1860s, the British government was actively encouraging its colonies in North America to unite into one country. Once the first four colonies were united in 1867, Ottawa adopted the British strategy to create a transcontinental nation. An important part of that strategy was to lure British Columbia into the "national fabric." The Canadian Pacific Railway was the first expression of this national policy.[2] In 1871, Prime Minister Macdonald promised that a railway to the Pacific Ocean would be built within 10 years after British Columbia joined Confederation. In Fort Victoria, however, some wanted to join the United States. By the middle of the nineteenth century, British Columbia had developed significant commercial ties with Americans along the Pacific coast. San Francisco was the closest metropolis and, with its railway to New York, offered the simplest and quickest route to London. In 1859, Oregon became a state and Washington was soon to follow. Commercial links with the United States were growing stronger. But the majority of people in Fort Victoria wanted to remain British. In 1871, the British Columbia government accepted the Prime Minister's offer and the province entered the new Dominion. Unfortunately, the slow progress in construction of the rail line caused friction and rekindled the movement to join the United States. While the Canadian government undertook surveys in the 1870s searching for the best route through the Cordillera, construction began in 1881 and on 7 November 1885 the "last spike" was driven at Craigellachie, BC (Photo 9.7). Finally, the Canadian Pacific Railway stretched across the country, ending at Port Moody on Burrard Inlet. In 1887, the railway

Alexander Ross/Library and Archives Canada/C-003693

Photo 9.7 Sir Donald Alexander Smith, a powerful banker and major financier of the Canadian Pacific Railway, drives the last spike at Craigellachie, just west of Eagle Pass in the Monashee Mountains, thus symbolizing completion of the CPR. The town of Revelstoke lies 20 km to the east of this famous pass. The divide of the Monashee Mountains separates the Columbia and Fraser drainage basins. Rogers Pass in the Selkirk Mountains lies further east. Rogers Pass, with its steep grade, high elevation, and frequency of avalanches, proved too difficult to maintain in later years. The answer was tunnels through the mountains—the Connaught Tunnel (1916) and the Mount Macdonald Tunnel (1988).

was extended 20 km westward to the small sawmill town of Vancouver.

Years later, in 1914, the Grand Trunk Pacific Railway, which connected with other rail lines to the east, was completed from Winnipeg to Prince Rupert, BC. All but the CPR were amalgamated as a Crown corporation, Canadian National Railways, in 1923 to give Canada two intercontinental railways.

Post-Confederation Growth

At first, Confederation had little effect on British Columbia. The province was isolated from the rest of Canada, and goods still had to come by ship from San Francisco or London. When the Canadian Pacific Railway was completed in 1885, British Columbia truly became part of the Dominion, and BC's role as a gateway to the world began.

With the CPR line in place, Vancouver grew quickly and soon became the major centre on the west coast. By 1901, Vancouver had a population of 27,000 compared to Victoria's 24,000. As the

THINK ABOUT IT

The Chinese population in British Columbia doubled from 4,200 in 1881 to 8,910 in 1891 (Roy, 1989: Table 1B). During this period, what construction project drew many from China to British Columbia?

terminus of the transcontinental railway, Vancouver became the transshipment point for goods produced in the Interior of BC and Western Canada. As coal, lumber, and grain were transported by rail from the Interior and the Canadian Prairies, the Port of Vancouver spearheaded economic growth in the southwest part of the province. It was then possible to tap the vast natural resources of BC and ship them to world markets. By the twentieth century, Vancouver had become one of Canada's major ports. Unlike Montréal, Vancouver has an ice-free harbour, and as Canada's major Pacific port, Vancouver became the natural transportation link to Pacific nations. With the opening of the Panama Canal in 1914, British Columbia's resources were more accessible to the markets of the United Kingdom and Western Europe.

While BC's economy and population continued to grow in the 1920s, the Great Depression of the 1930s caused the province's economy to stall as exports declined. World War II called for full production in Canada, thereby pulling British Columbia's depressed resource economy out of the doldrums. Military production, including aircraft manufacturing, greatly expanded BC's industrial output. As well, resource industries based on forestry and mining (especially coal and copper) were producing at full capacity.

When the war ended in 1945, BC's resource boom continued. With world demand for forest and mineral products remaining high, the provincial government focused its efforts on developing the resources of its hinterland, the Central Interior of British Columbia. The first step was to create a transportation system from Vancouver to Prince George, the major city in the Central Interior. The highway system was improved and extended from Prince George to Dawson Creek in 1952. But the completion of the Pacific Great Eastern Railway to Prince George in 1956 and then to Dawson Creek in 1958 opened the country, allowed for exports to foreign markets, and triggered economic growth, especially in the forest industry. With rail access to Vancouver, forestry, as well as other resource industries, expanded rapidly, thereby leading to the integration of this hinterland into the BC and global industrial core.

Over the past two decades, BC's increasing economic strength, partly driven by the Asian economy, has outpaced that of all other regions in Canada. Trade is a dynamic force propelling British Columbia's economy, and as China and other Pacific Rim countries have led the world in economic growth, this growth has created new markets for Canadian products shipped through Vancouver. Trade opportunities are almost endless between British Columbia and the population of 2.5 billion people in the Pacific nations. In BC's export-oriented economy, it is usually much less expensive to ship the raw material than the finished product. This has led to trade focused on resources. High labour costs, a relatively small local market, and distance from world markets have inhibited the development of manufacturing in BC.

British Columbia Today

British Columbia is heading toward a greener and more technically advanced economy. The foundation of its economy rests on its resources and its advanced economy. Trade facilitates resource development and innovative firms. Most trade flows through the Port of Vancouver (Photos 9.8 and 9.9). In 2015, the value of exports reached a record $36 billion (Table 9.1).

The value of exports in 2015 reached $36 billion, with forest products and coal representing the top exports from BC, while Western Canada's exports of coal, grain, potash, and oil/bitumen add to the volume passing through BC ports. Imports consist of a variety of consumer goods, including automobiles and textiles, and they flow to all parts of Canada. The geopolitical significance of the United States in BC's trade pattern is clear—52 per cent of the value of exports flows to the United States. However, the remarkable decline from 2001 to 2015 in exports to the US, coupled with an increase to China, reveals an important trend. Softwood lumber is a major export to the US, but with the expiration of the Softwood Lumber Agreement in October 2016 the United States has signalled that it intends to impose tougher restrictions in the agreement. Negotiations following President Trump taking office pose a serious challenge to BC.

Container traffic represents the fastest-growing form of trade. Within the Pacific Rim, the flow of containers from China to BC ports continues to

Ellen Atkin/Getty Images

Photo 9.8 Vancouver's magnificent harbour has facilitated trade with Pacific Rim countries. The Burrard and Granville Street bridges cross False Creek, separating Kitsilano from downtown Vancouver. Just beyond the West End lies Stanley Park. Across the harbour, West and North Vancouver occupy the lower slopes of the North Shore Mountains.

increase. BC has a decided advantage because its ports, especially Prince Rupert, provide the shortest North American sea links to China, Japan, and South Korea. According to the BC government, container traffic to all west coast ports is forecast to rise a staggering 300 per cent by 2020, thus reaching 9 million TEU (BC Ministry of Transportation, 2007). A measure of accuracy of that forecast comes from the 2014 data for Port Metro Vancouver, which recorded that the Port of Vancouver handled 2.9 million TEU of container cargo (TEU refers to containers measuring 20 feet) while the Port of Prince Rupert reached a record 620,000 TEU, increasing its container traffic by 26 per cent over its 2013 traffic (Port of Prince Rupert, 2016).

Industrial Structure

Is British Columbia turning into a core region? For over 50 years, developed nations have undergone

TABLE 9.1 Exports through British Columbia, 2001, 2006, 2009, and 2015

Country	2001 (%)	2006 (%)	2009 (%)	2015 (%)
US	69.8	61.3	51.3	52.0
China	2.3	4.4	10.2	16.8
Japan	12.8	14.1	13.7	10.0
South Korea	2.2	4.1	6.6	5.1
Other countries	12.9	16.1	18.2	14.8
Value in billions of dollars	31.7	33.5	25.2	36.0

Source: Adapted from BC Stats (2012, 2016a).

THE CANADIAN PRESS/Darryl Dyck

Photo 9.9 CP's Port Metro in Vancouver, one of the busiest shipping hubs on the continent. Port Metro Vancouver handled 140 million tonnes of cargo in 2014, up from the previous year's 135 million tonnes (Port Metro Vancouver, 2015). The Asia-Pacific Gateway and Corridor project is facilitating the flow of goods from Western Canada to the Pacific coast ports by upgrading highways and rail lines.

a shift from primary and secondary industries to tertiary ones, where most innovative activities take place. This trend is taking place within British Columbia where 80 per cent of the labour force is employed in the tertiary sector (Table 9.2). The advanced economy, driven by technological innovations, exists in all sectors. In the primary sector, for example, technical advances in oil and gas operations permit **horizontal drilling**, which, when combined with **hydraulic fracturing**, has unlocked natural gas deposits in northeast BC.

See Chapter 5 for a discussion of the economic shift to the tertiary sector and for economic change in the twenty-first century.

Some of BC's knowledge-based companies are local firms while others are associated with multinational corporations. Microsoft, for instance, with its home base in Seattle, opened its first Canadian Development Centre in Richmond, BC, employing 300 researchers from around the world. However, the knowledge-based economy is not limited to the computer world; it permeates all avenues of the economy.

Knowledge-based Economy

The tertiary sector is a mirror image of the new economy with the emphasis on technology and

TABLE 9.2   British Columbia Industrial Sectors by Number of Workers, 2005 and 2016

Economic Sector	Workers, 2005 (000s)	Workers, 2005 (%)	Workers, 2016 (000s)	Workers, 2016 (%)	% Difference
Primary	76.2	3.6	76.4	3.2	–0.4
Secondary	376.5	17.7	393.2	16.6	–1.1
Tertiary	1,677.8	78.7	1,895.0	80.2	+1.5
Total	2,130.5	100.0	2,364.6	100.0	11.0%

Source: Statistics Canada (2006, 2012, 2016f).

innovation, plus an expansion of service industries that support such an economy. Following the concept of a creative class, these service industries include a vibrant entertainment and filmmaking sector coupled with outstanding arts and drama performances. In short, a Canadian version of a laid-back, "California" lifestyle, with hints of California's Silicon Valley, has taken root in Greater Vancouver. Firms like MacDonald, Dettwiler and Associates (MDA), with its RADARSAT invention, and Ballard Power Systems, with its fuel cell development, provide the innovative leadership. MDA is a world leader in the design and development of radar satellite missions and provides Canada with three observation satellites that record shipping activities over the Arctic Ocean, including the Northwest Passage. This system is known as RADARSAT Constellation Mission. Funded by the federal government, the three-satellite configuration tracks Canada's Arctic Ocean on a daily basis. In this way, RADARSAT Constellation Mission is defending Canada's Arctic sovereignty with a broad-area maritime surveillance system using the RADARSAT Constellation (Keyzer, 2016).

The evidence is clear—British Columbia's economy is changing and diversifying, but growth in the manufacturing sector remains elusive. In the past two decades, however, BC has experienced growth in high technology. As the front edge of the structural shift in the manufacturing industry across Canada, high-tech firms are playing a greater role in BC's economy and are providing jobs for highly skilled workers. High technology involves cutting-edge research in the manufacture of electronics, telecommunications equipment, and pharmaceuticals. BC has the fourth-largest high-tech workforce in Canada.[3] According to Schrier and Hallin (2016), Ontario has the largest high-tech workforce, with 354,110 people, or 39 per cent of all Canadian high-tech workers, followed by Québec (26 per cent), Western Canada (15 per cent), and BC (10 per cent).

The sharp edge of the advanced economy based on innovative industries lies in a variety of areas: fuel cell development by Ballard Power Systems; possible new technology applied to the shipbuilding in BC, especially the polar class icebreaker; and RADARSAT inventions by MacDonald, Dettwiler and Associates, Canada's principal space company. According

to John MacDonald (2012), the co-founder of MacDonald, Dettwiler, "This cutting-edge project will create highly skilled jobs, and attract the world's best scientists, technicians and engineers to Canada's world-renowned space industry."

Technical Spearheads

Each region has a distinct set of economic spearheads that reflect the major economic advances taking place in the region. In the case of BC, three economic high-growth industries—shipbuilding, filmmaking, and natural gas—are of special note.

Seaspan Shipyard

In 2011, Vancouver's Seaspan Shipyard (Photo 9.10) was awarded a federal contract under the National Shipbuilding Procurement Strategy valued at $8 billion for building 17 vessels, including a polar-class icebreaker (Chase and Marotte, 2011: A1). By 2016, construction of a Canadian Coast Guard vessel and an offshore fisheries ship was well underway (Seaspan, 2015).

The economic impact on Vancouver and the BC economy is huge. According to Jonathan Whitworth, CEO of Seaspan: "This is going to be a boom. It's not like building a (liquefied natural gas) plant or a mine, where there are 1,500 jobs for about two years. This is work for decades. It's like winning the 2010 Olympics every two years" (Alldritt, 2012).

Filmmaking

Vancouver is known as "Hollywood North," and the Vancouver area has become a major film production centre (Photo 9.11). Filmmaking represents one aspect of the emerging highly diversified urban "knowledge economy," which has taken hold in Toronto and Montréal as well. In 2013–14, the Vancouver film industry generated $1.6 billion and directly employs about 20,000 people (Bailey, 2015).

Advanced Drilling Techniques

Gas or oil deposits sometimes are found in horizontal strata in sedimentary basins. The Western

Copyright © Seaspan

Photo 9.10 Seaspan Shipyard in North Vancouver. Across Burrard Inlet lies downtown Vancouver and Stanley Park. In 2011, the federal government awarded Seaspan an $8 billion contract to build 17 vessels.

The Canadian Press/Darryl Dyck

Photo 9.11 A stuntman dressed as Ryan Reynolds's Marvel Comics character Deadpool flips over a vehicle during filming on the Georgia Viaduct in Vancouver, 6 April 2015.

Canadian Sedimentary Basin contains such deposits trapped in horizontal shale strata. The Bakken Shale Formation in southern Saskatchewan and northern North Dakota is one example; the Montney gas field in northeast BC and northwest Alberta is another. In each case, the oil or natural gas is trapped in a shale formation. Convention drilling cannot access such deposits. The technological breakthrough in drilling techniques involves a combination of multi-stage hydraulic fracturing and long-reach horizontal drilling able to access these "elephant" deposits. As a result, BC could become one of the world's largest natural gas producers. According to the National Energy Board (2015), Montney, Horn River, and the Liard Basin contain the three largest reserves of natural gas in Canada. Globally, these deposits are among the 10 largest shale gas deposits in the world (National Energy Board, 2015). Until recently, technology to extract such deposits did not exist, but recent advances in drilling technology, including multi-stage hydraulic fracturing, have allowed these natural deposits to be exploited. As shown in Figure 9.9,

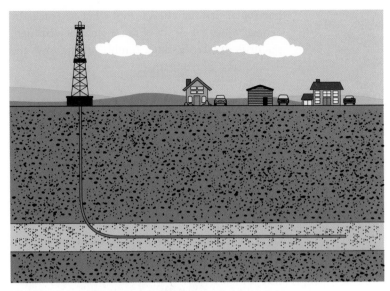

FIGURE 9.9 Horizontal drilling

Horizontal drilling takes place after vertical drilling has reached the horizontal shale strata. The next step requires the driller to alter the direction of the drilling to a horizontal one. At that point, fracking begins by pumping large quantities of pressurized, chemically treated water into the formation to fracture the rocks, allowing the natural gas to escape to the surface.

Contested Terrain 9.2

Is Fracking Harmless?

Fracking is a controversial technique that many oppose because of its potential threat to drinking water due to the release of chemically treated water. While enormous economic benefits come with shale gas projects, scientific evidence so far suggests that the impacts of hydraulic fracturing are harmful for a variety of reasons.

In the United States, where 1.1 million of these gas wells were operating in 2015, that total operation required 72 trillion gallons of water combined with 360 billion gallons of radioactive and carcinogenic chemicals. The process also involves quantities of silica sand added to this toxic stew, and the need for silica has led to a boom in sand mines, which can cause lung diseases for people living in the vicinity. Near fracking sites, on the other hand, birth defects and low birth weight have been recognized. Of the vast amounts of water used in fracking, 90 per cent never returns to the water cycle, and much of this wastewater is injected into deep underground disposal wells, a procedure that is identified as causing earthquakes (Loki, 2015). And, of course, the loss of water can be problematic for local communities, especially in arid regions, and, more generally, for the entire planet.

To top it off, quantities of methane leak out in the fracking process, so much so, in fact, that any "clean energy" effect of using natural gas rather than coal as an energy source may well be nullified. Methane is a much more potent greenhouse gas than carbon dioxide, trapping 86 times more heat in the atmosphere (Loki, 2015).

Public concerns have resulted in Québec and Nova Scotia outlawing fracking.

horizontal drilling allows the driller to reach the deposit. Once the depth of the shale is determined, the driller inserts a "bit assembly" that allows the drill to turn horizontally.

British Columbia's Economic Anchor: Forestry

The forest has long been British Columbia's greatest natural asset. With just over 60 per cent of the province covered by forests, British Columbia contains about half of the nation's softwood timber and leads the nation in the export of forest products. With such a dominant position, this region is easily Canada's leading supplier of wood products. With effective access to ports and rail, forest firms are ideally located to supply the needs of the US and global markets. At the same time, forests play an important role in the tourist industry with the growing recreational use of forest and wilderness areas by campers, hikers, and whitewater adventurers.

Logging and wood processing remain important, but forestry no longer dominates the province's economy. Fifty years ago forestry alone accounted for 50 per cent of the provincial economy and for most of the employment. By the late 1990s, the industry comprised only 17 per cent of BC's economy and 14 per cent of employment (Barnes and Hayter, 1997: 5). This decline continued into the twenty-first century (Schrier, 2012: 1). As well, the plight of wood processing and paper manufacturers remains particularly bleak and that situation partly accounts for the decline in BC's manufacturing sector. Another measure of the state of the forest industry is revealed by the annual value of exports. From 2002 to 2014, the annual value has fluctuated from a high of $15.1 billion in 2004 to a low of $8.2 billion in 2009. By 2014, the value of exports had increased to $12.4 billion (Barnes, 2015: 4).

The forest industry is particularly important to the BC Interior. Unlike the more heavily populated areas of BC, the Interior is much more reliant on the resource sector, especially the forest industry. The very survival of single-industry towns often depends on the logging, sawmills, and trucking associated with the forest industry. Even tree planting plays a small role by providing employment and thus keeping these small communities functioning.

Paper Excellence

Photo 9.12 Pulp and paper mills such as that in Mackenzie, BC, are struggling. In 2007, pulp prices hit a new low, causing Worthington Mackenzie to abandon the mill, forcing the BC government to take over operations. Prices improved and, in April 2010, Paper Excellence purchased the mill and invested $75 million, allowing the mill to successfully restart its operation and bring back over 200 jobs to the community.

The forest town of Mackenzie illustrates both dependency on the forest industry and community resilience. Located at the south end of Williston Lake
in the Northern Forest Zone (Figure 9.10), the community's economy has been tugged and pulled over
the years by fluctuations in lumber and pulp prices,
but the town has gained more economic stability
with the 2015 construction of a biomass electricity-
generating facility that consumes residue from the
sawmill (Photo 9.12).

Forest Regions

British Columbia's forest consists almost entirely
of coniferous softwood forest. Climate and topography have divided this vast forest into two distinct regions—the rain forest along the coast and
the boreal forest in the much drier Interior. Four
sub-regions are found in the Interior: the Northern Forest, the Nechako Forest, the Fraser Plateau
Forest, and the Columbia Forest (Figure 9.10). Size,

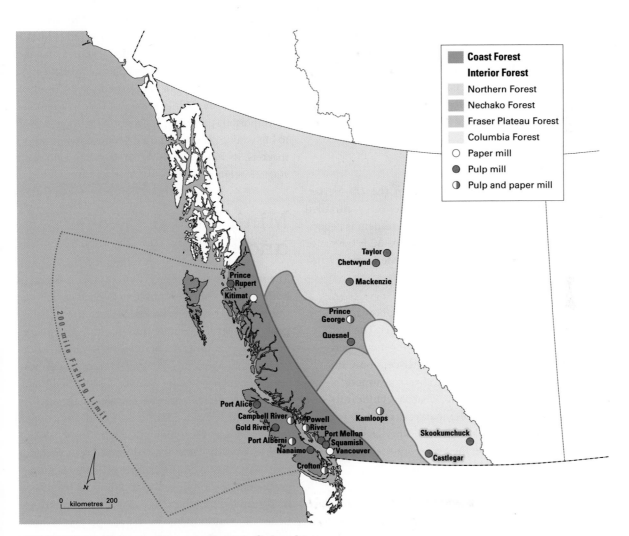

FIGURE 9.10 Forest regions in British Columbia

The Coast Rainforest is the most luxuriant coniferous forest in Canada. With its wet and mild marine temperatures and abundant rainfall, the Coast Rainforest is found almost entirely in mountainous terrain. The key species are Douglas fir, western red
cedar, and western red hemlock. The Interior Forest is subdivided into four areas that reflect variations in growing conditions.
The two main elements are lower temperature towards the north and, because of the warmer summer temperatures, drier
conditions.

age, and species vary. Within the rain forest, the mild, wet climate allows trees to grow to great heights for hundreds, even thousands, of years. Old-growth trees that are at least 250 years old are located along the Pacific coast, where fires are rare because of heavy precipitation throughout the year. The major species harvested are spruce and Douglas fir. In the Interior, the main species logged is the lodgepole pine. Since the climate in the Interior is much drier as well as colder in the winter and hotter in the summer than along the coast, the lodgepole pine and other trees are smaller and forest stands less dense. Trees have a shorter lifespan (120 to 140 years). While forest fires occur in all parts of BC, most occur in the dry, hot Interior. Here, forest fires are a constant threat and, more recently, pine beetle infestations have become a significant environmental and commercial problem.[4]

Dependency on the US Market

Most softwood lumber is sold in the US market. However, such exports may be seriously curtailed when a new Softwood Lumber Agreement is negotiated in 2017. Of Canada's six regions, BC is the major softwood lumber exporter. As McKenna (2016) reported:

> The essence of the fight is about how much of the U.S. market Canada will get. The U.S. industry is reportedly pushing for a permanent cap as low as 22 per cent on Canada's share of U.S. lumber consumption, enforced by a quota. That is significantly below Canada's 2015 market share of 30 per cent and well below the 33-per-cent level reached before the two countries signed their last managed trade deal in 2006.

Over the years, the United States has sought to reduce the volume of Canadian softwood lumber imports because such imports affect American producers. Yet, Canadian softwood lumber is highly valued by American construction firms and often its price is lower than the US softwood lumber. The 2017 Softwood Lumber Agreement negotiations seek to find a compromise. In 2015, Canadian softwood lumber made up about 30 per cent of the US market. The US position is strongly influenced by the US lumber lobby's demand that Canadian imports make up no more than 22 per cent of the US softwood lumber market. Such a drop in exports would have a drastic impact on the BC forestry industry and many small forestry-dependent communities.

The forest industry in British Columbia faces many difficulties. For softwood lumber producers, the problem is not a declining US market but the threat of limited access because of the new Softwood Lumber Agreement.[5] An optimistic interpretation, though, is of a kind of industrial renaissance, of a newly fashioned forest products industry that emphasizes high-value products, skilled labour, and leading-edge technology, plus a diversification of export markets with most attention focused on China and Japan. While the forest industry remains an important part of BC's economy, without a shift to high-value products and a diversification of export markets, its future is limited by its dependency on a single foreign market.

Mining, Energy, and Fisheries

The mineral wealth of British Columbia is found in both of the province's physiographic regions—the Cordillera and the Interior Plains. Each has a distinct geological structure and mineral and energy deposits. The Cordillera contains a wide variety of ore bodies ranging from diamonds to iron to uranium, while the Interior Plains with its Western Sedimentary Basin contains coal and petroleum deposits. In 2015, mineral production, led by coal and copper, totalled almost $6 billion (BC Stats, 2016c). While coal is king in mineral production, natural gas is soon expected to lead in terms of value of energy production. BC produced $3.0 billion worth of coal in 2015 and $2.3 billion in copper (BC Stats, 2016c). Canada's commitment to reduce its greenhouse gases suggests that the future of BC's coal production may be affected. Coking coal exported to Asian steel mills may continue at its current level but thermal coal used for producing electricity is already under pressure. For example, the Burrard thermal electric generating station located at Port Moody ceased production in 2016.

Natural Gas Exports: Dream or Reality?

Unlike the two bitumen pipelines proposed to reach the Pacific coast, natural gas pipelines are viewed by BC in a favourable light. The chief reason is that a leak in a natural gas pipeline or ship evaporates and thus has much less potential impact on the local environment than does a bitumen spill that soaks into the land or sinks to the bottom of lakes, rivers, or oceans. In the coming years, export of liquefied natural gas (LNG) to Asian countries could constitute a major export industry for British Columbia. This expectation is based on two world-class deposits: the Horn River shale gas deposits north of Fort Nelson and the Montney Basin reserves further south around Fort St John and Dawson Creek. The obstacles facing such huge developments are their high cost; the current low price of natural gas; and

surplus natural gas in the United States. Of these three obstacles, the most critical one is current low natural gas prices. Since commodity prices are cyclical, global companies have the financial resources to wait for an upswing in gas prices. A fourth obstacle, the environmental consequences of fracking (see Contested Terrain 9.2), so far has not made a dent in the political determination to pursue LNG exploitation despite ongoing protests by "fractivists."

The BC government hopes that at least two liquefied natural gas terminals—one at Kitimat and the other at Prince Rupert—will be built. One of the world's leading energy companies, Malaysia's state-owned Petronas, received federal approval for its Prince Rupert project in September 2016. The company expects that natural gas from the North Montney deposit in the Interior Plains of northeast BC will arrive in Asian ports as liquefied gas sometime in the next five years (Figure 9.11). Given

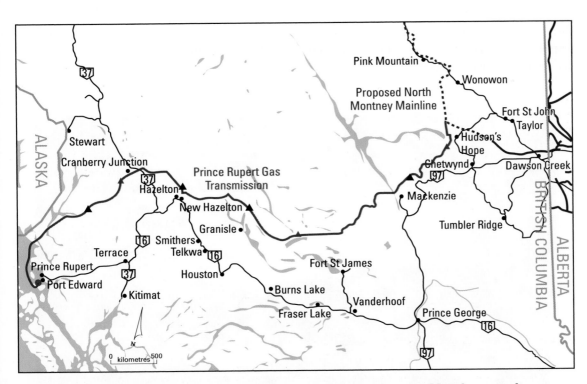

FIGURE 9.11 Prince Rupert Gas Transmission and North Montney Mainline pipelines

The Prince Rupert Gas Transmission pipeline from Hudson's Hope to the terminal on Lelu Island stretches across 900 km of land and sea with 120 km under the ocean. TransCanada Pipelines has approval to build a 301-km pipeline from Hudson's Hope to the North Montney deposit some 100 km northwest of Fort St John. The pipelines have the capacity to carry 2.0 billion cubic feet of natural gas per day.

Source: Prince Rupert Gas Transmission Project, 2016, at: http://www.princerupertgas.com/about-2/route-maps/.

the enormous size of the two natural gas deposits, export of liquefied natural gas is expected to continue for another 40 years. The $36 billion Petronas project consists of three parts:

1. Progress Energy Canada (with Petronas the principal shareholder) will extract the natural gas from the North Montney deposit first and later from the Horn River deposit.
2. TransCanada Pipelines, under contract with Petronas, will build and operate the Prince Rupert Gas Transmission and North Montney pipelines that will connect the North Montney natural gas deposit with the LNG terminal on Lelu Island near Prince Rupert.
3. Pacific NorthWest LNG will transform the natural gas into a liquefied state on Lelu Island near Port Edward and then load the liquefied gas into double-hulled freighters for shipment to Asian and other customers (Photo 9.13).

There is no guarantee of smooth sailing, however. Despite Ottawa's approval, opposition to the project remains. Environmental groups condemned the approval and First Nations oppose it. As Donald Wesley, a hereditary chief of the Gitwilgyoots tribe of the Tsimshian Nation, stated: "We have no alternative now but to take it to the courts" (Tracy Johnson, 2016).

Mining Industry

Both coal and copper remain important exports for British Columbia (Figure 9.12). BC coal production depends heavily on world demand for metallurgical coal used in steel mills, which fluctuates according to the global economic cycle. Since Ottawa has signalled that coal used to produce electricity will be phased out by 2030, BC metallurgical coal production should not be affected. Copper, because it conducts electricity well, finds a market in electric power systems, wiring of buildings and houses, and in the field of electronics. Boom-and-bust cycles are characteristic of the BC coal and copper industries. During resource booms, huge investments are made on new developments. Such was the case in the late 1970s when private and public funds went into the development of the vast Peace River coalfields near the Alberta border. Known as the Northeast Coal

Photo 9.13 Huge liquefied natural gas tankers like this one at Tokyo are anticipated to be plying the waters near Prince Rupert in the coming years. If all goes to plan, by 2022 the first such LNG tanker could dock at Lelu Island and then transport its cargo to any of several Asian ports, such as Tokyo, Hong Kong, or Mumbai.

Project, production began in 1984 about the time demand for coal slumped. Struggling to hang on, the coal companies squeaked by until 2000 when the project collapsed. By 2014, the demand and prices for coal began to soften, foreshadowing another "bust" in BC's coal industry.

Transportation costs are critical and these have been minimized by unit trains and bulk-loading facilities. Unit trains consist of a large number of ore cars, sometimes over 100, pulled by one or more locomotives. The Roberts Bank terminal on the Strait of Georgia in Delta, BC, south of Vancouver, was designed as a large bulk-loading facility where coal in rail cars is dumped and then the coal is moved by conveyor belts to the ship's hold. These ships must be moored in deep water, which necessitated building a long causeway to reach the ships. Similar arrangements take place at Prince Rupert.

Fishing Industry

British Columbia, like Atlantic Canada, has an important fishery. The BC fishery, as a renewable resource, ranks fourth in value of production among resource industries behind mining (including natural gas), forestry, and agriculture. Fish processing plants employ 25,000 full-time and part-time employees. More than 100 species of fish and marine animals are harvested from the Pacific Ocean, freshwater bodies, and aquaculture areas. Salmon is the most valuable species, followed by herring, shellfish, groundfish, and halibut. In 2013, the landed value from the sea reached $763 million with two-thirds associated with aquaculture (Fisheries and Oceans Canada, 2015).

Wild salmon catches vary from year to year. Salmon (chinook, sockeye, coho, pink, and chum) spend several years in the Pacific Ocean before returning to spawn in the Fraser and other rivers. The principal BC salmon-spawning rivers are the Fraser and the Skeena. In 2010, the Fraser River sockeye salmon return was the largest since 1913, with an estimated run of 34 million. The previous year, the Fraser River experienced one of the biggest salmon disasters in recent history. Between 10.6 million and 13 million sockeye were expected to return to the Fraser but less than 2 million arrived (Hume, 2009).

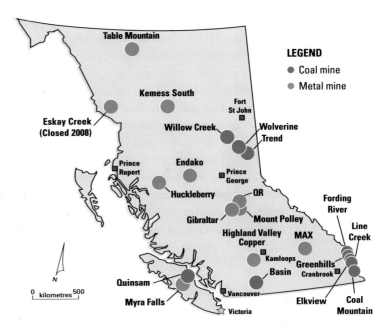

FIGURE 9.12 Mines in British Columbia

Most coal mines lie along the eastern flank of the Rocky Mountains while the metal mines are located in the Interior. Mount Polley's open-pit copper mine, for example, is situated in the Interior Plateau near the town of Williams Lake. Its production was halted following the breach of its tailing pond but within two years the mine was back to full production. The impact of the breach on the landscape is shown in Photo 9.4.

Source: Adapted from Mineral Resources Education Program of BC (2009).

Unfortunately, BC shares another similarity with Atlantic Canada—overexploitation of fish stocks, particularly the valuable salmon stocks. Pressure on the fish stocks, especially salmon, comes from four sources—Canadian commercial fishers, American commercial fishers, the Aboriginal fishery, and the sports fishery. All want larger catches.

Management of the salmon fishery falls under the Pacific Salmon Treaty, which was signed by Canada and the United States in 1985 and sets long-term goals for the sustainability of this resource. The Pacific Salmon Commission, formed by the governments of Canada and the US to implement the Pacific Salmon Treaty, does not regulate the salmon fisheries but provides regulatory advice and recommendations to the two countries. In Canada, Fisheries and Oceans Canada, in consultation with the Pacific Salmon Commission (www.psc.org/), has set annual quotas for salmon in Canadian waters.

Salmon are migratory fish, so regulating salmon fishing is particularly challenging. Like other fish, they are common property until caught. This principle is based on the "rule of capture." Fishers therefore try to maximize their share of a harvest so no one else will take "their" fish. The problem is complicated further because the Canadian government cannot regulate the "Canadian" salmon stocks, i.e., those that spawn in Canadian rivers, because they migrate to American waters, where the American fishing fleet harvests them. The result is that the salmon stocks are threatened. This problem is commonly referred to as the **tragedy of the commons** and is compounded by the economic cycle, whereby resource extraction accelerates during periods of high global demand for natural resources.[6]

Hydroelectric Power

Hydroelectric energy is a renewable energy source dependent on the hydrologic cycle of water, which involves evaporation, precipitation, and the flow of water due to gravity. British Columbia, with abundant water resources and a geography that provides many opportunities to produce low-cost energy, produces more hydroelectric power than all other provinces except Québec. Major generating stations on the Peace River and Columbia River produce

80 per cent of BC Hydro power. The two power stations on the Peace River are the massive W.A.C. Bennett Dam with its G.M. Shrum generating station (completed 1968) and the Peace Canyon Dam (completed 1980); a third station, Site C, is nearing the construction phase (Figure 9.13). In 2016, Victoria approved the first phase of this project. When completed, Site C will increase electrical production for the province by 8 per cent. However, this project continues to dodge protests from First Nations and environmental organizations. One reason is that it will flood 55 km² of river valley and could affect wildlife that local Treaty 8 First Nations harvest.

The Columbia River has a combination of dams and generating stations. The 1964 Columbia River Treaty with the United States called for Canada to construct and store water at three dams, the Duncan (1967), Hugh Keenleyside (1968), and Mica (1973) dams, in exchange for electricity generated at the Grand Coulee generating station in Washington State. The Mica Dam, from the outset, was built with a generating station while the other two were only for water storage, although in 2002, immediately downstream from the Keenleyside dam, a new Arrow Lakes generating station was completed. The

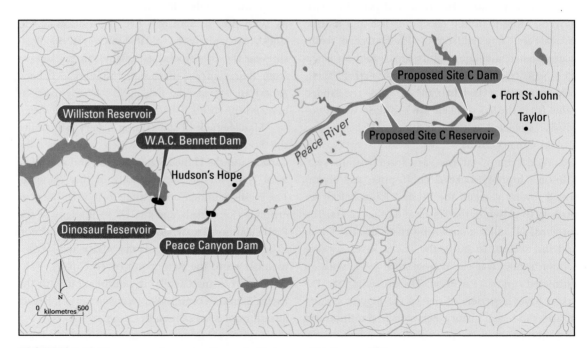

FIGURE 9.13 Dams and generating stations on the Peace River
Source: BC Hydro.

Photo 9.14 One of BC's most important processing plants, Rio Tinto's Kitimat aluminum smelter, uses low-cost hydroelectric power from the Kemano generating station to process bauxite from foreign countries.

THINK ABOUT IT

In 1951, Alcan began construction on the Kenney Dam across the Nechako River to create a huge reservoir. With the dam operational in 1954, these waters now flowed westward through a tunnel bored through the Coast Mountains to the Kemano generating station rather than eastward to the Fraser River. Why did Alcan have no legal cause to consult with the Cheslatta First Nation whose traditional lands were flooded?

Mica, Arrow Lakes, and Revelstoke facilities, the latter completed in 1984 upriver on the Columbia, have produced most of the power on the BC side of the Columbia River.

Rio Tinto (formerly Alcan) owns and operates the Kemano hydroelectric plant, which was completed in 1954. The geographic area controlled by Rio Tinto extends far inland beyond the Coast Mountains to the Fraser/Nechako plateau. This large area of northwest British Columbia extends from Kitimat to Kemano on the coast and then to the Kenney Dam on the Nechako River southwest of Vanderhoof. A 75-km transmission line takes electrical power to Rio Tinto's Kitimat aluminum smelter (Photo 9.14). Since its reservoir lies on the east side of the Coast Mountains, a 16-km tunnel drilled through the mountains connects Tahtsa Lake to the Kemano Powerhouse. Most power is consumed in the smelting of bauxite ore but the surplus energy is sold to BC Hydro.

These three giant industrial construction efforts—one on the Columbia River, another on the Peace River, and the third on the Nechako River—had enormous impacts on the economy and environment. They all involved the harnessing of waterpower from the province's rivers to generate low-cost electrical power, but they also flooded valuable farmland and First Nations lands and led to the loss of salmon spawning grounds. Such major engineering projects took place before environmental legislation became the law of the land and prior to the duty to consult First Nations being a requirement of resource projects. In today's world, such projects may have run into serious problems getting their environmental impact statements approved and receiving support from First Nations.

British Columbia's Urban Core

The most striking aspect of the urban geography of British Columbia is the concentration of people in the Lower Mainland. Close to 60 per cent of the population of British Columbia resides in the Lower Mainland (Figure 9.14). The four census metropolitan areas of Vancouver, Abbotsford, Kelowna, and Victoria provide another view of this concentration. Together, they comprise 69 per cent of the population of British Columbia.

As well, they are the fastest-growing urban places in the province, with a combined population increase of just over 25 per cent from 2001 to 2015 (Table 9.3). By comparison, the other urban centres grew by about 8.5 per cent from 2001 to 2011 (Table 9.4). Universities provide an incubator for the advanced economy and add to Florida's concept of an "interesting" city. Eight universities, led by the University of British Columbia and Simon Fraser University, are located in the Metro Vancouver region. On Vancouver Island are the University of Victoria (Photo 9.15) and Vancouver Island University, in Nanaimo.

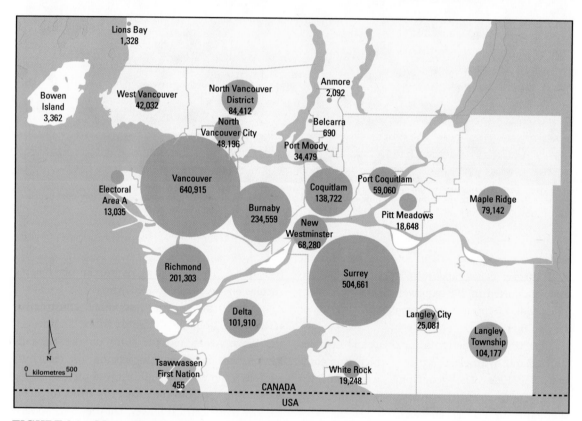

FIGURE 9.14 Metro Vancouver

Metro Vancouver consists of 21 municipalities and one First Nation reserve, and has a single amalgamated government comprised of elected officials from each local authority. Metro Vancouver delivers services such as drinking water, wastewater treatment, and solid waste management; monitors air quality; and is involved in planning, parks, affordable housing, and other issues of governance. Its boundaries correspond with the Vancouver census metropolitan area. The Lower Mainland of British Columbia, with Vancouver as the focal point, dominates British Columbia's population geography. BC's fourth-largest city, Abbotsford, is part of the Lower Mainland but is to the east of Metro Vancouver.

Source: Metro Vancouver (2015).

Greater Vancouver

With one of the most spectacular physical settings in the world, Vancouver, located on the shores of Burrard Inlet, is framed by the snow-capped peaks of the North Shore Mountains. The Lions Gate Bridge passes over Burrard Inlet, thereby linking Vancouver with the North Shore and its main urban centres of West Vancouver and North Vancouver. From West Vancouver, the Sea-to-Sky Highway leads to the Whistler ski resort. To the west is the island-studded Strait of Georgia, while the Fraser River and its deltaic islands (flat, low islands composed of silt and clay near the mouth of the river) mark Vancouver's southern edge. Vancouver has a mild, marine climate, with a California-like dry, warm summer. Winter, however, with its overcast skies and rainy weather, is less appealing to some people.

As one of the great ports on the Pacific coast of North America and the largest in Canada, Vancouver's economic strength stems partly from its role as a trade centre. With most of the world's population located along the Pacific Rim, Port Metro Vancouver handles over $65 billion worth of trade goods annually (Port Metro Vancouver, 2013).

Vancouver's rich and vibrant culture provides a suitable base for attracting the "creative class" members of the information society, with places like Granville Island (Vignette 9.4) as one element in the broad cultural world that appeals to "creative" people. But all is not well in Vancouver's housing market, which has priced many out of the market. In fact, a survey by Demographia declared

Photo 9.15 Campus of the University of Victoria with the Pacific Ocean in the background.

Courtesy of the University of Victoria, Community-Based Research Canada.

that Vancouver is the third-least-affordable city in the world, just behind Hong Kong and Sydney, Australia. Demographia found that the average family dwelling costs nearly 11 times more than the average household income, making it virtually impossible for those families to purchase a house (Schmunk, 2016). In July 2016, the provincial government sought to reduce the hot housing market by allowing the city to introduce a 15 per cent tax on residential properties sold to foreign nationals and foreign-controlled corporations. Most foreign buyers are from China. To further discourage foreign buyers, who see housing as an investment rather than a place to live, Vancouver in 2017 will assess owners of vacant houses and condos a 1 per cent tax based on the value of their housing units (CBC News, 2016).

THINK ABOUT IT

When 2016 census data are released, what economic developments might turn the population losses into gains for Terrace, Kitimat, and Prince Rupert?

TABLE 9.3 Census Metropolitan Areas in British Columbia, 2001–2015

Centre	Population 2001	Population 2015	Percentage Change
Abbotsford	147,370	183,652	24.6
Kelowna	147,739	197,274	33.5
Victoria	311,902	365,291	17.1
Vancouver	1,986,965	2,504,340	26.0
Total	2,593,976	3,250,557	25.3
British Columbia	3,907,738	4,703,939	20.4

Sources: Adapted from Statistics Canada (2007, 2016e).

TABLE 9.4 Urban Centres in British Columbia, 2001–2011

Centre	Population 2001	Population 2011	Percentage Change
Kitimat	10,285	8,335	−19.0
Dawson Creek	10,754	11,583	0.8
Prince Rupert	15,302	13,052	−14.7
Terrace	19,980	15,569	−22.1
Powell River	16,604	16,689	0.0
Squamish	14,435	17,479	21.1
Salmon Arm	15,388	17,683	14.9
Williams Lake	19,768	18,490	−6.4
Quesnel	24,426	22,096	−10.0
Cranbrook	24,275	25,037	−3.1
Port Alberni	25,299	25,465	0
Fort St John	23,007	26,380	9.3
Parksville	24,285	27,822	9.2
Campbell River	35,036	36,096	4.1
Penticton	41,564	42,361	4.2
Duncan	38,613	43,252	6.6
Courtenay	45,205	55,213	8.9
Vernon	51,530	58,584	7.5
Prince George	85,035	84,232	−2.1
Chilliwack	74,003	92,308	9.3
Nanaimo	85,664	98,021	7.8
Kamloops	86,951	98,754	4.4
Total	787,409	854,501	8.5
British Columbia	3,907,738	4,703,939	20.4

Source: Adapted from Statistics Canada (2007, 2011).

Vignette 9.4

Granville Island

Granville Island is the site of a well-known public market in the heart of downtown Vancouver. Situated in False Creek and lying beneath Granville Bridge, the island has turned into a key gathering spot for both locals and tourists. For many years, Granville Island was a sawmilling centre as logs could be towed through False Creek. In the 1970s, everything changed—sawmilling was out and an upscale residential and specialized commercial area was in. Besides Granville Island Public Market, other enterprises have widened its appeal—artists' studios and shops, a wide variety of restaurants, and features like the Kids Market, Maritime Market, and Coast Salish Houseposts, a joint endeavour between the Emily Carr College and First Nations. Granville Island is unique to Vancouver and has added another dimension to the wide-ranging cultural attractions in the Greater Vancouver area.

© Al Harvey/slidefarm.com

Photo 9.16 Aerial view of Granville Island.

SUMMARY

Situated at a critical geographic intersection with Asia, British Columbia benefits from an increasing volume of trade between Asia and North America. With a technically advanced economy and abundant natural resources, BC is well positioned for the future. In fact, two major projects, one in hand (the massive shipbuilding contract) and the other promised (the huge natural gas pipeline and LNG terminal project), are driving the BC economy forward. The combination of natural resources and an advanced economy, as exemplified by "spearhead" industries, is propelling British Columbia's economy well ahead of other regions. Given that momentum, BC's share of population and therefore political power in Ottawa can only increase in the years to come. As one of six regions, BC's population growth remains well above the national rate, while its export-oriented economy is poised to expand with the additional facilities at the Port of Prince Rupert.

One geographic fact remains irrefutable: the **grooves of geography**, in this case the north–south mountain ranges of BC, tend to align this region with the adjacent US Northwest and, despite modern transportation methods, set it apart from the rest of Canada. Yet, the heavy investment in transportation infrastructure—the superhighway corridor to Vancouver and the expansion of port facilities at Vancouver and Prince Rupert, plus the promise of an LNG terminal at Prince Rupert—creates an east–west groove and encourages links with Pacific Rim countries. The expansion of port facilities at Prince Rupert alone has provided another and shorter outlet for natural resources and agricultural products from Western Canada to reach markets in Asia. In addition, the prospect of a new energy corridor for Alberta's oil sands across the Cordillera to Vancouver and then by ship to Asian countries would greatly strengthen trade. Once the global economy regains its steam, exports to the United States and Pacific Rim countries are anticipated to return to previous or even higher levels. Finally, BC's natural setting makes it a world-class tourist destination. The main challenge facing BC is to diffuse its technically advanced economy to a broader range of economic activities.

Challenge Questions

1. Do you believe the appeal of Cascadia, rooted in the "grooves of geography," discourages west–east interactions? Historically and in recent years, Ottawa has been accused of ignoring the needs and wants of BC. How does the federal government approval of the Trans Mountain Expansion affect these "grooves"?

2. Why does BC's population geography represent both a demographic and cultural divide?

3. Discuss why the decision to create a UNESCO biosphere reserve for the Great Bear Rainforest may herald a path for solutions to other environment issues and lead to sustainable development involving local First Nations.

4. Why has the Trans Mountain Expansion been opposed by the city councils of Burnaby and Vancouver?

5. Explain why the US wants to limit BC's ability to ship lumber to US markets while the US places no such limits on BC's export of electricity to the Pacific Northwest.

Essay Questions

1. Housing prices in Vancouver are at record highs. For Vancouverites, the rate of house price increases is much greater than the rate of family incomes. Have foreign investors squeezed out Vancouver's middle class from the housing market?

    References:
    Gold, Kerry. 2016. "The Highest Bidder." *Walrus* 13, 4: 22–32.
    Kay, Jonathan. 2016. "Vancouver's Offshore Problem." *Walrus* 13, 4: 74.
    Woo, Yuen Pau. 2016. "It's Too Easy to Blame 'Outsiders' for Vancouver's Housing Woes." *Globe and Mail*, 5 Apr. At: http://www.theglobeandmail.com/opinion/its-too-easy-to-blame-outsiders-for-vancouvers-housing-woes/article29514052/.
    Yan, Andy. 2015. "Ownership Patterns of Single Family Home Sales on Selected West Side Neighborhoods in the City of Vancouver." At: http://www.slideshare.net/ayan604/ownership-patterns-of-single-family-homes-sales-on-the-west-side-neighborhoods-of-the-city-of-vancouver-a-case-study.

2. Toponymy is the study of geographic place names that reflect the political landscape. This expression of the political landscape takes on a "sense of place," but when it is contested, the outcome can take the form of decolonizing the map. For example, the insertion of Indigenous place names on the Canadian landscape represents the reclaiming of the names of lands and seas by those peoples, as has been done with Haida Gwaii (formerly the Queen Charlotte Islands). But is the geographic designation of the Salish Sea that replaces the Strait of Georgia, Puget Sound, and Juan de Fuca Strait a strictly Indigenous matter?

References:

Corntassel, J. 2012. "Re-envisioning Resurgence: Indigenous Pathways to Decolonization and Sustainable Self-determination." *Decolonization: Indigeneity, Education and Society* 1, 1: 86–101.

Tucker, Brian, and Reuben Rose-Redwood. 2015. "Decolonizing the Map? Toponymic Politics and the Rescaling of the Salish Sea." *Canadian Geographer* 59, 2: 194–206.

Further Reading

Molloy, Tom. 2000. *The World Is Our Witness: The Historic Journey of the Nisga'a into Canada.* Calgary: Fifth House.

On 11 May 2000, the Nisga'a Final Agreement Act passed into law, marking a historic treaty agreement between this small group of First Nations people and the rest of Canadian society. The Nisga'a, after all, had been the plaintiffs in the landmark *Calder* case of 1973, which they lost on a technicality, but which recognized the existence in law of Aboriginal rights to unceded traditional lands. The Nisga'a Agreement broke new ground in the search by First Nations for a place within Canadian society. As well, the Agreement offered one solution to the question of resource-sharing.

In *The World Is Our Witness*, Molloy, who was the chief federal negotiator, describes how the Agreement ends the period of colonization by the British and, later, Canadians of the Nisga'a lands and people. Molloy not only provides an insider's view of the struggle to achieve an agreement, but also explains its significance to Canadians. The Nisga'a treaty represents a compromise between the Nisga'a and other Canadians on how to share the lands and resources found in the traditionally occupied lands of the Nisga'a.

Some 15 years later, the theme of resource-sharing took the form of the Nisga'a Nation's governing body accepting $6 million from the BC government to allow a pipeline to bring natural gas to Prince Rupert to feed hoped-for liquefied natural gas plants. This proposed pipeline would cut across a provincial park in the Nass Valley that the Nisga'a co-manage with the province.

⑩ Atlantic Canada

CHAPTER OVERVIEW

Important issues and topics examined in this chapter include:

- Atlantic Canada's physical and historical geography.
- Population, urban centres, and economic affairs.
- Opportunity gained: the shellfish industry; opportunity lost: the cod fishery.
- Low energy and mineral prices.
- The economic boost provided by shipbuilding.

Introduction

For many centuries, the vast expanse of the Atlantic Ocean has shaped every aspect of Atlantic Canada. This undeniable connection to the sea has marked the region and its people. History, plus the geographic fact that this region lies far from the places of economic and political power in Canada, defines Atlantic Canada and separates it from the other regions. As an older part of Canada, its prime resources, whether coal, northern cod, or timber, have been consumed and those remaining are only a shadow of their original state. Adding to its challenges, the region's fractured geography limits economic growth, leads to high unemployment levels, and encourages out-migration. While geography did endow Atlantic Canada with vast offshore oil and gas, fossil fuel prices collapsed in 2014, thus greatly diminishing their value. Not surprisingly, then, Atlantic Canada remains the weak sister of Canada's regions. Nevertheless, sparks of economic rejuvenation are emerging in its major cities, especially Halifax, Moncton, and St John's.

While the task of revitalizing Atlantic Canada's economy remains a work in progress, four trends suggest a more positive future:

- the shellfish fishery is profitable;
- a large federal shipbuilding contract represents a long-term investment;
- the recently approved trade agreement with the European Union augurs well for a surge in transatlantic container traffic;
- the global price cycle, now at a bottom point, will no doubt return to higher prices for oil and minerals produced in Atlantic Canada.

In this chapter, we examine the fishing industry as the region's economic anchor—as it has been for centuries—and look at the growing importance of the shellfish industry. Potential economic spearheads include shipbuilding and hydroelectric development.

← The small fishing village at Cape St Charles, Labrador, Canada. Although Newfoundland and Labrador's economy has become increasingly tied to the oil and gas industry, fisheries remain an important part of province's economic and cultural identity.

Atlantic Canada within Canada

Stretching along the country's eastern coast, Atlantic Canada consists of two parts: the Maritimes (Nova Scotia, Prince Edward Island, and New Brunswick) and Newfoundland and Labrador[1] (Figure 10.1). Separated from the mainland by Cabot Strait, the island of Newfoundland stands alone in the Atlantic Ocean while the Labrador Peninsula abuts Québec. Still, in spite of its fractured geography, Atlantic Canada retains its rich and enduring sense of place that has grown out of the region's history, its original British and French settlements, and its close ties to the North Atlantic.

The Atlantic Ocean has dominated this region from the early days of the fishery to the "Golden Age of Wooden Ships and Iron Men" and through two world wars, to the economic dream of an Atlantic Gateway to Europe. In recent times, offshore petroleum developments have had positive impacts while the collapse of the northern cod fishery served a deadly blow to coastal communities and resulted in the end of a way of life. The future lies not in the fading image of outports like Diamond Cove (Photo 10.1) but in the vibrant urban centres, led by the ports of Halifax (Photo 10.2) and St John's.

Dale Wilson/All Canada Photos

Photo 10.1 The sharp interface between land and sea demonstrates why fishing was a way of life. Outports like Diamond Cove, situated along the isolated coastline of southwest Newfoundland, are a dying breed. Since the closure of the cod fishery in 2003, outports no longer have an economic base and many families abandoned these tiny fishing communities. Diamond Cove is hanging on, but its demographics tell the sad tale: a tiny and dwindling population (66 in 2006, down to 53 in 2011); an older population with an average age of 56 and no one under the age of 20.

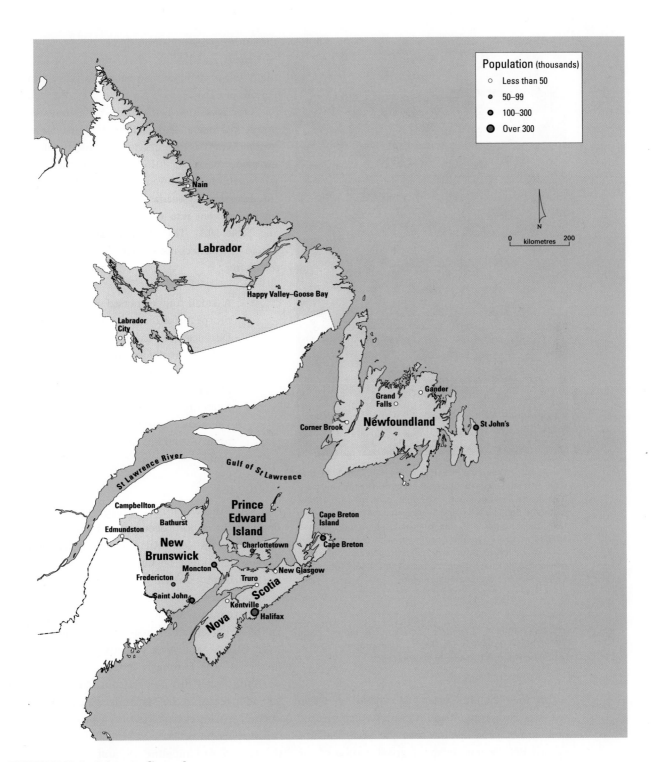

FIGURE 10.1 Atlantic Canada

Atlantic Canada contains four provinces, Nova Scotia, New Brunswick, Newfoundland and Labrador, and Prince Edward Island. Atlantic Canada has the smallest population and the weakest economy—except for the Territorial North—of Canada's six regions. Geography endowed the sea with rich fish stocks and petroleum deposits, but not with an abundance of fertile soils. Oil has made Newfoundland and Labrador a "have" province—at least for now. The others are classified as "have-not" provinces and receive equalization payments from the federal government. The largest city is Halifax, with a population of just under 420,000 followed by St John's at 212,000.

Russ Heinl/All Canada Photos

Photo 10.2 When the British founded Halifax in 1749, they were attracted by its magnificent harbour. The high hill overlooking the harbour offered a perfect location for a fortress to defend the new town and its naval base. Named the Halifax Citadel (upper left), this fortress is an impressive star-shaped masonry structure complete with defensive ditch, earthen ramparts, musketry gallery, powder magazine, garrison cells, guard room, barracks, and school room. The Citadel is now a National Historic Site.

In Chapter 1, "Canada's Geographic Regions," page 5, the rationale for Canada's six geographic regions, including Atlantic Canada, is elaborated.

As the region in Canada first exploited and then settled by Europeans, Atlantic Canada has experienced both growth and decline over the years. Atlantic Canada has become, in the regional version of the core/periphery model, a slow-growing region. Past exploitation of its renewable resources, especially cod and timber resources, has diminished its resource base. Atlantic Canada's troubles are epitomized by

the subpar economic performance relative to the rest of Canada and by the seemingly unstoppable out-migration of its more able people to faster-growing regions of Canada.

One measure of Atlantic Canada's overall economic performance is reflected in its per capita gross domestic product figures and its level of unemployment. In 2015, except for the Territorial North, Atlantic Canada's GDP per capita was the lowest in Canada, while the region's 2015 unemployment rate was the highest (Figure 10.2 and Table 10.1). The primary reasons for Atlantic Canada's weak economic performance include the following:

- A small and dispersed population limits prospects for internal economic growth.
- Distance from national and global markets stifles its manufacturing base.
- Fractured geography and four distinct political jurisdictions discourage an integrated economy.
- The natural resource base is restricted and some resources, such as cod, coal, and timber, were exploited in the past and have lost their importance.

All of these factors have made it extremely difficult for the region's economy to flourish. Furthermore, over the years Atlantic Canada has become heavily dependent on Ottawa for economic support through equalization payments and social programs. Yet, Atlantic Canada has received a second chance with the discovery of offshore oil and gas deposits and a huge shipbuilding contract from Ottawa, and most recently, the trade agreement with the European Union. In addition, the possibility of hydro power from Muskrat Falls in Labrador reaching the Maritimes could mean a reduction in electricity rates plus a profit from selling surplus power to New England markets; and the Energy East pipeline, if built, could delivery bitumen to the Irving refinery near Saint John, New Brunswick. By taking full advantage of these new opportunities, could Atlantic Canada shed its moniker as a "have-not" region?

Atlantic Canada's Population

Since Confederation, Atlantic Canada's population has increased at a rate well below the national average. From 2001 to 2016, Atlantic Canada's population has actually increased by only 38,000, and the anemic annual growth rate of less than 1 per cent is predicted to continue into the future (Chaundry, 2012: 95). Internal differences in population growth also persist. From 1996 to 2015, for example, the region's population increased in the Maritimes but decreased in Newfoundland and Labrador (Table 10.5). Over this span of 20 years, the Maritimes saw a modest increase of 63,000 souls, chiefly in Nova Scotia. Newfoundland and Labrador, on the other hand, lost nearly 25,000 residents.

In 2015, Atlantic Canada, with nearly 2.4 million people, comprised 6.6 per cent of Canada's population (Figure 10.2). Its population size ranks fifth out of the six Canadian regions, thus providing a rough measure of its importance within Confederation. In 1871, Atlantic Canada' share of the nation population was 20 per cent; now it is under 7 per cent (Figure 1.3). Its fragmented geography makes economic growth difficult; and without economic growth, large population increases are not possible.

Regional population distribution falls into six clusters around the principal cities—Halifax, St John's, Saint John, Moncton, Fredericton, and Charlottetown. Accounting for nearly 1.1 million people, these six urban centres comprise 46 per cent of Atlantic Canada's population.

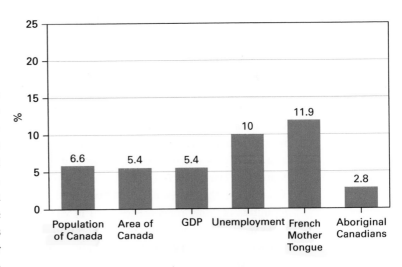

FIGURE 10.2 Atlantic Canada basic statistics, 2015

One measure of Atlantic Canada's weak economic performance is revealed by the following figures: the region has 6.6 per cent of Canada's population but produces only 5.4 per cent of the country's GDP.

Percentages of population, area, and GDP are for Canada as a whole; unemployment, French home language, and Indigenous population percentages are for Atlantic Canada. Percentages for French mother tongue and Indigenous Canadians are for 2011.

Sources: Tables 1.1, 1.2, and 5.6.

Atlantic Canada's Physical Geography

Two of Canada's physiographic regions are found in Atlantic Canada: the Appalachian Uplands and the Canadian Shield. The Appalachian Uplands are located in the Maritimes and the island of Newfoundland while Labrador is part of the Canadian Shield. In terms of geologic time, the Appalachian Uplands

TABLE 10.1 Basic Statistics for Atlantic Canada by Province, 2015

Province	Population (000s)	Population Density	% of National GDP	Unemployment Rate (%)
Prince Edward Island	147	24.7	0.3	10.4
Newfoundland and Labrador	528	1.4	1.5	12.8
New Brunswick	754	10.5	1.6	9.8
Nova Scotia	922	17.4	2.0	8.6
Atlantic Canada	2,351	4.7	5.4	10.0
Canada	35,986	3.8	100.0	6.9

Sources: Statistics Canada (2016a, 2016f).

326 The Regional Geography of Canada

represents the worn-down remnants of an ancient mountain chain. Formed in the Paleozoic era, the Appalachian Mountains have been subjected to erosional forces for some 500 million years. As Photo 2.8 illustrates, streams have cut deeply into the Cape Breton Highlands of the Appalachian Uplands, resulting in rugged, hilly terrain. In Labrador, the most prominent feature of this portion of the Canadian Shield is the uplifted and glaciated Torngat Mountains (Photo 10.3). Unlike the rest of the Canadian Shield, the Labrador portion was subjected to a mountain-building process (orogeny) in which the rocks were folded and faulted some 750 million years ago. More recently in geologic time, these mountains were covered with glaciers, which, as the glaciers slowly moved down slope, carved the mountain features and eventually reached the sea, where they created a fjorded coastline (see Photo 2.2).

The weather of Atlantic Canada is quite varied because of the frequent meeting of continental air masses with marine air masses. The flow of continental air masses from the northwest brings warm weather in the summer and cold weather in the winter. Yet, with no part of Atlantic Canada more than 200 km from the Atlantic Ocean or Gulf of St Lawrence, moderate, marine-type weather predominates. The result is generally unsettled weather. Still, Atlantic Canada, especially Labrador, has a strongly continental aspect to its climate and, coupled with the cold Labrador Current, takes on a more Arctic-like climate. Storms are not uncommon, especially in the fall when hurricanes reach the Maritimes. Usually tropical storms lose their punch by the time they reach Nova Scotia, but sometimes this is not the case. Hurricane Juan, for example, made landfall on 29 September 2003, bringing its full fury.

Alexndra Koblenko/All Canada Photos

Photo 10.3 The Torngat Mountains, a national park reserve since 2005, stretch along the fjorded coast of northern Labrador. One such fjord is Ramah Bay (with an iceberg floating in its waters). The mountains were recently, in geologic time, subjected to alpine glaciation, resulting in extremely sharp features, including arêtes, cirques, and horns. These mountains, including Mount Caubvik (also known as Mont D'Iberville), straddle the Québec/Labrador boundary. They attain heights of 1,652 m (5,420 ft) above sea level and are located near the sixtieth parallel. For both reasons—high elevation and high latitude—the Torngat Mountains lie beyond the tree line.

The clash of cold Arctic air with warmer, humid air from the south results in winter storms. In summer, occasional incursions of hot, humid air from the Gulf of Mexico occur, but the dominant weather is cool, cloudy, and rainy. In the winter, influxes of moist Atlantic air produce relatively mild snowy weather except in Labrador (and to a lesser extent in the New Brunswick interior), where it can become extremely cold for extended periods.

Annual precipitation is abundant throughout Atlantic Canada, averaging around 100 cm in the Maritimes and 140 cm in Newfoundland, but this gradually diminishes further north in Labrador. Much precipitation comes from nor'easters—strong winds off the ocean from the northeast—that draw their moisture from the Atlantic Ocean. Atlantic Canada, especially the Maritimes and the island of Newfoundland, has foggy weather. Thick, cool fog forms in the chilled air above the Labrador Current when it mixes with warm, moisture-laden air from the Gulf of Mexico. With onshore winds these banks of fog move far inland, but the coastal communities experience the greatest number of foggy days. Both St John's and Halifax, for instance, experience considerable foggy and misty weather (Vignette 10.1).

With such varied weather conditions, Atlantic Canada has three climatic zones—Atlantic, Subarctic, and Arctic zones. The great north–south extent of this region is one reason. For example, the distance from the southern tip of Nova Scotia (44°N) to the northern extremity of Newfoundland and Labrador (60°N) is over 2,000 km. Then, too, Atlantic Canada is the meeting place of Arctic and tropical air masses and ocean currents, resulting in wet, cool, and foggy weather. In addition, close proximity to the Atlantic Ocean exerts a moderating effect on the region's climate.

North of 55 degrees latitude is the Arctic zone in northern Labrador, in the Torngat Mountains and then along its coast. An Arctic storm track funnels extremely cold and stormy weather along the Labrador coast while the Labrador Current (Figure 10.3) brings icebergs from Greenland to the Labrador and Newfoundland coastlines and its cold waters contribute to the formation of land-fast ice along the Labrador and northern coastlines of Newfoundland. Beyond the land-fast ice in the open sea, the Labrador Current carries ice floes and icebergs as far south as the Grand Bank. By July, Labrador waters are ice-free.

The Arctic zone is associated with tundra vegetation as the summers are too cool for tree growth. The Subarctic climate zone exists over the interior of Labrador. The interior of Labrador experiences much warmer summer temperatures than its forested coastal areas. The Atlantic zone includes the Maritimes and the island of Newfoundland. For most of the year, this more southerly area is influenced by warm, moist air masses that originate in the tropical waters of the Caribbean Sea and the Gulf of Mexico. Only in the winter months does the Arctic storm track dominate weather conditions. The coastal areas of the Maritimes and Newfoundland can be affected by tropical storms in the late summer and fall.

The main air masses affecting the region originate in the interior of North America and from the Gulf of Mexico and the North Atlantic Ocean. Consequently, summers are usually cool and wet, while winters are short and mild but often associated with heavy snow and rainfall. Most precipitation falls in the winter, and temperature differences between inland and coastal locations are striking. Temperatures are usually several degrees warmer in the winter near the coast than at inland locations. During the summer, the reverse is true, with coastal areas usually several degrees cooler.

Along the narrow coastal zone of Atlantic Canada, the climate is strongly influenced by the Atlantic Ocean. The summer temperatures of coastal settlements along the shores of Newfoundland are markedly cooled by the cold water of the Labrador Current. Another effect of the sea occurs in the spring and summer—fog and mist result when the warm waters of the northeast-flowing Gulf Stream, which originates in the Gulf of Mexico, mix with the cold, southerly flowing Labrador Current. In the winter, the clash of warm and cold air masses sometimes results in severe winter storms characterized by heavy snowfall (Conrad, 2009: 36–7).

Vignette 10.1

Weather in St John's

While occupying a more southerly location than Victoria, British Columbia, St John's has a cooler climate, partly because of its very cold offshore waters (Table 2.2). Even so, St John's, like Victoria, is an ice-free port. However, unlike Victoria, a winter ice pack lies offshore, and spring-time icebergs are not uncommon off the coast (Photo 10.4). Melting of sea ice begins in spring, retreating northward along the landfast ice attached to the Labrador coast.

Generally speaking, weather is characterized by fog, overcast skies, and frequent storms and rain. Fog is common from April to September. Throughout the year, a salty smell is in the air. While most of the year has mild temperatures, strong northwest winds result in heavy winter snowfalls. Also, St John's does not escape the wrath of tropical storms—such as Hurricanes Igor (2010) and Leslie (2012)—that leave behind a path of destruction that includes toppled trees, torn power lines, and roofs ripped from buildings. Jutting into the Atlantic Ocean, St John's feels the full brunt of strong winds from the North Atlantic. As David Phillips (1993: 155), a climatologist and the spokesperson for Environment Canada's Meteorological Service, explains, "Of all major Canadian cities, St John's is the foggiest, snowiest, wettest, windiest, and cloudiest."

Brian Bursey. From postcard entitled, "Iceberg at St John's, Newfoundland"/M&B postcards, © 1996

Photo 10.4 Icebergs, calved from the Greenland Ice Sheet, frequently float near shore and into harbour entrances, as here in the Narrows off St John's harbour. While tourist viewing of the icebergs in late spring has become a popular attraction, the icebergs pose a threat to vessels and shipping.

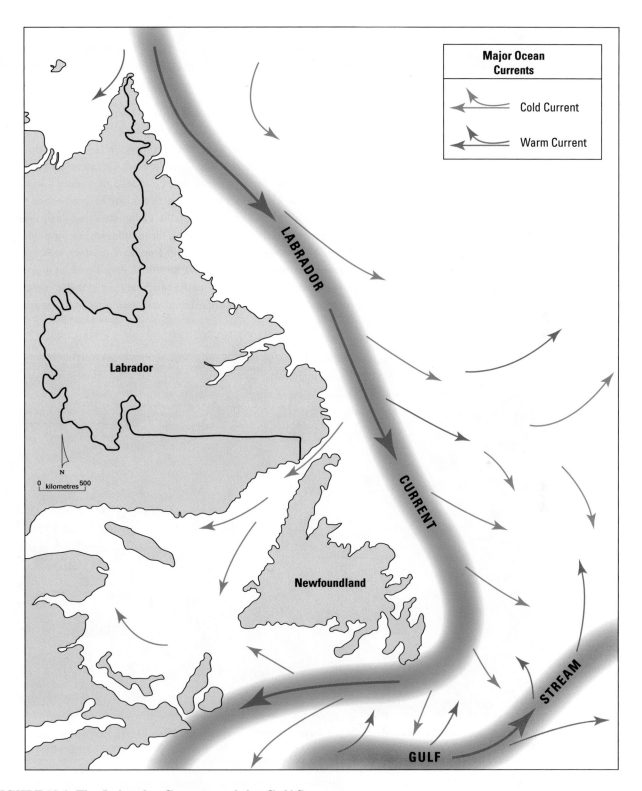

FIGURE 10.3 The Labrador Current and the Gulf Stream

Source: Macpherson (1997). Modified by Duleepa Wijayawardhana, 1998. Reproduced by permission of Gary E. McManus and Clifford H. Wood, *Atlas of Newfoundland and Labrador* (St John's: Breakwater Books, 1991), Plate 5.2.

Vignette 10.2

The Annapolis Valley

The Annapolis Valley is a low-lying area in Nova Scotia. At its western and eastern edges the land is at sea level, but it rises to about 35 m in the centre. The area is surrounded by a rugged, rocky upland that reaches heights of 200 m and more. The fertile sandy soils of the Annapolis Lowlands originate from marine deposits that settled there about 13,000 years ago. After glacial ice retreated from the area, seawaters flooded the land, depositing marine sediments that consisted of minute sand and clay particles. Isostatic rebound then caused the land to lift and slowly these lowlands emerged from the sea. In the seventeenth century, the favourable soil of the Annapolis Valley attracted early French settlers, the Acadians, who built dikes to protect parts of this low-lying farmland from the high tides of the Bay of Fundy and Minas Basin. Today, the Annapolis Valley's stone-free, well-drained soils and its gently rolling landforms provide the best agricultural lands in Nova Scotia. In Photo 10.5, at high tide, waters from the Minas Basin (seen in the background) extend into the low, wet land in the foreground. Land use is changing with vineyards replacing apple orchards. Local wineries now are common in Annapolis Valley.

Barrett & MacKay /All Canada Photos

Photo 10.5 Nova Scotia's Annapolis Valley, just north of Wolfville near Cape Blomidon. In the foreground is a small apple orchard, for which the Annapolis Valley is famous; in the middle is a tidal stream; in the background are the waters of the Minas Basin. As in other apple-growing areas in Canada, vineyards are replacing fruit trees.

Environmental Challenges/Disasters

Atlantic Canada has faced several environmental challenges with disastrous consequences. Three are discussed: hydroelectric projects and their effect on traditional lands and possible mercury poisoning of fish and wildlife; the Sydney tar ponds; and the collapse of the cod fishery.

Muskrat Falls

Across Canada, hydro projects have involved the flooding of Indigenous lands and the decaying of submerged vegetation that produces methylmercury. In turn, methylmercury can work its way through the food chain and lead to high levels of mercury in fish and other forms of wildlife. The James Bay hydro developments resulted in high levels of mercury in the reservoirs, much to the anguish of the Québec Cree. This lesson is well documented in scientific literature and etched in Indigenous memories; but the consequences of flooding of forested lands has been lost in the memory banks of project leaders of the ongoing Muskrat Falls hydro development in Labrador. Fortunately, the Labrador consumers of wildlife have not forgotten.

History should be a good teacher. But David Massell (2016) casts doubt on this idea with his historical account of the Muskrat Falls project. The Inuit and Innu were not part of the conversation when the Churchill Falls hydro project was undertaken in 1971–4, prior to the establishment of legal rights to Indigenous lands. By the time of the Voisey's Bay nickel project and the proposed Muskrat Falls project on the Lower Churchill River, the Inuit and Innu had the courts on their side. More than that, the New Dawn Agreement of 2008 between the Innu Nation and the Newfoundland and Labrador government contained compensation to the Innu (worth about $100 million over 30 years) for the flooding of hunting grounds that occurred when the Churchill Falls hydroelectric project was built in the early 1970s.

Yet, in 2016, with the construction of the Muskrat Falls hydro project, the same issues arose once again. Only protests by Labrador Indigenous peoples caught the attention of Premier Dwight Ball. In October of 2016 protestors occupied the site and blocked access to workers, demanding both the clearing of all vegetation and removal of soil before the first phase of reservoir flooding, planned for the fall of 2016, could begin (Bailey, 2016). An agreement was struck that the removal of the vegetation from the flood zone would be monitored by an independent expert advisory committee made up of provincial, federal, municipal, and Indigenous groups (CBC News, 2016). In stripping the land clean, the chances of vegetative material decomposing and producing methylmercury leading to high levels of mercury in fish and other wildlife would be eliminated or at least greatly reduced.

Sydney Tar Ponds

An older challenge, but one that may still cause problems in the future, was the Sydney tar ponds. In 1998, Ottawa and Halifax began one of Canada's biggest environmental cleanup projects—a remnant of the iron and steel industry at Sydney. The cost reached $400 million, with the federal government contributing 70 per cent and the province the remainder. By 2012, the reclamation project was completed and, instead of an old industrial eyesore, the area consisted of a 39-hectare green area that features several sports fields, walking trails, art installations, a playground, and panels chronicling the plant's troubled history. Controversy remains, however, because the toxic wastes were not removed but buried about 2 m below the surface. The buried toxic wastes leave one question unanswered: will this toxic sludge remain stable or will it seep into the local environment? Long-term monitoring and maintenance were built into the project and findings in the decades to come will answer that question.

Where Have All the Codfish Gone?

The habitat of the northern cod ranges from Georges Bank and the Bay of Fundy in the south to the Grand Banks and inshore of Newfoundland and Labrador to southern Baffin Bay, located between the southwest coast of Greenland and Baffin Island. Yet, these huge stocks collapsed under the onslaught of the international industrial fishing industry, which employed more advanced fishing technology and a strategy of processing the cod on factory ships. The demise of the northern cod stocks represents a classic example of the tragedy of the commons where public control of the resource, in this case by Fisheries and Oceans Canada, was unable to exert its power beyond Canada's maritime border. Not only did the cod stocks lose their way but so did the inshore fishers. In turn, coastal communities, such as Great Harbour Deep, were abandoned. In the case of Great Harbour Deep, located on Newfoundland's Northern Peninsula, people had fished for cod for centuries. In 2003, its remaining residents accepted the provincial government offer of a cash settlement to leave Great Harbour Deep.

Robert Clapp (1998: 129) examined the issue of overexploitation of the northern cod and attributed its collapse to technological advances that permit larger and larger catches until the resource is exhausted. Clapp offers the resource cycle in an unregulated environment as an explanation for ecological crises; in other words, what begins as a rich resource leads to overexploitation and the collapse of the resource.

The cause of overexploitation of the northern cod is well known. Much is due to the use of bottom draggers by the Canadian and foreign fishing fleets. The attraction of this form of fishing is its cost-efficiency, but scraping the seafloor for fish is environmentally disastrous. Fleets of trawlers create enormous waste because "non-commercial" fish—i.e., species of fish not being specifically sought, called the bycatch—are simply discarded. In addition, the trawlers destroy fragile ocean-floor ecosystems, including reefs and breeding habitat. As fishing technology advanced, catches of cod jumped from 400,000 metric tonnes per year to nearly 1 million metric tonnes in the 1950s. By the 1960s, the annual catch reached a peak of almost 2 million metric tonnes. European and Soviet trawlers accounted for most of this catch.

Ironically, the local inshore fishers did not employ such highly sophisticated technology but rather employed a simple hook-and-line system, as well as gillnets and cod traps (Photo 10.6). Yet, even though the coastal fishers did not have the capacity

John Eastcott & Yva Momatiuk/National Geographic/Getty Images

Photo 10.6 The inshore fishery involved more than making an economic return. It was a way of life.

to overfish, they suffered the most as their way of life and their communities disappeared.

With the cod stocks failing, the Canadian government announced in 1992 a moratorium on cod fishing in the waters of Atlantic Canada. By then, the foreign fishing vessels had left because their chances of catching sufficient cod had diminished. Twenty-five years later, inshore fishers observed signs of a recovery but federal officials were not convinced and recommended a continuation of the "controlled catch," which has involved quotas for only a few fishers that hardly amount to sustainable livelihoods for communities (Fisheries and Oceans Canada, 2015b).

Atlantic Canada's Historical Geography

Atlantic Canada was the first part of North America to be discovered by Europeans. In 1497, John Cabot reached the rocky shores of Atlantic Canada (the exact location, Cape Bonavista, Newfoundland, or Cape Breton Island, Nova Scotia, is in dispute). Yet, Newfoundland and Labrador, the first stretch of North America's Atlantic coastline explored by Europeans, was one of the last areas to be settled and formally colonized. In sharp contrast, French colonies found root in the Maritimes, where the land and climate were more favourable for agriculture, early in the seventeenth century.

In England, Cabot's report of the abundance of groundfish—cod, grey sole, flounder, redfish, and turbot—in the waters off Newfoundland lured European fishers—chiefly English, French, and Basque—to make the perilous voyage across the Atlantic to these rich fishing grounds, though some, especially the Basques, possibly had been fishing these waters at an earlier date. In any event, the Newfoundland coast quickly became a popular area for European fishers and though landings on shore took place—for drying the fish and establishing temporary habitation during the fishing season—permanent settlements were slow to take hold in this part of North America. This pattern of migratory fishing dominated the Newfoundland fishery for some 300 years until political circumstances changed in Europe and North America.

During this time, the French presence in the Newfoundland fishery was particularly strong, and Plaisance on the Avalon Peninsula's southwest coast was its largest settlement. With the defeat of the French in 1760, two events shaped the settlement of Newfoundland. First, French access was limited to what was called the French Shore, after 1783 stretching from Cape St John on the north coast around the Northern Peninsula and along the west coast of the island to Cape Ray in the far southwest, and permanent French settlement was restricted to the islands of Saint-Pierre and Miquelon. These French fishing rights did not end until 1904. Today, descendants of early French settlers reside in several communities along Newfoundland's southwest coast. Second, the emergence of a strong resident fishery marked the foundation of a Newfoundland society. English Protestant and Irish Catholic families settled along the Newfoundland coast, each locating in distinct places, and by the 1750s over 7,000 permanent residents, mostly English, lived in hundreds of small fishing communities along the Newfoundland coast.

At the dawn of the eighteenth century, British possessions in Atlantic Canada contained few people and were little more than names on a map. On the ground, the French colony of l'Acadie and their allies, the Mi'kmaq, were the most numerous inhabitants of the Maritimes, while French and English settlers occupied coastal settlements in Newfoundland with the Beothuk still occupying the interior of Newfoundland.

Over the first half of the eighteenth century, war between the two European colonial powers in North America—England and France—was almost continuous. During that time, the French forged an alliance with the Mi'kmaq and Maliseet, drawing them into the conflict with the English and their Iroquois allies. Under the terms of the 1713 Treaty of Utrecht, France surrendered Acadia to the British. However, many French-speaking settlers, the Acadians, remained in this newly won British territory, which was renamed Nova Scotia. During the previous century, the Acadians had established a strong presence in the Maritimes with settlements and forts. Most Acadians lived in the Annapolis Valley, near the Bay of Fundy coast, tilling the soil; others farmed on Île Saint-Jean (Prince Edward

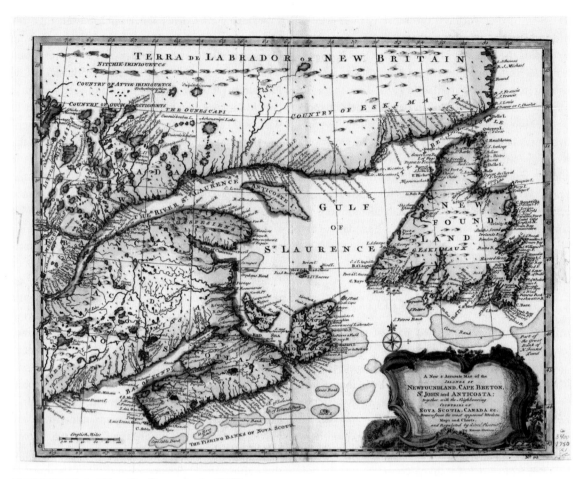

FIGURE 10.4 Atlantic Canada in 1750

European settlement in Atlantic Canada was concentrated in the Maritimes. In 1605, a handful of French settlers established the first permanent European settlement in North America north of Florida, at **Port Royal** on the Bay of Fundy coast of present-day Nova Scotia. During the seventeenth and part of the eighteenth century, French settlers spread into the Annapolis Valley (Vignette 10.2) and other lowlands in the Maritimes. By 1750, French-speaking Acadians numbered over 12,000. These French settlements, united by culture, language, and a common economy, became known as Acadia. In the coming decade, the British deported Acadians to various English colonies in North America and back to Europe.

Source: Emanuel Bowen, A new & accurate map of the islands of Newfoundland, Cape Breton, St. John and Anticosta. London, William Innys et al., 1747 BAnQ, G 3400 1750 B6.

Island). Until the mid-1700s, Britain made little effort to colonize these lands, leaving the Acadians to till the land in this British-held territory (see Figure 10.4). The Mi'kmaq remained close to the Acadians, but as the British power took hold they became strangers in their own land. Between 1725 and 1779, the Mi'kmaq signed a series of peace and friendship treaties with Great Britain, but events turned against the Mi'kmaq and Acadians with the founding of Halifax in 1749. The expulsion of the Acadians in 1755 from Nova Scotia, and in 1758 from Île Royale (Cape Breton Island) and Île Saint-Jean, eliminated the Mi'kmaq's ally, and relations between the British and the Mi'kmaq deteriorated. British rangers were unleashed to harass the Natives, to destroy their villages, and to drive them far beyond the British settlements. After the British defeated the French, the Treaty of Paris in 1763 ceded all French territories in North America to the British except for the islands of Saint-Pierre and Miquelon near the southern coast of Newfoundland.

The next event to influence the evolution of the Maritimes was the American Revolution. Following victory by the American colonies, approximately 40,000 Loyalists made their way to Nova Scotia and New Brunswick where they occupied the fertile lands of the recently departed Acadians and the prime hunting lands and fishing areas of the Mi'kmaq. With its superb harbour for ships of the British navy, Halifax became known as the "Warden of the North." Over the next 100 years, more and more British settlers came to the Maritimes. Nova Scotia alone received 55,000 Scots, Irish, English, and Welsh. Most Scots went to Cape Breton and the Northumberland shore. The driving forces pushing them from the British Isles were the Scottish Highland clearances and the Irish famine, which resulted in large influxes of migrants with Celtic cultural roots. These immigrants helped to define the dominantly Scottish character of Cape Breton and the Irish character of Saint John. The cultural impact of these Celtic peoples still resonates, and people of Scottish descent are still the largest ethnic group in Nova Scotia ("New Scotland").

⟳ For more details on Loyalist migrations to Canada, see "The Loyalists" in Chapter 3, page 104.

Head Start, Slow Start

In the early nineteenth century, the harvesting of Atlantic Canada's natural wealth increased. This frontier hinterland of the British Empire exploited its rich natural resources—the cod off the Newfoundland coast and the virgin forests in the Maritimes—and became heavily involved in transatlantic trade of these resources. Furthermore, the availability of timber and the region's favourable seaside location provided the ideal conditions for shipbuilding. By 1840, Nova Scotia and New Brunswick entered the "Golden Age of Sail," becoming the leading shipbuilding centres in the British Empire.

After the American Civil War, New England industrialized, leading to greater trade between the Maritimes and New England. In addition, Britain's move to free trade in 1849 meant the loss of Atlantic Canada's protected markets for its primary products, resulting in even greater interest by Maritime firms in the American market. Just before Confederation, the end of the Reciprocity Treaty cut off access to the Maritimes' natural trading partner, New England, resulting in the deterioration of the Maritimes' economic position.

The Maritimes Join Confederation—Reluctantly

The provinces of Atlantic Canada joined Canada at different times and for different reasons. Nova Scotia and New Brunswick entered at the time of Confederation; Prince Edward Island followed in 1873 (Figure 10.5); Newfoundland rejected the proposal and did not come on board until 1949.

With Central Canada now the main market for Maritime goods, distance became an enemy. To offset the disadvantage of geography, Ottawa's answer was the Intercolonial Railway (completed in 1876) that linked the Maritimes with Central Canada. The Intercolonial was operated and subsidized by the federal government: freight rates were kept low to promote trade, and Ottawa paid the annual deficits. Even so, manufacturing in the Maritimes declined. One exception was the production of steel rails as the completion of the CPR to the Pacific coast led to increasing railway construction and to a need for steel in the early twentieth century. By taking advantage of Cape Breton's coalfields and iron ore from Bell Island, Newfoundland, the steel industry[2] in Sydney prospered, accelerating Nova Scotia's economic growth well above the national average. However, in 1919, the Maritime economy suffered a deadly blow when federal subsidies for freight rates were eliminated. Immediate access to the national market became more difficult and, with the loss of sales, many firms had to lay off workers, while others were forced to shut down. Even before these troubled times, the Maritimes economy was unable to absorb its entire workforce, leading many to migrate to the industrial towns of New England and Central Canada. From then on, out-migration was a fact of life in the Maritimes.

⟳ See "The Territorial Evolution of Canada" in Chapter 3, page 71.

FIGURE 10.5 The Maritime Provinces: First to enter Confederation

New Brunswick and Nova Scotia joined the Province of Canada (Québec and Ontario) to form the Dominion of Canada in 1867; Prince Edward Island entered Confederation six years later.

Sources: *Atlas of Canada* reference map—Maritime Provinces, at: atlas.nrcan.gc.ca/data/english/maps/reference/provincesterritories/maritimes/map.pdf. Natural Resources Canada, 2000. Reproduced with the permission of the Minister of Public Works and Government Services Canada, 2013.

Newfoundland Joins Confederation

The political process of Newfoundland joining Canada had two steps. First, a rejection took place; second, some 80 years later, an acceptance was barely won in a referendum. In the first referendum of 1948, Newfoundlanders faced three choices—continuance

of the Commission of Government for five years, joining Canada, and a return to responsible government (i.e., quasi-independence within a fast-fading British Empire). An independent Newfoundland took 44.5 per cent of the vote, followed by joining Canada at 41.1 per cent. In the second referendum, Commission of Government was dropped off the ballot

Contested Terrain 10.1

Is the Economy All That Matters in a Hinterland?

In 1968, Professor David Erskine drew a rather dismal picture of Atlantic Canada as a declining hinterland. While Professor Erskine correctly assessed the economic situation, did he give full recognition to the "social value" of living in small communities in Atlantic Canada?

The region is, in the Canadian context, one of "effort" rather than of "increment." Small scale resources once encouraged small scale development, but only large scale resources encourage modernization. The small scale and lack of concentration of its resources makes the region one in which government investment is easily dispersed without bringing about growth. Low levels of professional services and low levels of education result from the high taxes from low incomes; thus, still further retardation of economic growth occurs. (Erskine, 1968: 233)

Fast-forward to 2016. After a culinary holiday trip with friends from Toronto, a columnist for the *Globe and Mail*, Margaret Wente, recanted her earlier position that "the province [Newfoundland and Labrador] was a vast and scenic welfare ghetto populated by ingrates on pogey." The headline of her recent article tells it all: "Please forgive me, and slap me with a cod."

and voters faced two choices, with a slim majority, 52.3 per cent, voting for joining Canada over an independent Newfoundland.

Atlantic Canada Today

The sea has moulded Atlantic Canada. As a result, Atlantic Canada contains a natural beauty and captivating cultural roots that continue to foster a quality of life for Atlantic Canadians. Yet, the economy of Atlantic Canada remains the weakest of the regions in southern Canada. Within Atlantic Canada, Newfoundland and Labrador (Figure 10.6), after riding the oil boom for more than a decade, has fallen on hard times. Across the region, major projects have closed, such as the potash mine in New Brunswick, or slowed production, such as the iron ore mines in Labrador. The prospect for strong economic growth remains elusive until oil and ore prices rebound to former levels. In addition, the loss of jobs in the Alberta oil sands has brought to an end the Great Commute. On the bright side, tourism is benefiting from the low Canadian dollar while shellfish fishing and shipbuilding remain the key pillars.

But opportunities do exist.

The first opportunity was the discovery and exploitation of offshore oil and gas deposits, which began the process of rejuvenating Newfoundland and Labrador's economy. Geography dictated that, because large oil deposits are located 200–300 km east of Newfoundland beneath the seafloor of the Grand Banks, Newfoundland and Labrador received the economic stimulus and royalties. From 2008 to 2014, offshore royalties have exceeded $2 billion annually and formed over one-third of the province's revenues. With the sharp fall of oil prices in 2015, offshore royalties may decline to under $1 billion.

Nova Scotia's promise of a similar oil bonanza failed and only minor deposits of natural gas have been exploited near Sable Island. With gas production declining from Sable Island and uncertainty surrounding the remaining life of Deep Panuke's output, Nova Scotia seems unlikely to enjoy an energy windfall.

The second opportunity—again, centred on Newfoundland and Labrador—stems from the huge nickel deposit at Voisey's Bay, Labrador, and the hydrometallurgy processing of nickel concentrate into nickel at the Long Harbour facility near St John's. The Long Harbour plant started production in

FIGURE 10.6 Newfoundland and Labrador

When Newfoundland entered Confederation in 1949, Canada gained a territory, population, and the remaining part of Britain's North American Empire. While an integral part of Atlantic Canada, Newfoundland and Labrador occupies a different space, economy, and culture from the Maritimes. In many ways, each has gone its own way, but the ongoing Muskrat Falls hydroelectric system might bind them closer together.

Source: *Atlas of Canada* reference map—Newfoundland and Labrador, at: atlas.nrcan.gc.ca/data/english/maps/reference/provincesterritories/newfoundland/map.pdf. Natural Resources Canada, 2002. Reproduced with the permission of the Minister of Public Works and Government Services Canada, 2013.

July 2014, and represents a value-added component rarely associated with resource development in Atlantic Canada.

A third opportunity is linked to Canada's largest oil refinery, an ocean location, and the proposed Energy East pipeline. The Irving refinery near Saint

TABLE 10.2   Atlantic Canada Industrial Sectors by Number of Workers, 2005 and 2016

Economic Sector	Workers, 2005 (000s)	Workers, 2005 (%)	Workers, 2016 (000s)	Workers, 2016 (%)	% Difference
Primary	62.5	5.8	53.7	4.9	−0.9
Secondary	171.7	16.0	172.7	15.6	−0.4
Tertiary	841.6	78.2	878.7	79.5	1.3
Total	1,075.8	100.0	1,105.1	100.0	2.7

Source: Statistics Canada (2006, 2016d).

John is designated as the end point of the pipeline. On the shore of the Bay of Fundy, the Irving refinery could process some bitumen from Alberta for consumption in Atlantic Canada and ship the rest to world markets.

Equalization Payments

Atlantic Canada has long benefited from equalization payments. While the calculations are complex, the funds come from the federal government out of its general tax revenues. Only recently has Newfoundland and Labrador broken from the pattern of dependency as a consequence of its offshore oil royalties. Lower oil prices may force the province back into the "have-not" category of provinces receiving equalization payments.

In 2015–16, Atlantic Canada received just over $3.7 billion in equalization payments (Canada, Department of Finance, 2015). Unless some spectacular event takes place of the magnitude of the discovery of vast offshore oil deposits, the Maritimes is destined to remain dependent on equalization payments.

For more on equalization payments, see Chapter 5, "Equalization Payments," page 169.

Industrial Structure

Atlantic Canada's primary resources are fish, forests, minerals, and petroleum, but the region's economic future lies in its tertiary sector, especially high-technology industries, including those that focus on ocean technology and shipbuilding.

Employment statistics provide a picture of the basic economic structure of Atlantic Canada. In 2016, employment in primary activities accounted for 4.9 per cent of the labour force; secondary employment constituted 15.6 per cent; and tertiary employment was 79.5 per cent (Table 10.2). Like other regions, Atlantic Canada has experienced the same trends with percentage decreases in the primary and secondary sectors and an increase in the tertiary sector. But unlike other regions, the total number of workers has increased only slightly, indicating a stagnant economy (Table 10.2). Another indicator of the weak economy is the high rate of unemployment—in 2015, Atlantic Canada's unemployment rate was 10 per cent compared to the national average at 6 per cent (Table 10.1).

Technical Spearheads

Atlantic Canada has its economic spearheads. These spearheads represent a major economic thrust for the region and also illustrate the region's unique character as it moves into the knowledge-based economy. The rapid growth of ocean technologies in Atlantic Canada is fuelled in part by the strong growth of the offshore oil and gas industry. The giant oil and gas companies are providing the capital and two provinces, but particularly Newfoundland and Labrador, receive substantial royalties. Conversely, the federal government's need for ships resulted in a huge federal government contract to Irving Shipbuilding in Halifax. Both employ advanced technology.

Shipbuilding at Halifax

Under the National Shipbuilding Procurement Strategy, Irving's Halifax Shipyard is building the Royal Canadian Navy's future fleet, beginning with Arctic offshore patrol vessels. On the Pacific coast, North Vancouver's Seaspan is building coast guard ships. Irving Shipbuilding has received a $25 billion federal contract to build 21 combat ships for the Canadian navy over 30 years. To undertake this massive project, the company built the largest shipyard in North America (Photo 10.7). Most importantly, this federal contract is triggering a series of complementary economic activities designed to create a world-class shipbuilding industry in Halifax. Already, Irving has issued over 200 contracts to Canadian companies worth over $1 billion (Irving, 2016). Further in the future, maintenance of these ships would cost billions. Having built the ships, the Irving shipyard will have an inside track on a maintenance contract that would extend over another 30–50 years. Yet, this massive defence spending is both expensive and slow moving. For example, "cutting steel" is just starting because Irving had to look for expertise outside of Canada and turned to Odense Maritime Technology, a Danish engineering and naval architectural firm (Doucette, 2013). Cutting steel for the eight Arctic and Offshore Patrol Ships (AOPS) began in 2015; if all goes well, the first patrol ship should have its maiden voyage in 2018.

Megaproject of the Century or a White Elephant?

The Muskrat Falls and Gull Island hydroelectric projects on the Lower Churchill River represent either the megaproject of the twenty-first century or a giant white elephant (Figure 10.7). The proposal involves two power stations, at Gull Island and Muskrat Falls on the Churchill River. Together, these stations would produce 3,074 megawatts (MW) of electricity (Churchill Falls power station, which achieved full production in 1971, produces 5,425 MW). Like Churchill Falls, the market for the generated electricity lies in distant markets, except for that which would go to the island of Newfoundland. The logical transmission line to these markets runs through Québec. Even though more costly and risky, the selected all-Atlantic Canada route was a political decision. The attraction of this route lies in the unification of the electrical power system for Atlantic Canada and exports to New England. The transmission route involves subsea cables, one under the Strait of Belle Isle from Labrador to Newfoundland and the other beneath the Cabot Strait between Newfoundland and Nova Scotia. From Nova Scotia, the power will move through high-voltage transmission lines to New Brunswick and then to New England.

Another attraction, for Newfoundland and Labrador, was that the Atlantic Canada route could bypass Québec. Feelings have run high for many in Newfoundland and Labrador because of the 1969 deal with Hydro-Québec over Churchill Falls (see Contested Terrain 10.2).[3]

© iStock/shaunl

Photo 10.7 The Halifax Shipyard facility is the largest single building for constructing ships in North America. From 2013 to 2015, Irving Shipbuilding invested over $350 million to create the Halifax Shipyard in order to accommodate the production of the Royal Canadian Navy's future combat fleet.

Work on the Muskrat Falls project began in 2012, with an estimated cost at $7.4 billion. Four years later, the cost estimate had ballooned to $11.4 billion and Stan Marshall, the newly appointed CEO of **Nalcor Energy**, the provincial energy corporation, stated that what he now had to oversee was a "boondoggle." As he said, "It was a gamble and it's gone against us" (Roberts, 2016b). Among the problems, according to Marshall, have been: a lack of Nalcor experience and that of its principal—Italian—contractor on such a large project in a cold environment; a project too large for the energy needs of the province; lower

THINK ABOUT IT

Hard feelings? Do you think that the long-term strategy of Nalcor is to transmit a portion of both the Churchill Falls and the Muskrat Falls power to New England utilities? Remember that the 1969 agreement over Hydro-Québec purchase of electricity from Churchill Falls runs out in 2041.

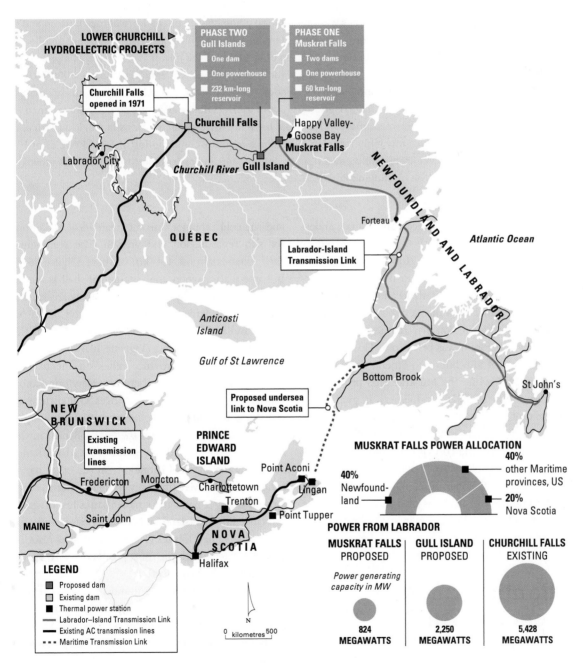

FIGURE 10.7 Lower Churchill hydroelectric projects

Source: Adapted from McCarthy (2011).

Contested Terrain 10.2

Churchill Falls: Bonanza for Québec

From Hydro-Québec's perspective, a contract is a contract (Canadian Press, 2016). The terms reached in the late 1960s between the Newfoundland government and Hydro-Québec for the sale and transmission of hydroelectric power from Churchill Falls were negotiated when energy prices were at rock bottom and the Churchill Falls project was on the verge of failure. Hard bargaining with a desperate opponent resulted in very favourable terms for Hydro-Québec—purchase of virtually all the power for 40 years at a price of under 30 cents per 1,000 kWh and the option to renew for another 25 years at only 20 cents per 1,000 kWh.

From the perspective of Newfoundland and Labrador, the contract represents an enormous windfall to Québec because electricity prices have risen sharply over the decades, well above power, maintenance, and transmissions costs. While customers in Montréal have the lowest electric rates in North America, those in Atlantic Canada have much higher rates. Based on a monthly consumption of 1,346 kWh, as of 1 July 2016 a customer in Montreal would pay $97, in St John's $145, in Fredericton $161, in Charlottetown $207, and in Halifax $210 (Newfoundland Power, 2016).

demand and falling energy prices; and a gross underestimate of cost to begin with (a problem shared by many megaprojects) (Roberts, 2016b).

But that's not all. Part of the deal is that the undersea cable between Newfoundland and Nova Scotia is to be provided by Emera Inc., a publicly traded Nova Scotia energy transmission firm that used to be Nova Scotia Power before it was privatized. This Maritime Link, at a cost of $1.6 billion to Emera, will be completed in 2017 while the Muskrat Falls project will be fully online by 2020, and Emera is guaranteed 20 per cent of the Muskrat Falls power generation for the next 35 years—all for the cost of providing the link. By 2016, the cost of cancelling the project had become prohibitive. And added to Nalcor's woes, local protests in October 2016, which could end up costing hundreds of millions of dollars, delayed the partial flooding of the reservoir at Muskrat Falls, a necessity to protect the infrastructure before winter (Bailey, 2016; Roberts, 2016b).

Atlantic Canada's Economic Anchor: The Fishing Industry

Nature has given Atlantic Canada a vast continental shelf that provides an excellent physical environment for fish: the warm ocean currents from the Gulf of Mexico and the cold Labrador Current create ideal conditions for fish reproduction and growth. The continental shelf extends almost 400 km offshore (Figure 10.8). In some places, where the continental shelf is raised, the water is relatively shallow. Such areas are known as banks. The largest banks are the Grand Banks off Newfoundland's east coast and Georges Bank off the south coast of Nova Scotia (Vignette 10.3).

Although each province relies on the fishery, striking differences exist between Newfoundland/Labrador and the Maritime provinces. One difference is fishing grounds. Newfoundlanders, traditionally, have fished in the waters of the Grand Banks, in the inshore fishery around the island of Newfoundland, and along the shore of Labrador. On the other hand, fishers from the Maritimes ply more southern waters around Georges Bank and smaller banks just offshore of Prince Edward Island and Nova Scotia. Fishing for the highly valued lobster (Figure 10.9) takes place in shallow waters, with the most productive area found near Yarmouth, Nova Scotia.[4]

A second difference is found in the nature and value of the catch. While the value of the Atlantic fisheries reached a record high of $2.4 billion in 2014 (Fisheries and Oceans Canada, 2016), shellfish, led by lobster, crab, and shrimp, made up 88 per cent of the total value (Table 10.3). Geography plays a role, too, as lobster is the most valuable fish harvested by Maritimers while Newfoundlanders focus on queen crab

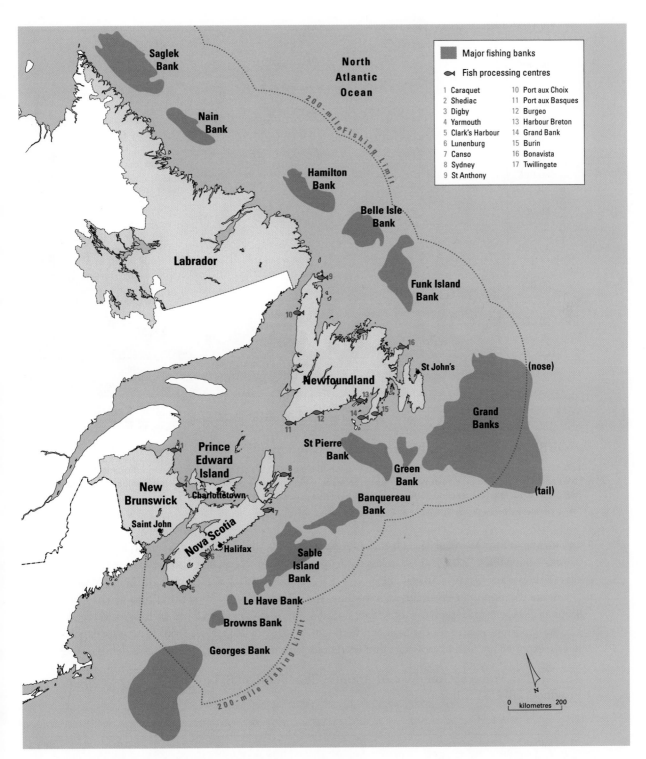

FIGURE 10.8 Major fishing banks in Atlantic Canada

The Atlantic coast fishery operates within a vast continental shelf that extends some 400 km eastward into the Atlantic Ocean, southward to Georges Bank, and north to Saglek Bank. Within these waters are at least a dozen areas of shallow water known as "banks." The Grand Banks of Newfoundland is the most famous fishing ground while Georges Bank contains the widest variety of fish stocks. Scallops, for instance, are harvested in beds on Georges Bank and Browns Bank.

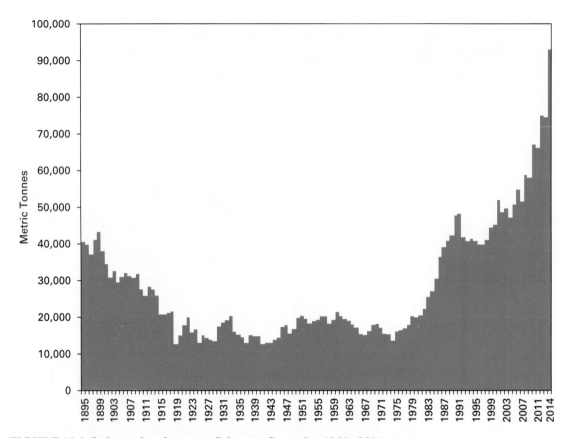

FIGURE 10.9 Lobster landings in Atlantic Canada, 1895–2014

Lobster is by far the most valued species, accounting for 40 per cent of the catch by value in Atlantic Canada. Lobster landings reached a historic high in 2014 at 92,779 metric tonnes and higher prices combined to push the value of this catch to $942 million. In 2015, lobsters reached $6/lb, well above previous prices (FFAW, 2016).

Source: Fisheries and Oceans Canada (2015c).

and shrimp, which provided 73 per cent of the value of their landed fish in 2014; cod fell to less than 5 per cent (Fisheries and Oceans Canada, 2016).

Seafood export is an expanding industry in Nova Scotia and less so in other provinces of Atlantic Canada. Yet, the opportunity exists. At the moment, fresh lobster are exported to China in growing numbers (Photo 10.8), thus providing a boost to Maritime fishers. Chinese companies also are entering the Nova Scotia fish business. For example, in 2014 the Chinese firm Zoneco (better known in China as Zhangzidao) purchased Capital Seafoods in Eastern Passage (Withers, 2016). By 2013, Nova Scotia firms were exporting fresh lobster by air to China. Chinese demand is driven by

TABLE 10.3 Value of Commercial Atlantic Coast/Gulf of St Lawrence Fish Landings, by Province, 2014 ($ millions)

Species	NS	NB	PEI	Québec	NL	Total
Groundfish	76.0	1.2	0.4	14.7	90.0	183.0
Pelagic fish	45.5	16.3	6.1	3.5	17.1	88.5
Shellfish	924.5	280.2	130.1	204.4	579.6	2,101.5
Others	>0.1	0.6	0.6	0	14.1	15.3
Totals	1,046.0	298.3	137.2	222.6	700.8	2,404.9

Note: Totals may not add up due to rounding.

Source: Adapted from Fisheries and Oceans Canada (2015a).

Vignette 10.3

Georges Bank

As part of the Atlantic continental shelf, Georges Bank (Figure 10.10) is a large shallow-water area extending over nearly 40,000 km². Water depth usually ranges from 50 to 80 m, but in some areas the water is 10 m or less. Georges Bank is one of the most biologically productive regions in the world's oceans because of the tidal mixing that occurs in its shallow waters. This brings to the surface a continuous supply of regenerated nutrients from the ocean sediments. These nutrients support vast quantities of minute sea life called plankton. In turn, large stocks of marine life, including cod, flounder, haddock, lobster, and scallops, feed on plankton.

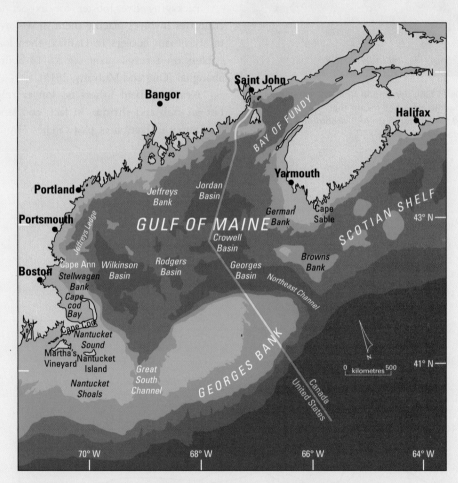

FIGURE 10.10 Georges Bank: The Canada–US Boundary

In the nineteenth century, both American and Canadian fishing vessels plied the waters of Georges Bank for groundfish and shellfish. After World War II, Canada claimed the northern half of Georges Bank but the United States claimed the entire area. In 1984, the World Court established the boundary for the disputed territory. The US received two-thirds of the disputed area. Canada obtained the rights to the northeast corner, which is particularly rich in shellfish, including lobsters and scallops.

Source: http://celebrating200years.noaa.gov/magazine/globec/map_gulfofmaine_650.jpg

Photo 10.8 Live lobster is in high demand in Chinese restaurants. The rapidly growing Chinese middle class has meant that "there is an exponential increase in demand for lobster in China," according Peter Hall of Export Development Canada (Withers, 2016).

Atlantic Canada's competitive price and high quality of lobster. As Ong and Mulvany (2015) reported:

> Chinese importers shopping on Alibaba .com can buy live Canadian lobsters prized for their tail meat and big claws for US$6 to US$10 a pound, according to the website, compared with US$20 to US$33 for Australia's Southern rock lobsters—a different species that doesn't have claws.

Packaging live lobster for export to distant countries involves placing them in wet newspapers in styrofoam coolers in Halifax, then loading the coolers on a cargo plane for an 18-hour flight to Shanghai (Ong and Mulvany, 2015).

Newfoundland fishers no longer rely on cod but on crab and shrimp. In fact, cod landings are a minuscule fraction of past catches (Figure 10.11).

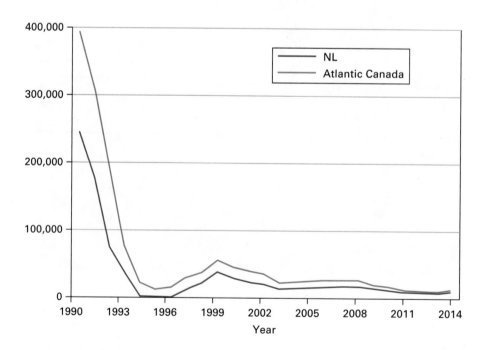

FIGURE 10.11 Cod landings for Newfoundland/Labrador and Atlantic Canada, 1990–2014 (metric tonnes live weight)

Source: Based on data from Fisheries and Oceans Canada (2015a).

In 2014, cod landings were only 10,000 tonnes; in contrast, over 245,000 metric tonnes were landed in 1990, shortly before the closure of the fishery. In 2014, Newfoundland reported that the total value of the fisheries catch was just over $700 million, with less than 2 per cent of that attributed to cod; queen crab and shrimp accounted for 37 and 36 per cent, respectively (Fisheries and Oceans Canada, 2016).

In addition, fewer fishing licences are allotted for crab compared to the old days when Newfoundlanders focused on cod. As a result, the fishery is concentrated in fewer and fewer hands and that fact has led to the demise of many coastal fishing villages. Another change in the fisheries is that the Mi'kmaq fishers are active in lobster fishing in the Maritimes (Photo 10.9). Their involvement stems from the Supreme Court of Canada's landmark 1999 *Marshall* decision that opened the door for a share of the commercial fishery.

Photo 10.9 Captain Gary Denny of the Pictou Landing First Nation is one of the beneficiaries of the 1999 Supreme Court of Canada ruling that acknowledged the treaty right of Mi'kmaq fishers to make a moderate livelihood from the commercial fishery. Gary and his crew are busy throughout the year. In May and June, they set lobster traps near Cheticamp. Starting in July, the crew fish for snow crab in the Gulf of St Lawrence and by fall they return to Pictou Landing to fish herring and rock crab. When those seasons close in November, Denny heads to Nova Scotia's South Shore to crew on a boat in the winter lobster fishery. In 2015, Fisheries and Oceans Canada estimated that about 365 land-based workers and 1,310 fishers participate in the Indigenous commercial fishery in Atlantic Canada (Beswick, 2015).

Atlantic Canada's Resource Wealth

For over a decade, Atlantic Canada put its stock in energy—as we have seen in regard to Muskrat Falls—and mineral development. In 2014, the leading sectors of the resource economy were petroleum, minerals, fishing, agriculture, and forestry (Table 10.4). In 2016, this decision looks less promising and the ranking could change with petroleum and minerals dropping and fisheries improving. Fisheries have provided the bright spot in Atlantic Canada's resource wealth. The sharp drop in prices for oil and iron brought to an end the boom conditions of earlier years while the rise

in fish prices has had the opposite effect. Of course, the global economy has its boom-and-bust cycle for prices and both the energy and mineral industries can expect to see boom times again. Agriculture and forestry, two renewable resource activities, trail far behind in value of output and number of workers.

Petroleum Industry: The Leading Edge

Offshore oil production provides the leading edge for resource development in Atlantic Canada, but this production is found only in Newfoundland

TABLE 10.4 Value of Resources, 2014 ($ millions)

Product	NL	PEI	NS	NB	Atlantic Canada
Minerals	3,160	4	204	381	3,749
Petroleum	7,696	0	156	0	7,852
Farm cash receipts	120	440	560	560	1,680
Fisheries	701	137	1,047	298	2,183
Primary wood exports	>1	>1	26	1,204	1,230
Total	11,677	581	1,993	2,443	16,694

Sources: Natural Resources Canada (2015, 2016); Canadian Association of Petroleum Producers (2015); Fisheries and Oceans Canada (2016); Statistics Canada (2015c).

Photawa/Dreamstime/Getstock.com

Photo 10.10 Neil's Harbour is a small fishing village on the northern tip of Cape Breton. The protected harbour is ideal for mooring small fishing boats.

and Labrador. Natural gas, by comparison, is a weak sister and generates far less revenue. Furthermore, natural gas production takes place offshore of Nova Scotia and this production is declining. The hoped-for oil deposits off of Nova Scotia have failed to materialize and its limited gas production comes from two projects—the Sable Offshore Energy Project (SOEP) and the Deep Panuke Offshore Gas Development (Figure 10.12). The gas production, valued at an estimated $156 million in 2014, goes mainly to New England markets via a series of pipelines (Statistics Canada, 2016b).

The oil and gas deposits off Canada's east coast were identified in the late twentieth century, but the high cost and technological challenges delayed full-scale exploitation. In 1985, for example, during the exploratory phase of Newfoundland offshore development, a huge mobile drilling rig, the *Ocean Ranger*, went down in a violent storm.

Eighty-four-workers died, with no survivors. The oil deposits, consisting of a **light sweet crude**, are situated in sedimentary basins near the Grand Banks. Within the Jeanne d'Arc Basin, oil and natural gas deposits have been discovered and three oil projects—Hibernia, Terra Nova, and White Rose—are now operating. In 2014, production totalled 12.5 million m^3, which amounted to 15 per cent of Canada's output (Canadian Association of Petroleum Producers, 2015). These three oil projects, unlike those in Alberta, receive the Brent price for their oil. Even so, the province is no longer enjoying record levels of royalties because of low oil prices. Low prices, if they continue, could drive the province back into "have-not" status.

These megaprojects have added a new dimension to Newfoundland and Labrador's economy. In 1997, the Hibernia oil project began producing oil; Terra Nova followed in 2002, and White Rose in

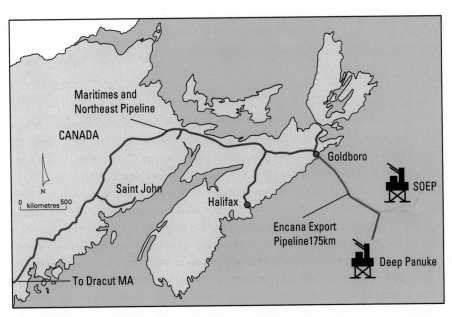

FIGURE 10.12 Nova Scotia offshore gas sites and pipeline system

Source: Adapted from Canada–Nova Scotia Offshore Petroleum Board (2016).

2005. Another project, Hebron, has an anticipated start-up for 2017. All of these oil fields are located some 300 km east of St John's, in water ranging from 80 to 120 m deep. The oil deposits extend another 2,500 to 4,000 m below the seabed. These projects required huge capital investments. In turn, they generated construction booms by creating a high demand for workers, especially skilled tradesmen, and for a variety of products and services. Once these developments were operational, employment in the construction industry dropped sharply, and the number of permanent workers required for the oil production is relatively small. Fortunately, Exxon is moving forward with development of its Hebron oil field, and the company agreed to build most of the platform locally and compensate the province $150 million for that portion built outside the province (Tait, 2013).

Hibernia (Vignette 10.4) uses a fixed platform while the Terra Nova and White Rose oil fields employ floating production storage and offloading (FPSO) vessels. Oil is offloaded from the FPSOs onto a shuttle tanker. Workers are taken to the offshore sites by helicopter on an in-and-out basis, and in 2009 a helicopter taking workers to a White Rose FPSO and to Hibernia went down at sea, killing 17 with only one survivor.

Today, the Hibernia drilling site has an annual output of about 30 million barrels and adds greatly to Newfoundland's energy output and provincial royalties. Based on an average price of $80 per barrel, the annual value of production is $2.4 billion. However, the price of oil fluctuates widely. In, February 2016, the Brent price hit a low of US$30/barrel, but back a few years the price was over $100/barrel (Index Mundi, 2013). Over the next 10 years, the price of oil will likely vary from a low of $30/barrel to a high of over $100/barrel. According to the owners, the Hibernia Consortium, production should continue until 2030.

Vignette 10.4

The Hibernia Platform

The Hibernia oil project is located 315 km east of St John's, Newfoundland, on the Grand Banks. To tap the estimated 615 million barrels of oil from the Hibernia deposit, an innovative offshore stationary platform was needed. About 4,000 workers built a specially designed offshore oil platform that can withstand the pounding storms of the North Atlantic and crushing blows from huge icebergs. The massive concrete and steel construction sits on the ocean floor, with 16 "teeth" in its exterior wall designed to absorb the impact of icebergs.

The 111-m-high Hibernia platform, which includes oil-storage units, weighs over 650,000 tonnes, and is the largest gravity base structure of its kind in the world. In the summer of 1997 the platform was placed on the ocean floor just above the oil deposits. The depth of the water at this point is about 80 m, leaving the oil platform approximately 30 m above the ocean surface. This structure is designed as a platform for the oil derricks, and houses pumping equipment and living quarters for about 185 offshore workers, as well as a storage facility for the crude oil. The rig extracts oil from the Avalon reservoir (2.4 km under the seabed) and from the Hibernia reservoir (3.7 km deep). The crude oil is then pumped from the Hibernia storage tanks to an underwater pumping station and then through loading hoses to three 900,000-barrel supertankers for shipment to foreign refineries.

Source: Adapted from Cox (1994).

Suncor Energy Inc.

Photo 10.11 The Hibernia platform has a massive concrete base that supports its drilling and production facilities as well as the workers' accommodations. Since the platform, with a topside length of 98 m and width of 34 m, was positioned on the ocean floor in 1997, the province has joined the ranks of other oil-producing provinces. The government of Newfoundland and Labrador at first received half of the royalties generated by these offshore developments. With a new agreement with Ottawa, in 2006 the province received all of the oil revenues. By 2009, oil revenues had made Newfoundland and Labrador a "have" province. With the sharp drop in oil prices in 2015, oil revenues dropped by half, causing the provincial budget to slip into the red.

Megaprojects boost regional development, but they also present problems related to boom–bust conditions. First, they are capital-intensive undertakings. During the construction phase a large labour force is required, but in the operational phase relatively few employees are needed. Second, megaprojects in resource hinterlands lose much of their spinoff effects to industrial areas. As a consequence, economic benefits related to the manufacture of the essential parts for building a megaproject go outside the hinterland, as does the processing of the resource once the project is up and running. Interventions by the government of Newfoundland and Labrador to address this classic problem have had mixed results. The biggest success story comes not from the petroleum industry but from the agreement with the developers of the Voisey's Bay nickel mine whereby the government of Newfoundland and Labrador obtained a commitment from the company, Vale,[5] to process the ore at Long Harbour in Placentia Bay. In 2013, operations to process the ore began.

The Mining Sector: Boom-and-bust Performer

Atlantic Canada is endowed with world-class mineral deposits. The Canadian Shield in Labrador has rich deposits of iron ore and nickel (Figure 10.13). In 2011, with high commodity prices, the value of mineral production in Atlantic Canada reached a record $6.8 billion. By 2014, however, lower commodity prices saw this figure drop by almost half to $3.8 billion (Table 10.4). Prices on the two leading minerals, nickel and iron, fell by over 50 per cent (Natural Resources Canada, 2015). As well, the lead-zinc mine near Bathurst, New Brunswick, ceased production in 2015. More bad news fell on the mining industry when, in 2016, the Potash Corporation announced the temporary closure of its mine near Sussex, New Brunswick, because of weak demand.

Nickel Mining and Processing

Discovered in 1993, the Voisey's Bay nickel deposit lies along the coast of Labrador approximately 350 km north of Happy Valley–Goose Bay. In 1996, Inco Ltd acquired the rights to the Voisey's Bay property and then sold it nearly a decade later to Vale, the giant Brazilian-owned mining company. Vale began its production in 2005. At its Ovoid site, mining operations are employing an open-pit system (Photo 10.12). The more expensive underground mining will take place at two other deposits—the Western Extension and Eastern Deeps. Since the Ovoid deposit lies close to the surface and is only a short distance from open water, the Voisey's Bay mine is one of the lowest-cost nickel mines in the world. It consists of 32 million tonnes of relatively rich ore bodies—2.8 per cent nickel and 1.7 per cent copper.

A concentrator reduces the ore into three parts: nickel, copper, and waste ore. The copper concentrate is sent to Europe while the nickel concentrate goes to Long Harbour on Newfoundland's Avalon Peninsula for final refining. This processing at the mine site and at Long Harbour represents the much desired "value-added" that all resource-based provinces seek but rarely obtain.

Resource Development and Indigenous Rights: Voisey's Bay

The Voisey's Bay mining development sparked a renewed interest in comprehensive land claim settlements.[6] At the time the proposed development was taking form in 2003, neither Indigenous group in Labrador had reached such an agreement. Consequently, Inco (now Vale) negotiated impact and benefit agreements (IBAs) with the Labrador Inuit and Innu, thus allowing the project to proceed before comprehensive agreements were reached. For the Inuit and Innu, the IBAs included employment opportunities, provided the Indigenous workers had a basic command of English necessary for the workplace and at least a high school education. Unfortunately, relatively few qualified.

The next order of business was to settle land claims. By 2005, the Labrador Inuit and the federal government signed the comprehensive land claim agreement that created the Inuit government of Nunatsiavut. By 2016, the Innu had not yet reached a similar agreement with the federal government. However, in 2011, the New Dawn Agreement between the Innu Nation of Labrador and the province established the parameters—in regard to claim area and compensation—for an eventual agreement with

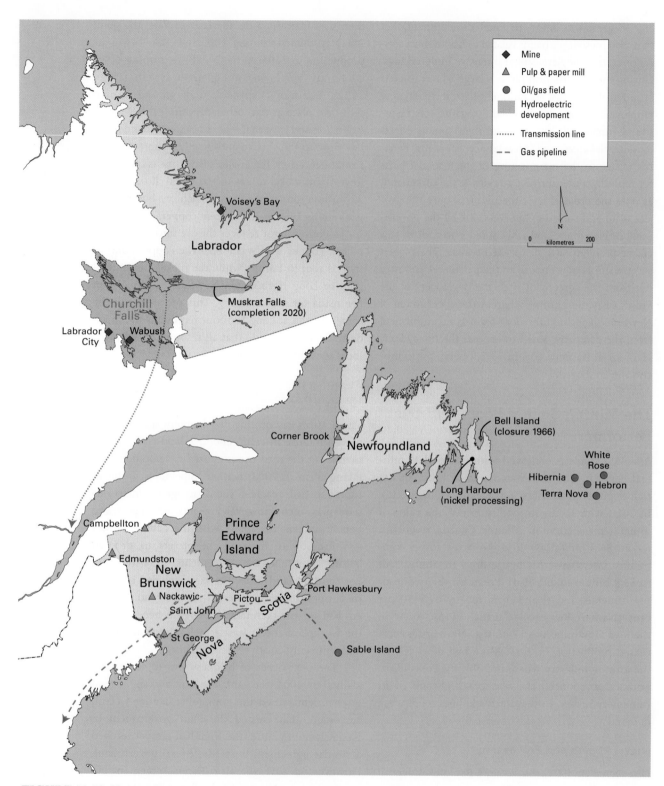

FIGURE 10.13 Natural resources in Atlantic Canada

Photo 10.12 The Voisey's Bay mine in Labrador.

Ottawa. In the following year, the Innu had reached an agreement-in-principle but no final agreement had been reached by the end of 2016.

Forest Industry: A Weak Sister

Beyond the sea, Atlantic Canada's most important renewable resource, historically, has been its forests. The rugged Appalachian Uplands in Atlantic Canada encompass 22.9 million ha of forest. The forest industry, both logging and pulp and paper processing, is concentrated in New Brunswick. Logging is both an important employer and an income generator for woodlot owners. Unlike in the rest of Canada, where forest land is usually Crown land, the proportion of private timberlands to Crown lands in the Maritimes is extremely high. Private timberlands make up 92 per cent of the commercial forest in Prince Edward Island, 70 per cent in Nova Scotia, and 50 per cent in New Brunswick. In Newfoundland and Labrador, like the rest of Canada, private ownership makes up only 2 per cent of the forested area. On average, the rate of logging on private lands is very high, sometimes exceeding the annual allowable cut estimated by the province. The high rate of logging often takes place on farms where timber sales are an important source of income.

Yet, the best days for this industry are long gone. In fact, the forest industry in Atlantic Canada (and across Canada's boreal forest) is contracting due to diminishing demand and low prices in the US. Other factors contributing to the weak state of the forest industry are declining demand for newsprint due to a slumping newspaper industry; rising electricity costs in Atlantic Canada, which constitute a large portion of operating costs in pulp and paper; and the expiration of the Canada–US lumber agreement in 2016. The weak nature of the forest industry is revealed by the drop in the value of forest products from $4 billion in 2001 to just over $2.5 billion in 2014 (Table 10.4). The downward cycle, as elsewhere in Canada, is linked to the collapse of the US housing market. All forest operations have suffered: logging, sawmilling, and pulp and paper plants. Pulp and paper mills have been hit hard, with numerous mills closing in recent years—in New Brunswick, at Bathurst, Dalhousie, Newcastle, South Nelson, and Saint John; in Nova Scotia, at Port Hawkesbury, Liverpool, and Hantsport; and in Newfoundland, at Stephenville and Grand Falls. Nonetheless, some mills, including two in New Brunswick owned by an India-based company that produce a quality product with newer technology, continue to operate (Photo 10.13).

THINK ABOUT IT

Atlantic Canada, unlike Western Canada, struggles to shift from a resource economy to a more diversified one. Is this a flaw in the staples thesis or a difference in the two resource bases?

Photo 10.13 Located in the Saint John River Valley, the Nackawic kraft mill, owned by the Indigenous firm Aditya Birla, manufactures dissolving grade pulp from various hardwood species, including maple, aspen, and birch. Further north on the Restigouche River at Atholville, near Campbellton, its second plant also produces high-quality dissolving grade pulp from a mix of hardwood and softwood.

In addition, Indigenous right to timberlands has projected another player into the forest industry. In 2005, the Supreme Court of Canada ruled that the Mi'kmaq of Nova Scotia and New Brunswick have the right to participate in commercial logging activities but that they must have permits from their respective provinces. The two provincial governments purchased timberlands from Irving Forest Corporation and then allocated logging permits to the Mi'kmaq loggers.

Agriculture: Limited in Size

Agriculture is limited by the physical geography in Atlantic Canada. Arable land constitutes less than 5 per cent of the Maritimes. Arable land is scarcer in Newfoundland and Labrador, making up less than 0.1 per cent of its territory. This province has the least amount of farmland—just over 6,000 ha.

Though limited in size, agricultural production significantly contributes to the economy of Atlantic Canada. In 2014, the value of agricultural production in the region was about $1.7 billion (Table 10.4). New Brunswick, Nova Scotia, and Prince Edward Island provide 98 per cent of this figure. Specialty crops, especially potatoes and apples, account for much of this value.

Atlantic Canada has nearly 400,000 ha in cropland and pasture. Almost all of this farmland is concentrated in three main agricultural areas—Prince Edward Island, the Saint John River Valley in New Brunswick, and the Annapolis Valley in Nova Scotia. Potatoes and tree fruit are important cash crops, though vineyards are gaining ground in the Annapolis Valley. In all three agricultural areas, dairy cattle graze on pasture land. The dairy industry in Atlantic Canada has benefited from the orderly marketing of fluid milk products through marketing boards.

© barrettmackay.com

Photo 10.14 The rich, red soils of Prince Edward Island are famous for growing potatoes, which are the primary cash crop in the province. Prince Edward Island is Canada's leading potato province, responsible for almost one-third of Canadian production. Its potatoes are grown for three specific markets: seed, table potatoes, and processing. Seed potatoes are sold to commercial potato growers and home gardeners to produce next year's crop; table potatoes go to the retail and food service sectors; and processing potatoes are manufactured into french fries, potato chips, and other processed potato products.

Prince Edward Island is the leading agricultural area in Atlantic Canada (Photo 10.14). It has almost half of the arable land in the region. Most of Prince Edward Island's 155,000 ha of farmland are devoted to potatoes, hay, and pasture, with the principal cash crop being potatoes. Since the 1980s, most potato growers have had contracts with the island's major potato-processing plants—Irving's processing plant near Summerside and McCain's plant at Borden–Carleton now dominate the potato industry on the island. The second major agricultural area, the Saint John River Valley, is in New Brunswick. Its 120,000 ha of arable land make up about one-third of Atlantic Canada's farmland. The Saint John River Valley has the best farmland in New Brunswick. Nova Scotia has nearly one-quarter of Atlantic Canada's farmland, with 105,000 ha. Nova Scotia's famous Annapolis Valley, the region's third agricultural area, is the site of fruit orchards and market gardens. The valley's close proximity to Halifax, the major urban market in Atlantic Canada, has encouraged vegetable gardening. In both New Brunswick and Nova Scotia, potatoes are a major cash crop. Almost all potato farmers in these two provinces

seed their potatoes under contract to McCain Foods, a multinational food-processing corporation based in New Brunswick. The company has benefited from NAFTA after the removal of tariffs on its food products, especially french fries and potato chips, for export to the United States.

Atlantic Canada's Core

Atlantic Canada's population has grown at a very low rate over time (Figure 1.3 and Table 10.5). Much of that growth has taken place in its major cities. In fact, this trend shows no sign of changing. At the same time, people are leaving rural Atlantic Canada. Over the last 20 years St John's and Newfoundland and Labrador recorded the greatest change in concentration. In 1996, 31.5 per cent of the population of the province resided in St John's; by 2014, this had risen to 40.2 per cent (Statistics Canada, 2016c). One of the most powerful factors causing this shift was related to the collapse of the inshore fishery, which resulted in the demise of small coastal communities and the relocation of those residents to larger cities, especially to St John's. The second event

Photo 10.15 With the city of Saint John in the background, the strategic location of Canaport LNG facility, Canada's only operational LNG terminal, is ideal for access to the huge New England energy market. Liquefied natural gas arrives from a variety of locales, including the Caribbean and Middle East. Here, the liquefied gas is stored in containers at −162°C, then is regasified and sent by pipeline to New England markets.

was the economic oil boom that drew workers to Fort McMurray (Vignette 10.5). In the same time span, Halifax saw its percentage of the province of Nova Scotia increase from 37 per cent to 41.7 per cent (Statistics Canada, 2016c). Within New Brunswick, the two principal cities, Moncton and Saint John, shifted their positions. In 1996, Saint John was the largest city with 17 per cent of New Brunswick's population while Moncton had 15.5 per cent. Twenty years later, Moncton was the largest city, at 19.4 per cent of the provincial population, while Saint John had 16.9 per cent. Together, Moncton and Saint John comprise 36.3 per cent of New Brunswick's population (Statistics Canada, 2016c).

A fractured physical geography also applies to the region's urban geography. The four cities with

TABLE 10.5 Population Change in Atlantic Canada, 1996–2016

Province	1996	2006	2011	2016*	Change 1996–2016	% Change 1996–2016
PEI	134,557	135,851	140,204	146,933	12,376	+9.2
NL	551,792	505,469	514,536	528,336	23,456	−4.3
NB	738,133	729,997	751,171	754,735	16,602	+2.3
NS	909,282	913,462	921,727	945,834	36,552	+4.0
Atlantic Canada	2,333,764	2,284,779	2,327,638	2,375,828	42,064	+1.8

Note: Population figures for 2016 are first-quarter estimates by Statistics Canada.

Sources: Statistics Canada (2002a, 2007, 2012a, 2016e).

Vignette 10.5

The Passing of the Big Commute

The attraction of the **Big Commute** from Newfoundland to the Alberta oil sands was steady, high-paying jobs. Many thousands of Newfoundland trades workers have regularly commuted to Alberta to work for salaries that started above $100,000 a year, not including overtime. Oil sands companies paid for their air travel from St John's to Fort McMurray, and once there they have been fed and housed at company expense (CBC News, 2007, 2009; Storey, 2009). It is believed that they have brought back hundreds of millions of dollars—for Newfoundland and Labrador, a hidden economic boost for a recently anointed "have" province and a monetary infusion that has kept some communities viable, and at the same time dependent on the fortunes of an industry practically at the other end of the country. The hidden costs—to families, to social structure, to individual lives and values—are perhaps even more difficult to discern. Commuting across the country has entailed working 14 days on site, flying for 16 hours, and spending six days at home. The alternative was living hand-to-mouth in Newfoundland (Quinn, 2012).

But all good things end eventually. In the case of long-distance commuting from St John's to Fort McMurray, the end began with the economic downturn in the oil industry in 2014. In that year, as many as 30,000 Newfoundland workers were regularly moving through the St John's airport per week, en route to jobs in the oil patch and in Canada's North by company charter flights. Two years later, the numbers of commuters had greatly dwindled, and those still working in high-paid, faraway jobs had often taken pay cuts or were paying their own airfare on commercial flights to reach their work (Roberts, 2016a). Needless to say, many other Newfoundlanders who had relocated to Fort McMurray lost their homes in the 2016 wildfire.

populations over 100,000 are Saint John, Moncton, St John's, and Halifax, which are separated from each other by great distances. While Moncton is the fastest-growing city, Halifax serves as the economic capital of the Maritimes; St John's fills the same role for Newfoundland and Labrador (Table 10.6). These cities comprise 38 per cent of the population of Atlantic Canada. Significantly, the population growth of these four cities from 2001 to 2015 easily outpaced the overall growth of Atlantic Canada—17 per cent to 4 per cent (Table 10.6). From 2001 to 2011, this pattern of smaller growth in the centres with a population under 50,000 is confirmed by 10 of 11 of these cities having a population increase below 6 per cent (Table 10.7). Labrador City jumped by 19.2 per cent because it was undergoing an expansion of its iron

TABLE 10.6 Census Metropolitan Areas in Atlantic Canada, 2001–2015

Centre	Population 2001	Population 2015	Percentage Change
Saint John, NB	122,678	126,912	3.5
Moncton, NB	118,678	147,968	24.7
St John's, NL	172,918	214,285	23.9
Halifax, NS	359,183	417,847	16.3
Total	773,457	907,012	17.3
Atlantic Canada	2,285,729	2,374,154	3.9
Canada	30,007,094	35,985,751	19.9

Source: Adapted from Statistics Canada (2002b, 2007, 2016g).

TABLE 10.7 Urban Centres in Atlantic Canada, 2001 and 2011

Urban Centre	Population 2001	Population 2011	% Change
Labrador City, NL	7,744	9,228	19.2
Gander, NL	9,651	10,234	6.0
Bay Roberts, NL	10,531	10,871	3.2
Grand Falls–Windsor, NL	13,340	13,725	2.9
Campbellton, NB	18,820	17,842	−5.2
Edmundston, NB	22,173	21,903	−1.2
Kentville, NS	25,172	26,359	4.7
Corner Brook, NL	26,153	26,623	1.5
Bathurst, NB	32,523	33,484	3.0
New Glasgow, NS	36,735	35,809	−2.5
Truro, NS	44,276	45,888	3.6
Charlottetown, PEI	57,234	64,487	12.7
Fredericton, NB	81,346	94,268	15.9
Cape Breton, NS*	109,330	101,619	−7.1

*Cape Breton, which consists of Sydney and Glace Bay as well as other municipalities, has too low a population density to be classified as census metropolitan area.

Sources: Statistics Canada (2002b, 2012a).

mining operation. By 2016, Labrador City may see a population drop because of the drastic slowdown in the mining. Urban centres losing population over this 10-year period were led by Cape Breton, a former coal mining and steel centre, which experienced a population decline of 7.1 per cent.

In sum, Atlantic Canada remains the least urbanized region of Canada with just over half of its population living in urban centres. In comparison with other southern regions, the difference is both striking and an indicator of how much more urban growth (or rural decline) in Canada's regions is likely. At the top end of the scale, Ontario and British Columbia have close to 90 per cent of total population classified as urban. As well, Atlantic Canada has none of Canada's largest cities: Halifax (Vignette 10.6)

Vignette 10.6

Halifax

Halifax, the capital of Nova Scotia and the largest city in Atlantic Canada, was founded in 1749. By 2015, Halifax had a population of nearly 418,000. As in the past, its strategic location allows Halifax to play a major role on the Atlantic coast as a naval centre, an international port, and a key element in the Atlantic Gateway concept. Along the east coast of North America, its deep, ice-free harbour is ideally suited for huge post-Panamax ships. Yet, because of its relative distance from the major markets in North America and its reliance on transferring goods between ships, trains, and trucks, Halifax cannot provide lower transportation costs than New York. The economic strength of Halifax rests on its defence and port functions, its service function for smaller cities and towns in Nova Scotia, and its role as a provincial administrative centre. Halifax also has a small manufacturing base and a growing service sector, as well as a small but growing high-technology industry. In 2013, the federal government awarded a 30-year shipbuilding contract to Irving Shipbuilding, which is expected to stimulate the economy of Halifax and result in a surge in population.

Barrett & MacKay/All Canada Photos

Photo 10.16 The Confederation Bridge reduces Atlantic Canada's fractured geography by connecting Prince Edward Island with New Brunswick. As an integral part of the Trans-Canada Highway system, at 12.9-km it is the longest bridge over ice-covered waters in the world. After the bridge's opening in 1997, the economic impact on Prince Edward Island has been significant in four areas: increased tourism; a real estate boom; expanded potato production and potato-based processed foods; and greater export of time-sensitive and high-priced seafood. These economic gains help to account for the province's increased population.

ranks twelfth in population. Equally significant, Atlantic Canada's fractured geography prevents Halifax from serving as the primary city for the region. Instead, Halifax serves as the urban focal point for the Maritimes, while St John's fills a similar role for Newfoundland and Labrador. Halifax's advantage is its deep, ice-free harbour, its role as a naval base, and its relatively large population/market. Halifax serves as a major container port and shipbuilding centre. The Confederation Bridge, of course, serves to bind PEI to New Brunswick and Nova Scotia (Photo 10.16). On the other hand, St John's today is focused on offshore oil, the fishing industry, and government services, and is a centre for Arctic marine research and resupply. The only other CMAs in the Atlantic region are Moncton and Saint John, New Brunswick. Within the Maritimes, Saint John is ideally situated as an energy hub (see Photo 10.15). Moncton is a "gateway" to both Nova Scotia and PEI, and with a large francophone population is a "gateway," too, to the Acadian French area of northern New Brunswick.

See Chapter 4, "Urban Population," page 125, for further understanding of Atlantic Canada's lagging urbanization.

See Chapter 4, "Urban Population," page 125, for further understanding of Atlantic Canada's lagging urbanization.

THINK ABOUT IT

Would national unity be served if Alberta crude supplied the oil refineries in Montréal and Saint John?

SUMMARY

Atlantic Canada, on the eastern rim of Canada, remains a slow-growing region. High unemployment and strong out-migration are common to all four provinces. Yet, Atlantic Canada has a second chance. Its major cities, led by Halifax, exhibit strong growth.

Within Atlantic Canada, Newfoundland and Labrador has taken the megaproject road, pushed along by its offshore petroleum resources, rich Labrador nickel deposits, and the potential of hydroelectric power from the Lower Churchill River. This province has already shaken off the mantle of a "have-not" province, but the sudden drop in oil and commodity prices has forced a detour. Added to low prices, its declining population and high unemployment do not augur well for the future. Within the province, St John's provides a flash of hope with its economic and population growth. The Maritime Provinces, still among the "have-nots," are struggling to move forward. Economic rejuvenation has appeared in the few major cities, while the surge in lobster exports has breathed new life into the fisheries.

What does the future for Atlantic Canada hold? Is Atlantic Canada destined to remain a slow-growing region? Outside the urban centres, the economic situation is vulnerable. Within the core/periphery construct, Atlantic Canada fits the model of a declining region, and past efforts to break out of that mould have failed. But then, who is looking through the right lens—Erskine or Wente? (Contested Terrain 10.1).

The hope for a better future in massive resource developments has been stalled by low global prices. Yet, the trade agreement with the European Union achieved in 2016 could be a tremendous boost. Finally, global demand for fish products is on the rise, and a possibility remains that the lobster boom might spread to other fish stocks, thus adding another powerful leg to the economic platform of Atlantic Canada. But the chances of Atlantic Canada turning into a regional engine of growth with GDP exceeding the national average, unemployment declining, and out-migration slowing are not yet in sight.

Challenge Questions

1. Offshore oil and iron/nickel mining have provided Newfoundland and Labrador with an opportunity to break its downward economic spiral, but why did these developments fail to slow the province's population decline?
2. From an economic perspective, why does it make sense for New Brunswick to refine Alberta crude at the existing Irving refinery in Saint John rather than for a new refinery to be built in Alberta?
3. Fishing technology was critical to the destruction of the cod stocks. What is preventing a similar "tragedy of the commons" from happening to the shellfish stocks?
4. Why are the major cities of Atlantic Canada enjoying rapid population growth while rural areas are either stagnant or losing population?

Essay Questions

1. Under Premier Smallwood, the huge Churchill Falls hydro project was built a half-century ago but the power was sold to Hydro-Québec. Now the prospects for Muskrat Falls hydro development look bleak. In April 2016 the new CEO of Nalcor Energy, the provincial energy corporation, called Muskrat Falls a "boondoggle" but said it was too late to back away from the project. What are the inherent problems and what do you believe are the best-case and worst-case scenarios for Newfoundland and Labrador and for Atlantic Canada?

Suggested References:

Corcoran, Terence. 2016. "How Muskrat Falls Went from a Green Dream to a Bog of Red Ink." *National Post*, 22 Apr. At: http://business.financialpost.com/fp-comment/terence-corcoran-how-muskrat-falls-went-from-a-green-dream-to-a-bog-of-red-ink.

Massell, David. 2016. "History Lingers at Muskrat Falls." *Niche*, 21 Sept. At: http://niche-canada.org/2016/09/21/history-lingers-at-muskrat-falls/.

Nalcor Energy. 2016. "Muskrat Falls Project Construction: March 2014." At: https://muskratfalls.nalcorenergy.com/newsroom/photo-video-gallery/project-construction-march-2016-2/.

Nalcor Energy. 2016. "Project Overview." At: https://muskratfalls.nalcorenergy.com/project-overview/.

2. Is shipbuilding in Halifax a real hope for the long-term future? What problems need to be considered before one can assume this will be a gravy train for the Atlantic Canada economy?

Suggested References:

MacIvor, Angela. 2016. "Irving Shipbuilding's Deal to Build Arctic Patrol Vessels Questioned." CBC News, 4 Mar. At: http://www.cbc.ca/news/canada/nova-scotia/irving-shipbuilding-contract-questioned-1.3486609.

Withers, Paul. 2016. "Irving Shipbuilding Shows Off World's Most Modern Shipyard." CBC News, 4 Mar. At: http://www.cbc.ca/news/canada/nova-scotia/irving-shipyard-halifax-1.3476760.

Further Reading

Coates, Ken S. 2000. *The Marshall Decision and Native Rights*. Montréal and Kingston: McGill-Queen's University Press.

On 7 September 1999 the Supreme Court of Canada ruled in a case involving Donald Marshall Jr that the Mi'kmaq could earn a "modest income" from the fishery in the Maritimes. In one swoop, Atlantic Canada woke up to the Aboriginal desire and right to participate in the fishery, especially the lucrative lobster fishery. This is easier said than done because sharing of natural resources, such as lobsters, means taking away from those who already have the right to harvest such resources. The lobster solution involved the federal government obtaining lobster fishing licences from non-Aboriginal fishers and allocating them to the Mi'kmaq fishers.

Fifteen years later, Professor Coates revisited this concept of sharing resources within a national context in his seminal paper, "Sharing the Wealth: How Resource Revenue Agreements Can Honour Treaties, Improve Communities, and Facilitate Canadian Development," published by the Macdonald-Laurier Institute. His online paper is available at: http://www.macdonaldlaurier.ca/files/pdf/MLIresourcerevenuesharingweb.pdf.

11 The Territorial North

Chapter Overview

Topics and issues examined in this chapter include the following:

- The dualistic nature of the region's population and economy.
- The birth of Nunavut, and the impact of modern land claims.
- Climate change, the Northwest Passage, Arctic sovereignty, and cruise ship tourism.
- Megaprojects: good or bad?

Introduction

The Territorial North is Canada's last frontier, but it is also a homeland for Indigenous peoples, who form the majority of its population (Table 1.2). Located in the highest latitudes of Canada, the Territorial North, remote and permafrost-affected, remains a paradox—rich in natural resources but slow to develop. Two other challenges unique to Canada face this most northerly region: finding a more secure place for Indigenous peoples within the unfolding modern version of territorial society and its resourced-based economy; and dealing with Arctic sovereignty issues. With these challenges, plus climate change, land claim settlements, and increasing world demand for its resources, what does the future hold for the Territorial North?

In Friedmann's regional scheme of the core/periphery model, the Territorial North would be described as a resource frontier. Like developing frontiers around the world, the Territorial North's economic performance is measured by its oil and mineral production, not by its sustainable economy based on harvesting from the land and sea. On the one hand, the Territorial North's economy is vulnerable to sharp fluctuations in global demand for its exports. On the other hand, the harvesting economy provides country food but inadequate income for Indigenous peoples. For these reasons, one focus in this chapter is megaprojects, which in one guise or another have been an economic anchor for centuries—if not for the peoples of the North, then for Europeans who have ventured into Canada's North. A second focus deals with the struggle by Indigenous peoples to find a place in the commercial economy. Arctic tourism may be an economic spearhead in the years to come as the North becomes more accessible with global warming.

← Caribou crossing the Dempster Highway in Yukon Territory. Tensions between resource development and the environment exist throughout the Territorial North.

Theo Allofs/Getty Images

The Territorial North within Canada and the World

The Territorial North has the <u>largest geographic area</u> of the six regions, but the <u>smallest population</u> and economy (Figure 11.1). Its geographic area stretches over 3.9 million km² with roughly 70 per cent lying within the natural zone of the Arctic and 30 per cent in the Subarctic. Beyond its land base, the Arctic Ocean provides another world for the Territorial North. Normally a frozen body of water, the Arctic Ocean has seen more open water in the late summer than ever before, thus allowing a tourist industry associated with cruise ships crossing the Northwest Passage.

Its <u>tiny population of just over 100,000 persons spread over a vast land mass</u> makes the Territorial

FIGURE 11.1 The Territorial North

The Territorial North consists of three territories. Their borders are fixed, although marine boundaries are unclear between Yukon and Alaska and in regard to the seabed beneath the international waters of the Arctic Ocean. At the moment, three countries—Russia, Denmark, and Canada—all claim the seabed beneath the North Pole.

Source: Atlas of Canada, 2006, "The Territories," at: atlas.nrcan.gc.ca/site/english/maps/reference/provincesterritories/northern_territories. Natural Resources Canada, 2006. Reproduced with the permission of the Minister of Public Works and Government Services Canada, 2013.

North one of the world's most sparsely populated areas. As a **resource frontier,** its narrowly based mining economy depends on global markets and prices, leaving the region extremely vulnerable to **boom-and-bust cycles.** At the moment, this cycle is at a low point, causing a contraction in the North's economy.

The Territorial North's demographic features have been shaped by five factors. The first, its small population, is due to the limited capacity of the land to support people. The second is (the Indigenous population—especially the Inuit, whose very high birth rate and extremely low death rate account for the population growth in the Territorial North. Third, the levels of education and job experience in the Indigenous labour force fall short of the non-Indigenous counterpart. Fourth, (the northerners, but particularly non-Indigenous residents, move to job opportunities in other regions when the North's economy stalls) Fifth, in the age of air commuting, the majority of workers at resource projects live in southern Canada and work in the North.)

The discussion in **Chapter 4,** "Population Density," page 120, provides insight into the issue of the limited capacity of the land to support people.

As a resource frontier, the Territorial North has an economy based on the exploitation of its energy and mineral resources, and this exploitation depends on world demand and high commodity prices. From a theoretical perspective, the Territorial North is encased in the global core/periphery strait-jacket as a supplier of resources to world markets. Such industrial activities normally take the form of megaprojects that require huge capital investments and run the risk of failure. The Mackenzie Gas Project is an example of a failed **megaproject** that never got off the ground, while the falling prices of iron ore have placed the Mary River Project on the skids.

Two Visions

The people of the Territorial North have two powerful and seemingly contradictory visions—one is of a **northern frontier,** while the other is of a **homeland.** The traditional image of the northern frontier is one of great wealth just waiting to be discovered. For example, during the Klondike gold rush (1897–8), prospectors flooded the Yukon to pan for gold along the Klondike River and its tributaries. A more contemporary version of this image consists of large multinational corporations with their vast capital and advanced technology undertaking megaprojects—mining for gold, diamonds, lead, and zinc, and drilling for oil and gas. Megaprojects, large-scale resource developments financed and managed by multinational corporations, are designed to meet global needs for primary products. Such projects create an economic boom during the construction period, but in their operational phase fewer employment opportunities are available and economic spinoffs for local businesses are limited. Because of the risks associated with developing resources in a frontier—from overcoming physical barriers unique to the Territorial North to coping with downturns in world prices for resources—such projects usually

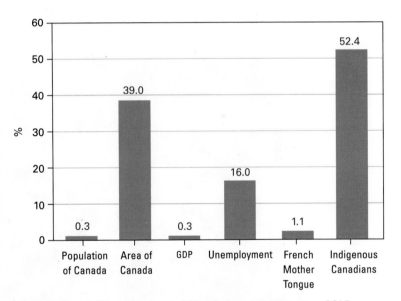

FIGURE 11.2 The Territorial North basic statistics, 2015

Though the region is the largest in Canada, its population and economy are the smallest. The Indigenous population continues to increase, jumping from 51.7 per cent of the total population in 2001 to 52.4 per cent in 2011, and possibly reaching 53 per cent by 2015. Paradoxically, the Territorial North suffers from a shortage of skilled workers and a high level of **underemployment**; i.e., when no jobs are available, individuals do not seek employment and hence are not classified as unemployed. Again, this dichotomy takes place in two different geographic areas: mining towns and Indigenous communities.

Percentages of population, area, and GDP are for Canada as a whole; unemployment, French home language, and Indigenous population percentages are for the Territorial North. Percentages for French mother tongue and Indigenous Canadians are for 2011.

Sources: Tables 1.1, 1.2, and 11.3.

THINK
ABOUT IT

If population density were to be measured by physiological density or the carrying capacity of the land to sustain life, how would the Territorial North compare with the other five geographic regions? See Chapter 4 for a discussion of physiological density and carrying capacity.

are undertaken by large corporations. Normally, these corporations reap large profits and supply the industrial cores of the world with raw materials, precious minerals, and energy. Exceptions do occur. The Snap Lake diamond mine failed to make a profit after seven years, costing De Beers $2.2 billion on mine construction and operation up to the end of 2014 (Reuters, 2016).

Northerners, particularly Indigenous peoples, see the North as a homeland where their culture, language, and spirituality can flourish. This perception is based on a special, deep commitment to the North, which cultural geographers often attribute to a sense of place. Indigenous peoples have a strong appreciation for natural features, cultural traits, and the political and economic issues affecting their homeland. A sense of place evokes a feeling of belonging as well as a commitment to a particular place. This commitment can take the form of protests against mega developments, such as the

Muskrat Falls hydroelectric project. While this hydro project lies outside of the Territorial North, the Subarctic area of Labrador falls within the natural extent of the North, and the Innu and Inuit believed the flooding involved in such a development would threaten wildlife, including the marine life in Hamilton Inlet.

For more on the issues related to Muskrat Falls, see Chapter 10, "Environmental Challenges/Disasters," page 331.

Sense of place is discussed further in Chapter 1, "Sense of Place," page 8.

In the Territorial North, the concepts of homeland and regional consciousness have resulted in the devolution of political power from the federal government to the territorial governments. Elected governments exist in the three territories and eight land claim agreements with First Nations have been concluded, the most recent being the Déline Final Self-Government Agreement (2015). Significantly,

Clara Parsons/Valan Photos

Photo 11.1 The South Nahanni is one of the world's great wild rivers. Located in the boreal wilderness of Nahanni National Park Reserve in the southwest part of the Northwest Territories, this untamed river is seen surging through the steep-walled First Canyon. Downstream, its waters rush past hot springs, plunge over a waterfall twice the height of Niagara, and cut through canyons more than 1 km deep.

the Déline Agreement includes provisions for self-government for the Sahtu Dene and Métis who live on the western shore of Great Bear Lake in the Northwest Territories. Future comprehensive land claim agreements are likely to include a section on self-government. Indigenous self-government received an enormous boost in 1992 when the provision for the territory of Nunavut was placed in the Nunavut Land Claims Agreement under the Nunavut Political Accord. Unlike Yukon and the Northwest Territories, Nunavut is an expression of "ethnic" regional consciousness and yet Nunavut is a public government and therefore is different from First Nations' "ethnic" self-governments, which are exclusive to members of specific First Nations. The next challenge facing the Territorial North, but especially Nunavut, is to generate sufficient economic growth and to create a labour force that can take advantage of such growth. The mismatch between the education/job experience of the Indigenous labour force and the employment needs of the companies and governments must be overcome. While a tall order, if achieved, then the Territorial North's economic dependency on Ottawa would diminish. At the same time, the Territorial North, while blending Western and Indigenous ways, would create a homeland accepted by all.

Physical Geography of the Territorial North

The Territorial North extends over four of Canada's physiographic regions: the Canadian Shield, the Interior Plains, the Cordillera, and the Arctic Lands (including the Arctic Archipelago) (Figure 2.1). While not unique to the Territorial North, the illuminations of the aurora borealis or northern lights occur regularly in the long winter nights, causing spectacular displays of shifting or streaming coloured light in northern skies.

The physical geography of the Territorial North is governed not so much by physiography as by a cold environment. Cold persists throughout most of the year and in many ways affects human activities. The cold environment includes permafrost (Figure 2.8) and long winters with sub-zero temperatures. The

Territorial North was subjected to glaciation except for much of Yukon. For that reason, the scouring effects of the Cordillera ice sheets did not affect the rich Klondike placer deposits. The region's main climate zones, the Arctic and the Subarctic (Figure 2.4), are characterized by very short summers.[1] In the Arctic climate, summer is limited to a few warm days interspersed with colder weather, including freezing temperatures and snow flurries. The Subarctic climate has a longer summer that lasts at least one month. During the short but warm summer, the daily maximum temperature often exceeds 20°C and sometimes reaches 30°C.

Arctic air masses dominate the weather patterns in the Territorial North. They are characterized by dry, cold weather and originate over the ice-covered Arctic Ocean, moving southward in the winter. The Arctic zone has an extremely cold and dry climate. Distinguished by long winters and a brief summer, the Arctic climate is normally associated with high latitudes and lower levels of solar energy. The Arctic Ocean and continuous permafrost keep summer temperatures cool even though the sun remains above the horizon for most of the summer. These cool summer temperatures, which Köppen defined as an average mean of less than 10°C in the warmest month, prevent normal tree growth. For that reason, the Arctic climate region has tundra vegetation, which includes lichens, mosses, grasses, and low shrubs. In the very cold Arctic Archipelago, much of the ground is bare, exposing the surface material. As there is little precipitation in the Arctic Archipelago (often less than 20 cm per year), this area is sometimes described as a "polar desert."

Beyond 70°N, growing conditions for the hardy tundra vegetation reach a limit. With lower temperatures and less precipitation than in the lower latitudes of this climatic zone, tundra vegetation cannot survive, giving the land a "Mars"-like landscape. The Arctic climate, however, does extend into lower latitudes in two areas: along the coasts of Hudson Bay and the Labrador Sea. These cold bodies of water chill the summer air along the adjacent land mass. In this way, the Arctic climate extends along the coasts of Ontario, Québec, and Labrador well below 60°N, sometimes extending as far south as 55°N.

THINK ABOUT IT

Does Nunavut represent a merging of the two visions of the Territorial North, or is it falling into a staples trap?

Bill Terry/Take Stock Inc

Photo 11.2 The Yukon River Valley at Dawson City. For Indigenous peoples as well as for fur traders and prospectors, this long and winding river has been an important transportation route in the history of the Territorial North.

The geology of the Territorial North provides much of its wealth. For example, the sedimentary basins of the Interior Plains and Arctic Lands contain large deposits of oil and natural gas (Vignette 11.1). Even the sedimentary strata beneath the Arctic Ocean just beyond Canada's current jurisdiction hold vast energy deposits. The Cordillera and Canadian Shield of the Territorial North have already yielded some of their mineral wealth to prospectors and geologists. These minerals include diamonds, gold, lead, uranium, and zinc. Since its discovery in 1962, an extremely high-grade iron deposit on Baffin Island has attracted mining companies. The Mary River Project, underway since 2015, originally called for mining the ore, shipping to port by rail, and then to markets in Europe by ship, but falling iron ore prices have put some of these plans on hold.

Vignette 11.1

Sedimentary Basins

The Territorial North has many sedimentary basins, some of which contain petroleum deposits. Those containing petroleum are the Western Sedimentary Basin, the Mackenzie Basin, and the Canadian Arctic Basin. The Canadian Arctic Basin contains several smaller basins, including the Sverdrup Basin. Offshore reserves in the seabed of the Arctic Ocean are vast, but for the most part these remain undiscovered and, ultimately, are potential deposits. While drilling has taken place in discovered resources, which are thus "proven" deposits, such is not the case with undiscovered and therefore potential resources. When Arctic navigation becomes a reality, these offshore petroleum reserves could become a commercial reality.

Contested Terrain 11.1

Less Ice, More Whales

Climate change affects the Inuit way of life, which is dependent on shore ice for hunting seals and other sea mammals. Thinner ice than normal endangers hunters travelling on snowmobiles, while less ice than normal reduces the time available for fishing and hunting marine mammals. Yet, the warming of Arctic waters as a consequence of climate change is causing a variety of whales found in the North Atlantic Ocean to spend more time in the Arctic Ocean, possibly providing a secure marine food source for the Inuit. But is this a realistic expectation?

Environmental Challenge: Climate Change

The Territorial North is faced with a major environmental challenge—the warming of the land and waters. The forces of climate change are transforming the Arctic, tightening the links between this seemingly remote region and the rest of the world in matters of resource development, sustainable development, and the pursuit of peace.

Climate change is more rapid in the Arctic than the rest of the world. Temperature increases in the Arctic are much higher than in the provinces because of the albedo effect, whereby greater solar warming of the land and water occurs because of the reduction of ice and snow cover. The Arctic Ocean is particularly vulnerable to this change. In the late summer of 2012, Arctic Ocean sea ice reached its lowest extent in the twenty-first century with only 3.41 million km^2 of sea ice (Environment Canada, 2012). The previous low of 4.2 million km^2 occurred in 2007. Equally telling, satellite measurements for September 2016 found that this year matched or exceeded the second-lowest total from 2007, and the extent of sea ice following initial freeze-up, as measured in late October, was the lowest on record (NSIDC, 2016).

As discussed in Chapter 2, global warming is the increase over time of the earth's average surface temperature. Several factors are involved in greater temperature increases occurring in the Arctic, such as heat transfer from lower latitudes to higher ones, but the primary factor is the albedo effect. Light from the sun takes the form of short-wave radiation while energy emitted from the earth's surface takes the form of long-wave radiation. Long-wave radiation is more readily absorbed by the atmosphere and thus warms the atmosphere whereas short-wave radiation escapes into outer space without warming the atmosphere. The Arctic, historically, has had a high albedo because of its cover of snow and ice, which means most solar energy is reflected back into outer space without warming the atmosphere. However, as ice and snow cover decreases in the Arctic, its albedo will shift from high to low, meaning that the solar energy reaching the Arctic will be more effective in warming the atmosphere and thus raising temperatures well above their long-term averages.

The impact of global warming in the Arctic is expected to have both positive and negative impacts on the wildlife and northern peoples. By the end of the twenty-first century, global warming may result in an ice-free Arctic Ocean each summer, thus allowing for unimpeded ocean transportation across the Northwest Passage, including shipments of petroleum and mineral deposits in the Arctic. The vast copper and zinc deposits located inland at Izok and High Lake in Nunavut are a case in point. Land transport, with the melting of permafrost, will be another matter. Wildlife will be affected. Already scientists have noted negative impacts on polar bears but a positive effect on seal populations. The huge migrating caribou herds that have their calving grounds in the Arctic could be affected. The reduction of the size of calving grounds would have a negative impact on preferred space for reproduction. The Dene and Inuit communities that rely on these herds for much of their country food may have to purchase more of their food from local stores. On the other hand, more open and warmer seas would permit a return of large numbers of bowhead whales, which used to sustain the Thule.

Historical Geography of the Territorial North

European Contact

At the times of initial contact with Europeans, seven Inuit groups and seven Indigenous groups belonging to the Athapaskan language family (also known as Dene) occupied the Territorial North. The Inuit stretched across the Arctic: the Mackenzie Delta Inuit lived in the west; further east were the Copper Inuit, Netsilik Inuit, Iglulik Inuit, Baffinland Inuit, Caribou Inuit, and Sadlermiut Inuit. Inuit also lived in northern Québec and Labrador. By the early twentieth century, two groups (most of the Mackenzie Delta Inuit and all of the Sadlermiut Inuit) would succumb to diseases that European whalers brought to the Arctic. The Indigenous tribes that resided in what is today the territorial Subarctic were the Kutchin, Hare, Tutchone, Dogrib, Tahltan, Slavey, and Chipewyan. More recently, these tribes are known in the aggregate as the Dene. These Indigenous peoples had developed hunting techniques well adapted to two cold but different environments. Cultural traits, such as the ethic of sharing, developed from this dependency on the land and sea for food.[2]

Early European Exploration

Though the Vikings were the first to make contact with northern Indigenous peoples around 1000, little is known of those encounters. At that time, the

Arctic Ocean had much less ice cover because of a warmer climate. Five centuries later, the Arctic had become much colder. In 1576, Martin Frobisher, in searching for a Northwest Passage to the Far East, reached Baffin Island.[3] Unfortunately for Frobisher, his expedition took place at the height of the Little Ice Age, and his ships met with heavy ice conditions in Davis Strait (which separates Baffin Island from Greenland).

 The Little Ice Age is discussed in Vignette 2.13, "Fluctuations in World Temperatures," page 46.

Over the next three centuries, the search for a Northwest Passage through Arctic waters led to misadventure for various European explorers, including John Franklin, whose famous last expedition ended in disaster with all hands lost (Vignette 11.2). However, cultural exchange between Europeans and the original inhabitants of these lands remained limited until the nineteenth century, when the trade in fur pelts and whaling peaked in North America.

Whaling and the Fur Trade

Whaling began in the late sixteenth century in the waters off Baffin Island. During those early years, whalers had little opportunity or desire to make contact with the Inuit living along the Arctic coast. The Inuit probably felt the same, particularly those who had heard stories of the nasty encounter with Frobisher's men. During early summer, whaling ships set sail from British, Dutch, and German ports for Baffin Bay, where they hunted whales for several months. By September, all ships would return home. In the early nineteenth century, the expeditions of John Ross (1817) and William Parry (1819) sailed farther north and west into Lancaster Sound. Their search for the Northwest Passage had limited success but opened virgin whaling grounds for whalers. These new grounds were of great interest as improved whaling technology had reduced the whale population in the eastern Arctic. In fact, the period from 1820 to 1840 is regarded as the peak of whaling activity in this area. At that time, up to 100 vessels were whaling in Davis Strait and Baffin Bay.

THINK ABOUT IT

Photo 3.2, page 64, illustrates a skirmish between Frobisher's men and the Baffin Island Inuit. Such hostilities were not unusual. In the late nineteenth century, for example, the Labrador Inuit and settlers still had bloody encounters. Do such encounters in the form of vigorous protests still occur in Labrador along the Indigenous/non-Indigenous faultline?

Vignette 11.2

The Northwest Passage and the Franklin Search

In 1845, Sir John Franklin headed a British naval expedition to search for the elusive Northwest Passage through the Arctic waters of North America. This British naval expedition set out at the end of the Little Ice Age, meaning that ice conditions would have been much more challenging than those occurring today. Franklin and his crew never returned. Their disappearance in the Canadian Arctic set off one of the world's greatest rescue operations, which involved upward of a dozen search parties and was conducted on land and by sea and stretched over a decade. The British Admiralty organized the first search party in 1848. Lady Franklin sent the last expedition to look for her husband in 1857. These expeditions accomplished three things: (1) they found evidence confirming the loss of Franklin's ships (the *Erebus* and *Terror*) and the death of their crews; (2) one rescue ship under the command of Robert McClure almost completed the Northwest Passage; and (3) the massive rescue effort resulted in a greater knowledge and mapping of the numerous islands and various routes to the north and west of Baffin Island in the Arctic Ocean. The exact sequence of events that led to the Franklin disaster is not known. However, archaeological work, conducted in the early 1980s on the remains of members of the expedition, revealed that lead poisoning, possibly caused by the tin cans in the ships' food supplies, may have contributed to the tragic demise of the Franklin expedition. In 2010, Parks Canada began a serious underwater search for the two ships. At the end of the summer of 2016, both ships, the HMS *Erebus* (2014) and the HMS *Terror* (2016), had been located about 100 km apart—the *Terror* in Terror Bay offshore of King William Island and to the south the *Erebus* on the bottom of Queen Maud Gulf near O'Reilly Island just off the coast of the Adelaide Peninsula. Survivors made a desperate decision—to march south to the Back River and to follow that river to a Hudson's Bay Company fur-trading outpost. No one made it to the Back River.

As whaling ships went further to find better whaling grounds, it became impossible to return to their home ports within one season. By the 1850s, the practice of "wintering over" (that is, allowing ships to freeze in sea ice along the coast) was adopted by English, Scottish, and American whalers. This allowed whalers to get an early start in the spring, providing for a long whaling season before the return trip home at the onset of the next winter. Wintering over took place along the indented coastlines of Baffin Island, Hudson Bay, and the northern shores of Québec and Yukon. Permanent shore stations were established at Kekerton and Blacklead Island in Cumberland Sound, at Cape Fullerton in Hudson Bay, and at Herschel Island in the Beaufort Sea. Life aboard whaling ships was dirty, rough, and dangerous, and many sailors died when their ships were caught in the ice and crushed.

Despite earlier unfortunate encounters with European explorers, the Inuit welcomed the whaling ships because of the opportunity for trade. The Inuit were attracted to shore stations and often worked for the whalers by securing game, sewing clothes, and piloting the whaling ships through difficult waters to promising sites for whale hunting. Some Inuit men signed on as boat crew and harpooners. In exchange for this work, the Inuit obtained useful goods, including knives, needles, and rifles, which made domestic life and hunting easier. While this relationship brought many advantages for the Inuit, there were also negative social and health aspects, including the rise in alcoholism and the spread of European diseases (Vignette 11.3). Perhaps the most devastating result of this trade relationship for the Inuit was the unexpected end of commercial whaling—for example, at Herschel Island in the western Arctic,

American whalers remained for barely 20 years, until 1908—and this represented the loss of access to highly valued trade goods. Just as the twentieth century began, demand for products made from whales—whalebone corsets, lamp oil—decreased sharply, halting the flow of whalers, and thus trade goods, that were sailing into Arctic waters. By this time, however, the Inuit depended on trade goods for their hunting activities. Somehow, they had to find other means of obtaining these useful goods.

Fortunately, European fashion had taken a liking to Arctic fox pelts, which caused the Hudson's Bay Company to establish trading posts in the Arctic. This provided a replacement for whaling and associated trade. The fur trade had already been successfully operating in the Subarctic for some time—a relationship between European traders and the Subarctic Indigenous peoples was established through the trade of fur pelts, especially beaver. Soon the Inuit were deeply involved in the fur trade. The working relationship between the Hudson's Bay Company and the Inuit was based on barter: white fox pelts could be traded for goods.

Dependency

Did the fur trade and Arctic whaling create a form of dependency whereby First Nations peoples and Inuit could not survive without trade goods? The answer is a qualified "yes." At first, Indigenous people had a form of partnership with European traders and whalers. Each side had power—for instance, the European traders needed the Indigenous peoples to trap beaver and, often, to show them how to survive in the harsh climate, and the Indigenous peoples needed the traders to obtain European goods and technology. Gradually, however, the power relationship shifted in favour of the European traders. By the nineteenth century, the fur companies controlled the fur economy. Fur-trading posts dotted the northern landscape. Indigenous peoples, who had long ago integrated trade goods into their traditional way of life—including their hunting techniques and their migration patterns—were therefore heavily dependent on trade. In fact, when game was scarce, tribes relied on the fur trader for food. Ironically, by securing game for the traders, Indigenous people reduced the number of animals that would be available for their own sustenance. In

Vignette 11.3

European Diseases

Whalers, fur traders, and missionaries introduced new diseases to the Arctic. As the Inuit had little immunity to measles, smallpox, and other communicable diseases such as tuberculosis, many of them died. In the late nineteenth century, the Sadlermiut and the Mackenzie Delta Inuit were exposed to these diseases. According to Dickason (2002: 363), in 1902 the last group of Sadlermiut, numbering 68, died of disease and starvation on Southampton Island, "a consequence of dislocations that ultimately derived from whaling activities." The Mackenzie Delta Inuit, whose numbers were as high as 2,000, almost suffered the same fate but managed to survive. Herschel Island, lying just off the Yukon coast, was an important wintering station for American whaling ships. Whalers often traded their manufactured goods with the local Mackenzie Delta Inuit, who became involved with the commercial whaling operations. Through contact with the whalers, European diseases, such as smallpox, took their toll. By 1910, only about 100 Mackenzie Delta Inuit were left. Gradually, Inupiat Inuit from nearby Alaska and white trappers who settled in the Mackenzie Delta area intermarried with the local Mackenzie Delta Inuit, which secured the survival of these people. Today, their descendants are called Inuvialuit. After World War I, the worldwide flu epidemic reached Canada and by the 1920s had spread along the Mackenzie River, infecting Dene tribes; many people died.

the Territorial North, game became scarce around fur-trading posts from overexploitation.

The problems of a growing dependency on European goods and a changing way of life for northern Indigenous peoples were compounded by the arrival of Western culture in the late nineteenth century. Indigenous peoples were subjected to Western ideas and rules propagated by missionaries and police, who now lived at the trading posts. On the one side, the NWMP (which added "Royal" to its name in 1904 and, in 1920, was renamed the Royal Canadian Mounted Police) imposed Canada's system of law and order on Indigenous people. On the other side, missionaries challenged Indigenous spiritual values. Worse yet, on behalf of the Canadian government, both Anglican and Catholic missionaries placed young Indigenous children in church-run residential schools, where they were taught in either English or French. In this failed assimilation, most children learned to read and write in English or French, but they were inadequately prepared for northern life. As they lost the opportunity to learn from their parents about how to live on the land, they became trapped between the two very different worlds of their Indigenous communities and that of the larger Canadian society. Under these circumstances, many lost their Indigenous language, animistic beliefs, and cultural customs.

Fur traders opposed many of these imposed Western cultural adaptations because they needed the Indigenous people on the land to trap. Nevertheless, the influence of the churches, the power of the state, and the number of non-Indigenous residents in the North increased in the twentieth century, placing Indigenous cultures under siege and crippling their land-based economy. However, political and social changes were occurring at this time that would lead to territorial governments, then to relocation of Indigenous people to settlements, and most recently to land claim agreements and self-government.

From the Land to Indigenous Settlements

While many complained about relocation to settlements in the years following World War II, virtually no one chose to remain on the land. The attraction of settlement life with its security of food supply and government support, whether in the form of public housing or family allowance monthly payments, was too powerful for the few who tried to stay behind on the land. The freedom and risks of living on the land were exchanged for a regulated and more secure life in settlements.

The relocation from the land to these tiny settlements marks the beginning of a new way of life, with some good aspects and some bad ones. Advantages included food security, access to medical services, and public education. Food security eliminated hunger and starvation but it also meant more store foods and less country food in their diet. And relocation had many negative impacts, including destroying the traditional social hunting/trapping unit from a family-based one to a male one. Children were required to attend schools so mothers stayed in the settlements. In fact, the much-needed family allowance payments to the mothers, introduced in 1945, only took place if the children remained in school. Finally, being based in settlements, the old style of extended family units living on the land and following the seasonal cycle of wildlife movements fell into history's dustbin.

Relocation continues to be a controversial subject in northern history. Williamson (1974), Elias (1995), Marcus (1995), and Rowley (1996) provide different perspectives. However, leaving the Indigenous people in what was seen to be a failing hunting/trapping economy was not an option. Living off the land was sometimes a challenge, but the shortage of cash/credit from trapping to purchase goods was critical. One option might have been to subsidize the hunting/trapping economy by providing the necessary cash to Indigenous families as well as more time to adjust to relocation, as is now done in northern Québec where Cree hunters and trappers are paid for living on the land and acquiring country food for themselves and others. When relocation to settlements became the order of the day, few of the people had a full command of English (or French in Québec), which would become so necessary for participating in the affairs of settlement life. Still, the apparent political urgency of the day caused Ottawa to push for relocation, and these settlements and the newcomers were both ill-prepared. Hunters and their families had their lives turned upside down.

THINK ABOUT IT

If you were the Minister of Northern Affairs and Natural Resources in the 1950s, what policy would you have proposed for northern peoples living on the land?

In the early 1950s, federal officials saw relocation from two perspectives. First, it was deemed a necessary step in protecting northern peoples from the hardships of living on the land, such as life-threatening food shortages, as well as a means of dealing with the world press that accused Ottawa of neglecting its "starving Indians" and Inuit. Second, concentrating Indigenous people in settlements allowed Ottawa to provide a variety of services, including schooling for the children. The relocation plan was designed to "modernize" the Inuit and First Nations populations and allow them to function within Canadian society. One could argue that, since few Indigenous families abandoned settlement life to return to the land, the attractions of settlement life outweighed the disadvantages.

Yet, how serious was the hardship of living on the land? The search for game might not always be successful and so periodic hardship, hunger, and starvation were characteristic of their traditional culture. Accordingly, Indigenous populations were balanced with their wildlife food supply. After the relocation process, this balance was lost and a population explosion took place. The consequences remain with us today, and that demographic explosion accounts for an increasing demand for public services that outstrips the capacity of government to meet that demand, notably for public housing.

Some areas were more risky for hunting peoples. The **Barren Grounds** of the central Arctic were a particularly challenging place to live off the land because of the heavy dependence for sustenance on the migrating caribou herds. Most of the time, however, their hunting, fishing, and trapping lifestyle was entirely satisfying. When game was scarce, hunger could be severe and starvation did occur, but these troubles were not an accepted or acceptable part of the culture of modern Canadian society. Failure to find the caribou translated into hunger and even starvation. Reports of deprivation and even death by starvation among the Caribou Inuit had reached Ottawa before, but no action was taken.

In the early 1950s, however, the Canadian media reported that about 60 Caribou Inuit starved to death. How could people living in a modern country like Canada starve to death? This sad event pushed the government into action, leading to a relocation policy. By

1958, Ottawa made the decision to relocate the Caribou Inuit to settlements, such as Baker Lake and Eskimo Point, but by then starvation had taken its toll—the Caribou Inuit population had dropped from "about one hundred and twenty in 1950 to about sixty in 1959" (Williamson, 1974: 90). At the same time, Ottawa extended this relocation program to coastal Inuit and to First Nations people and Métis in the Subarctic who also lived off the land. However, Ottawa was unprepared for the economic, psychological, and social consequences of settlement life for hunting peoples.

After 60 years of settlement life, access to store food and medical services has resulted in a population boom. Today, the Indigenous population forms a clear majority in the Territorial North, especially in Nunavut. On the other hand, the increased population has not matched the availability of public housing and jobs, resulting in overcrowding and chronic underemployment. As well, Indigenous communities face deep-rooted social dysfunctions, resulting in extremely high suicide rates among young people. The causes are various: some are traced back to cultural dislocation and devaluation while others are related to the social stress found in small Indigenous communities. A key factor, especially among young people, is the cultural shock of living within a dominant nation-state. Pressures to accept the ways and language of the nation-state are relentless though sometimes subtle. Such an oppressive political situation of internal colonialism was termed the "Fourth World" in the 1970s by Canadian First Nation scholar and leader George Manuel (Manuel and Posluns, 1974; see Bone, 2016: 12). When Indigenous people speak of the need to consider the impact of current actions and inactions on those seven generations from now, this is not merely a poetic manner of expression. Past actions—whether social engineering or the environmental impacts of megaprojects—can reverberate for generations to come. High suicides rates are one measure of this cultural shock (Figure 11.3).

Another, more tangible factor contributing to social dysfunction is the fact that Native communities have no solid economic base, resulting in heavy dependency on government for the impoverished and few opportunities for young people. The two principal sources of income are wages and various

Rate of death by suicide, Inuit men in Nunavut (2004–2008 average) and all men in Canada (2004), by age cohort.

■ Inuit men in Nunavut (2004–2008)
■ All men in Canada (2004)

Annual rate of death by suicide/ per 100,000 population

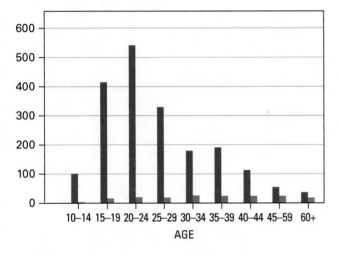

Rate of death by suicide, Canada (all) and Inuit in Nunavut (5-year rolling average), 1972–2013.

—— Inuit in Nunavut
—— Canada (all)

Annual rate of death by suicide/ per 100,000 population

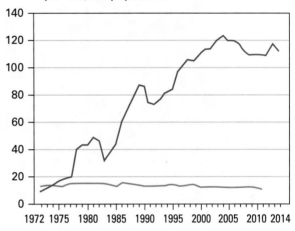

FIGURE 11.3 Nunavut's suicide spike

Source: Contenta (2015).

forms of government payments, including social assistance. The major employer is the government. As well, lower-income households, especially the elderly, rely on the sharing of country food by those who can afford to hunt and fish. Another alarming trend reported by Chan (2006) is that the increase in the consumption of store food rich in carbohydrates, particularly by younger generations, has already caused obesity and diabetes.

Perhaps the most positive outcome of settlement life is the emergence of educated Indigenous leaders. This new generation of leaders has had a hand in transforming the Indigenous society and economy in new directions through successful negotiations for comprehensive land claim agreements, for the first effectively Indigenous territory within Canada (Nunavut), and for their international involvement in the Arctic Council.

Comprehensive land claim agreements are discussed in Chapter 3 under the heading "Modern Treaties," page 90.

Territorial Expansion: Rupert's Land, the Arctic Islands, and the Arctic Seabed

The Territorial North fell under Canadian jurisdiction in three stages. First, the transfer of Rupert's Land to Canada by Britain took place in 1870. Second, Great Britain transferred the Arctic Islands to Canada in 1880. Third, in 1985, Canada declared a 200-mile economic zone that extended its control over the Arctic Ocean. In addition, in the same year Canada announced its Arctic Waters Pollution Prevention Act. Still, the last remaining territory that may become part of Canada consists of a portion of the seabed of the Arctic Ocean, which now lies in international waters. Canada intends to submit its claim to the United Nations Convention on the Law of the Sea (UNCLOS) for an extension of its continental shelf that reaches to the North Pole in 2018 (Sevunts, 2016).

THINK ABOUT IT

Canada, Russia, and Denmark all claim the North Pole as part of their extended continental shelves and hence under their jurisdiction. Apart from laying claim to Santa Claus (!), why would these countries want control of an immeasurably small compass point known as the North Pole?

Alexndra Koblenko/All Canada Photos

Photo 11.3 Pangnirtung is a small but fast-growing hamlet on the coast of Baffin Island. Like most Inuit communities, its natural increase far outstrips other Canadian urban centres. From 2006 to 2015, Pangnirtung's population grew from 1,325 to 1,645, an increase of 24.2 per cent. Most significant, 35 per cent of its population was under the age of 15. Such an age structure is common in developing countries. Unlike many Arctic communities, Pangnirtung has a strong fishing industry based on turbot (Greenland halibut). Besides involving fishers, the community-owned Pangnirtung Fisheries Ltd employs local workers to process the fish. Demand is strong, with exports of turbot to China increasing each year.

Forgotten Frontier: Confederation to World War II

Until after World War II, Canada never paid much attention to the Territorial North. In fact, the region was a forgotten part of Canada: it had little value for agricultural settlement or, because of its remote location, for resource development; Ottawa had its hands full with the provinces where almost all Canadians lived; and the fur trade in the North depended on the Indigenous people living on the land. In short, the Territorial North was not a "priority" region and thus received minimum attention. With the exception of the Klondike gold rush in the Yukon, the North's economy was left in the hands of the nomadic Dene and Inuit who hunted and trapped, moving seasonally with the wild animals, such as the caribou. Ottawa had adopted a laissez-faire policy to minimize federal expenditures,

leaving the fur traders and missionaries to deal with the food and health needs of a hunting society.

With the outbreak of World War II, the Territorial North became a strategic frontier. Military investments and activities included military bases, highways, landing fields, and radar stations. While the nature of its strategic role changed over time, the Territorial North served as a buffer zone between North America and the Soviet Union for over 50 years. This role ceased with the collapse of the Soviet Union and the end of the Cold War in 1991.[4]

Strategic Frontier, Arctic Sovereignty, and the Northwest Passage

In the twenty-first century, Arctic sovereignty took on a fresh urgency (Bone, 2016: ch. 8). This urgency has several elements. First, global warming has meant more open water in the Arctic Ocean, making trans-Arctic shipping a reality. In addition, circumpolar nations are in the process of claiming the Arctic seabed, and Canada must exert control over these waters and seabed or forfeit its claim. Four methods are employed to maintain surveillance. Patrolling this vast region by aircraft based in southern Canada provides one method; the Canadian Rangers, "Indigenous foot soldiers," offer a second method. More recently, RADARSAT satellite surveillance has introduced an innovative means that provides more accurate and fuller coverage of the entire area. Coming soon, perhaps by 2018, a fourth method—surface patrol ships, perhaps based at Cambridge Bay and Resolute—will supplement the first three surveillance systems. By 2018, the first

of six Arctic offshore patrol ships should arrive in the Northwest Passage (Royal Canadian Navy, 2015).

For discussion of the program to build patrol ships for the Arctic, see the section "Shipbuilding at Halifax" in Chapter 10, page 339.

In 2007, then Prime Minister Harper firmly declared that "the first principle of Arctic sovereignty is use it or lose it" (BBC News, 2007). What prompted this sense of urgency is pressure from Russia and other circumpolar countries that are actively staking their claims to the Arctic seabed and from shipping nations that want the Northwest Passage to be defined as lying in international waters. National borders have yet to be set for the Arctic Basin (Figure 11.4). Pressure to do so is mounting as global

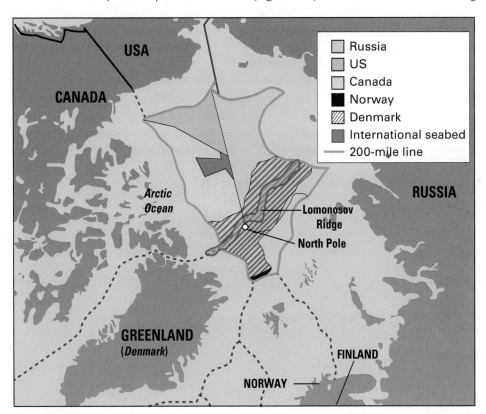

FIGURE 11.4 The Arctic Basin and national borders

Now that four of the five countries (excluding the United States) have made their initial claims to the Arctic seabed, the remaining issue is to resolve the overlapping claims. The elephant in the room is the 2014 claim by Denmark that extends into areas claimed by Canada and Russia. Applications to claim parts of the "international zone" of the Arctic seabed are restricted to five countries: Canada, Denmark (Greenland), Russia, the United States, and Norway, the first three of which are seeking to claim the North Pole. One exception is the International Seabed that represents an area too deep for claims, i.e., the seabed lies beneath over 2,500 metres of water.

Source: Milne (2016).

THINK ABOUT IT

Denmark has rejected Russia's call for bilateral negotiations over disputed "ownership" of seabed in the Arctic Ocean because Denmark is following the rules of UNCLOS while Russia is attempting to make a deal outside of UNCLOS. Yet, Canada has agreed to such negotiations. By examining the map (Figure 11.4), offer an explanation for Denmark's refusal to meet with Russian officials and Canada's willingness to do so.

warming has opened a short summer ice-free shipping route through the Northwest Passage. In 2013, the *Nordic Orion* sailed from Vancouver through the Northwest Passage with a cargo of coal for a Finnish destination. In the following year, the MV *Nunavik* delivered nickel ore from a mine in Arctic Québec to China by sailing through the Northwest Passage.

For Canada, the Arctic Basin possibly is its last territorial acquisition. Ottawa recognizes that:

- Vast quantities of petroleum deposits lie beneath the floor of the unclaimed zone of the Arctic Ocean (Table 11.1).
- Global warming may turn the frozen Arctic Ocean into a commercial ocean route.
- Canada's international position within the Arctic Council and, by extension, within the Circumpolar World is at stake (Vignette 11.4).

In a provocative book, *Arctic Front: Defending Canada in the Far North*, Coates et al. (2008: 1) describe Ottawa's efforts to claim Arctic waters and resources:

Arctic sovereignty seems to be the zombie—the dead issue that refuses to stay dead—of Canadian public affairs. You think it's settled, killed and buried, and then every decade or so it rises from the grave and totters into view again. In one decade the issue is the DEW Line, then it's the American oil tanker *Manhattan*, steaming brazenly through the Northwest Passage, then the *Polar Sea* doing the same thing. In August 2007, a Russian submarine planted a flag at the North Pole. Or perhaps it was under the North Pole, as the UK *Daily Telegraph* reported, raising an image of a striped pole floating in the ocean, with the devious Russians diving underneath it. Perhaps the flag did land on the pole, though good luck with that, since the pole is a point with no size at all, so the Russians likely missed it. However it was, they are up there, and the zombie has come to life once more.

The international community recognizes Canada's ownership of the islands in the Arctic Ocean. (There is one exception, however. Hans Island, a 1.3-km^2 rock, lies between Greenland and Ellesmere Island [see Photo 11.4].) The ownership of

TABLE 11.1 Petroleum Resources in the Territorial North

Oil Resources

Region	Discovered Resources 10^{6}m^3	Million bbl	Undiscovered Resources 10^{6}m^3	Million bbl.	Ultimate Potential 10^{6}m^3	Million bbl.
Northwest Territories and Arctic offshore	187.9	1,182.5	799.7	5,032.6	987.6	6,215.0
Nunavut and Arctic offshore	51.3	322.9	371.8	2,339.4	423.1	2,662.3
Arctic offshore Yukon	62.5	393.8	412.7	2,596.8	475.2	2,990.6
Total	301.7	1,899.1	1,584.1	9,968.8	1,885.9	11,867.9

Gas Resources

Region	Discovered Resources 10^{9}m^3	Trillion cubic feet	Undiscovered Resources 10^{9}m^3	Trillion cubic feet	Ultimate Potential 10^{9}m^3	Trillion cubic feet
Northwest Territories and Arctic offshore	457.6	16.2	1,542.2	54.8	1,999.8	71.0
Nunavut and Arctic offshore	449.7	16.0	1,191.9	42.3	1,641.6	58.3
Arctic offshore Yukon	4.5	0.2	486.6	17.3	491.1	17.4
Total	911.8	32.4	3,220.7	114.3	4,132.6	146.7

Sources: Compiled and integrated from several published sources that may underestimate or overestimate actual field resources. Volumes and distribution should be regarded as approximate. Numbers may not add due to rounding.

Source: Indigenous and Northern Affairs Canada, Northern Oil and Gas Branch (2012: Table 2). Reproduced with the permission of the Minister of Public Works and Government Services Canada, 2013

deadlyphoto.com/Alamy Stock Photo

Photo 11.4 The barren Hans Island lies in Nares Strait midway between Greenland and Canada. While the ocean border between the two countries is settled, Hans Island remains a sovereignty puzzle because it lies within the territorial waters of both Canada and Denmark (Greenland). The logical decision would be to divide the island into two parts, one Danish and the other Canadian, but so far this diplomatic decision has not been reached. Rather, on the infrequent occasions that Danish or Canadian troops have set foot on the island, they have left a bottle of liquor with a note saying either "Welcome to the Danish Island" or "Welcome to Canada" (World Atlas, 2016).

the waters lying between Canada's Archipelago does not have the same international understanding. Some countries, including the United States, consider the Northwest Passage to be international waters. Over the years, Canada has sought to legalize its sovereignty over the Arctic. In 1907, Canada

Vignette 11.4

The Arctic Council and the Circumpolar World

The Circumpolar World is an enormous area, sprawling over one-sixth of the earth's landmass and spanning 24 time zones. The Arctic Council focuses its attention on this massive land area, its environment, and its peoples. The member states are Canada, Denmark (including Greenland and the Faeroe Islands), Finland, Iceland, Norway, the Russian Federation, Sweden, and the United States of America. Most importantly, the various national organizations of Indigenous peoples are represented as permanent participants. Canada has a number of permanent participants on the Arctic Council, including the Athabaskan Council, the Gwich'in Council, and Canadian Inuit through their participation on the Inuit Circumpolar Council. With the Northwest Passage now becoming a commercial shipping route, a growing number of states, including China, have received observer status.

first announced the "sector principle," which divided the Arctic Ocean among those countries with territory adjacent to the Arctic Ocean. More recently, Canada has looked to environmental legislation as a means of exercising its sovereignty over Arctic waters. In the age of supertankers, container vessels, and cruise ships, the threat of toxic spills is more likely than ever before.[5] The Arctic Council provides a diplomatic means to maintain Canada's sovereignty, and direct negotiations with Russia provide another avenue.

The Territorial North Today

The Territorial North remains a resource frontier far from world markets. In such a harsh environment, almost everyone lives in a settlement, town, or city. Rural communities and farms, as found in southern Canada, do not exist. Another surprising fact is that mining sites are no longer associated with resource towns. Industry has opted for air commuting. This long-distance system sees southern workers flown to the mine site where they work for a week or so; then they are returned to the pickup point, often their hometown (Quenneville, 2014; NWT Bureau of Statistics, 2014). The three diamond mines provide examples. Each is located in an isolated area but the companies house their workers in camps and fly them to and from Yellowknife and Edmonton rather than build a permanent community where the workers' families would live.

Within the North, another difference is apparent—Arctic urban centres are very small and isolated from one another (Figure 11.5). From Statistics Canada's perspective, these settlements do not qualify as **urban areas** because their populations are less than 1,000. In 2011, for example, approximately three-quarters of these centres had populations under 1,000 and more than 40 per cent of the Territorial North's population lived in three cities: Whitehorse (26,898), Yellowknife (19,234), and Iqaluit (6,254). By 2015, the urban pattern remained the same, though the populations of the three largest centres increased (Table 11.2). Most significantly, these three centres accounted for 48 per cent of the Territorial North's population. Equally significant, Iqaluit experienced the greatest rate of increase from 2006 to 2015.

Population

Several demographic factors stand out for the Territorial North. Of most importance, its population is increasing at a rapid rate. From 2001 to 2015, the population of the Territorial North increased by 28 per cent, reaching a figure of 118,567 (Table 11.3). This population growth is due exclusively to a high rate of natural increase (Table 11.4). Most of this increase comes from the Indigenous population, especially the Inuit. Nunavut, for example, exhibits the highest rate of natural increase of the three territories while Yukon reflects a strong in-migration, largely due to job opportunities. Not surprisingly, isolated resource projects, ranging from diamond to iron mines, rely heavily on air commuting for their labour force with the vast majority coming from southern locations.

According to the 2011 census, Indigenous people made up 52 per cent of the northern population. However, the percentage of Indigenous people varies widely between the three territories. In 2011, Nunavut had the highest percentage at 86 per cent, followed by the Northwest Territories at 52 per cent and Yukon at 23 per cent (Table 11.3). By 2016, the same demographic pattern existed, but the Indigenous percentages for the North and Nunavut likely increased.

A second key demographic factor is natural increase. Unlike the rest of the country, natural increase accounts for most of the population growth. However, the rate of natural increase among the Indigenous population is declining. Evidence for this shift is indirect, i.e., both the birth and death rates for the Territorial North declined from 2012 to 2015, suggesting a trend towards the national average has begun. In 2015, the birth rate in the Territorial North was 17.1 births per 1,000 persons—down from 23.5 births per 1,000 in 2012. Within the three territories, the same pattern exists, though birth rates in the Territorial North vary with the percentage of Indigenous peoples (Tables 11.3 and 11.4). While birth and death rates are not

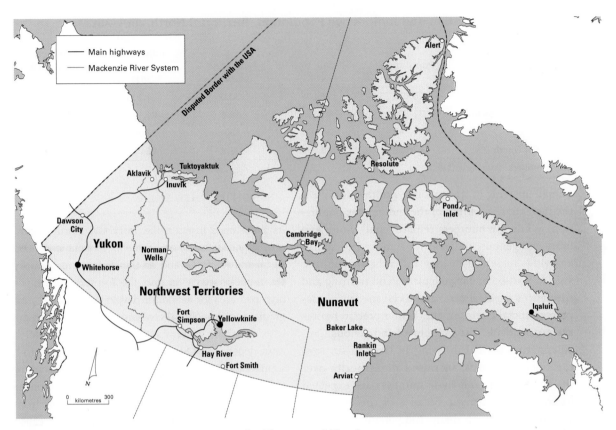

FIGURE 11.5 Major urban centres in the Territorial North

The major cities are the territorial capitals, Whitehorse, Yellowknife, and Iqaluit. With most government jobs in these cities, under-employment is much less a problem than in many smaller centres, especially Native settlements. Alert, located at the northern tip of Ellesmere Island, remains a military base from the Cold War, while military operations at Resolute are to be expanded.

collected by ethnicity, given the proportion of Indigenous people in each territory the association of high birth rates with a high percentage of Indigenous population indicates the highest birth rates are among Indigenous people, especially among the Inuit in Nunavut (Table 11.4).

The population of the Territorial North also is affected by migration (Table 11.4). Migration to the North normally occurs when economic expansion creates jobs, thus drawing workers and their families from southern Canada. When economic contraction takes place, these same workers and their families often return to southern Canada. As Table 11.4 indicates, the outflow from the Northwest Territories and Nunavut reflects a sluggish economic situation while the inflow in Yukon marks

TABLE 11.2 Capital Cities in the Territorial North

Capital	Population 2006	Population 2015	Percentage Change	Percentage of Territory Population, 2006	Percentage of Territory Population, 2015
Iqaluit	4,796	7,543	57.3	16.3	20.9
Yellowknife	18,700	20,637	10.4	45.1	45.2
Whitehorse	22,898	28,872	24.3	75.4	77.0

Sources: Statistics Canada (2012a, 2016a); Nunavut Bureau of Statistics (2016); NWT Bureau of Statistics (2016b); Yukon Bureau of Statistics (2016).

TABLE 11.3 Population and Indigenous Population, Territorial North, 2001–2015

Territory	Population 2001	Population 2015	% Change, 2001–15	Indigenous Population, 2011	% Indigenous of Total 2011 Population
Yukon	28,674	37,288	30.0	7,705	23.1
Northwest Territories	37,300	44,253	18.6	21,160	51.9
Nunavut	26,745	37,026	38.4	27,360	86.3
Territorial North	92,719	118,567	27.9	56,225	52.4

Sources: Statistics Canada (2012a, 2014b, 2016a).

a small upswing in its economy. Another feature is the increase in mobility of the Indigenous population. While the numbers remain small, more and more Indigenous migrants have moved to southern cities in search of jobs and urban amenities, such as post-secondary education and training and specialized medical care, and to escape from a depressed social environment. While precise figures are not available, the number of Indigenous Canadians from the North living in large urban centres appears to have increased dramatically over the last 20 years and these numbers are expected to continue to increase because of the economic and social state of many Indigenous communities. Precise figures are available for the Inuit. Until relatively recently, virtually all Inuit lived in the Arctic. By 2011, the census revealed that over 1,000 called Edmonton home, 900 lived in Montréal, 735 in Ottawa, another 735 in Yellowknife, and 680 in St John's (Statistics Canada, 2014a). The geographic pattern of this drift to the south reflects the location of these major cities and the four Inuit regional homelands. Edmonton, for instance, houses mainly Inuit from the western Arctic; Montréal, from Nunavik and Nunavut; Yellowknife, from the western Arctic and Nunavik; and St John's, from the Inuit living in Labrador (see Figure 11.6).

Industrial Structure

As a northern frontier, the Territorial North's economy depends heavily on private investment to develop its natural resources and on transfer payments to pay for its public sector.[6] In sum, the Territorial North is a high-cost area for economic development, social programs, and geopolitical challenges. With a limited tax base, the three governments of the Territorial North must depend on Ottawa. All of this translates into a simple fact: Canadians in other parts of the country will be called on to invest in the country's last frontier for decades to come. Canadians should take solace from the territorial version of equalization payments called Territorial Formula Financing—transfer payments and the cost of sovereignty are essential to nation-building.

In terms of employment, the primary sector in the Territorial North accounts for a much larger proportion of the workforce than it does in other geographic regions. For example, in 2015, approximately 15 per cent of the workers were in the primary sector compared to less than 2 per cent in Ontario. The reverse is true for secondary employment, with Ontario having 18.5 per cent of its workforce in this sector compared to only 2 per cent in the Territorial North. Both the Territorial North (83 per cent) and Ontario (80 per cent) have a large tertiary or service sector (Table 11.5).

TABLE 11.4 Components of Population Growth for the Territories, 2015

Demographic Event	Canada	Yukon	NWT	Nunavut	Territorial North
Births/1,000 persons	10.8	12.0	15.6	24.3	17.1
Deaths/1,000 persons	7.5	6.2	4.7	5.1	5.3
Natural rate of increase (%)	0.3	0.6	1.1	1.9	1.2
Net interprovincial migrants		90	−452	−133	−495.0

Source: Adapted from Statistics Canada (2016b).

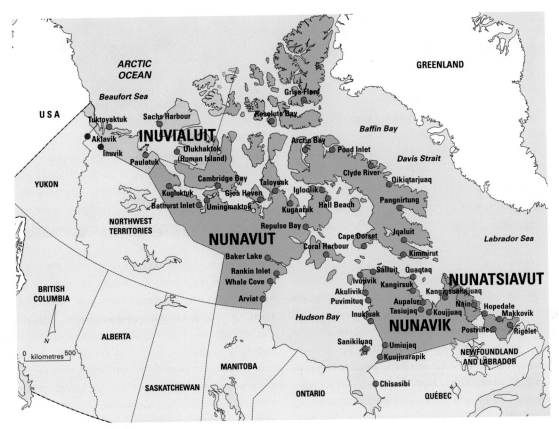

FIGURE 11.6 Inuit Nunangat

This map shows the four Inuit regions of Canada. Three regions—Inuvialuit in the NWT, Nunavik in Québec, and Nunatsiavut in Newfoundland and Labrador—have attained some degree of autonomy within long-established political jurisdictions, but only the territory of Nunavut is a stand-alone political entity within Canada.

Changing Governance

The Territorial North consists of three territorial governments: Yukon, the Northwest Territories, and Nunavut. Territorial governments have fewer powers than provincial governments, and in this sense they are political hinterlands. Devolution of powers is happening, however. For example, the federal government is now sharing its power over natural resources and the substantial amount of tax revenue from companies extracting natural resources is now shared with Yukon and the Northwest Territories (Vignette 11.5).

The Territory of Nunavut

The new territory of Nunavut was made possible through a land settlement agreement between Canada and the Inuit of the eastern Arctic in 1993. The terms of the agreement included the use of Crown lands for the Inuit to hunt, fish, and trap, and the transfer of part of the land to the Inuit, with a portion of this area involving rights to subsurface minerals. The same year the land agreement was reached, the federal government made

TABLE 11.5 Estimated Employment by Industrial Sector, Territorial North, 2015

Economic Sector	North Workers (%)	Ontario Workers (%)	Percentage Difference
Primary	15.0	1.6	13.4
Secondary	2.0	18.4	−16.4
Tertiary	83.0	80.0	3.0
Total	100.0	100.0	

Source: Table 5.5; author's estimate.

Vignette 11.5

Resource-Sharing with the Northwest Territories, 2015

In 2014, the federal government and the government of the Northwest Territories (GNWT) concluded a resource-sharing arrangement whereby half of the revenues generated by resource developments would flow to the GNWT. In turn, the GNWT shares up to 25 per cent of its portion of resource revenues with participating Indigenous governments. This new revenue is in addition to any amounts Indigenous governments previously received under land claim and self-government agreements. In the Territorial North, resource revenue-sharing arrangements are negotiated within the context of the comprehensive land claims process.

the commitment to create a new territory by passing the Nunavut Act. This Act, which provided the legal basis for the creation of a distinct territory and territorial government, also allowed for a six-year transition period, giving the Inuit time to form the government, recruit civil servants, and select a capital city. By means of a plebiscite, Iqaluit was selected as the capital of the new territory. Following an election in February 1999, the 19 members of the Nunavut Assembly took office on 1 April 1999. Unlike First Nations, the Inuit created a public form of government, meaning that every resident—Indigenous and non-Indigenous—has the same political rights.

The creation of a separate territory for the Inuit brought hopes for a brighter future. Through an Inuit government, a sustainable economy was thought to be achievable within 20 years. The Bathurst Mandate (Nunavut, 1999) gave voice to that hope, but the cruel reality told a different story. As Légaré (2008: 367) writes:

> For now, though, the urgent socio-economic plight of Nunavut does not bode well for the future. The vision of a viable Nunavut society by the year 2020, as expressed through the Bathurst Mandate, seems to be, at least for now, an illusion.

Indigenous Economy

Indigenous people participate in both the land-based and wage economies. This mixed economy is an adaptive response to make the best out of close contact with the capitalist economy, which often takes the form of mining operations. Geographically speaking, the traditional part of this mixed economy is most prevalent in small, isolated communities. The reverse is true in larger communities, especially the capital cities of each territory where administrative employment prevails. Not surprisingly, Indigenous workers are drawn to employment opportunities in the public side of the tertiary sector (Table 11.5). Few opt for jobs in mining projects.

As emphasized in the commentary for *Indigenous Peoples and Resource Development* (Bone and Anderson, 2017), sustainable development is the preferred route to their version of an advanced economy. One example presented in this chapter is the success of locally owned fisheries companies on Baffin Island. Another involves control of commercial enterprise. Such control results from comprehensive land claim agreements that have provided capital for investment in business enterprises. Oddly, global warming has played a part in exposing new opportunities for the Inuit. Two examples are Arctic tourism and Arctic fisheries.

While such moves into the global economy proceed, trapping, hunting, and other land-based activities endure. These traditional pursuits persist not so much because of their commercial value but largely because of their cultural importance. For instance, hunting produces food for the family and country food remains a core cultural feature among northern Indigenous families. While trapping and hunting sometimes go hand in hand, interest in trapping has diminished because of low prices for furs and because of the effective lobbying of the European Union by animal rights groups. The value of fur production in the Northwest Territories, for instance, hovers around $1 million annually—the 2014–15 figure was $985,039 (NWT Bureau of Statistics, 2016a). This is far below the figure of $6.1 million in 1987–8 (NWT Bureau of Statistics, 1990).

Economic Spearheads

It may seem odd to speak of "economic spearheads" for a resource frontier, but the dual economy of the Territorial North is reflected in certain unique qualities, tied to the people and the land, that spur the economy in Indigenous communities (Bone and Anderson, 2017). An early spearhead, the fruits of which are still manifest, was the encouragement and marketing of Inuit soapstone carving by Canadian artist and writer James Houston in the late 1940s and 1950s. In 1957 Houston introduced printmaking to Inuit artists at Cape Dorset (Barz and Roed, 2008), and for many years now the works of Nunavut artists have been highly valued in Canadian and international markets.

Local artists and communities today are beginning to benefit from Arctic tourism via large cruise liners, and this boon to local economies, a product of global warming, can be expected to grow. For example, at the three shore visits in 2016 from the *Crystal Serenity* (Photo 11.5), cruise passengers spent and left behind an estimated several hundred thousand dollars, an amount of no small significance for individuals and communities (George, 2016). With sophisticated marketing directed towards these visits and by working closely with the cruise lines, as happened with Crystal Cruise Lines, more can be expected in this realm.

Another spearhead for the North has been the Indigenous development corporations established through land claim agreements. These corporations use cash settlements from the agreements to support local business and to establish new business entities. A shining example has been the Inuvialuit Development Corporation, which is involved in such enterprises as shipping, air transport and travel, energy services, and catering to project developments in Canada's North, and the Inuvialuit also have investment,

land, and petroleum corporations. Their success is reflected by the fact that in 2014, for example, the Inuvialuit Regional Corporation—the governing institution of the Inuvialuit—made annual distribution payments of over $550 each to 4,360 Inuvialuit members over the age of 18 (IRC, 2014).

Global trade has allowed fishers from Baffin Island to market their product in China. Chinese restaurants demand fresh fish. The Inuit-owned and Iqaluit-based Baffin Fisheries Coalition, one of several Baffin Island fisheries companies, harvests turbot (Greenland halibut) and northern shrimp from Baffin Bay. The company is owned by five hunter and trapper associations (HTAs): Amarok HTA (Iqaluit), Pangnirtung HTA (Pangnirtung), Mayukalik HTA (Kimmirut), Mittimatalik HTA (Pond Inlet), and Namautaq HTA (Clyde River). The company owns and operates the 64-m Arctic shrimp trawler, the *Sivulliq*, and has two factory-freezer, fixed-gear vessels and two large factory-freezer multi-species trawlers (Baffin Fisheries, 2016). Similarly, the operations of the community-owned Pangnirtung Fisheries are expanding because of high demand from Chinese buyers—a similar pattern as has occurred with

Chris Corday/CBC Licensing

Photo 11.5 In August 2016, the *Crystal Serenity*, a 280-m-long luxury cruise liner, became the largest commercial cruise ship to sail through the Northwest Passage. Every summer in recent years, about 10 cruise ships carrying a total of about 2,600 passengers have sailed through all or part of the Northwest Passage. The *Crystal Serenity*, with 1,000 passengers and a crew of 600, stopped at Ulukhaktok (formerly Holman Island), Cambridge Bay, and Pond Inlet. Vicki Aitaok, cruise ship co-ordinator for Cambridge Bay, was responsible for five cruise ship visits over a tight two-week window in late August. The hamlet typically welcomes 100 passengers from small cruises for an afternoon visit. But with the *Crystal Serenity*'s stop, 150 passengers arrived at a time by zodiac "so as to not overwhelm the community" (Brown, 2016).

Contested Terrain 11.2

Global Warming and Arctic Tourism

The warming climate has opened the Northwest Passage and allowed Arctic cruise ships to reach small Arctic communities for a few weeks each summer. Cruise lines that arrange these tours profit greatly from the high-end tourists who seek such exotic "adventure"—though some on the *Crystal Serenity*'s 2016 trip across the Arctic reportedly were surprised by the lack of ice—and local residents in the very few communities where these ships stop stand to profit from the influx of wealthy visitors. Many others, however, do not benefit, and the threat to the environment is real from an oil spill, or worse, a cruise ship sinking. As the larger cruise liners sail through the Northwest Passage, will a point be reached beyond which local people will find the flood of tourists for a few short weeks unacceptable? Will an environmental or human disaster give cruise lines or local residents pause? Or as ice melt in the Arctic Ocean increases, will the Far North no longer be an attractive destination for restless consumers?

Nova Scotia lobster. The path to a sustainable fisheries economy, like the boost to Arctic tourism from global warming, owes its success from the turbot reaching higher latitudes because of the warming of the waters of Baffin Bay (Bone, 2016: 293).

As pointed out above, Arctic tourism has reached several Inuit communities along the Arctic coast. At Cambridge Bay, Arctic tourism has become an important element of the local economy. In 2016, the largest cruise ship ever to pass through the Northwest Passage arrived on 29 August (Photo 11.5). To take advantage of the visit, the annual Nunavut Arts Festival was held to coincide with the ship's arrival and Nunavut artisans found that the wealthy tourists (passage for the cruise ranged from $22,000 to over $100,000 per person) purchased many of their carvings and other works of art, netting northern artisans many thousands of dollars (Brown, 2016).

Comprehensive Land Claim Agreements

Though the JBNQA (1975) represents the first modern treaty, it preceded the federal negotiating system for treaties known as comprehensive agreements. The JBNQA was the result of a court-imposed negotiation over the construction of the first hydroelectric dam and reservoirs associated with the James Bay Project.

 For further discussion of land claims, see Chapter 3, "Modern Treaties," page 90.

Comprehensive land claim agreements (Table 11.6) are designed to satisfy Indigenous land claims based on the long-time use of the land for hunting, fishing, and trapping. In Canada, Indigenous land claims are settled by treaty: the Indigenous tribe surrenders its claim to all the land in exchange for title to a smaller amount of land, a cash settlement, and, in most instances, usufructuary right to a larger territory owned by the Crown for hunting and fishing. In simple terms, land claims are an attempt by Indigenous peoples and the federal government to resolve the issue of Indigenous rights.[7] Each agreement is very similar to the 1984 Inuvialuit Final Agreement (IFA). One common feature repeated in future agreements is that

TABLE 11.6 Comprehensive Land Claim Agreements in the Territorial North

Indigenous Group	Date of Agreement	Cash Value	Land (km²)
Inuvialuit	1984	$45 million (1977 $)	90,650
Gwich'in	1992	$75 million (1990 $)	22,378
Sahtu/Métis	1993	$75 million (1990 $)	41,000
Inuit (Nunavut)	1993	$580 million (1989 $)	350,000
Yukon First Nations	1993	$243 million (1989 $)	41,440
Dogrib (Tlicho)	2003	$152 million (1997 $)	39,000
Déline (Sahtu/Métis)	2015	Self-government	

Sources: Canada (1985: 6, 31; 1991: 3; 1993a: 3; 1993b: 81, 215; 2004); Indigenous and Northern Affairs Canada (2015, 2016).

dual institutions allow one foot in the marketplace and the other in the traditional world. In the case of the IFA, the economic sector is the Inuvialuit Regional Corporation, which manages and invests the cash settlement received as part of the agreement through other separate corporations, such as the Inuvialuit Development Corporation. The second sector, the Inuvialuit Game Council, is responsible for environmental issues that affect their hunting economy. These two distinct structures were the Inuvialuit's attempt to straddle two worlds: their old world based on harvesting game and a new world as part of the Canadian and global economies. The IFA was silent on one important element so necessary for Indigenous peoples—self-government—although an agreement-in-principle for self-government was signed in 2015 by the federal and NWT governments and by the long-time chair of the Inuvialuit Regional Corporation, Nellie Cournoyea. In 2006, self-government became part of comprehensive land claim agreements.

Figure 3.11, "Modern treaties," page 90, shows the geographic extent of modern land claim agreements in the Territorial North.

Country Food

While store-bought food dominates the table of many Indigenous families, country food holds a special place. It carries with it a connection to the spirituality of the past and remains a key element of Indigenous culture and practices. While Indigenous cultural identities vary across the Territorial North, certain core elements maintain their distinctness. These core elements include a strong attachment to the land, to country food, and to the ethic of sharing. Country food is food obtained from the land, a preferred source of meat and fish. As equivalent store-bought foods are expensive, most Indigenous northerners keep their food costs low by consuming country food. While it is true that there are substantial costs expended in harvesting country food, to some degree this cost is offset by the pleasure and spiritual rewards of being on the land and participating in hunting and fishing. Sharing also remains an important component in the harvesting and distribution of country food among family members, relatives, and close friends.

Early contacts and European hopes of discovering wealth in the North are discussed in Chapter 3, "Initial Contacts," page 64.

Frontier Vision of Development in the Territorial North

Until Prime Minister John Diefenbaker's "Northern Vision" in the late 1950s, Ottawa paid little attention to the Territorial North. With his Roads to Resources program, Ottawa began to invest in highway construction with the goal of encouraging resource developments. But the Territorial North is so vast and so sparsely populated, the case for spending large sums on road-building is difficult to make—the cost of highway construction is extremely expensive, which accounts for the paucity of highways in the Territorial North. One reason for the high cost is the presence of permafrost; another is the distance between places, which translates into extra expenses to assemble road-building equipment and materials.

The Territorial North has few highways. Nunavut has none that connect to the national highway system. The most prominent highways in the North are Yukon's Alaska Highway and the Dempster Highway and several in the Northwest Territories, including the Mackenzie Highway, Yellowknife Highway, Fort Smith Highway, and Liard Trail. Winter roads greatly extend the road system, making the trucking of heavy equipment, building supplies, and other goods possible in the winter. In late 2012, the completion of the Deh Cho Bridge (Photo 11.6) greatly reduced the cost of trucking goods to Yellowknife and other centres along the Mackenzie River served by road. CN operates on a single track to Hay River, Northwest Territories, where it connects with the river barge system on the Mackenzie River.

In assessing the cost of transportation, the value of the mineral is taken into account. For example, copper, lead, nickel, and zinc are low-grade ores (much of the ore has no commercial value). Even after the first-stage separation of some of the waste material from the valuable mineral, the enriched ore still remains a bulky product, with significant waste material remaining that can be removed only

Don Johnston_NC/Alamy Stock Photo

Photo 11.6 The Deh Cho Bridge crosses the Mackenzie River near Fort Providence. The bridge replaced the ferry system in the summer and the ice road in the winter.

through smelting. Shipping such a low-value commodity is very expensive. Ideally, such ore is transported to a smelter by ship (Vignette 11.6). Railways are the second-most effective transportation carrier for low-grade ore. The critical nature of transportation for such mines is clear in the example of the

Vignette 11.6

Sea Transportation on the Arctic Ocean

Arctic transportation takes advantage of nature. In late summer when the shore ice melts along the western Arctic, a narrow stretch of water opens between the shore and the polar pack ice. Small ships take advantage of this open water to bring supplies to communities located along the coast of the Beaufort Sea. Most of these supplies are transported by barge northward along the Mackenzie River. In the eastern Arctic, after the shore ice has retreated, ocean-going ships bring fresh supplies to Arctic communities. The Arctic pack ice covers most of the Arctic Ocean in the winter. Here, only specially reinforced ships and icebreakers can traverse the ice-covered waters. How thick is the ice? One-year ice is about 1 m thick while older ice can reach 5 m thick. Such voyages by icebreakers in older ice are not common. In August 1994, two icebreakers, the American *Polar Sea* and the Canadian *Louis S. St Laurent*, ploughed through thick ice on a scientific voyage to the North Pole. Canada has commissioned a new icebreaker, CCGS *John G. Diefenbaker*, costing just over $1 billion. The construction job for this icebreaker was awarded to Vancouver's Seaspan Shipyard with a delivery date of 2022.

lead-zinc deposit at Pine Point in the Northwest Territories. Discovered in 1898 by prospectors heading overland to the Klondike gold rush, the Pine Point deposit was not developed until 1965, when a railway was extended to the mine site. With a means of transporting the ore to a smelter, the company, Cominco, could send massive amounts of ore by rail to its smelter at Trail in British Columbia. The mine closed in 1983, leaving Pine Point a ghost town.

In the past, companies built resource towns near their mining sites—Pine Point, for example. However, the life expectancy of resource towns tends to be short because when the mine closes, no economic support remains for the community. Some companies have avoided this problem by turning to air commuting, which may be an effective way to obtain skilled southern workers for remote resource projects but does have drawbacks for the North. Southern-based air commuting systems hurt the North's economy because: (1) workers spend their wages in their home communities in southern Canada, thereby stimulating provincial, not territorial, economies; and (2) workers who reside in a province but work in the territories pay personal income tax to provincial rather than to territorial governments, thereby depriving territorial governments of valuable personal income tax. For Indigenous communities, air commuting is advantageous because it provides access to high-paying jobs in the mining industry and, at the same time, allows workers' families to remain in their Indigenous communities. Known as "cultural commuting," the fly-in and fly-out work schedule has another attraction by allowing workers time to hunt and fish on their week(s) off.

The Territorial North's Economic Anchor: Megaprojects

Resource megaprojects provide a connection to the global economy and an economic anchor for the territorial economies. On a resource frontier like Canada's North, megaprojects rely on external factors such as capital, mining expertise, and southern labour through fly-in/fly-out systems for their workers. Indigenous workers and business do participate,

but only on the margins. It is paradoxical to think of megaprojects as an anchor because of their reliance on commodity prices and their often short lifespans, but this is the reality for the Territorial North. In the mid-twentieth century, the region entered a new phase of resource development characterized by megaprojects controlled by multinational companies. Megaprojects have three critical features:

- huge capital investment, often exceeding $5 billion;
- long construction period, usually over five years to complete;
- profitability affected by the commodity price cycle.

Megaprojects have integrated the Territorial North's economy into the global economy, thereby firmly locking the North into a resource hinterland role in the world economic system. These huge undertakings are vulnerable to construction cost overruns and deteriorating commodity price fluctuations associated with the downside of the global boom-and-bust cycle (Flyvbjerg, 2014). Cost overruns are often attributed to an underestimation of the costs and time required to complete a megaproject in the challenging physical setting of the North.

The recent megaprojects in the Territorial North involved diamond mines and the massive Mary River iron ore project, owned by Luxembourg-based ArcelorMittal and Baffinland Iron Mines, which began production in 2015. As well, an even more ambitious project announced in 2012 remains on the drawing board, the Izok Corridor proposal of the Chinese state-owned MMG Ltd (formerly Minmetals Corporation), which calls for five underground and open-pit mines producing lead, zinc, and copper (Weber, 2012: B1). Since 2014, commodity prices for these minerals dropped sharply, pushing the Izok Corridor project well outside of the magic circle of viability.

Gold mining at the Discovery mine came to an end in 1969, causing the economy of the Northwest Territories to slip into troubled waters. The discovery of diamonds in the Northwest Territories in the mid-1980s brought new hope (MacLachlan, 1996). Yet, the time from discovery to production was over 10 years. By 1998, diamond mining at Ekati mine had rejuvenated the economy of the Northwest Territories. By 2014, two other mines, Diavik and Snap Lake, were operating and, along with Ekati, were supplying the world with around 15 per cent of the annual production of diamonds. Unexpectedly, in 2015, De Beers announced the closing of Snap Lake due to high levels of water seeping into the underground mining operations. Efforts to control the water problem proved expensive, causing the mine to lose money each year (see Quenneville, 2015a). By 2016, another De Beers mine, Gahcho Kué, came into production.

Miners are flown to the mine sites while bulky supplies, such as the annual supply of diesel fuel, are trucked along ice roads to the remote mines, thus keeping transportation costs relatively low. All of these diamond mines are located in the Slave Geological Province that straddles the border between the Northwest Territories and Nunavut.

Proponents of resource development describe megaprojects as the economic engine of northern development, though others challenge this assumption, claiming that they offer few benefits to the region and, more particularly, to the Indigenous communities (Bone, 2016: 133–5). These large-scale ventures are designed for the export market. By injecting massive capital investment into the construction of giant engineering projects, megaprojects create a short-term economic boom. However, most construction expenses are incurred outside hinterlands because the manufactured equipment and supplies are produced not in hinterlands but in core industrial areas. This reduces the benefits of megaprojects to the hinterland economy and virtually eliminates any opportunity for economic diversification. As well, since all megaprojects in the Territorial North are based on non-renewable resources, these developments last for a limited time. At the end of a project, the local economy suffers a collapse. The impact of mine closures has affected each of the three territories. Four examples are the lead/zinc mine at Faro, Yukon (1998); the gold mine Discovery near Yellowknife (1969) and the Snap Lake diamond mine (2015), both in the Northwest Territories; and the Jericho diamond mine (2014) in Nunavut.

In spite of these shortcomings, megaprojects offer the only route to large-scale mining operations. Such projects are not sustainable but they do inject much-needed capital and create short-term development. Megaprojects in resource hinterlands are high-risk ventures to both the operator and the region. The region is vulnerable to the boom-and-bust cycle and the inevitable closure of the mine. From this, there is no escape. On the other hand, multinational companies can reduce their risks in three ways. First, they can create a consortium of companies and thereby spread the investment risk among several firms. Second, they can arrange for long-term sales of the product at a fixed price before proceeding with construction. Third, they can obtain government assistance, which often takes the form of low-interest loans, cash subsidies, and tax concessions.

Four megaprojects are discussed in the following sections: the Mackenzie Gas Project; the Norman Wells Oil Expansion and Pipeline Project; the NWT Diamonds Project; and the Mary River Project. Not all proposals are successful. For example, the Mackenzie Valley Pipeline Project of the 1970s looked like a game-changer for the Northwest Territories, but the project stumbled during its inquiry and ended in the dustbin. The same fate met the Mackenzie Gas Project.

The Mackenzie Gas Project, 2000

Near the mouth of the Mackenzie River, large deposits of natural gas exist. The three natural gas fields in the Mackenzie Delta are Taglu, Parsons Lake, and Niglintgak. In 2000, Imperial Oil proposed the Mackenzie Gas Project, which would see a 1,220-km pipeline system along the Mackenzie Valley, linking northern natural gas sources to southern US markets. In 2003 the pipeline was estimated to cost $5 billion, but by 2007 Imperial Oil reassessed the cost of the pipeline, the gas fields, and the gas-gathering system at $16.2 billion (CBC News, 2007).

With more and more gas deposits discovered due to the fracturing technique that releases gas from shale deposits, North America is awash in natural gas, driving its price to new lows. The Mackenzie Gas Project, like the Mackenzie Valley Pipeline

Project, failed the commercial test and Imperial Oil was forced to shelve it.

The Norman Wells Oil Field, 1920–2016

The Norman Wells oil field was discovered in 1920. Until the pipeline to southern Canada was built, production was limited to providing for local communities and mining sites along the Mackenzie River and briefly, during World War II, as the central component of the Canol Project. In 1982, Esso Resources Canada (Imperial Oil) obtained federal permission to build a pipeline and ship the oil to Canadian and US markets (Figure 11.7). Prior to the pipeline, annual output was less than 180,000 m³. With the completion of the pipeline in 1985 and the expansion of oil production by a factor of 10,

the Norman Wells oil field became a major player in the Territorial North. Since 2002, however, production from the Norman Wells field has decreased from nearly 1.4 million m³ to just under 600,000 m³ in 2015 (NWT Bureau of Statistics, 2015: 21). With this oil deposit still producing, the role of Norman Wells in the northern resource economy continues but it takes second fiddle to diamond production.

The NWT Diamonds Project

Canada is now the third-largest producer of diamonds in the world, behind Botswana and Russia, and accounts for 15 per cent of the world supply, thanks in large part to the three operating diamond mines in the Northwest Territories—Ekati, Diavik, and Gahcho Kué.

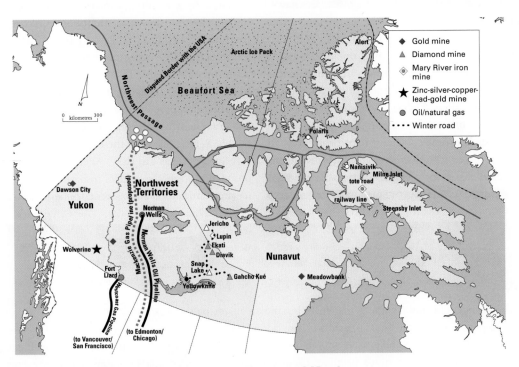

FIGURE 11.7 Resource development in the Territorial North

The mineral wealth of the Territorial North lies mainly in the Northwest Territories. Diamonds, gold, natural gas, and oil drive this territory's resource economy. In contrast, the resource economies of Yukon and Nunavut are much smaller. Petroleum exploration in the Beaufort Sea is complicated by the border dispute between Canada and the United States. The US claims a narrow strip of the Canadian section of the Beaufort Sea—an area of 21,436 km². Mines often have a short lifespan. Jericho, Polaris, Snap Lake, and Nanisivik are abandoned mines. Also, major new developments, such as the Mary River Project in Nunavut, are at the whim of commodity prices. When iron ore prices fell, the Mary River plans for a railway to an all-season port at Steensby Inlet were set aside.

How did this remarkable and unexpected discovery come about? Until 1991, geologists believed that the Canadian Shield was not a geological structure where diamonds could be formed. Two prospectors, Charles Fipke and Stewart Blusson, proved them wrong and turned conventional thinking on its head when they discovered diamond-bearing kimberlite near Lac de Gras in the Northwest Territories. The output figures are dazzling—Northwest Territories diamond production has gone from zero in 1997 to a high of $2.1 billion in 2011. Two years later, the value of diamond production had dropped slightly to $1.6 billion, but it is expected to increase sharply with the opening in 2016 of De Beers's Gahcho Kué mine, the largest diamond mine in Canada.

Not only is diamond mining the leading resource sector in the Northwest Territories, its production came on stream just as gold mining was ending. With the closing of the Giant gold mine at Yellowknife (Vignette 11.7), the last gold was mined in 2004 but closing down operations lasted until 2005. Already Diavik mine has gone to the more expensive underground mining, causing its output to slow. Unless new discoveries take place, Diavik mine will close in 2023 and Ekati in 2030. With non-renewable resource projects as an economic base, the Northwest Territories' economy could fall into a staples trap, that is, economic collapse when the staples run out because the region has been unable to diversify its narrow resource-based economy.

The Mary River Project

Nunavut is now the site one of the major iron mines in the world. This enormous deposit of high-grade iron ore was first recorded by Murray Watts in 1962. At the time, Watts was conducting airborne reconnaissance prospecting across central and northern Baffin Island. Back in 1962, mining companies were not interested in deposits located in remote areas of the Arctic, and so this extremely large and rich deposit remained untouched for many years. Rising demand and prices for iron ore altered the dynamics of its profitability. With China's industrialization taking hold, its iron and steel industries needed more and more coal and iron—two of China's major imports. As a result, the price of iron ore soared during the first decade of the twenty-first century, reaching a peak in 2011. During that time, interest in the Mary River deposit turned from a dream into a commercial reality. In 2013, the Nunavut Impact Review Board accepted the environmental and social reports prepared by the company, Baffinland. At the same time, the company concluded its impact benefit agreement with the Baffin Island Inuit.

Such projects are risky. After five years to reach production stage, the price of iron ore fell from a high in January 2011 of $180/metric tonne to $50/metric

---

Vignette 11.7

Toxic Time Bombs: The Hidden Cost of Mining

Mining brings jobs and wealth to the North but it also leaves behind toxic wastes. The short lifespan of most mines—less than 20 years—results in a geography of toxic time bombs. But why don't companies accept the social responsibility for cleaning up their mess? The answer is that they wish to skirt the high cost of cleanup. New and more stringent regulations have corrected this situation—except in cases of bankruptcy, which are not uncommon in the mining industry. For example, gold mining near Yellowknife has ended but hidden costs remain. The refining of gold at the Giant gold mine at Yellowknife left residues of arsenic. Now closed, this mining operation has left behind 237,000 tonnes of arsenic trioxide, a by-product of gold refining. Since the last mining company (Royal Oak Mines) declared bankruptcy, the cost of the cleanup, estimated at a quarter of a billion dollars, is left to the federal government—and that means the Canadian taxpayer (Bone, 2016: 187; Danylchuk, 2007).

Baffinland Iron Mines http://www.baffinland.com/latest-news/first-shipment-of-baffinlands-mary-river-iron-ore/?lang=en

Photo 11.7 The bulk carrier *Federal Tiber* departs from Baffinland's Milne Inlet port with a full load of iron ore bound for Nordenham, Germany.

tonne in January 2015. The impact on the Mary River Project was severe. The plan to build a railway to Steensby Inlet and then construct port facilities was cancelled and the company opted for a less expensive road route to Milne Inlet—costing some $4 billion less. Shipment of ore from Milne Inlet began in August 2015 (Photo 11.7). The company's proposal to expand the mine's shipping schedule out of Milne Inlet to include the winter months was initially rejected in April 2015 by the Nunavut Planning Commission, but now this proposal is before the Nunavut Impact Review Board, where it will undergo an environmental assessment.

Megaprojects: Achilles Heel?

Megaprojects have made important contributions to the northern economy. Table 11.7 shows the value of production for minerals and petroleum for the year 2014. Often, these projects and the resources extracted are touted in the press as "the engines of economic growth." Certainly, megaprojects give the regional economy a boost, but is that boost enough to lead to regional diversification in the Territorial North? One problem is that megaprojects in the Territorial North are based on non-renewable resources and

therefore do not allow for sustainable growth. Regional economic growth heavily based on non-renewable resources gives rise to a fatal long-term weakness—the Achilles heel of boom-and-bust cycles. As well, the spin-off effects of resource development in the North leak to southern Canada because the economic structure in the Territorial North is so small and because most workers at mines reside outside of the region (Quenneville, 2014; NWT Bureau of Statistics, 2014; Skura, 2016). Consequently, diversification of the North's economy is much slower than in more developed regions. From this scenario, some would suggest that the Territorial North is doomed to slip into a staples trap.

TABLE 11.7 Mineral and Petroleum Production in the Territorial North, 2014 ($ millions)

Mineral Product	Yukon	NWT	Nunavut	Territorial North
Metals	420	89	642	1,151
Non-metals	9	1,799	0	1,808
Petroleum*	0	350	0	350
Total	429	2,238	642	3,309

*Value of oil and gas production is an estimate.

Sources: Adapted from Natural Resources Canada (2015); NWT Bureau of Statistics (2015).

SUMMARY

Social and economic life in the North reflects a struggle between two visions—a resource frontier and an Indigenous homeland. The Territorial North as a frontier is a product of the global economy while the homeland vision has its roots in the North and its original (and predominant) inhabitants. The former is focused on non-renewable resource development while the latter is concerned about sustainability. But those two visions are not exclusive to one another. One economic path for Indigenous peoples goes well beyond the traditional harvesting of the land and sea into commercial but sustainable enterprises. Another path calls for educated Indigenous workers filling administrative and professional jobs in both public and private institutions. Indigenous corporations and businesses have already begun to find a place within the evolving northern economy by participating in resource projects and by creating commercial ventures. From the perspective of the federal government, Canada has no choice but to invest heavily in infrastructure to support Arctic sovereignty and encourage resource development, but at the same time Canada must back the peoples of the Territorial North as they find their way in an advanced economy.

Challenge Questions

1. How have comprehensive land claim agreements equipped Indigenous peoples to chart a new and brighter future?

2. Why would the British naval expedition led by Sir John Franklin stand a better chance of navigating the Northwest Passage today than in 1845?

3. How has global warming improved the lot of Inuit commercial fishers?

4. Megaprojects are the driving force behind the economy of the Territorial North. What is it about these projects that encourages the employment of southern workers and prohibits the diversification of the territorial economy?

5. Why has the old sector principle coloured Canada's claim to the North Pole?

Essay Questions

1. Arctic sovereignty involves several political hot spots. One is the Beaufort Sea boundary dispute with the US, another is the Northwest Passage, and the last major one is the control of the Arctic seabed. How will these be resolved, and why is Hans Island not considered a hot spot?

   References:

   Bone, Robert M. 2016. "Geopolitics, Climate Warming, and the Arctic Ocean." Chapter 8 in Bone, *The Canadian North: Issues and Challenges*, 5th edn. Toronto: Oxford University Press Canada.

   Charron, Andrea. 2008. "The Northwest Passage in Context." At: http://www.journal.forces.gc.ca/vo6/no4/north-nord-02-eng.asp.

2. Arctic cruises have increased dramatically in the last two decades. The Northwest Passage alone attracts around 10 to 12 cruise ships each summer, bringing nearly 2,500 passengers to visit Arctic communities. In August 2016, the scale of cruise ships crossing the Northwest Passage reached record levels, with the passage of the *Crystal Serenity* representing a quantum leap in regard to tourism. Could this form of tourism lead to a sustainable industry for Arctic communities?

   References:

   Dawson, J., P.T. Maher, and D.S. Slocombe. 2007. "Climate Change, Marine Tourism and Sustainability in the Canadian Arctic." *Tourism in Marine Environments* 4, 2: 69–83.

   Stewart, E.J., J. Dawson, and M.E. Johnston. 2015. "Risks and Opportunities Associated with Change in the Cruise Tourism Sector: Community Perspectives from Arctic Canada." *Polar Journal* 5, 2: 403–27.

Further Reading

Bone, Robert M. 2016. *The Canadian North: Issues and Challenges*, 5th edn. Toronto: Oxford University Press.

In this book the author discusses, among other subjects, the geopolitics of the Territorial North (Chapter 8). Bone identifies and analyzes the impact of climate warming on sea ice, and, with the loss of summer sea ice, the possibility of the Northwest Passage becoming a reality, thus connecting Asia and Europe. The author expresses his concern for the preparedness of the federal government to monitor and control shipping through the Northwest Passage, and to proceed with the huge investment to build ice-worthy patrol ships in Halifax and an icebreaker in Vancouver. Both take both time and money, with the cutting of steel for the $1.3 billion *John G. Diefenbaker* icebreaker scheduled for 2017 and with a delivery date of 2022 (Pehora, 2016). In the meantime, the last large land rush—for the unclaimed seabed of the Arctic Ocean— is underway. Here, perhaps 30 per cent of the world's untapped oil and gas deposits are found. Canada was expected in 2013 to submit its well-documented claim to the United Nations but the Danish claim to the North Pole and surrounding areas prompted former Prime Minister Harper to make a counter-claim. Accordingly, the scientists were instructed to take a second look at the geological evidence. In late 2016, Ottawa and Moscow announced that they are holding bilateral meetings to resolve the boundary issue.

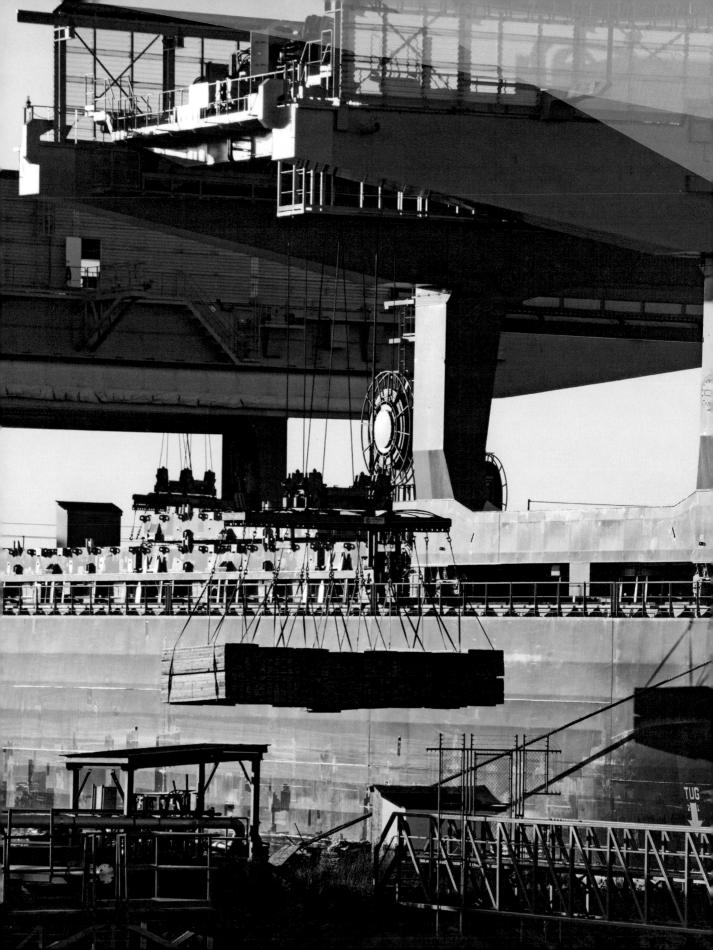

12 Canada: A Country of Regions within a Global Economy

Introduction

"Canada is big—preposterously so," wrote geographer Kenneth Hare (1968: 31). The sheer size of Canada has meant that the country spans a diverse set of physical and cultural geographies, thus transforming the nation into a country of regions. Since the 1960s, other perspectives have emerged. More open immigration policies have transformed Canada into a multicultural society, and old and new social issues, no longer invisible, have come to the surface. The attempts to address these issues are transforming social relationships between Canadians and reshaping the "Canadian identity." For instance, the relationship between Indigenous people and the rest of Canada is now under serious review, partly through the recognition of past hurts to Indigenous people led by the Truth and Reconciliation Commission of Canada (Sinclair, 2015) and poignantly expressed by Gord Downie in his story of Chanie Wenjack (Figure 12.1).

Most importantly, Canadian participation in the global economy has affected each region and its workers—sometimes positively and other times negatively. Most recently, the global economic slowdown and the dramatic drop in commodity and oil prices have forced hard-rock mining companies to curtail or halt production and oil producers to swallow lower prices. At the same time, manufacturing-oriented regions like Ontario and Québec have an opportunity to regain their economic momentum by increasing exports to the United States, helped by the low dollar.

◄ A freighter is loaded with lumber in Nanaimo, BC. Despite activity in high-tech sectors, Canada's economy relies heavily on natural resource extraction and the processing of those resources.

Keith Douglas/Getty Images

Art by Jeff Lemire.

FIGURE 12.1 Gord Downie's *The Secret Path* and the death of Chanie Wenjack

Gord Downie, the Tragically Hip frontman and songwriter, has hoped that his graphic novel, *Secret Path*, with art by Jeff Lemire, and Downie's album of the same name will help to inform others of the dark side of Canada's residential schools. Downie sings about Chanie, a young boy who, in October 1966, fled from the Cecilia Jeffrey Indian Residential School in Kenora and tried to walk to his home at Ogoki Post on the Marten Falls Reserve some 500 km north of Thunder Bay. His body was found along the railway tracks leading to Thunder Bay.

Source: Still from the animated version of *Secret Path*; art by Jeff Lemire.

Canada's economy, while full of challenges and uncertainty, has not shaken off its reputation as being based on natural resources and manufacturing. That said, Canada has taken the first steps into a high-tech advanced world where automation, digitalization, and robotics dominate. This world, troubled by the negative effects of globalization, has its challenges. In *The Collapse of Globalism*, John Ralston Saul (2009) brings a fresh argument to bear: globalization has spread wealth to many nations through international trade but also has caused many in developed countries to "bump along an unregulated road." With all the twists and turns in the world economy, Canada, so reliant on exports to drive its economy, continues to seek its place in the swirling waters of the global economy. And those waters, in certain ways, could become a torrent as a nationalistic, anti-free trade, and possibly protectionist Donald Trump presidency arises in the United States. Klaus Schwab's Fourth Industrial Revolution has arrived, but for Canada to create a knowledge-based industrial structure within a technologically advanced world, and to avoid dark waters, is no mean trick.

Coupled with adjusting to new economic circumstances, three federal policies—multiculturalism, immigration, and reconciliation—have pushed Canada's population in a new direction. In fact, Canada is well on the way to having the most diverse ethnic composition of any country in the world, reflecting more and more a "global-like" population; to recognizing Indigenous peoples and their special place and rights; and to taking on an increasingly tolerant view of cultural and racial differences. Inclusion, while not perfect, has opened the door to Pride parades across the country that have become part of Canada's diverse culture and open society (Photo 12.1), and when inclusion and tolerance have been found wanting, social movements like Idle No More and Black Lives Matter—and some politicians, such as Newfoundland and Labrador's Cathy Bennett and Alberta's Sandra Jansen[1]—try to remind us all how we have come up short. Fitting into Richard Florida's theory of the creative class, such a diverse society hopefully provides an advantage in the creation of a knowledge-based economy unique to Canada and its regions. Canada's advantage, then,

Don Marce/CBC Licensing

Photo 12.1 Vancouver Mayor Gregor Robertson, at the city's 2016 Pride Parade. "This is one of the biggest days of community celebration," said Robertson, who added that "it's all about inclusion in Vancouver, it's great to have the prime minister here too" (Pawson, 2016).

is the capacity to respect others. Founded on one truth flowing out of its history, Canada's strength lies in its ability to reconcile cultural, regional, and even global differences. Canada was not born out of revolution and bitter warfare, and today this distinction shows. In Saul's view (1997: 8–9), Canada is a "soft" country "because the classic nation-state is hard—hard in the force of its creation and its maintenance."

In this concluding chapter, five critical topics are addressed: Canada's regional character and structure; the role of cities in the advanced economy; Canada's faultlines; globalization; and future directions.

Regional Character and Structure

Canada's character—you might even say what makes it interesting—is its regional diversity and the ensuing political struggle to balance regional interests

Vignette 12.1

Canadian Identities

Saul's concept of a "soft" Canada is based on its heterogeneous nature, which fits nicely with the concept of Canada as a country of regions. An identity quandary reflected in the regional nature of the country, multiculturalism, and the arrival of immigrants from all corners of the world has created an inclusive aspect to Canadian identity not found in other countries. Pluralism, which is hardly a national identity, prevails. Each region has its own character, though "Canadian" values thread their way through regional identities. Québec, with its Québécois culture and French language, stands out, but still falls within the Canadian community. The identity quandary, ironically, has helped make Canada freer of prejudice than is the case in some other countries, and, at the same time, more of a place where newcomers can feel comfortable.

FIGURE 12.2 Fighting over oil revenues

British Columbia and Alberta have had difficulties resolving their differences over whether or not BC should receive compensation for environmental damage caused by the construction of pipelines across BC to oil terminals on the Pacific coast and for the potential threat of a pipeline leak and/or bitumen spill in the coastal waters of BC. The federal government is caught on the horns of a dilemma—pipelines to tidewater versus the risk of catastrophic damage to the marine environment. The Energy East pipeline to Saint John and the Trans Mountain Expansion to Burnaby would stimulate the Alberta and Canadian economies, but past performance tells us that the risks of pipeline ruptures and mishaps with oil tankers are real.

Source: Brian Gable/The Globe and Mail/Canadian Press Images

with national ones. Oil, pipelines, and tidewater offer a glimpse into regional conflicts, national goals, and the global economy (Figure 12.2).

The character of Canada flows from its six geographic regions—Ontario, Québec, Western Canada, British Columbia, Atlantic Canada, and the Territorial North. These regions have been shaped by history and, more recently, by global forces. While each region has a unique economy, global trade and immigration are playing a powerful role in shaping these regional economies. Ontario's automobile industry has increased its exports to the United States, and Ontario receives the bulk of the newcomers to Canada. On the eastern edge of the country, Atlantic Canada is not a preferred destination for immigrants, but exports to China have given new life to its fisheries, especially the lobster fishery.

Canada's regional structure is best described by the Canadian version of the core/periphery model.

According to this model Canada has two core regions, Ontario and Québec, two rapidly growing regions, Western Canada and British Columbia, one slow-growing region, Atlantic Canada, and one resource frontier, Territorial North. Canada's regional structure is not static, however; it is subject to forces that push and pull each region. Two such forces are global prices and global trade. Global prices for energy and commodities are one of the major forces affecting the well-being of regions, particularly those with abundant energy and mineral resources. Since global prices fluctuate in accordance with the global business cycle, a resource-rich province like Alberta undergoes a boom when prices are high and a bust when prices are low. Global prices can even drive a perennial "have-not" province into the group of "have" provinces, as happened in 2009 with Newfoundland and Labrador and its offshore oil. In sum, global prices exert a cyclical impact on the economies of resource-rich regions, giving a boost when prices are high and forcing a retreat when prices are low.

Global trade is another external force that affects regions. Canada's international trade no longer sees energy as its number-one export by value. In 2017, motor vehicles and parts took first place, followed by consumer goods and energy (Statistics Canada, 2017). Energy's fall from the top was not due to a decrease in quantity of exports but to a drop in price for energy, notably oil. In this switch in exports by value, Ontario is the chief beneficiary while Alberta is the principal loser. Similarly, the next Softwood Lumber Agreement could greatly reduce forestry exports to the US.

Today, globalization is on everyone's lips. While economists foretold of the bountiful benefits of globalization, many workers in developed countries, like Canada, felt its cold shoulder. Led by international companies operating in Canada, the race to the bottom of the wage ladder seems relentless. With the mobility of capital and open markets, manufacturing companies turn to outsourcing and offshore production because of low-wage countries where they can reduce their manufacturing costs and ship their products to markets in developed countries. One unfortunate outcome results in fewer high-paying jobs in manufacturing firms, forcing surplus workers to accept lower-wage jobs often in the service industry. Since prices for imported goods became lower than for similar domestic goods, a hollowing out of manufacturing has taken place, especially in the core regions of Ontario and Québec. Across Canada but especially in the core regions, the percentage of workers in the secondary sector, which is made up primarily of those engaged in manufacturing, has declined. This trend is repeating itself in other developed economies. Another global trend is that more and more workers in developed countries are moving from primary and secondary employment into the tertiary or services jobs. Knowledge-based innovations spur technical advancements in all three sectors. Lastly, automation, with robotic and technical innovations, is spurring greater efficiencies in all three industrial sectors and these efficiencies are reducing the need for employees.

Urban Canada and the Advanced Economy

Within Canada's regional character and structure, the driving force of change and innovation is urban Canada. The greater share of Canada's population and its advanced economy are found in metropolises, particularly Toronto, Montréal, and Vancouver. For these urban centres and smaller urban centres to flourish, they need to attract the creative class; to make their cities more livable; and to focus on urban sustainability. One urban expression of the creative class takes the form of innovative clusters, the most famous of which is Silicon Valley in California. Not only are cities competing for creative people and innovative clusters, but they have recognized the need for a quality of urban life that demands a fresh vision of the design and functioning of cities. So critical is quality of life to Canada's future that Alan Wallace (2016), the former Director of Planning and Development for Saskatoon, stated that urban Canada stands on the "threshold of pivotal change" where cities are not just growing bigger but more sustainable. In this vein, Vancouver Mayor Gregor Robertson has put his city on a path to become "the greenest city in the world." While the larger cities are reinventing themselves into more attractive

places to live through gentrification of old industrial areas and environment-friendly innovations such as green roofing, smaller cities can learn from their experience and avoid their mistakes in urban design and planning (see Photo 6.9). As Wallace (2016) points out, cities like Saskatoon, "London, St Catharines, Halifax, Oshawa, Victoria, Windsor, Regina, and Sherbrooke, to name a few, all have populations under half a million. These cities are growing but hopefully not just bigger." Traffic congestion and satellite towns are common features of urban Canada, but these mid-sized cities can rejig their future by making three critical choices between:

- automobile traffic or rapid transit;
- suburban expansion or development of the downtown core;
- invest in roads and freeways or promotion of education and research.

Canada's Faultlines

Tensions naturally arise in a country of regions. In 2012, a powerful eruption took place along the regional faultline between Alberta and British Columbia when the premiers of Alberta and British Columbia took strikingly different positions on the proposed Northern Gateway pipeline. BC's negative position was based on three main factors:

- A major bitumen spill in the coastal waters of BC could have consequences similar to or worse than what occurred in 1989 with the *Exxon Valdez* oil disaster in Prince William Sound, Alaska.
- Opposition from First Nations along with concerns held by BC citizens must be addressed.
- BC, which would take the bulk of the environmental risks and costs, wants a "fair" share of the revenue.

Alberta, of course, wants oil pipelines to access tidewater because such pipelines would lower the cost of transportation, obtain a higher profit for Alberta oil, and ensure oil sands expansion. On the other

THINK ABOUT IT

While major oil spills in the Pacific Ocean are rare, the enormous damage caused by the *Exxon Valdez* oil spill in March 1989 served notice not only that such marine accidents are possible, but also that they represent an ecological catastrophe that seems to have no end. Under those circumstances, is it fair that Alberta gains while BC shoulders most environmental costs and future risks?

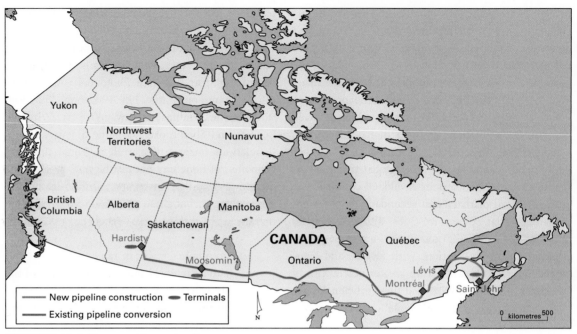

FIGURE 12.3 Energy East pipeline route

TransCanada's proposed pipeline project extends from Hardisty, Alberta, to Saint John, NB. Heavy oil would be delivered to refineries at Montréal, Québec City, and Saint John. Most of TransCanada's existing gas pipeline would be converted to an oil pipeline while new pipeline construction would take place in Québec and New Brunswick. Opposition, centred in Québec, involves a wide range of groups including the city of Montréal and the Mohawks of Kanesatake.

Source: TransCanada Pipelines (2016).

hand, British Columbia stands to gain little and lose much. Its potential losses flow less from the environmental damage associated with the construction of oil pipelines, but more from the potential disaster caused by a major bitumen spill.

More recently, the Energy East pipeline has been proposed. The project would deliver oil sands bitumen to existing refineries in Montréal, near Québec City, and in Saint John. Québec has expressed similar concerns to those of British Columbia. This proposal and other pipeline proposals must obtain a recommendation for construction from the National Energy Board and then the government of Canada. In the case of pipeline proposals, Ottawa must balance national interests against provincial concerns. Ottawa relies on the National Energy Board to evaluate such projects, but the federal government must either approve or reject such proposals (Figure 12.3).

Contested Terrain 12.1

Are the Oil Sands in Canada's Economic Future?

Political columnist Lawrence Martin (2016) wrote: "Two major pipeline projects, Keystone XL and Northern Gateway, are dead or all but dead. That leaves two others, Energy East and Kinder Morgan. If they don't get done, if much of our most precious resource faces a landlocked future, consequences are predictable." What consequences do you believe he is speaking of? Martin was writing in September 2016. Have more recent geopolitical events altered his sour prediction? For that matter, do you believe the oil sands are "our most precious resource"?

Canada and the Global Economy

With the global economy spinning its wheels, what happens in the next few years will have a direct impact on Canada and its six regions. The most positive scenario is that the global business cycle has already reached its low point and that, after 2016, it will begin to recover, led by a resurgence of the economies of the United States, China, and the European Union. When full recovery takes place, the economies of resource-rich regions should recover their strength, and with the injection of knowledge-based innovations in processing firms, the core regions should again provide economic leadership for Canada. The Territorial North may well play a more prominent role because of global warming and the resulting increase in open water in the Arctic Ocean. Already, international tensions over claims for the seabed of the Arctic Ocean are realigning Canada's geopolitical stance (Photo 12.2)

Along with the hope for a resurgence of the global economy, other hard issues face Canada and the world. Rapidly advancing technology in the form of artificial intelligence, nanotechnology, and robotics is already upon us. According to Martin Ford, job losses in manufacturing in the United States from 1950 to the present are due primarily to advancing technology and the offshoring of production but not to trade (Ford, 2015: 54–5). As Ford (55) puts it, "We are making more stuff, but doing so with fewer and fewer workers."

Advancing technology has already made inroads in the primary sector—think of how mechanized agriculture has become—and is poised to overcome

Photo 12.2 In September 2016, Foreign Minister Stéphane Dion announced that Canada will seek to actively co-operate with Russia in the Arctic. Since Canada and Russia control 75 per cent of the Arctic: "Co-operation with Russia on the full range of Arctic issues is simply in our best interests. The North is not a place for military confrontation or buildup" (Byers, 2016). At the same time, Canada continues to shore up its submission for seabed territory in the Arctic Ocean by undertaking research, in some cases in co-operation with Denmark and the United States. Here, the Canadian Coast Guard icebreaker *Louis S. St Laurent* and the US Coast Guard cutter *Healy* engaged in a joint Arctic survey mission in 2009 to explore largely unknown parts of the Canada Basin, north of the Beaufort Sea.

THINK ABOUT IT

Does the core/periphery spatial structure, even if bent or broken, illustrate the value of a theoretical framework in regional geography?

significant elements of the tertiary sector. Already banks have moved into online banking, allowing them to reduce the number of bank branches, tellers, and support staff. Robotic advancing technology is no longer found only in science fiction. Sometimes its debut occurs in small ways, such as robotic vacuum cleaners; in other ways its impact is large, such as in assisting doctors to perform surgery. Down the road, driverless cars are coming. Two consequences might be a reduction in traffic accidents and the demise of taxi drivers. Martin Ford's fear that the developed world faces mass unemployment and economic collapse may be far-fetched, but perhaps his idea of a guaranteed income is worth thinking about.

The Future

Change is inevitable. In the next decades, the country needs to build cultural and economic bridges between its regions; to provide more powers and revenue to its cities; and, in so doing, to strengthen the economy and national unity. Such unity in a country like Canada, however frail or fractured it sometimes appears, is the linchpin holding the nation and its six regions together; if strengthened, unity can empower regional bonds and drive their economies into the futuristic knowledge-based world.

The key to Canada's economic future lies in global trade and partaking in the advanced economy with all its robotic twists and turns. The trade agreement with the European Union and the creation in 2016 of the Advisory Council on Economic Growth represent two steps in that direction (McKenna, 2016). Already, the federal Liberal government is exploring much deeper ties with China, is planning to create an infrastructure bank to attract foreign investors, and appears willing to run large budget deficits to jump-start the stalled economy and to inject more knowledge-based innovations into all economic sectors.

Over the long run, Canada's economy and population are destined to expand through global trade and immigration. Much of the economic expansion will be due to the fast-growing Asian countries, led by China and India. While Asia is finding its way through industrialization, China, Japan, and India will require more energy and oil from Alberta and natural gas from BC, and pipelines, if built, could bolster trade with Asia and stimulate the Alberta and BC economies. Saskatchewan, in addition to potash and uranium exports, sees Asia's middle class demanding more of its processed canola and lentils. At the other end of the country, Ontario and Québec, by moving into more sophisticated and high-value manufacturing products, will find global markets; and Atlantic Canada fisheries may repeat the recently booming lobster trade with China with other fish stocks. The Territorial North, limited to its non-renewable resources, will have to wait for commodity and energy prices to recover. Caught in this general resurgence are four significant factors:

- The six geographic regions will continue to define Canada within the core/periphery framework, but global forces—and forces within a polarized United States—will help shape and reshape their economies.
- The outcome of the environment and pipelines debate will determine the fate of the Alberta oil sands and the future of fossil fuels in Canada.
- Canada's major cities will house and drive the knowledge-based economy.
- Urban Canada is moving to a softer, gentler, and more inclusive society where the creative class, as proposed by Richard Florida (e.g., 2002, 2012), flourishes, where downtowns become more pedestrian- and cycle-friendly, and where newcomers to cities, both immigrants and Indigenous people, find their footing.
- This softer, gentler, and more inclusive society remains a work in progress, but in spite of bumps in the road Canada is heading in the right direction in addressing its social imperfections and evolving identity.

Tomorrow, while full of uncertainty, contains three certainties. (1) Canada will remain a country of six geographic regions and will continue to experience regional tensions in its search for an advanced economy. (2) Compromise remains a special strength. By engaging in open and vigorous debate, compromises—not solutions—will follow (Frye, 1971: i–iii). Compromise works at the heart of the

Photo 12.3 One dream of resurgence sees Toronto as a leading global financial centre and as Canada's leading centre for knowledge-based activities. As the headquarters for Canadian banks—seen on the world stage as reliable, stable, and profitable—plus several important universities, a creative class, and **ethnoburbs** (Li, 2009), Toronto is well positioned to take the next step as a world financial hub and centre for innovations.

exercise of democratic power in a diverse society by demanding a balance between individual and collective rights, between regional and national interests, and between those with power and those in need of it. The ability to strike this balance is critical to Canada's well-being and social harmony. (3) Geography dictates that Canada's economy will continue to rely on natural resources to fuel it and to drive its exports.

Challenge Questions

1. "Canada is big—preposterously so," wrote geographer Kenneth Hare in 1968. What spatial theory helps explain relations between regions?

2. If push comes to shove, which of the oil sands pipeline proposals stands the best chance of gaining federal government approval?

3. Canada's economic future depends on global trade. Explain.

4. The global business cycle is a fact of life. Why is its effect on Canada's regions so uneven?

5. Has John Ralston Saul fallen either into postmodern relativism (a recent trap for social thinkers) or into **environmental determinism** (an old trap for geographers) when he writes that "in spite of intellectual claims to the contrary, not religion, not language, not race but place is the dominant feature of civilizations. It decides what people can do and how they will live"?

Essay Questions

1. In November 2015 Prime Minister Trudeau announced that Canada is on board with "Mission Innovation," a grouping of 20 countries with private-sector sponsors such as Bill Gates that is committed to clean energy development and research. Can such an initiative bring about real change?

   References:

   Bennet, James. 2015. "We Need an Energy Miracle." *The Atlantic* (Nov.). At: http://www.theatlantic.com/magazine/archive/2015/11/we-need-an-energy-miracle/407881/.

   Campbell, Bruce, Seth Klein, and Marc Lee. 2016. "We Can Afford the Leap." Canadian Centre for Policy Alternatives. At: https://leapmanifesto.org/wp-content/uploads/2015/09/Afford-en1.pdf.

   Natural Resources Canada. 2016. "Mission Innovation." 3 Feb. At: http://news.gc.ca/web/article-en.do?nid=1037519.

2. Canada's diverse geography reflects the four faultlines. From time to time, one of these faultlines flares into the national spotlight. In 2015, the pendulum of economic power swung in favour of Central Canada, setting in motion a reversal of Ontario and Alberta as "have" and "have-not" provinces. Examine the power pendulum by considering the relationship between the price of oil and the Canada/US exchange rate.

   References:

   Brown, Kario-Paul A. 2016. "How and Why Oil Impacts the Canadian Dollar (CAD)." *Investopedia*. At: http://www.investopedia.com/articles/investing/021315/how-why-oil-impacts-canadian-dollar-cad.asp.

   Fitz-Morris, James. 2015. "Tom Mulcair's 'Dutch Disease' Diagnosis Was Poor Politics, but Sound Economics." CBC News, 14 Apr. At: http://www.cbc.ca/news/politics/tom-mulcair-s-dutch-disease-diagnosis-was-poor-politics-but-sound-economics-1.3028343.

   Spurr, Ben. 2015. "Alberta to Introduce Economy-wide Carbon Tax in New Climate Change Strategy." *Toronto Star*, 22 Nov. At: http://www.thestar.com/news/canada/2015/11/22/alberta-premier-proposes-carbon-tax-emissions-cap-to-fight-climate-change.html.

3. Can you make a case that Canada's six regions reflect the spatial perception of people, that is, that they are vernacular regions? Also known as popular or perceptual regions, vernacular regions are those perceived to exist by their inhabitants, as evidenced by the widespread acceptance and use of a special regional name.

Further Reading

Saul, John Ralston. 2009. *The Collapse of Globalism and the Reinvention of the World*, 2nd edn. Toronto: Penguin Canada.

The Collapse of Globalism brings a fresh argument to the question: Has globalization spread wealth to all nations through international trade but, at the same time, disadvantaged workers in developed countries? No one doubts the world is a "richer" place, but the bumps along an unregulated road have displaced workers. His argument has implications for Canada's regions. Essentially, Saul calls for more regulations of capitalism: "Are political decisions meant to be made in deference to the economy and markets, or are political institutions meant to shield us from harsh realities of globalization?" As a case in point, should Alberta allow the marketplace to determine where its bitumen is upgraded, even if this means that the processing and the jobs involved are lost to Alberta and Canada?

Glossary

age dependency ratio   The ratio of the economically dependent sector of the population to the productive sector, arbitrarily defined as the ratio of the elderly (those 65 years and over) plus the young (those under 15 years) to the population of working age (those 15 to 64 years); the old-age dependency ratio is similar to the age dependency ratio except that it focuses only on those over 64.

agricultural fringe   Agriculture at its physical limits. Along the southern edge of the boreal forest and in the Peace River country, farmers have cleared the land, but the short growing season prevents most crops from maturing, and consequently many farmers turned instead to cattle.

air commuting   Travel to a work site in a remote area, such as a mine, by aircraft owned or hired by the company. Until the 1970s, companies built resource towns to house workers and their families. Employees remain at the work site for a week or longer, working long shifts (often 12 hours per day), then have a week or two at home. The company pays for the air transportation and for food and lodging at the work site.

air drainage   The movement of colder, heavier air to lower elevations, leaving warmer, lighter air in the higher elevations.

air pollution   Any chemical, physical, or biological agent that modifies the natural characteristics of the atmosphere.

Alaska Panhandle   A strip of the Pacific coast north of 54° 40'N latitude that was awarded to the United States in 1903 following what is known as the Alaska boundary dispute.

albedo effect   Proportion of solar radiation reflected from the earth's surface back into the atmosphere.

Alberta clipper   A low pressure system that begins when warm, moist winds from the Pacific Ocean come into contact with the Rocky Mountains and then the winds form a chinook in southern Alberta; winter storms occur over the Canadian Prairies when it becomes entangled with the cold Arctic air masses. Eventually, the storm reaches Ontario and Québec. Also, "Alberta Clipper" is the name of a natural gas pipeline that runs from Alberta to the US Midwest.

allophones   A term used by Statistics Canada to identify those whose mother tongue is not English, French, or one of the Aboriginal languages.

alpine permafrost   Permanently frozen ground found at high elevations.

anglophones   Those whose mother tongue is English.

Arctic Circle   An imaginary line that signifies the northward limit of the sun's rays at the time of the winter solstice (21 December). At a latitude of 66° 32'N, the sun does not rise above the horizon for one day of the year (the winter solstice). Except for a short period of twilight, darkness prevails for 24 hours. At the summer solstice (21 June), the sun's rays do not fall below the horizon, providing constant daylight for 24 hours.

Arctic ice pack   Floating sea ice in the Arctic Ocean that has consolidated into an ice pack, with an extent of over 10 million km^2. New sea ice (less than one year in age) is often about 1 m thick; old sea ice can reach 5 m in thickness. Ice ridges are formed, reaching 20 m in thickness. Scientists have found that higher temperatures are reducing the geographic extent and thickness of the Arctic ice pack.

arêtes   Narrow serrated ridges found in glaciated mountains. Arêtes form when two opposing cirques erode a mountain ridge.

Asia-Pacific Gateway and Corridor   A system of transportation infrastructure, including British Columbia's Lower Mainland and Prince Rupert ports, road, and rail connections, that reaches across Western Canada and into the economic heartlands of North America, including major airports and border crossings.

Assembly of First Nations (AFN)   National advocacy organization for status Indians, i.e., the more than 630 First Nations in Canada.

Athabasca tar sands   The largest reservoir of crude bitumen in the world and the largest of three major oil sands deposits in Alberta; also known as the oil sands.

Bakken formation   A geological structure containing large quantities of oil trapped in shale. It lies in Williston Basin in southern Saskatchewan and Manitoba and extends into North Dakota, Montana, and South Dakota.

Barren Grounds   The area of tundra stretching from the west coast of Hudson Bay to Great Slave and Great Bear lakes and northward to the Arctic Ocean. The barren ground caribou use this region for calving each summer before migrating to the boreal forest.

basins   Structural depressions in sedimentary rock caused by a bending of sedimentary strata into huge bowl-like shapes. Petroleum may accumulate in sedimentary basins.

Beothuk   Before the arrival of fishing boats from Europe, the Beothuk, who probably spoke an Algonkian language, hunted and fished on the island of Newfoundland. Relations with fishers and settlers often resulted in conflicts, which confined the Beothuk to the inland. With access to coastal resources cut off and under attack by settlers, the Beothuk struggled to survive in the resource-poor interior. In 1829, the last of the Beothuk died.

Big Bear   The last of the great chiefs prior to widespread European settlement of the Prairies, who had a vision to unite the Plains Cree to stand together against the impending wave of settlers and to find a way to sustain their culture.

Big Commute   Air travel by Newfoundland trades workers to and from the Alberta oil sands, on a cycle such as 20 days in Alberta and eight days back home in Newfoundland.

biosphere reserve   Designation by the United Nations of lands and waters that in turn are protected by provincial or state legislation. Such UNESCO reserves contain core areas where no resource development is permitted; buffer zones where limited resource extraction is permitted; and transition zones where resource development takes place in a sustainable manner.

bitumen   A tar-like mixture of sand and oil.

Black Lives Matter   A social movement by the African-American community against police violence towards black people in the United States; now active in some Canadian urban centres such as Toronto.

boom-and-bust cycle   A rapid increase in economic activities in a resource-oriented economy, often based on the value of a single commodity, quickly followed by a downturn when the commodity price(s) falls due to a drop in world demand, which is usually associated with a contraction in the business cycle.

Brent oil price   A major trading classification of sweet light crude oil that serves as a major benchmark price for purchases of oil worldwide; named for a North Sea oil field, the Brent price in recent years has been slightly higher than the continental North American West Texas Intermediate price. *See* oil prices.

business cycle   A series of irregular fluctuations in the pace of economic activity in the world market (capitalist) economy. These fluctuations consist of four phases: "contraction" (a slowdown in the pace of economic activity); "trough" (the lowest level of economic activity); "expansion" (a sharp increase in the pace of economic activity); and "peak" (the maximum level of economic activity).

Calder   Supreme Court of Canada ruling in 1973 that Aboriginal peoples have some undefined collective rights, based on historic occupation, possession, and use of traditional territories, known as "Indian title" (now called "Indigenous [or Aboriginal] title"). These rights are not property rights, which involve the full weight of ownership.

carbon sequestration   Carbon capture and storage technology involving the capture of CO_2 and other greenhouse gas (GHG) emissions from fossil-fuel power stations or other large carbon emitters and storage of the CO_2 in deep, stable geological formations.

Cascadia   The name proposed for an independent sovereign state advocated by a grassroots movement in the Pacific Northwest, which would include British Columbia, Washington, and Oregon.

census metropolitan area   An urban area with a population of at least 100,000, with at least 50,000 people residing in the core, together with adjacent smaller urban centres and even rural areas that have a high degree of economic and social integration with the larger urban area.

Château Clique   The political elite of Lower Canada, composed of an alliance of officials and merchants who had considerable political influence with the British-appointed governor; similar to the Family Compact in Upper Canada.

chernozemic   A soil order identified by a well-drained soil that is often dark brown to black in colour; associated with the grassland and parkland natural vegetation types and located in the Prairies climatic zone.

chinook   A dry, warm, downslope wind in the lee of the Rocky Mountains in Alberta. Also called a rain shadow wind because it has dropped most of its moisture on windward slopes.

circumpolar countries   The eight nations associated with the circumpolar area are Canada, Denmark (including Greenland and the Faeroe Islands), Finland, Iceland, Norway, Russian Federation, Sweden, and the United States of America. Five of these—Canada, Denmark, Norway, Russia, and the US—have a territorial claim to portions of the Arctic seabed.

cirques   Large, shallow depressions found in mountains at the head of glacial valleys that are caused by the plucking action of alpine glaciers.

Clayoquot Sound   Located on the west coast of Vancouver Island, Clayoquot Sound in 1993 became the centre of environmental protests against logging in old-growth rain forests.

climate   An average condition of weather in a particular area over a very long period of time.

climate change   Change in global climate patterns, with most change apparent since the mid-twentieth century; attributed largely to the increased levels of atmospheric carbon dioxide produced by the use of fossil fuels.

climatic zone   A geographic area where similar types of weather occur.

commercial forest   Forest lands able to grow commercial coniferous (softwoods), deciduous (hardwoods), and mixed woods timber within an acceptable time frame.

comprehensive land claim agreement   Agreement based on territory claimed by an Indigenous group that was never ceded or surrendered by treaty. Such agreements extinguish the Indigenous land claim to vast areas in exchange for a relatively small amount of land, capital, and the organizational structure to manage their lands and capital.

container   A sealed steel "box" of standardized dimensions (measured in 20-foot equivalent units or "TEU") for transporting cargo by ship, rail, and truck.

continental air masses   Homogeneous bodies of air that have taken on moisture and temperature characteristics of the land mass of their origin. Continental air masses are normally dry and cold in the winter and dry and hot in the summer.

continental effect   Land masses heat up and cool more quickly than oceans.

continentalism   Policies, like the Free Trade Agreement, that promote Canadian trade and economic ties with the United States.

continuous permafrost   Extensive areas of permanently frozen ground in the Arctic, where at least 80 per cent of the ground is permanently frozen.

convectional precipitation   An upward movement of moist air that causes the air to cool, resulting in condensation and then precipitation.

conventional oil and gas   Deposits that can be recovered through natural flow or pumping to the surface.

core   An abstract area or real place where economic power, population, and wealth are concentrated; sometimes described as an industrial core, heartland, or metropolitan centre.

core/periphery model   A theoretical concept based on a dual spatial structure of the capitalist world and a mutually beneficial relationship between its two parts, which are known as the core and the periphery. While both parts are dependent on each other, the core (industrial heartland) dominates the economic relationship with its periphery (resource hinterland) and thereby benefits more from this relationship. The core/periphery model can be applied at several geographical levels: international, national, and regional.

country food   Food, primarily game, such as caribou, fish, and sea mammals, obtained by Indigenous people from the land and sea. Although First Nations, Inuit, and Métis now live in settlements, they fish and hunt for cultural and economic reasons.

creative class   Culture workers, from artists to computer programmers, who, Richard Florida argues, are the key to a flourishing and progressive city and who are attracted to urban centres rich in diversity and culture.

crude birth rate   The number of births per 1,000 people in a given year.

crude death rate   The number of deaths per 1,000 people in a given year.

culture   The sum of attitudes, habits, knowledge, and values shared by members of a society and passed on to their children.

culture areas   Regions within which the population has a common set of attitudes, economic and social practices, and values.

Delgamuukw   Supreme Court of Canada case in 1997 that defined how Aboriginal title may be proved in a court of law, which includes oral historical accounts of the people in question.

demographic transition theory   The historical shift of birth and death rates from high to low levels in a population. The decline in mortality precedes the decline in fertility, resulting in a rapid population growth during the transition period.

demography   The scientific study of human populations, including their size, composition, distribution, density, growth, and related socio-economic characteristics.

denudation   The process of breaking down and removing loose material found at the surface of the earth. In this way, erosion and weathering lead to a reduction of elevation and relief in landforms.

deposition   The deposit of material on the earth's surface by various processes such as ice, water, and wind.

dilbit   Bitumen diluted with a diluent.

diluent   A hydrocarbon substance used to dilute crude bitumen so that it can be transported by pipeline.

discontinuous permafrost   Permanently frozen ground mixed with unfrozen ground in the Subarctic. At its northern boundary about 80 per cent of the ground is permanently frozen, while at its southern boundary about 30 per cent of the ground is permanently frozen.

dispute settlement mechanism   Binding arbitration to resolve trade disputes, as built into the FTA and NAFTA.

drainage basin   Land sloping towards the sea; an area drained by rivers and their tributaries into a large body of water.

Drive Clean program   Requirement in Ontario that older vehicles must pass an emissions test.

drumlins   Low, elliptical hills created by the deposit of glacial till, believed to be from subglacial megafloods, and shaped by the movement of the ice sheet; also called whalebacks or hogbacks.

Dry Belt   An agricultural area in the semi-arid parts of Alberta and Saskatchewan, primarily devoted to grain farms and cattle ranches, where crop failures due to drought are more common. *See* Palliser's Triangle.

Eastern Townships   An area of Québec in the Appalachian Uplands lying south and east of the St Lawrence Lowland and near the US border. The region is now referred to as Estrie.

economies of scale   A reduction in unit costs of production resulting from an increase in output.

ecumene   The portion of the land that is settled.

energy poverty   In the classical definition, developing countries where access to energy is limited; in the case of Ontario, the high cost of energy that reduces low-income families' access to energy.

environmental determinism   The assumption that human activities are controlled by the physical environment. Now considered far too deterministic, it was a popular philosophical position of geographers in the late nineteenth and early twentieth centuries.

erosion   The displacement of loose material by geomorphic processes such as wind, water, and ice by downward movement in response to gravity.

eskers   Long, sinuous mounds of sand and gravel deposited on the bottom of a stream flowing under a glacier; eskers appear on the land surface after the glacier has retreated.

Estrie   An administrative region that overlaps most of the area formerly called the Eastern Townships.

ethnic group   People who have a shared awareness of a common identity and who identify themselves with a particular culture.

ethnic origin   A Statistics Canada definition, which refers to the ethnic or cultural origins of the respondent's ancestors. An ancestor is someone from whom a person is descended and is usually more distant than a grandparent.

ethnoburbs   Suburban residential and business areas with a significant ethnic character composed of new Canadians.

ethnocentricity   The viewpoint that one's ethnic group is central and superior, providing a standard against which all other groups are judged.

evapotranspiration   Part of the water cycle: the sum of evaporation of water from the soil and water bodies to the air and the transpiration of water from plants and its subsequent loss as vapour.

Family Compact   A group of officials who dominated senior bureaucratic positions, the executive and legislative councils, and the judiciary in Upper Canada.

faulting   The breaking of the earth's crust as a result of its differential movement; often associated with earthquakes.

fault line   A crack or break in the earth's crust. A complex fault line is known as a fault zone; major fault lines exist between two tectonic plates.

faultlines   Application of a geological phenomenon to the economic, social, and political cracks that divide regions and people.

Fertile Belt   Area of long-grass and parkland natural vegetation in Western Canada associated with black and dark-brown chernozemic soils. It supports a mixed farming area where crop failures due to drought are less common.

fertility rate   The number of live births per 1,000 women aged 15 to 44 in a given year; also known as the general fertility rate. The fertility rate is much more indicative of changes in fertility behaviour than is the crude birth rate because it is based on those women of child-bearing age rather than the general population.

First Nations people　By Statistics Canada definition, those Indigenous persons who report a single response of "North American Indian" to the Indigenous identity census question.

folding　The bending of the earth's crust.

fracking　A technique involving the injection of water and unidentified chemicals underground at very high pressure to create fractures in the underlying shale rock formations, thus releasing the oil or gas for extraction; hydraulic fracturing.

francophones　Those whose mother tongue is French.

Free Trade Agreement (FTA)　Trade agreement between Canada and the United States enacted in 1989.

French Canadians　Canadians with roots to Québec and who likely still speak French.

frontal precipitation　Condensation and then precipitation that occur when a warm air mass is forced to rise over a colder air mass.

glacial erosion　The scraping and plucking action of moving ice on the surface of the land.

glacial spillways　Deep and wide valleys formed by the flow of massive amounts of water originating from a melting ice sheet or from water escaping from glacial lakes.

glacial striations　Scratches or grooves in the bedrock caused by rocks embedded in the bottom of a moving ice sheet or glacier.

glacial troughs　U-shaped valleys carved by alpine glaciers.

global circulation system　The movement of ocean currents and wind systems that redistribute energy around the world.

globalization　An economic/political/social process driven by international trade and investment, as well as by migration and the spread of Western popular culture, that leads to a single world market and wide-ranging impacts on the environment, cultures, political systems, and economic development.

global warming　An increase in global temperature due to the greenhouse effect caused by increased levels of carbon dioxide, chlorofluorocarbons, and other pollutants in the atmosphere; the main contributor is the burning of fossil fuels.

Great American Desert　The treeless Great Plains as described by American explorers in the nineteenth century; in fact, this region has a semi-arid climate and a grasslands vegetation cover.

Great Bear Rainforest　Temperate rain forest along British Columbia's central and north coast, an area of 6.4 million hectares with 85 per cent of the old-growth forest designated as protected from logging by the BC government in 2016.

greenhouse effect　The absorption of long-wave radiation from the earth's surface by the atmosphere.

greenhouse gases　Water vapour, carbon dioxide, and other gases that make up less than 1 per cent of the earth's atmosphere but are essential to maintaining the temperature of the earth.

grooves of geography　Physiographic structure, such as plains and mountains, that facilitates or impedes movement between adjacent regions.

gross domestic product (GDP)　An estimate of the total value of all materials, foodstuffs, goods, and services produced by a country or province in a particular year.

groundfish　Fish that live on or near the bottom of the sea. The most valuable groundfish are cod, halibut, and sole.

Gulf Stream　A warm ocean current paralleling the North American coast that flows from the Gulf of Mexico towards Newfoundland.

habitants　French peasants who settled the land in New France under a form of feudal agriculture known as the seigneurial system.

"hard" and "soft" countries　Portrayal by John Ralston Saul of countries as "hard" and "soft" in terms of their relationships with minority groups. Hard nations with homogeneous populations tend to treat minorities harshly. Soft nations have more diverse populations and as a result of a history of interaction among different cultural groups, the value of harmonious relations has taken root.

heartland　A geographic area in which a nation's industry, population, and political power are concentrated; also known as a core.

"hewers of wood and drawers of water"　Biblical phrase applied by sociologists and others to the labouring classes of capitalism doing the most menial, low-paid work necessary for the operation of capitalist society. Within the context of the core/periphery model, this term refers to periphery regions where primary production prevails; core areas, on the other hand, focus on the processing of those raw products. Its application to a country's economy refers to the export of raw materials rather than of finished goods.

hinterland　A geographic area based on resource development that supplies the heartland with many of its primary products; also known as a periphery.

hollowing-out　The relocation of manufacturing plants in one country to another, which leaves the economy of the original country much weakened.

Holocene epoch　The current geological division of the Geological Time Chart. It began some 11,000 years ago and is associated with the warm climate following the last ice age.

homeland　A land or region where a relatively homogeneous people and their ancestors have been born and raised, and thus have developed a strong attachment to that place; a sense of place.

homesteader　A settler who obtained land. In Western Canada, quarter sections of 160 acres were available as homesteads under the federal government's plan known as the Dominion Lands Act where a settler paid a $10 fee for a quarter section.

horizontal drilling　Recently developed technology used in drilling for oil and gas, as opposed to vertical oil and gas drilling, which has existed for a long time.

hydraulic fracturing　A method used to fracture rock formations in order to allow oil or natural gas to flow from impervious geological strata; fracking.

hydrometallurgy　A process that produces nickel, copper, and cobalt directly from ore, thus avoiding the smelting process and eliminating environmentally unfriendly sulphur dioxide and dust emissions.

ice age　A geological period of severe cold accompanied by the formation of continental ice sheets. The most recent ice age, the Pleistocene, began some 2 million years ago and ended with the beginning of the Holocene epoch some 11,000 years ago.

igneous rocks　Rock formed when the earth's surface first cooled or when magma or lava that has reached the earth's surface cools.

Indigenous ancestry According to Statistics Canada, those who report an Aboriginal identity as well as those who report being Aboriginal to the ethnic origin question, which focuses on the ethnic or cultural origins of a person's ancestors.

Indigenous identity According to Statistics Canada, those persons identifying with at least one Aboriginal group, that is, North American Indian, Métis, or Inuit, and/or those who report being a treaty Indian or a registered Indian, as defined by the Indian Act, and/or those who report they are members of an Indian band or First Nation.

Indigenous peoples All Canadians whose ancestors lived in Canada before the arrival of Europeans; includes status and non-status Indians, Métis, and Inuit.

Indigenous rights The practices, customs, and traditions that Aboriginal peoples practised prior to contact with or large-scale settlement by Europeans. One Aboriginal right, the right to hunt and fish on Crown lands, has legal status and is protected by the Canadian Constitution. Given the diversity among Aboriginal peoples, Aboriginal rights vary from group to group. Indigenous people whose chiefs signed treaty agreements on behalf of their tribes also have treaty rights.

Indigenous settlements Small Indigenous centres, often found on reserves or in remote, northern locations.

Indigenous title A legal term that recognizes an Aboriginal interest in traditionally occupied land.

industrial structure The sectors of a national, regional, or local economy—primary (e.g., resource extraction and harvesting), secondary (e.g., manufacturing, construction), and tertiary (services)—and the extent to which the whole economy is driven by each of these sectors.

Inland Passage The protected waterway of the Pacific Ocean lying between the BC mainland and Vancouver Island and Haida Gwaii.

Inuit People descended from the Thule, who migrated into Canada's Arctic from Alaska about 1,000 years ago. The Inuit do not fall under the Indian Act, but are identified as an Aboriginal people under the Constitution Act, 1982.

Irish famine The great famine in Ireland that took place between 1845 and 1852 when the principal crop and source of food, the potato, was devastated by blight, causing widespread crop failures. Many Irish immigrated to Atlantic Canada, especially to Saint John, New Brunswick.

isostatic rebound The gradual uplifting of the earth's crust following the retreat of an ice sheet that, because of its weight, depressed the earth's crust. Also known as postglacial uplift.

James Bay and Northern Québec Agreement (JBNQA) A 1975 agreement between the Cree and Inuit of northern Québec and the federal and Québec governments that allowed the James Bay Project to proceed and provided the Indigenous peoples with specific rights and benefits.

just-in-time A system of manufacturing in which component parts are delivered from suppliers at the time required by the manufacturer, so that manufacturers do not bear the cost burden of building and maintaining large inventories.

Kativik Regional Government Administrative organization for Inuit in Nunavik. Formed in 1978 after the James Bay and Northern Québec Agreement and given the responsibility to deliver public services to its residents and to provide technical assistance to the 14 Inuit communities with Nunavik.

kimberlite Intrusions of igneous rocks in the earth's crust that take a funnel-like shape. Diamonds are sometimes found in these rocks.

knowledge-based economy Sector of post-industrial economy based on the use of inventions and scientific knowledge to produce new products and/or services, often in engineering, management, and computer technology fields.

Labrador Current Cold ocean current flowing south in the North Atlantic from Greenland and Labrador.

Lake Agassiz Largest glacial lake in North America that covered much of Manitoba, northwestern Ontario, and eastern Saskatchewan.

latitude A measure of distance north or south, in degrees and minutes, along imaginary lines that encircle the globe parallel to the equator.

light sweet crude The most highly valued crude oil, which because of its low level of sulphur has a pleasant smell and, more importantly, requires little processing to become gasoline, kerosene, and diesel fuel.

liquefied natural gas (LNG) A liquid form of natural gas chilled to $-162°C$. The cooling process, called liquefaction, reduces the volume to one six-hundredth of its original volume.

longitude The distance east or west from the prime meridian at Greenwich, England, an imaginary line that runs through both the North and South poles, as measured in degrees and minutes.

Lower Mainland A local term describing Vancouver and the surrounding area extending from the North Shore Mountains to the border with the United States and eastward to include the Fraser Valley.

Loyalists Colonists who supported the British during the American Revolution. About 40,000 American colonists who were loyal to Britain resettled in Canada, especially in Nova Scotia and Québec.

Makivik Corporation A non-profit organization owned by the Inuit of Nunavik and created in 1978 pursuant to the JBNQA. Its central mandate is to receive and manage the funds derived from the JBNQA.

Manifest Destiny The belief and subsequent political actions in nineteenth-century America that the United States, by divine right, should expand to the Pacific coast; in the view of some, this expansion was to include all of North America, thus incorporating Canada. The term was coined by journalist John L. O'Sullivan in 1845, in the context of the annexation of Texas and the Oregon Territory.

Manitoba Act of 1870 Legislative Act of Parliament that created Canada's fifth province. Also known as the "postage stamp" province, its initial territory only encompassed the Red River Colony.

manufacturing belt A contiguous industrial zone in North America noted for its manufacturing and heavy industry. In Canada, this belt extends from Windsor to Québec City, stretching across the Great Lakes and St Lawrence Lowlands.

marine air masses Large homogeneous bodies of air with moisture and temperature characteristics similar to the ocean where they originated. Marine air masses normally are moist and relatively mild in both winter and summer.

megaproject   A large-scale construction project, often related to resource extraction, that exceeds $1 billion and takes more than two years to complete.

metamorphic rocks   Rocks formed from igneous and sedimentary rocks by means of heat and pressure.

Métis   People of mixed biological and cultural heritage, usually either French–First Nations peoples or English– or Scottish–First Nations peoples.

modernization   A progressive transition from a traditional society to a modern one; underlying theme in Rostow's Stages of Economic Growth theory.

mortality rate   The number of deaths per 1,000 people in a given year; also called crude death rate.

muskeg   A wet, marshy area found in areas of poor drainage, such as the Hudson Bay Lowlands. Muskeg contains peat deposits.

Nalcor Energy Corporation   An energy Crown corporation created by the Newfoundland and Labrador government in 2007.

National Energy Program   A bold policy of the federal Liberal government in 1980 to keep Canadian oil prices lower than the rapidly rising world oil prices, provide manufacturers in Ontario and Québec with low-priced western oil, foster oil exploration in the Arctic, and increase federal government revenues from oil sales.

National Policy   A policy of high tariffs instituted in 1879 by the federal government of John A. Macdonald to insulate Canada's infant manufacturing industries from foreign competition and thus create a national industrial base.

Native settlements   *See* Indigenous settlements.

non-status Indians   Those of Amerindian ancestry who are not registered as Indians under the Indian Act.

nor'easters   Strong winds off the North Atlantic from the northeast that bring stormy weather.

North American Free Trade Agreement (NAFTA)   Trade agreement between Canada, the United States, and Mexico that came into effect in January 1994, forming the world's largest free trade area.

northern frontier   View of Canada's North as a place of resource wealth to be exploited.

northern lights   Aurora borealis, the visible portions of the dissipation of solar energy carried to the earth's magnetosphere by solar winds. The energy is visible, most commonly in higher latitudes, as rapidly moving light that appears as white, green, or red flashes or "curtains" of light across the sky.

Northwest Passage   Sea route(s) through the Arctic Ocean connecting the Atlantic and Pacific Oceans that can be traversed only in the summer.

North West Transportation Corridor   Stretching from Prince Rupert across northern BC and into Western Canada, the North West Transportation Corridor centres on the CN rail route and the Yellowhead Highway.

Nunavik   Homeland of the Inuit of northern Québec, with a semi-autonomous political unit known as the Kativik Regional Government.

oil prices   Either of two pricing systems for oil in North America. Tidewater cities use the Brent crude oil price while inland cities use the West Texas Intermediate (WTI) price.

Oregon Territory   Territory in the Pacific Northwest, the possession of which was disputed between the US and Great Britain. The Oregon Treaty of 1846 between the United States and Great Britain determined the boundary at the forty-ninth parallel but with Vancouver Island remaining within British North America.

orogeny   Mountain-building, a geologic process that takes place as a result of plate tectonics (movement of huge pieces of the earth's crust). The result is distinctive structural change to the earth's crust where mountains are formed.

orographic precipitation   Rain or snow created when air is forced up the side of a mountain, thereby cooling the air and causing condensation followed by precipitation.

orographic uplift   Air forced to rise and cool over mountains. If the cooling is sufficient, water vapour condenses into clouds and rain or snow occurs.

outsourcing   Arrangement by a firm to obtain some parts or services from other firms.

Paleo-Indians   Considered by archaeologists the first people of North America because they shared a common hunting culture, which was characterized by its uniquely designed fluted-point stone spearhead.

Palliser's Triangle   Area of short-grass natural vegetation in southern Alberta and Saskatchewan named after Captain John Palliser.

patterned ground   The natural arrangement of stones and pebbles in polygonal shapes found in the Arctic where continuous permafrost is subjected to frost-shattering as the principal erosion process.

Peace River Country   Aspen parkland region at the northern edge of agriculture in northwest Alberta and northeast British Columbia.

peneplain   A more or less level land surface caused by the wearing down of ancient mountains; represents an advanced stage of erosion.

periphery   The weakly developed area surrounding an industrial core; also known as a hinterland.

permafrost   Permanently frozen ground.

physiographic region   A large geographic area characterized by a single landform; for example, the Interior Plains.

physiography   A study of landforms, their underlying geology, and the processes that shape these landforms; geomorphology.

Pineapple Express   A strong and persistent flow of warm air from the southwest associated with heavy rainfall that originates in the waters adjacent to the Hawaiian Islands.

pingos   Hills or mounds that maintain an ice core and that are found in areas of permafrost.

placelessness   The reverse of "sense of place." Placeless landscapes have no distinguishing features and could be found in very many places. Examples are strip malls, cookie-cutter theme parks, and service stations.

plate tectonics   The study of movement in the seven large pieces or "plates" of the Earth's outermost layer, the lithosphere, as well as in smaller remnant plates, such as the Juan de Fuca plate south and west of Vancouver Island.

Pleistocene epoch   A minor division of the Geological Time Chart beginning nearly 2 million years ago and associated with several (likely, four) glacial advances interrupted by the retreat of these advances when comparatively warmer climate prevailed. The last advance, called the Wisconsin, ended about 11,000 years ago.

pluralistic society A society where small groups within the larger society are permitted to maintain their unique cultural identities; multiculturalism.

podzolic A soil order, often grey in colour, identified by poor drainage; associated with the boreal forest and the coastal rain forest and with climates that have large amounts of precipitation, such as the Pacific, Atlantic, and Subarctic climatic zones.

population density The total number of people in a geographic area divided by the land area; population per unit of land area.

population distribution The dispersal of a population within a geographic area.

population growth The rate at which a population is increasing or decreasing in a given period due to natural increase and net migration; often expressed as a percentage of the original or base population.

population increase The total population increase resulting from the interaction of births, deaths, and migration in a population in a given period of time.

Port Royal The settlement founded in the summer of 1605 on the north shore of the Annapolis Basin near the mouth of the Annapolis River by a French colonizing expedition led by Pierre du Gua de Monts and Samuel de Champlain.

postglacial uplift The gradual rising of the earth's crust following the retreat of an ice sheet that, because of its weight, depressed the earth's crust. Also known as isostatic rebound.

potash A general term for potassium salts. The most important potassium salt is sylvite (potassium chloride). Potassium (K) is a nutrient essential for plant growth.

Poundmaker An outstanding political leader of the Plains Cree who played a key role in setting the terms for Treaty No. 6.

primary products Goods derived from agriculture, fishing, logging, mining, and trapping; products of nature with no or little processing.

primary sector Economic sector involving the direct extraction/production of natural resources that includes agriculture, fishing, logging, mining, oil and gas, and trapping.

Provincial Agricultural Land Commission An independent British Columbia agency responsible for administering the province's land-use zone in favour of agriculture.

Provisional Government Government formed in 1869 by the Métis, under the leadership of Louis Riel, in order to negotiate the terms to permit the Red River Colony to join Canada as a province.

quaternary sector Knowledge-based economic activities that provide high-technology information services, such as computing, information and communication technologies, and research and development.

Québécois A term that has evolved from referring to French-speaking residents of Québec to meaning all residents of Québec.

Quiet Revolution A period in Québec during the Liberal government of Jean Lesage (1960–6) characterized by social, economic, and educational reforms and by the rebirth of pride and self-confidence among the French-speaking members of Québec society, which led to a resurgence of francophone ethnic nationalism.

rain shadow effect A dry area on the lee side of mountains where air masses descend, causing them to become warmer and drier.

rate of natural increase The surplus (or deficit) of births over deaths in a population per 1,000 people in a given time period.

recent immigrants Statistics Canada term that refers to landed immigrants who arrived in Canada within five years prior to a given census.

Red River migration British-instituted migration organized by the Hudson's Bay Company whereby perhaps as many as 1,000 settlers from Fort Garry travelled by horse-drawn wagons to Fort Vancouver in 1841 to shore up the British claim to the Oregon Territory.

region An area of the earth's surface defined by its distinctive human and/or natural characteristics. Boundaries between regions often are transition zones where the main characteristics of one region merge into those of a neighbouring region. Geographers use the concept of regions to study parts of the world.

regional consciousness Identification with a place or region, including the strong feeling of belonging to that space and the willingness to advocate for regional interests.

regional geography The study of the geography of regions and the interplay between physical and human geography, which results in an understanding of human society, its physical geographical underpinnings, and a sense of place.

regional identity Persons' association with a place or region and their sense of belonging to a collectivity.

regionalism The division of countries or areas of the earth into different natural/political/cultural parts.

regional service centres Urban places where economic functions are provided to residents living within the surrounding area.

relief A measure of elevation of the land relative to sea level, which is designated as zero; a relief map indicates elevation and/or topographic features, such as a mountain range, by different colours.

reserve Under the Indian Act, lands "held by her Majesty for the use and benefit of the bands for which they were set apart; and subject to this Act and to the terms of any treaty or surrender."

residential schools Boarding schools for Indigenous children and youth funded by the federal government and run by various churches from the 1880s to 1996 that effectively sought to acculturate Canada's First Peoples by taking away their cultural, language, and spiritual belief systems and replacing these with Euro-Canadian systems.

residual uplift The final stages of isostatic rebound.

resource frontier The perception of the Territorial North as a place of great mineral wealth that awaits development by outsiders.

resource town An urban place where a single economic activity focused on resource extraction (e.g., mining, logging, oil drilling) dominates the local economy; single-industry town. Also, a company town built near an isolated mine site to house the mine workers and their families.

restrained rebound The first stage of isostatic rebound.

restructure To make economic adjustments deemed necessary by fierce competition, whereby companies reduce costs by reducing the number of workers at their plants.

Robinson treaties   Two 1850 treaties signed between the Crown (Canada West) and the Ojibwa First Nations of Lake Superior and the Ojibwa Indians of Lake Huron. Under the terms of both agreements, the Crown secured an area of 52,400 square miles mostly in central and northern Ontario. For the first time, reserves were part of the agreement. The Crown paid the Ojibwa peoples a lump sum as well as an annual payment in perpetuity.

Scottish Highland clearances   Forced displacements of poor tenant farmers in the Scottish Highlands during the eighteenth and nineteenth centuries. Migration ensued, and in 1812 Scottish settlers arrived at Fort Garry to found Lord Selkirk's experimental colony. Most of the Scottish crofters who came to what would become Canada, perhaps 100,000, settled in Nova Scotia. The clearances were part of a process of change of estate land use from small farm leases to large-scale sheep herding.

scrip   Under the Manitoba Act of 1870, certificates issued by Ottawa to the Métis to settle their land claims and to allow them to obtain land. This scrip was issued to individuals and was redeemable in Dominion lands in Manitoba.

sea ice   Ice formed from ocean water. Types of sea ice include: (1) "fast ice" frozen along coasts and that extends out from land; (2) "pack ice," which is floating, consolidated sea ice detached from land; (3) the "ice floe," a floating chunk of sea ice that is less than 10 km (six miles) in diameter; and (4) the "ice field," a chunk of sea ice more than 10 km (six miles) in diameter.

Sea-to-Sky Highway   Highway that winds through the spectacular Coast Mountains, linking communities from West Vancouver to Whistler. Since rock slides occur frequently, the highway was widened and straightened to reduce the chances of rock slides and to improve safety and reliability for the 2010 Winter Olympic Games.

secondary sector   The sector of the economy involved in processing and transforming raw materials into finished goods; the manufacturing sector of an economy.

sedimentary rocks   Rocks formed from the layered accumulation in sequence of sediment deposited in the bottom of an ocean.

seigneurs   Members of the French elite—high-ranking officials, military officers, the nascent aristocracy—who were awarded land in New France by the French king. A seigneur was an estate owner who had peasants (habitants) to work his land.

sense of place   The special and often intense feelings that people have for the area where they live.

sex ratio   The ratio of males to females in a given population; usually expressed as the number of males for every 100 females.

shariah law   Islamic religious law based on the Koran, the Muslim holy book; under most interpretations, Islamic law gives men more rights than women in matters of inheritance, divorce, and child custody.

"soft" countries   See "hard" and "soft" countries.

softwood forest   The predominant forest in Canada. Softwood forests consist mainly of coniferous trees, characterized by needle-like foliage.

sovereignty-association   A concept designed by the Parti Québécois under the Lévesque government and employed in the 1980 referendum. This was based on the vision of Canada as consisting of two "equal" peoples. Sovereignty-association called for Québec sovereignty within a partnership with Canada based on an economic association.

specific land claims   Claims made by treaty Indians to rectify shortcomings in the original treaty agreement with a band or that seek to redress failure on the part of the federal government to meet the terms of the treaty. Many of these have involved the unilateral alienation of reserve land by the government.

sporadic permafrost   Pockets of permanently frozen ground mixed with large areas of unfrozen ground. Sporadic permafrost ranges from a trace of permanently frozen ground to an area having up to 30 per cent of its ground permanently frozen.

staples thesis   Harold Innis's idea that the history of Canada, especially its regional economic and institutional development, was linked to the discovery, utilization, and export of particular staple resources in Canada's vast frontier.

staples trap   The economic and social consequences on a region and its population following the exhaustion of its resources; the opposite outcome of the positive outcome of economic diversification anticipated in the staples thesis.

status (registered) Indians   Indigenous peoples who are registered as Indians under the Indian Act.

strata   Layers of sedimentary rock.

subsidence   A downward movement of the ground. Subsidence occurs in areas of permafrost when large blocks of ice within the ground melt, causing the material above to sink or collapse.

summer fallow   The farming practice of leaving land idle for a year or more to accumulate sufficient soil moisture to produce a crop or to restore soil fertility; summer fallowing is being replaced by continuous cropping.

super cycle   Concept based on two premises: (1) that demand will tend to outstrip supply and thus keep prices high; and (2) that in a global economic downturn, demand from industrializing countries will keep price declines to a minimum.

terraces   Old sea beaches left after the sea has receded; old flood plains created when streams or rivers cut downward to form new and lower flood plains. The old flood plain (now a terrace) is found along the sides of the stream or river.

terra nullius   The doctrine according to which European countries claimed legal right to ownership of the land occupied by First Nations peoples and Inuit because the land was not cultivated and lacked permanent settlements.

tertiary/quaternary sector   The economic sector engaged in services such as retailing, wholesaling, education, and financial and professional services; the quaternary sector, for which at present statistical data are not compiled, involves the collection, processing, and manipulation of information.

till   Unsorted glacial deposits.

topography   The shape of the surface of the land; contour maps, using isolines (contour lines), are one representation of topography and/or topographic features, with each line on the map representing the same elevation above sea level.

trade-off   Finding a balance between two things that cannot be had at the same time.

tragedy of the commons   The destruction of renewable resources that are not privately owned, such as fisheries and forests.

Trans-Pacific Partnership   Twelve countries (Canada, United States, Mexico, Australia, New Zealand, Peru, Chile, Singapore, Vietnam, Malaysia, Japan, and Brunei) that negotiated a free trade agreement. The agreement was effectively voided before ratification following the 2016 US presidential election when the President-elect reiterated his campaign promise to reject the TPP.

treaty Indians Aboriginal people who are descendants of First Nations peoples who signed a numbered treaty and who benefit from the rights described in the treaty. All treaty Indians are status Indians, but not all status Indians are treaty Indians.

treaty rights Specific rights that apply only to the First Nation(s) that signed the treaty in question. While no two treaties are identical, the list of rights always included land (reserves). These rights are protected in the Constitution Act.

Tyrrell Sea Prehistoric Hudson Bay as the Laurentide Ice Sheet receded. Its extent was considerably greater than that of present-day Hudson Bay because the land had been depressed by the weight of the ice sheet.

underemployment Generally, workers who are employed, but not in the desired capacity, whether in terms of compensation, hours, or level of education, skill, and experience. In this text, "underemployment" refers to persons in small communities where the very few jobs are already filled and, because these potential workers are aware that no job opportunities exist, they do not seek jobs elsewhere.

unemployment Lack of paid work, but this term and statistics based on it measure only those who are seeking paid employment.

upgrader A processing plant that breaks large hydrocarbon molecules (such as bitumen) into smaller ones by increasing the hydrogen-to-carbon ratio. The product is supplied to refineries, which will process it into gasoline, jet fuel, diesel, propane, and butane.

urban areas Communities with economic and social functions that differentiate them from rural places; the common practice of defining urban population is by a specified size that assumes the presence of urban economic and social functions. Statistics Canada considers all places with a combination of a population of 1,000 or more and a population density of at least 400 per km^2 to be urban areas. People living in urban areas make up the urban population. People living outside of urban areas are considered rural residents and, by definition, constitute the rural population.

value-added industry Manufacturing that increases the value of primary (staple) goods.

weathering The decomposition of rock and particles in situ.

western alienation Feeling on the part of those in Western Canada and BC—derived from past government actions and a natural periphery response to the core—that they have little influence on federal policy and that Central Canada controls the government in Ottawa.

Western Sedimentary Basin Within the geological structure of the Interior Plains, normally flat sedimentary strata that are bent into a basin-like shape. These basins often contain petroleum deposits.

winter roads Temporary ice roads over muskeg, lakes, and rivers built during the winter to provide ground transportation for freight and travel to remote northern communities and work sites.

Websites

CHAPTER 1

www.youtube.com/watch?v=NuZ6wWESCVg
Laurence C. Smith imagines the effect of climate change on the world of 2050. This YouTube video is based on his book *The World in 2050: Four Forces Shaping Civilization's Northern Future.*

http://news.nationalpost.com/news/canada/the-giant-flaw-in-canadian-maps-you-never-noticed-mapmakers-keep-pretending-we-own-the-north-pole
In 1907, Senator Pascal Poirier argued that Canada should claim lands and seas to the North Pole based on the sector theory. Accordingly, the 141° west longitude extends from Yukon to the North Pole. However, this boundary is not recognized in the international community. Instead, the Exclusive Economic Zone forms the outermost sea boundary to a maximum of 200 nautical miles.

geography.about.com/od/politicalgeography/a/coreperiphery.htm
The origins and transformation of the core/periphery theory are presented here.

http://staff/wwu/edu/stef/salish_sea.html.
Within Canada's six regions, smaller spatial areas exist that enrich the fabric of each region. One is the Indigenous Salish Sea.

CHAPTER 2

www.youtube.com/watch?v=6ZAuRpK4tkc
NASA illustrates the loss of the polar ice cap over time.

earthquakescanada.nrcan.gc.ca/histor/20th-eme/1949-eng.php
Details on the 1949 earthquake off Haida Gwaii.

www.theglobeandmail.com/technology/technology-video/video-carbon-capture-facility-aims-to-transform-carbon-dioxide-into-fuel/article28028038/
Can technological innovations halt global warming?

http://news.nationalpost.com/full-comment/canada-russias-toxic-waste-dump
Russia uses Baffin Bay as dumping ground for toxic materials from its space program.

www.cbc.ca/news/technology/polar-bear-populations-can-be-monitored-by-satellite-1.2710341
Satellite technology counts polar bears.

http://news.nationalpost.com/news/canada/the-beast-is-alive-how-the-fire-that-tried-to-destroy-fort-mcmurray-is-still-burning-near-the-albertasaskatchewan-border
Columnist Tristin Hopper reports on "The Beast" wildfire going underground.

www.theglobeandmail.com/news/british-columbia/tug-sinking-shows-oil-spill-response-resources-inadequate-transport-minister/article32694781/
Oil spill in BC waters demonstrates both the risk of oil spills and the lack of preparedness by federal marine operations.

CHAPTER 3

www.american-indians.net
North American Aboriginal culture regions are found at this site.

www.youtube.com/watch?v=OUwcDIyv_7U
Short historical film—"Scientific Trip into the Great Arctic"—of expedition under direction of Captain J.E. Bernier that sailed from Québec to Pond Inlet on northern Baffin Island in the summer of 1922.

http://geogratis.gc.ca/api/en/nrcan-rncan/ess-sst/c9bc8461-8893-11e0-baff-6cf049291510.html
The Hudson's Bay Company undertook a census of Aboriginal peoples in 1822. The *Atlas of Canada* has produced a map and accompanying text describing this very detailed census.

http://geogratis.gc.ca/api/en/nrcan-rncan/ess-sst/?q=territorial+evolution atlas.nrcan.gc.ca/sitefrancais/english/maps/historical/territorialevolution/territorial_animation.gif/image_view
Maps that illustrate the territorial evolution of Canada and an animated version of Canada's territorial development are found here.

faculty.marianopolis.edu/c.belanger/quebechistory/events/quiet.htm
An account of the Quiet Revolution in Québec.

archives.cbc.ca/politics/federal_politics/topics/1891/
CBC Digital Archives provides a close look at "separation anxiety" in Canada associated with the 1995 referendum.

www.mhs.mb.ca/docs/pageant/13/selkirksettlement1.shtml
The Manitoba Historical Society has documented Lord Selkirk's land grant of 1811.

http://en.wikipedia.org/wiki/Haldimand_Proclamation
The Haldimand Proclamation.

www.llbc.leg.bc.ca/public/PubDocs/bcdocs/322107/north_east_coal_facts.pdf
Boom and bust: the Northeast Coal Project.

CHAPTER 4

www.cbc.ca/history/EPISCONTENTSE1EP14CH3PA3LE.html
CBC provides an account of the internment of Japanese Canadians living in BC.

www.youtube.com/watch?v=yGd764YU9yc
Gord Downie's *The Secret Path*, the animated version of the graphic novel by Downie and artist Jeff Lemire, which aired on CBC television on 23 October 2016, the fiftieth anniversary of 12-year-old Chanie Wenjack's death. The young Indigenous boy fled from a residential

school in Kenora and died of exposure along the CN rail line as he sought to walk hundreds of kilometres to his home at Ogoki Post on the Marten Falls Reserve. The video includes opening and closing sequences of Downie visiting Chanie's sisters on the reserve in Northern Ontario, where Downie went right after completing his final tour with the Tragically Hip.

www.theglobeandmail.com/opinion/why-black-canadians-are-facing-us-style-problems/article30939514/
Columnist Doug Saunders describes the nature of discrimination faced by black Canadians.

www.idlenomore.ca
Official website of the grassroots Indigenous movement that emerged in late 2012.

www.statcan.gc.ca/daily-quotidien/121218/dq121218f-eng.htm?HPA
Statistics Canada's population estimates are provided quarterly.

www.theglobeandmail.com/news/toronto/the-quest-to-understand-kensington-market-torontos-weird-little-island/article32302041/
Does Toronto's Kensington Market fit Florida's image of a cultural diverse city?

www.youtube.com/watch?v=HJooje7taXU
Short video on effort to improve education for a First Nation in Northern Ontario.

CHAPTER 5

www.theglobeandmail.com/report-on-business/economy/poloz-expected-to-mark-down-recovery-hold-line-on-rates/article32423831/
Bank of Canada sees rough waters ahead for Canada's economy.

www.theglobeandmail.com/report-on-business/give-fuel-cells-a-chance-says-toyota-canada-president-larry-hutchinson/article32587525/
Discussion of the wave of the future: technology and electric cars lead to sharply reduced greenhouse gas emissions.

www.theglobeandmail.com/opinion/on-energy-pm-needs-to-lead-with-his-head-not-heart/article31727993/
Columnist Lawrence Martin offers his ideas on the controversial topic of pipelines.

www.theglobeandmail.com/report-on-business/top-business-stories/why-the-spike-in-ontario-electricity-prices-is-so-shocking/article31047552/
Fossil fuels provide the world with low-cost energy but they also emit greenhouse gases. Coal is the worst offender. Ontario has shut down its coal-burning electric generating plants and subsidized green sources of electricity. The result so far is much higher electrical rates for Ontario consumers.

www.theglobeandmail.com/report-on-business/rob-commentary/defence-rd-key-to-canadas-innovation-solution/article32085597/
Is defence spending key to creating an innovative Canada?

CHAPTER 6

www.statcan.gc.ca/kits-trousses/projet-cyber-project/manufact2-eng.htm
Students can test the premise: Ontario and Québec were the Canadian leaders in manufacturing at the time of Confederation and they maintained that dominance into the twentieth-first century.

www.theglobeandmail.com/report-on-business/economy/economic-insight/defining-canadas-place-in-an-era-of-digital-globalization/article32653280/
Advanced economy employs digital techniques.

www.nationalpost.com/m/story.html?id=1100168
Good public policy? Ottawa and Ontario dole out $4 billion to Chrysler and General Motors.

www.theglobeandmail.com/report-on-business/national-bank-of-canada-cuts-600-jobs-takes-175-million-charge/article32542536/
Technology and banks: another sign of a digital attack on jobs.

www.theglobeandmail.com/report-on-business/rob-magazine/how-waterloo-became-a-world-class-robotics-hub/article29784283/
Waterloo becomes a robotics hub of innovation.

www.aadnc-aandc.gc.ca/eng/1100100016337/1100100016338
Indigenous and Northern Affairs Canada offers a chronology of the Six Nations land dispute.

http://globalnews.ca/news/2664824/youtube-space-opens-toronto-studio-how-budding-creators-can-turn-youtube-into-a-career/
Article and short video on YouTube Space Toronto, a 3,500-square-foot facility for Canadian online creators opened in 2016 at George Brown College School of Design.

CHAPTER 7

www.theglobeandmail.com/report-on-business/ottawa-pledges-long-term-support-for-bombardiers-growth-prospects/article32481389/
Technology in Québec City—Québec Metro High Tech Park.

www.theglobeandmail.com/report-on-business/ottawa-pledges-long-term-support-for-bombardiers-growth-prospects/article32481389/
Despite Bombardier's troubles, Ottawa pledges support—but no money so far.

www.theglobeandmail.com/report-on-business/mega-brands-toy-maker-pushes-for-more-production-in-montreal/article31400900/
Toymaker Mega Brands, based in Montréal, wants to consolidate its production by bringing back its operations from China.

www.theglobeandmail.com/report-on-business/rob-commentary/quebec-hydro-project-northern-pass-powers-new-hampshire-campaign/article32550550/
Hydro-Québec's exports to New England run into an environmental challenge.

www.theglobeandmail.com/report-on-business/rob-commentary/canadas-dairy-producers-are-waking-up-to-the-realities-of-global-trade/article32279338/
The Canada–EU Comprehensive Economic and Trade Agreement (CETA) poses problems for Québec's dairy and cheese industries.

www.greatlakes-seaway.com/en/
Official site of the Great Lakes–St Lawrence Seaway system.

www.canadiangeographic.ca
History of the St Lawrence Seaway plus archival photographs and a tour of the seaway.

CHAPTER 8

http://news.nationalpost.com/news/businesses-drawn-to-saskatchewans-agriculture-sector?__lsa=9217-caa6.
Saskatchewan is the breadbasket of Canada, exporting its crops to world markets. But in recent decades, value-added processing is taking place with canola, lentils, and others crops.

www.theglobeandmail.com/report-on-business/top-business-stories/from-auto-crisis-to-oil-shock-windsor-rides-high-as-calgary-laid-low/article32346613/
Calgary and Windsor reflect the economic downturn in Alberta and upturn in Ontario.

www.theglobeandmail.com/report-on-business/economy/transalta-faces-winds-of-change-as-it-moves-towards-post-coal-future/article30745943/
Alberta follows Ontario to move away from coal-burning generating plants.

www.youtube.com/watch?v=j6zBun7zZso
Can carbon capture work?

www.saskmining.ca/commodity_info/Commodities/1/potash.html
The history of potash mining in Saskatchewan.

www.cbc.ca/edmonton/features/dirtyoil/
CBC Edmonton: "Alberta Oil Sands: Black Gold or Black Eye?"

www.youtube.com/watch?v=oWPnZv5TdYE
Pipeline technology.

CHAPTER 9

www.youtube.com/watch?v=eBirhxxA5Ro
BC launches $100 million tech fund.

www.theglobeandmail.com/news/british-columbia/bcs-foreign-buyer-tax-will-turn-political-liability-into-revenue-bonanza/article31112032/
Vancouver house prices reached record levels. Then the BC government approved of a tax on foreign home buyers for Greater Vancouver.

www.theglobeandmail.com/opinion/pipeline-protests-next-stop-vancouver/article32670440/
The prospects of the Kinder Morgan pipeline expansion reaching Burnaby may result in the largest and most spirited protest in Canada.

www.theglobeandmail.com/news/british-columbia/bc-oil-spill-shows-what-can-go-wrong-under-difficult-conditions/article32588037/
Did the National Energy Board underestimate the risk of an oil spill in BC waters?

www.theglobeandmail.com/report-on-business/industry-news/energy-and-resources/federal-government-to-weigh-in-on-trans-mountain-pipeline-extension/article32671559/
BC's bitumen pipeline to Vancouver—a final resolution to the duty to consult quandary?

www.th.gov.bc.ca/PacificGateway/documents/PGS_Action_Plan_043006.pdf
Pacific Gateway Strategy Action Plan.

CHAPTER 10

www.theglobeandmail.com/news/politics/atlantic-premiers-ottawa-announce-plan-to-boost-immigration/article30739787/
Can the three-year plan to direct immigrants to Atlantic Canada work to improve its economic and population situation?

www.theglobeandmail.com/report-on-business/energy-east-pipeline-will-happen-but-taking-too-long-arthur-irving/article32467000/
Energy East pipeline good or bad for the Maritimes?

www.eleanorbeaton.com/userfiles/file/Chatelaine%20-%20Oil%20Patch%20Widows.pdf
"No Man's Land"—story of Newfoundland and commuting.

www.theglobeandmail.com/news/national/premier-dwight-ball-paints-dire-picture-of-newfoundlands-economic-future/article32671914/
Newfoundland hits tough times.

www.offshore-technology.com/projects/hibernia/
Hibernia, Jeanne d'Arc Basin, and its technology.

www.sysco.ns.ca/history.htm
The history of the steel plant at Cape Breton.

www.nalcorenergy.com/Lower-Churchill-Project.asp
The Muskrat Falls hydroelectric project has the potential to create an Atlantic Canada electric power network but at a great cost.

www.youtube.com/watch?v=rnS5OkuFt5M
In 2014, Shell's Shelburne Basin Venture Exploration Project marks the first time 3D wide azimuth (WAZ) seismic technology was used in Canada. This technology provides much clearer data in water depths of 1,500 to 3,500 m.

CHAPTER 11

www.youtube.com/watch?v=lWg-fxpPSBs
Nunavut culture—Nunavut Arctic College at Cambridge Bay.

www.mmg.com/en/Our-Operations/Development-projects/Izok-Corridor.aspx
Before commodity prices fell, a Chinese company, MMG, proposed to develop the vast lead/zinc deposit in the Izok Corridor and ship the ore to China through the Northwest Passage.

http://news.nationalpost.com/news/world/russia-submits-claim-for-vast-arctic-seabed-territories-at-united-nations
Russia flexes its muscles with Denmark in claiming the Arctic seabed.

www.theglobeandmail.com/opinion/why-its-worth-it-for-canada-to-talk-to-the-russian-bear/article32429843/
Geopolitics at play: Canada to meet with Russia over Arctic Sea boundaries.

www.theglobeandmail.com/news/national/cruise-ship-looks-to-make-clean-journey-through-northwest-passage/article31478675/
Arctic tourism with Crystal Serenity: good or bad?

www.arctic-council.org/index.php/en/
Formation and mandate of the Arctic Council, as well as Canada's role in the Arctic Council.

www.statsnwt.ca/
The Bureau of Statistics of the Northwest Territories provides not only a wide variety of statistical data but also links to Yukon and Nunavut statistical data.

CHAPTER 12

www.theglobeandmail.com/report-on-business/economy/wto-cuts-2016-world-trade-growth-forecast-to-17-per-cent/article32071378/
World trade takes a hit—it's no longer a "rose garden" for continued growth.

www.foreignaffairs.com/articles/united-states/2016-10-17/populism-march0/7/3/8/7/pages73870/p73870-1.php
Populism on the march: nationalism trumps global states.

www.theglobeandmail.com/report-on-business/rob-commentary/ceta-puts-canadas-trade-debate-to-rest-once-and-for-all/article32620448/
Will CETA change the direction of Canada's international trade?

www.theglobeandmail.com/report-on-business/rob-commentary/canadians-need-to-understand-the-importance-of-oil-export-pipelines/article32492792/
Why are pipelines to tidewater so important for Canada's economic growth?

Notes

CHAPTER 1

1. In the late nineteenth century, geographers believed that the physical environment determined human affairs. That position was rejected, although geographers recognize that the environment does exert a strong influence on the nature of human activities in various regions of the world. Students can find a more complete discussion of environmental determinism and other philosophical options' in geography, including possibilism, positivism, humanism, and Marxism, in William Norton, *Human Geography*, 7th edn (Toronto: Oxford University Press, 2010). The writings of most geographers reflect one or some combination of these philosophical positions. The core/periphery model, for example, sprang from Marxist scholarship. Because of the model's powerful spatial implications, other scholars holding different philosophical positions have modified this theory by removing its economically deterministic character. Instead, they accept that external forces (such as global institutions like the World Trade Organization) and internal forces (such as federal–provincial agreements like equalization payments) can modify the impact of the physical environment on regional development. Hinterlands, therefore, are not locked into a single outcome because of their physical geography.

2. While Canadians and Americans occupy the same continent, historic events and geographic differences laid the foundation for the emergence of two different societies within one continent. These differences are found in many aspects of the two societies. Each country has a different approach to gun control legislation, multiculturalism, and a national health-care system. As a result of these and other differences, some scholars believe that Canadians are more trusting of their governments and more tolerant of social diversity than are Americans (Hartz, 1995; Lipset, 1990; Lemon, 1996; Saul, 1997).

3. A group of Muslim women led by Najat Boughaba visited the town council to present a fuller picture of Islam and its customs. "There was a real exchange," Najat Boughaba told Radio-Canada. "There were people who reached out to us. I really think our visit to Hérouxville benefited both sides" (CBC News, 2007). Najat Boughaba was struck by how little the townspeople knew about Islam and its customs. Following this exchange, the town council in Hérouxville amended its immigrant code of conduct to remove references to "no stoning of women in public" and "no female circumcision." The town council had designed the code "to inform the new arrivals that the lifestyle they left behind in their birth country cannot be brought here with them and they would have to adapt to their new social identity" (Hamilton, 2007: A7). In fact, the "code" clearly targeted Middle Eastern, North African, and South Asian immigrants whose cultural practices did not always sit well with the old-timers. The resulting firestorm within Québec society caused the provincial government to launch the Bouchard-Taylor Commission to address the issue of "accommodation practices related to cultural differences in response to public discontent concerning reasonable accommodation." On 8 February 2007, Québec Premier Jean Charest announced the establishment of the Bouchard-Taylor Commission, headed by sociologist Gérard Bouchard and philosopher Charles Taylor, formally known as the Consultation Commission on Accommodation Practices Related to Cultural Differences, in response to public discontent concerning reasonable accommodation. The Commission's report received mixed reviews and some felt that the Commission was "unreasonably accommodating."

4. In the early 1990s, the Ontario government allowed Catholic and Jewish faith-based arbitrations to settle family disputes, such as divorce, custody, and inheritances, outside of the Ontario court system—if the parties involved agreed. In 2004, the Islamic Institute of Civil Justice applied to establish its own faith-based arbitration panel under the Ontario Arbitration Act. Reaction from the public was swift, and strong opposition was voiced by officials from both the Muslim community and women's organizations: the Muslim Canadian Congress, the Canadian Council of Muslim Women, and the National Association of Women and the Law vigorously opposed such a move because, in their judgment, women are not treated equally to men. In September 2005, Ontario Premier Dalton McGuinty rejected the request from the Islamic Institute of Civil Justice and, at the same time, rescinded the operation of Catholic and Jewish tribunals.

5. Yet, by their very nature, theories must simplify the real world. In doing so, when applied to actual regions, they often lose touch with the complexity and variety of economic, political, and social forces at play. Added to this shortcoming, economic theories are based on past events, which means that, as the world changes, they must either be adjusted to fit the new economic circumstances or be replaced by more robust hypotheses.

CHAPTER 2

1. Canadians have various visions of themselves, their region, and their country. For the most part, these visions are rooted in the physical nature and historical experiences that have affected Canada and its regions. For example, people see Canada as a northern country because of its location in North America and because of its climates, which are often noted for long, cold winters. Louis-Edmond Hamelin's concept of nordicity exemplifies the impact of "northernness" from a geographer's perspective. Hamelin (1979) provides a measure of "northernness" according to five geographic zones—Extreme North, Far North, Middle North, Near North, and Ecumene (southern Canada). Songwriters, too, have been intrigued by Canada's northern nature, and well-known writers, from Jack London and Robert Service to Margaret Atwood, Pierre Berton, and Farley Mowat, have written about the North and, in doing so, have etched out another parameter of Canadian identity.

2. The Champlain Sea covered Anticosti Island and the northern tip of the island of Newfoundland. For the purposes of this text, the eastern extent of this physiographic region ends just east of Québec City.

3. The distance between latitudes is almost constant at 111 km. On the other hand, the distance between longitudes varies from 111 km to nearly zero because of the spherical shape of the earth, which causes longitude lines to become closer and closer towards the North Pole and South Pole. The distance between the equator (0°) and 1°N is approximately 111 km and between 89°N and the North Pole (90°N) is nearly zero.

4. The mean annual temperature of a location on the earth's surface is a measure of the energy balance at that point. Solar energy is the source of heat for the earth, and this energy is returned to the atmosphere in a variety of ways. Therefore, a global energy balance exists. However, there are regional energy surpluses and deficits in different parts of the world. For example, the Arctic has an energy deficit, while the tropics have a surplus. These energy differences drive the global atmospheric and oceanic circulation systems. When the mean annual temperature is below zero Celsius, it indicates that an energy deficit exists.

CHAPTER 3

1. Under the terms of the British North America Act, the Dominion of Canada was composed of four provinces (Ontario, Québec, New Brunswick, and Nova Scotia). Modelled after the British parliamentary and monarchical system of government, the newly formed country had a Parliament made up of three elements: the head of government (a governor general who represented the monarch), an upper house (the Senate), and a lower house (the House of Commons). This Act was modified several times to accommodate Canada's evolving political needs and its gradual movement to independent nationhood. The patriation of Canada's Constitution in 1982 removed the last vestige of Canada's political dependence on the United Kingdom, although Canada still recognizes the British monarch as its symbolic head.

   The British North America Act was based on the highly centralized government of the United Kingdom in the 1860s. However, this Act assigned specific powers to the provinces in order to satisfy Québec's demand for control over its culture. The Canadian political system that emerged, therefore, allowed for regionalized politics. For example, political parties in the House of Commons sometimes serve regional interests. In the 1920s, the Progressive Party represented the concerns of farmers in Western Canada, while the pro-independence Bloc Québécois, which was formed in 1990, not only serves the interests of Québec but is also active in the separatist movement. Furthermore, while the House of Commons is based on the principle of representation by population, Senate membership is based on the principle of equal regional representation. However, because senators are appointed by the Prime Minister and not elected by the people in the different regions of the country, the Senate fails to provide a regional counterweight to the House of Commons. With the election of the Justin Trudeau Liberal government in October 2015, the Senate currently is in the process of becoming a more non-partisan upper chamber.

2. A group of Irish Americans, known as Fenians, was struggling for Irish independence. They believed that attacking British possessions in North America would advance the cause of a free Ireland. Between 1866 and 1870, the Fenians launched several raids across the border into Canada. The United States did not encourage these raids and eventually forced the Fenians to disband. By the end of the American Civil War, Anglo-American relations again were strained because of Britain's tacit support for the Confederacy during the war. For that reason, the United States withdrew from the Reciprocity Treaty in 1866. This treaty, a free trade agreement between British North America and the United States, began in 1854; the subsequent years were prosperous ones for British North America, and the end of this agreement was a factor in the Province of Canada seeking an alternative economic union with the other British colonies in North America.

3. Progress at the community level often comes from local leaders and special circumstances that provide opportunities to engage in business opportunities rather than from the national lobby organizations. The explanation is simple: the national organizations are concerned about issues that affect all of their members, such as funding and control of education. Local governments, whether band or village councils, can make decisions that affect their local community. Some Indigenous communities have already moved in that direction. The Métis village of Pinehouse receives annual payments from its impact benefit agreement with Cameco, a uranium company; Onion Lake Cree First Nation owns and manages its oil fields that are located on its reserve; and the Whitecap Dakota First Nation is a centre of tourism based on its casino and world-class golf course. Other communities have also embraced business opportunities and their residents continue to practise their traditional values.

4. After the defeat of the French by the British in 1763, Pontiac, the Odawa chief in the Ohio Valley, led a successful uprising against the British. By capturing the forts in the Ohio Territory, he exposed Britain's precarious hold on this region, which the British had just obtained from the French. However, Pontiac and his followers could not hold these forts against the British because, with French forces driven back to France, Pontiac had no source of ammunition and muskets. He concluded that his best move would be to make peace with Britain. The British came to the same conclusion, though for other reasons. Without the help of Pontiac and the other chiefs in this region, Britain would lose control over these lands. Britain therefore had to form an alliance with them. With that objective in mind, George III announced an important concession to these Indigenous peoples in the Royal Proclamation of 1763, namely, that the King recognized them as valued allies and that the land they used to hunt and trap was "Indian land" within the British Empire. In 1783, the American revolt against Great Britain ended with an American victory, which opened the lands west of the Appalachian Mountains to settlement by New Englanders and, at the same time, ended the dream of a vast "Indian land" within the British Empire.

5. Governments like to change departmental names—to put their personal stamp on the government bureaucracy and its direction soon after they assume office, to indicate a directional shift in policy in a certain issue-area once in office, or as part of a reorganization of departments and lines of responsibility. This has been the case with what is today called Indigenous and Northern Affairs Canada. It began as the colonial Indian Department, after Confederation was

the Indian Branch within the Department of the Secretary of State and then within the Department of Interior, and in 1880 became the full-fledged Department of Indian Affairs, though with a close linkage to Interior. In the middle years of the twentieth century it was a branch within Mines and Resources and then within Citizenship and Immigration. In 1966 it became the Department of Indian Affairs and Northern Development (DIAND) and more recently was renamed Aboriginal Affairs and Northern Development Canada. Finally, when the Liberals took office in November 2015 the department was renamed Indigenous and Northern Affairs Canada (INAC), a reflection of the contemporary preference for "Indigenous" over "Aboriginal" among its constituency and perhaps, as well, to de-emphasize a view of the North as a hinterland to be exploited for "development."

6. The Manitoba Act of 1870 recognized the legal status of farms and other lands occupied by the Métis as "fee simple" private property. The lands allotted to the Métis were distributed after 1875, but much of the scrip land was sold and then occupied by non-Métis. For more on this subject, see Tough (1996: ch. 6). Flanagan (1991) argues that the federal government of the day, while often slow in settling the Métis claims, did not act in bad faith. Taking the opposite position, Sprague (1988) claims that the Métis were victims of a deliberate conspiracy by the federal government to prevent a Métis land base in Manitoba. Milne (1995) provides a summary of this controversy. The 2013 Supreme Court of Canada ruling stated that the federal government, over 140 years earlier, "acted with persistent inattention and failed to act diligently" in regard to the land grant provision of the Manitoba Act of 1870, and emphasized that "repeated mistakes and inaction . . . persisted for more than a decade" (CBC News, 2013b).

7. The original Magna Carta goes far back in history to 1215, when King John of England was forced to sign a charter known as the Magna Carta. In this charter, he promised to consult regularly with the country's nobles before collecting new taxes, and to stop interfering in affairs of the Church.

8. While the French language was not recognized by the Québec Act, 1774, the Governor made use of the French language in conducting his business with local officials. For example, the judges appointed by the Governor had to know both languages in order to facilitate the business of the court. In short, while English was the official language of British North America, the British colony of Québec functioned in both the French and English languages.

9. Riel is considered both a Father of Confederation and a traitor to the country. Born in the Red River Colony in 1844, he studied for the priesthood at the Collège de Montréal. The founder of Manitoba and the central figure in both the Red River Rebellion (1869–70) and the Northwest Rebellion (1885), he was captured shortly after the Battle of Batoche, where the Métis forces were defeated. After a trial in Regina, the jury found Riel guilty of treason but recommended clemency. Appeals were made to Manitoba's Court of Queen's Bench and to the Judicial Committee of the Privy Council. Both appeals were dismissed. A final appeal went to the federal cabinet, but the government of John A. Macdonald wanted Riel executed. Riel was hanged in Regina on 16 November 1885. His body was interred in the cemetery at the Cathedral of St Boniface in Manitoba.

Riel's execution has had a lasting effect on Canada. In Québec, French Canadians felt betrayed by the Conservative government and federalism: Canada's French-speaking population believed they could not count on the federal government to look after French-Canadian interests. It was also a blow against a francophone presence in the West. In Ontario, Riel's death satisfied the anti-Catholic and anti-French majority. In the West, Riel's hanging resulted in the marginalization of both the Métis and Indigenous tribes, especially those who participated in the uprising.

10. An example is the political fallout from the Québec referendum in 1995. Prime Minister Chrétien sought to fulfill his verbal promises made in the closing days before the referendum vote. In a House of Commons resolution, the federal government proposed three concessions to Québec: (1) a veto over constitutional changes; (2) recognition of Québec's distinct society status; and (3) devolution of federal powers to Québec. In the case of the veto, Ottawa was prepared to "lend" its constitutional veto to Québec, Ontario, Atlantic Canada, and the four western provinces. Not only was the federal government committing itself to seeking permission from these four regions before putting its stamp of approval on any constitutional change, it was also recognizing that Canada consisted of four major regions. The premiers of Alberta and British Columbia reacted negatively to that concept of regionalism. British Columbians in particular saw this arrangement as another example of Ottawa's failure to recognize the west coast as a "distinct and powerful" part of Canada. The federal government retreated from this issue and quickly amended its resolution to extend the veto to British Columbia. In December 1995, this resolution passed in both the House of Commons and the Senate. It then became the law of the land that Canada consists of five major regions!

11. Circumstances may force Ottawa to make a decision that is unpopular to some provinces but popular in others. In 1982, the patriation of the British North America Act, renamed the Constitution Act, 1867, was such a decision. The Constitution Act, 1982, which was entrenched at the same time, added to the British North America Act in several ways, but without a doubt the most important addition has been the Charter of Rights and Freedoms. These rights and freedoms strengthen the rights of individuals. Prime Minister Pierre Trudeau, who conceived of society as an agglomeration of individuals (not collectivities), whose rights accrued to them as individuals, saw the Charter as protecting individuals from governments that try to suppress individual rights. At the same time, the Charter changed the role of the Supreme Court of Canada, which has become more proactive with the adjudication of Charter cases, notably in regard to recognizing the collective rights of Indigenous groups.

CHAPTER 4

1. The debate between tolerance and intolerance is one of the great debates of our times. Canada, like many other countries, is a pluralistic, multicultural nation. It can move forward only by respecting the norm of tolerance. That does not mean that everything must be tolerated—a civilized society has no choice but to condemn practices that cause harm to others and injure citizens or undermine the fabric of peaceful coexistence. But it means the basic rule must be tolerance. Preserving that tolerance is grounded in respect for

the innate human dignity of each person. It compels us to cultivate and sustain inclusive institutions and attitudes. And it demands an unwavering commitment to the rule of law.

2. "Race," unlike ethnicity, is based on physical characteristics. Racial types are frequently assigned a set of social characteristics, which is known as "stereotyping." Sociologists define "race" as the socially constructed classification of persons into categories on the basis of real or imagined physical characteristics such as skin colour. Others consider "race" a means of creating major divisions of humankind on the basis of distinct physical characteristics.

3. When Baltej Singh Dhillon was accepted into the RCMP, he faced a choice—serving his country or wearing his turban. He chose to fight for his religious rights. Due to his effort, in 1990 the federal government finally removed the ban preventing Sikhs in the RCMP from wearing turbans.

4. French and English, as the official languages, represent the traditional duality of Canadian society. With the establishment of the Province of Canada in 1841, the relationship flowered into a partnership with English-speaking Canada West and French-speaking Canada East sharing political power. In 1867, the British North America Act (section 133) established that both French and English "may be used by any Person in the Debates of the Houses of Parliament of Canada and of the Houses of the Legislature of Quebec," as well as in federal courts, but it was not until the Official Languages Act of 1969 that French truly began to be entrenched in the institutions of Canadian society. The assignment of education to the provinces in the BNA Act (section 93) and the stipulation that Roman Catholic (i.e., francophone) schools had equal standing with Protestant (i.e., anglophone) schools ensured that French would retain a dominant position in Québec, at least for the time being.

5. In 1974, the Québec Liberal government passed Bill 22 (Loisur la langue officielle), which made French the language of government and the workplace. In 1977, the Parti Québécois government introduced a much stronger language measure in the form of Bill 101 (Charte de la langue française). This legislation eliminated English as one of the official languages of Québec and required the children of all newcomers to Québec to be educated in French. Four years later, Bill 178 required all commercial signs to use only French. The French language has made modest gains outside of Québec. In 1969, New Brunswick passed an Official Languages Act, which gave equal status, rights, and privileges to English and French, and the federal Parliament passed the Official Languages Act, which declared the equal status of English and French in Parliament and in the Canadian public service.

CHAPTER 5

1. Trade disputes remain troublesome. In April 2009, for example, the United States rekindled the softwood lumber dispute by imposing a 10 per cent tariff on lumber from four provinces that, according to Washington, exported more to the US than the 2006 lumber agreement specified. The Free Trade Agreement, which was replaced by the North American Free Trade Agreement, really means freer trade rather than free trade. As we have seen, three trade agreements—the Auto Pact (1965; nullified in 2001), the FTA (1989), and NAFTA (1994)—led to a realignment of the Canadian economy so that it was more thoroughly integrated with the North

American economy. These trade agreements saw more and more manufactured goods exported to the United States, thus breaking the old pattern of exporting primarily low-value unprocessed or semi-processed resource products, and the volume of exports to the United States grew dramatically. In spite of these trade agreements, however, Washington is prepared to defend US business interests by imposing trade barriers, as has been the case with duties on softwood lumber and grain, to restrict the natural flow of certain Canadian goods into the United States. The purpose of these duties is twofold: (1) to protect US farmers and forest companies in the short run by imposing duties on targeted Canadian exports, and (2) to force Canada to accept a long-term agreement that will limit its grain and lumber exports.

CHAPTER 6

1. By December 2012, the Ontario government decision to cancel the construction of two gas-fired plants, in Oakville and Mississauga, and relocate the projects elsewhere was estimated to cost the Ontario taxpayers between $800 million and $1.3 billion (Leslie, 2012).

2. In 1970, mercury was discovered in the fish near the Grassy Narrows Reserve, which is about 500 km downstream from the pulp mill. Levels of methyl mercury in the aquatic food chain were 10 to 50 times higher than those in the surrounding waterways (Shkilnyk, 1985: 189). These levels were similar to those found in the fish of Minamata Bay, Japan. Over 100 residents of this Japanese village died from mercury poisoning in the 1960s, and over 1,000 people suffered irreversible neurological damage. Because they depend on fish and game, the Ojibwa at the Grassy Narrows Reserve ate fish on a daily basis and many complained of mercury-related illnesses. Unlike the Minamata incident no one died, but the economic and social impact on the Ojibwa was an industrial tragedy of immense proportions. As we now know, this problem for Grassy Narrows has continued.

3. Both the federal and Ontario governments have propped up the automobile industry by supporting research into advanced technologies and by providing training in automotive manufacturing technologies at Ontario universities. For example, McMaster University and the University of Waterloo have established an Automotive Manufacturing Innovation initiative with 35 industry partners and support from the Ontario government. Another example is the Auto21 program at the University of Windsor from 2001 to 2016, with funding from the federal government. In 2011, the federal and Ontario governments provided $500 million to Toyota as an incentive to expand production at its Woodstock plant. By 2013, manufacturing of the RAV4, a crossover utility vehicle, expanded from 150,000 units per year to 200,000 units, with the bulk exported to the expanding market in the United States. Employment at the Woodstock plant increased from 2,000 to 2,400 (Keenan, 2012: B3).

4. Interestingly, both Canadian National Railway and most of the major banks have rebranded themselves with acronyms—CN, RBC, TD, BMO, CIBC—perhaps to mask their Canadian origins for the American market, where some people have a dim view of anything "foreign." The Bank of Nova Scotia might have rebranded as BNS but instead chose Scotiabank. Historically, there were close colony-to-colony trade ties between Nova Scotia and British colonies in the Caribbean, where Scotiabank now does much of its offshore business.

5. Until 2001, foreign motor vehicle manufacturers had to pay a 6.1 per cent import duty. Based on the fair trade stipulations that grew out the final round of the General Agreement on Tariffs and Trade and led to the establishment of the WTO, Japan and the European Union argued that the Auto Pact discriminated against their imported vehicles. In July 2001, as a consequence of a WTO ruling in favour of Japan and the EU that it did indeed amount to an unfair trade practice, the Auto Pact, which had helped to build Canada's automobile assembly and parts industry, ceased to exist.

6. Robotics have moved from simple to more complex work situations. These advances have played a key role in keeping Canadian assembly plants competitive in two ways. First, robotics technology has kept the cost of labour low by supplementing traditional workers' tasks with robotic ones. Over time, the role of robotics in assembly plants has expanded from welding to a variety of operations, including laser applications, palletizing, press loading, and the assembly line. Second, robotic "workers," programmed on the floor of the assembly line by a human worker, are extremely accurate, thus reducing flaws in assembly process.

7. The 2014 sale to Saudi Arabia of light armoured vehicles valued at $15 billion was questioned by human rights advocates because of Saudi Arabia's dire human rights record.

CHAPTER 7

1. For the 2015 federal election, the House of Commons had 338 seats. Reapportionment takes place every 10 years based on population figures from the census. The last reapportionment, based on the 2011 census, added 30 new seats to the Commons: Ontario (15), BC (6), Alberta (6), and Québec (3).

2. By responsible government, Lord Durham meant a "political system in which the Executive is directly and immediately responsible to the Legislature, in which the ministers are members of the Legislature, chosen from the party which includes the majority of the elected representatives of the people" (Lucas, 1912: I, 138).

3. In 1912, Québec gained northern territories inhabited by the Inuit and Cree. Ottawa ceded these lands to Québec with the understanding that the Québec government would be responsible for settling land claims with the Aboriginal peoples in these territories. At the time of the 1995 referendum, the Cree in northern Québec, in response to the separatist claim to territorial independence, declared that they have the right to secede from Québec. They argued that if Québec has the right to secede from Canada, then the Cree have the right to secede from Québec. From a geopolitical perspective, the partitioning of Canada or Québec makes sense only to those supporting ethnic nationalism.

4. The case of Churchill Falls is an interesting one. The divide between the Atlantic Ocean and Hudson Bay drainage basins marks the Labrador–Québec boundary. For historical reasons, the Québec government does not formally recognize this boundary, but it does treat the area as part of Newfoundland and Labrador. Newfoundland and Labrador, through its provincial corporation Nalcor Energy, owns the large Churchill Falls hydroelectric project, but virtually all of this power is purchased by Hydro-Québec at well below market value by the terms of a contract originally signed in 1969. Hydro-Québec then transmits it across Québec to markets in the Great Lakes–St Lawrence Lowlands and the United States. A 25-year renewal clause—at an even lower rate—kicked in on 1 September 2016 after the Québec Court of Appeal rejected Newfoundland and Labrador's claim that the terms of the original contract were unfair, and the Québec Superior Court ruled a week later that Hydro-Québec has the right to purchase all but two small blocks of Churchill Falls power (Boone, 2016).

CHAPTER 8

1. In the mid-nineteenth century, the British government faced the question as to how much of Rupert's Land was suitable for new settlement. The area under consideration was the grasslands found in what is now the Prairies. One thought was that the grasslands were an extension of the American Desert. In 1857, the Palliser Expedition set out from England to assess the potential of Western Canada for settlement. Well documented by Spry (1963), this expedition spanned three years (1857–60). In his report to the British government, John Palliser identified two natural zones in the Canadian Prairies. The first zone was described as a sub-humid area of tall grasses, while the second, located further south, was described as a semi-arid area with short-grass vegetation. Palliser considered the area of tall grasses to be suitable for agricultural settlement. He named this area the Fertile Belt. In Manitoba this belt is south of the Canadian Shield and stretches to the border with the United States. Palliser believed that the semi-arid zone, located in southern Alberta and Saskatchewan, was a northern extension of the Great American Desert. His belief was reinforced by the Great Sand Hills (Vignette 8.2). According to Palliser, these semi-arid lands were unsuitable for agricultural settlement. The area described by Captain Palliser became known as Palliser's Triangle—its area overlaps with, but is slightly larger than, the agriculture zone known as the Dry Belt (see Figure 8.4). Homesteaders called these lands "heartbreak territory" and most abandoned their attempts at farming because of the frequency of drought-induced crop failures. David Jones's *Empire of Dust* (1987) captures the settling and abandonment of homesteads in the 1930s while Arthur Kroeger's *Hard Passage* (2007) is a personal recollection of the struggle of the author's family to homestead in Palliser's Triangle and their eventual defeat.

2. The sudden need to adjust to British rule from the 1870s on caused shock waves among the Indigenous peoples on the Prairies. The building of the Canadian Pacific Railway announced the coming of settlers and marked the demise of the great buffalo herds. Two novels illustrate the powerful impact of agricultural settlement on the Indigenous peoples, while the Métis revolts paint another picture of the clash between the old and the new. Rudy Wiebe's *The Temptations of Big Bear* (1973) focuses on the Cree; Guy Vanderhaegh's *The Englishman's Boy* (1996) looks at the Cypress Hills Massacre; George Stanley's classic *The Birth of Western Canada: A History of the Riel Rebellions* (1992) is a valuable account of the Métis in a changing world.

3. Big Bear (Mistahimaskwa) is best known for his refusal to sign Treaty No. 6 in 1876 and for his band's involvement in violent conflicts associated with the 1885 North-West Rebellion. The last clashes between the Cree and the early settlers took place at Frog Lake, Fort Battleford, and Fort Pitt, and Cut Knife Hill. With the arrival of the Canadian militia from eastern Canada, the Cree were defeated.

CHAPTER 9

1. In December 2009 the British Columbia government, as part of a reconciliation agreement with the Haida, officially renamed the Queen Charlotte Islands as Haida Gwaii, which in Haida means "islands of the people." Since the 1980s the archipelago of more than 150 islands had commonly been referred to both as Haida Gwaii and as the Queen Charlottes (CBC News, 2009).

2. Besides the issue of luring British Columbia into Confederation, there were other political reasons for constructing a transcontinental railway. First, there was the urgent need to exert political control over the newly acquired but sparsely settled lands in Western Canada. As in British Columbia, the perceived threat to this territory was from the United States. Second, there was the need to create a larger market for manufactured goods produced by the firms in southern Ontario and Québec.

3. The provincial government created the Technical University of British Columbia in 1997 and this virtual university began to provide online courses in 2000. The objective is to prepare students for the high-tech industry. The university offers certificate programs in electronic commerce and software development. High-technology companies are encouraged to locate offices and research laboratories near its Surrey campus. Students undertake internships and co-operative work sessions with high-technology firms. Its theoretical basis lies in the concept of high-tech clusters around a university. In 2002, the BC government placed the Technical University under the aegis of Simon Fraser University and it was renamed SFU Surrey.

4. In the past, cold winters kept this pest under control. In recent years, however, pine beetles have spread and multiplied as a result of milder winters. Temperatures of at least −38°C for four days or longer are required to kill off pine beetle infestation. If cold winters return, then the pine beetles will be controlled. On the other hand, if milder winters are a feature of climate change, then there will be no stopping the pine beetle from spreading across Canada's boreal forest.

   Another terrain-related issue is clear-cut logging. BC forests often are found in mountainous areas. While the practice of clear-cut logging keeps costs down, it leads to soil erosion and sediment deposition in streams and rivers, particularly after a heavy rain. Beyond the environmental concern about clear-cut logging, this harvesting approach is antithetical to the sustainability of the BC forests. Along with this efficient but anti-sustainable logging system, economic cycles of high demand cause companies to accelerate logging in response to economic rather than environmental considerations (Clapp, 2008: 129).

5. Problems over free and fair trade have been particularly frequent in the forest industry. American lumber production, which operates mainly in the Pacific Northwest and Georgia, can produce a maximum of 15 billion board feet per year. Canadian lumber production nearly doubles the American figure. In fact, lumber production from British Columbia is roughly equal to that of the entire United States. The main difference is that US-produced lumber serves its domestic market, while most Canadian-produced lumber is exported to the United States, Japan, and other foreign customers. Trade disputes over lumber exports can therefore significantly affect BC's forest industry.

6. In 2000, Ottawa tried to alleviate the pressure on salmon stocks by reducing the fleet of 4,500 fishing vessels by about one-third. However, this announcement sparked a strong reaction and little was accomplished. At the same time, Ottawa allowed Indigenous fishers, who have treaty rights to harvest fish for subsistence purposes, a share of the commercial stock. In 1999 Ottawa successfully negotiated a new Pacific Salmon Treaty with the United States, which extends to 2018 (Fisheries and Oceans Canada, 2009). Ottawa is able to exert some management of fish stocks in the Pacific Ocean because of its 200-mile fishing zone and because of its role in the Pacific Salmon Commission. Salmon fishing on the Pacific coast is regulated, based on the Pacific Salmon Treaty, which determines the size of the catch taken by each nation.

CHAPTER 10

1. On 30 April 1999, the Newfoundland House of Assembly gave unanimous consent to a constitutional amendment that would officially change the name of the province to Newfoundland and Labrador. An amendment to the Canadian Constitution was proclaimed on 6 December 2001 formalizing the name change.

2. For over 100 years, coal and iron mining provided the basis for the Nova Scotia iron and steel industry. The iron and steel industry in Cape Breton Island near Sydney, Nova Scotia, was for a long time the heavy industrial heartland of Atlantic Canada. During that time, Sydney was the principal city on Cape Breton Island and the second-largest city in Nova Scotia. Sydney's fate was closely tied to its major industrial firm, the Sydney steel mill, and to Nova Scotia coal mines. The mill and mines prospered in the early part of the twentieth century, and both the town of Sydney and steel production expanded, with much steel exported as rails for the construction of railways in Western Canada. Two dark sides to this iron and steel complex existed. One was the loss of life in the coal mines. While the pay was good, danger went with the job, and for some the cost was their lives. In 1956 and again in 1958, the Springhill mine near the head of the Bay of Fundy was the site of two underground explosions that killed nearly 100 miners. In 1992, the Westray mine in Pictou County, Nova Scotia, was the site of another mine disaster that took 26 lives. The second dark side was the environmental degradation caused by seepage of toxic fluids from the steel mill, which resulted in the Sydney tar ponds.

   A major turning point occurred after World War II when demand for steel dropped and the size of the labour force was reduced. This process of deindustrialization, while delayed by federal and provincial subsidies, eventually saw the steel mill closed. By 2001, the dream of a heavy industrial base in Nova Scotia was gone. Without the steel and coal industry, Sydney and Cape Breton fell on hard times.

3. Of course, Québec still feels cheated over the 1927 Québec–Labrador boundary decision of the British Privy Council, a decision it continues not to recognize as final. In that year the colony of Newfoundland won the argument over the meaning of the word "coast." In previous historical descriptions of the Labrador boundary, the vaguely worded geographic zone of "coast" was not defined, but in the 1927 decision Newfoundland won the day when Britain's Privy Council accepted that the inland extent of "coast"

actually meant watershed (Budgel and Stavely, 1987). Geography had a hand in the conditions of the Churchill Falls agreement because the immediate market for Churchill Falls power was just across the border at the iron mines near Schefferville, Québec. Other factors were the huge cost of the project and its long construction period before returns would be realized. The long-term contract signed in 1969 allowed Churchill Falls a secure market for its power but at a low and "fixed" price. In this way, Hydro-Québec made the deal of a lifetime by obtaining vast quantities of low-cost power over 65 years at 1960 rates. While the initial agreement was made in 1969, its starting date began with the production of power in 1976. However, a "controversial" 25-year extension was added, pushing the expiry date to 2041. The problem with the agreement—at least for Newfoundland and Labrador—is obvious. Since the price of Churchill Falls power is fixed at 1960 levels (Feehan and Baker, 2005), the returns to Newfoundland and Labrador were always far below current market prices. In hindsight, fixing the price was a mistake for the province, but then, who would have predicted the jump in energy prices in the 1970s due to OPEC? Added to that unexpected boost in energy prices, the desire for "clean" energy towards the end of the twentieth century forced utilities in New England to reduce their power production from local coal-burning generating stations.

4. The lobster is found in the waters of Atlantic Canada. A nocturnal creature that hides under rocks or in crevices most of the day, the lobster is generally found in waters less than 50 m in depth. The largest populations are found on Georges Bank, around Nova Scotia, and in the southern Gulf of St Lawrence. The most productive grounds are near Yarmouth on the southern tip of Nova Scotia. Traps are set on the seabed either individually or in groups of up to eight on a line. The traps are hauled to the fishing vessel by powered winches, emptied, re-baited, and lowered again. The catch is transported live to harbour where it is often kept in seawater-permeated wooden crates for later sale.

5. In 2006 the Brazilian mining company CVRD (now named Vale) purchased the Canadian nickel-mining company Inco, including its Sudbury operations and the Voisey's Bay mine site, for approximately $17 billion. Its Canadian-based subsidiary, originally Vale Inco, is now named Vale Canada Limited or simply Vale.

6. On 26 May 2004 the Labrador Inuit voted 76 per cent in support of the agreement, with an 86.5 per cent voter turnout. The provincial and federal governments passed legislation in 2004 and 2005, respectively, giving legal effect to the Labrador Inuit Land Claims Agreement Act. This agreement contains the provision that the Labrador Inuit will receive 25 per cent of the revenue from mining and petroleum production on their settlement land, as well as 5 per cent of provincial royalties from the Voisey's Bay project. The federal environmental review panel examining the possible environmental and social impacts of the mine proposal at Voisey's Bay expressed concern about the disposal of the 15,000 tonnes of mine tailings to be produced each day. The mining company proposed to deposit the toxic tailings in a pond and prevent this from draining into surrounding streams and rivers by building two dams. While federal and provincial environmental officials are satisfied with the company's solution to the tailings problem, local people, especially the Inuit and Innu, are skeptical and worried about the effects of these toxins on the wildlife they depend on for food. In 2002, the Labrador Innu signed a Memorandum of Agreement in regard to Voisey's Bay that gives them 5 per cent of provincial revenues from the project and the assurance that a final land claim agreement will include a chapter on Voisey's Bay that would detail any further compensation and environmental protections. In 2011 the Innu Nation ratified the New Dawn Agreement with the province, an agreement that is expected to form the basis of a final agreement that also involves the federal government.

CHAPTER 11

1. There is a third climatic zone in the Territorial North—the Cordillera. However, the Cordillera climate, often described as a mountain climate, is affected by elevation (as elevation increases, temperature drops). North of 60°N, the Cordillera climate is also affected by latitude so that boreal natural vegetation is found at lower elevations and tundra natural vegetation at high elevations.

2. The Inuit employed the kayak and harpoon to hunt seals, whales, and other marine mammals, which enabled them to occupy the Arctic coast from Yukon to Labrador. The First Nations hunted and fished in the northern coniferous forest, where the birchbark canoe, the bow and arrow, and snowshoes enabled them to hunt in summer and winter. The Dene tribes relied heavily on big game like the caribou, the Chipewyans often following the caribou to their calving grounds in the northern barrens of the Arctic. Both the Inuit and the Dene moved across the land in a seasonal rhythm, following the migratory patterns of animals. Operating in small and highly mobile groups, these hunting societies depended on game for their survival.

3. Sometime around the year 1000 the Vikings made contact with the ancestors of the Inuit, the Thule (c. AD 1000 to 1600). The Thule originated in Alaska where they hunted bowhead whales and other large sea mammals. They quickly spread their whaling technology across the Arctic, travelling in skin boats and dogsleds. With the onset of the Little Ice Age in the fifteenth century, climate conditions affected the distribution of animals and the Thule who were dependent on them. An increased amount of sea ice blocked the large whales from their former feeding grounds, resulting in the collapse of the Thule whale hunt. With the loss of their main source of food, the Thule had to rely more on locally available foods, usually some combination of seal, caribou, and fish. By the eighteenth century, the Thule culture had disappeared and had been replaced by the Inuit hunting culture. In 1576, the Frobisher voyage to Baffin Island may have been the last European encounter with a group of Thule, some on land, others in their kayaks. Relations quickly soured. During a skirmish between Frobisher's men and the Inuit, five of his men were lost, three of the Inuit were captured, and Frobisher was hit by an arrow. The Inuit and one kayak were taken back to England, as often was done in the early years of European exploration, as proof of Frobisher's discovery. All three of the captives soon succumbed to European illness.

4. For the Americans, Canada's North provided a secure transportation link to the European theatre of war and, in 1942, to Alaska. The air routes consisted of the Northwest Staging Route and Project Crimson. Each consisted of a series of northern landing strips that

would enable American and Canadian warplanes to refuel and then continue their journey to either Europe or Alaska. In the Northeast, Project Crimson involved constructing landing fields at strategic intervals to allow Canadian and American planes to fly from Montréal to Frobisher Bay (now Iqaluit) and then to Greenland, Iceland, and, finally, England. In Canada's Northwest, American aircraft came to Edmonton and then flew along the Northwest Staging Route to Fairbanks, Alaska, where their major military base was located. The Alaska Highway, built at the same time, provided road access to the various landing fields and to Alaska. The US Army command had decided that the oil needed by the American armed forces in Alaska must be made secure by increasing oil production at Norman Wells in the NWT and sending it by pipeline across several mountain ranges to Whitehorse and then northward to the military facilities at Fairbanks. Known as the Canol Project, the oil pipeline was completed in 1944, but with the disappearance of the Japanese threat it was closed within a year.

After World War II, the geopolitical importance of northern Canada changed. The North's new strategic role was to warn of a surprise Soviet air attack. The defence against such an attack was a series of radar stations that would detect Soviet bombers and allow sufficient response time for American fighter planes and (later) American missiles to destroy the Soviet bombers. In the 1950s, 22 radar stations, called the Distant Early Warning (DEW) Line, were constructed in the Territorial North along 70°N. Before the end of the Cold War, these radar stations were abandoned and replaced with more sophisticated methods of detecting incoming Soviet planes or missiles. With the collapse of the Soviet Union, Ottawa withdrew its military establishment at Inuvik, did not proceed with its plans for a military base at Nanisivik, and downsized its operation at Alert.

5. The ownership of Arctic waters between the islands in Canada's archipelago remains unclear. Although this route has only recently been used for commercial purposes, a number of "unknown" countries have sent nuclear submarines under the ice cover, and the Americans in the past made several trips through the Northwest Passage on the surface without asking Canada's permission: in 1969, an American tanker, the SS *Manhattan*, to test the route's viability for shipping oil from Alaska's Prudhoe Bay; in 1970, the *Manhattan* again; in 1985, the US Coast Guard icebreaker *Polar Sea*. The political fallout over what was considered the most direct challenge to Canada's sovereignty in the Arctic led to the signing of the Arctic Co-operation Agreement in 1988 by Prime Minister Brian Mulroney and US President Ronald Reagan. The document states that the US is to refrain from sending icebreakers through the Northwest Passage without Canada's consent; in turn, Canada will always give consent. The issue of whether the waters are international or internal was left unresolved.

The seabed of the Arctic Ocean lies beyond the boundaries of the five Arctic countries. Each Arctic country is making a claim for a portion of the seabed to the United Nations. In 2014, the Danish government extended its claim to include the North Pole and areas formerly claimed by Canada and Russia. The 200-nautical-mile (370-km) line indicates the extent of each country's economic area. The reaction of Russia has been muted so far but Ottawa has sent its

scientists back into the field. Canada was expected to make its claim in 2014, but the Danish submission forced Ottawa to take a second look or lose much of the seabed and the North Pole.

6. With a small tax base, large transfer payments from Ottawa to the three territorial governments play a determining role in their budgets. Given the late start in the process of economic and social development, the Territorial North has a great deal of catching up in terms of infrastructure and in terms of equipping its Indigenous population with the skills and tools to compete in the market economy. From this perspective, transfer payments, as large as they are, are insufficient to narrow the gap between the North and the South.

Most workers are employed by one of three governments: federal, territorial, or local. Local governments are settlement councils, band councils, and other organizations funded by a higher level of government. The reason the tertiary sector is so large in the Territorial North is that geography demands such an investment of people and capital to ensure the delivery of public services. Territorial governments must spend more money per resident than do provincial governments to provide basic services, such as education and nursing services. Much of the cost differential is attributed to overcoming distance in the Territorial North and hiring staff for small communities. However, the social importance of the public service sector goes beyond the number of employees. The wide geographic distribution of public jobs across the North is a major social benefit to those in small communities. As a result, employment opportunities, while concentrated in the three capital cities, exist in every community. In small, remote communities, where few jobs exist and where potential workers have given up searching for jobs, underemployment rates are often as high as 60 per cent. The territorial governments' ability to implement affirmative action hiring practices runs up against the low levels of educational attainment among the Indigenous population.

7. In 1974, the first comprehensive land claim submission came from the Dene/Métis who claimed most of the Mackenzie Basin north of 60°N. This land was called Denendeh. While this was a bold attempt similar to that later pursued in the creation of Nunavut, chiefs and elders from the Great Slave Lake area refused to approve it, primarily because it contained no reference to self-government and it called for the surrender of Aboriginal rights.

As the first land claim agreement achieved under the federal system, the Inuvialuit Final Agreement served as a model for subsequent ones. Since 1984, as shown in Table 11.6, six more comprehensive agreements have been reached or extended. Self-government was not covered in the first agreements. The Nunavut (1993) and Tlicho (2003) final agreements did spell out the specific nature and unique structures of self-government for the Inuit and the Dogrib. In 2015, the Déline Self-Government Agreement (FSGA) provided the earlier Sahtu Dene and Metis Comprehensive Land Claim Agreement (1993) with the power of governance.

The Yukon First Nations agreement, signed in 1993, was different in that it only established the basic elements of final agreements for each of the 14 Yukon First Nations, leaving the negotiations for a final agreement to each Yukon First Nation. Known as the Umbrella Final Agreement, this 1993 arrangement provided the basic framework within which each of the 14 Yukon First Nations (Carcross/Tagish; Champagne and Aishihik; Tr'ondek Hwech'in; Kluane; Kwanlin Dun; Liard; Little Salmon/Carmacks; Nacho Nyak Dun; Ross River Dena; Selkirk; Ta'an Kwäch'än Council; Teslin Tlingit Council; Vuntut Gwitchin; and White River) could conclude a final claim settlement agreement. White River, Ross River Dena, and Liard never did complete final agreements and remain under the jurisdiction of the Indian Act (INAC, 2010). The other 11 First Nations achieved final agreements between 1995 and 2006.

CHAPTER 12

1. Cathy Bennett, Newfoundland and Labrador's Minister of Finance, who is also responsible for the status of women, revealed in December 2016 the death threats and other hateful messages she has received on social media. Weeks earlier, in late November 2016, Sandra Jansen, a backbencher in the Alberta legislature who crossed the floor from the Conservatives to the governing NDP, read in the legislature some of the cyber abuse she had been subjected to (see Bailey, 2016).

Bibliography

CHAPTER 1

Adams, Michael. 2003. *Fire and Ice: The United States, Canada and the Myth of Converging Values.* Toronto: Penguin.

Agnew, John. 2002. *American Space/American Place: Geographies of the Contemporary United States.* New York: Routledge.

Atlas of Canada. 2009. "Official Languages, 1996." 25 Feb. At: atlas.nrcan. gc.ca/site/english/maps/peopleandsociety/lang/officiallanguages/1.

Azzi, Stephen. 2006. "Debating Free Trade." *National Post*, 14 Jan., A18.

Bailey, Ian, and Bill Curry. 2011. "Health Proposal Divides the Provinces." *Globe and Mail*, 20 Dec., A1, A12.

Barnes, Trevor, ed. 1993. "Focus: A Geographical Appreciation of Harold A. Innis." *Canadian Geographer* 37, 4: 352–64.

Black, Conrad. 2016. "Conrad Black: WLU's Decision to Remove the Statue of John A. Macdonald Is Cowardly and Disgraceful." *National Post*, 12 Mar. At: http://news.nationalpost.com/full-comment/conrad-black-wlus-decision-to-remove-the-statue-of-john-a-macdonald-is-cowardly-and-disgraceful.

Blackwell, Tom. 2006. "Be 'Less Religious' about Sovereignty, Manley Urges." *National Post*, 7 Feb., A7.

Blanchfield, Mike. 2011. "Canada Won't Be 'Captive Supplier' of U.S. Energy, PM Says." *Globe and Mail*, 2 Dec., B1.

Bone, Robert M., and Robert B. Anderson, eds. 2017. *Indigenous Peoples and Resource Development in Canada.* Toronto: Captus Press.

Burney, Derek. 2007. "From the FTA, Lessons in Leadership: Free Trade Turns 20." *Globe and Mail*, 9 Oct., A19.

——— and Fen Osler Hampson. 2012. "The Last Thing We Need Is Another Foreign Policy Review." *Globe and Mail*, 20 Jan., A13.

Canadian Dairy Information Centre. 2015. "Number of Farms, Dairy Cows and Heifers." At: http://www.dairyinfo.gc.ca/index_e.php?s1=dff-fcil&s2=farm-ferme&s3=nb.

CBC News. 2007. "Hérouxville Drops Some Rules from Controversial Code," 13 Feb. At: www.cbc.ca/canada/montreal/story/2007/02/13/qc-herouxville20070213.html.

Chase, Steven, and Greg Keenan. 2012. "Iron, Steel for New Windsor Bridge Must Come from Canada or U.S." *Globe and Mail*, 15 June, B1, B8.

Coates, Ken. 2015. *Sharing the Wealth: How Resource Revenue Agreements Can Honour Treaties, Improve Communities and Facilitate Canadian Development.* Aboriginal Canada and the Natural Resource Economy Series 6. Ottawa: Macdonald-Laurier Institute. At: http://www.macdonaldlaurier.ca/files/pdf/MLIresourcerevenuesharingweb.pdf.

———. 2016. "10 Questions on Indigenous Futures." Macdonald-Laurier Institute. 5 May. At: http://www.macdonaldlaurier.ca/ken-coates-discusses-indigenous-futures-on-the-agenda/.

Columbo, John Robert, ed. 1987. *New Canadian Quotations.* Edmonton: Hurtig.

Cresswell, Tim. 2005. *Place: A Short Introduction.* London: Blackwell.

Dairy Farmers of Canada. 2016. "Dairy Farmers of Canada React to CETA Signing." 31 Oct. At: https://www.dairyfarmers.ca/news-centre/news/policy/dairy-farmers-of-canada-react-to-ceta-signing.

De Blij, H.J., and Alexander B. Murphy. 2006. *Human Geography: Culture, Society, and Space*, 8th edn. Toronto: John Wiley.

Department of Finance Canada. 2014. "Federal Support to Provinces and Territories." 15 Dec. At: http://www.fin.gc.ca/access/fedprov-eng.asp.

Desbiens, Caroline, Carole Lévesque, and Ioana Comat. 2016. "'Inventing New Places': Urban Indigenous Visibility and the Co-Construction of Citizenship in Val-d'Or (Québec)." *City & Society.* doi: 10.1111/ciso.12074.

Dicken, Peter. 2007. *Global Shift: Mapping the Changing Contours of the World Economy*, 5th edn. New York: Guilford.

Frank, A.G. 1969. *Capitalism and Underdevelopment in Latin America.* New York: Monthly Review Press.

Freelan, S. 2009. *The Salish Sea Map.* At: http://staff.wwu.edu/stef/salish_sea.shtml.

Friedmann, John. 1966. *Regional Development Policy: A Case Study of Venezuela.* Cambridge, Mass.: MIT Press.

Gagnon, Marc-André, and Camille Laurin-Desjardins. 2015. "Montreal Mayor Denies Building Permit to Controversial Imam." *Toronto Star*, 31 Jan. At: http://www.torontosun.com/2015/01/31/montreal-mayor-denies-building-permit-to-controversial-imam.

Garreau, Joel. 1981. *The Nine Nations of North America.* Boston: Houghton Mifflin.

Hamilton, Graeme. 2007. "Welcome! Leave Your Customs at the Door." *National Post*, 30 Jan., A1, A7.

Hare, Kenneth F. 1968. "Canada." In John Warkinton, ed., *Canada: A Geographical Interpretation.* Toronto: Methuen, 3–12.

Hart, Michael. 1991. "A Lower Temperature: The Dispute Settlement Experience under the Canada–United States Free Trade Agreement." *American Review of Canadian Studies* (Summer/Autumn): 193–205.

Hartshorne, Richard. 1939. *The Nature of Geography: A Critical Survey of Current Thought in the Light of the Past.* Lancaster, Penn.: Association of American Geographers.

Hartz, Louis. 1995. *The Liberal Tradition in America.* New York: Harcourt Brace Jovanovich.

Hayter, Roger, and Trevor J. Barnes. 2001. "Canada's Resource Economy." *Canadian Geographer* 45, 1: 36–41.

Hazell, Elspeth, Har-Fai Gee, and Andrew Sharpe. 2012. *The Human Development Index in Canada: Estimates for the Canadian Provinces and Territories, 2000–2011.* Research Report of the Centre for the Study of Living Standards. At: www.csls.ca/reports/csls2012-02.pdf.

Heap, Alan. 2005. "China—The Engine of a Commodities Super Cycle." Citigroup, 31 Mar. At: www.fallstreet.com/Commodities_China_Engine0331.pdf.

Hiller, Harry. 2000. "Region as a Social Construction." In Keith Archer and Lisa Young, eds, *Regionalism and Party Politics in Canada.* Toronto: Oxford University Press.

Howlett, Karen, Dawn Walton, and Shawn McCarthy. 2012. "McGuinty–Redford War of Words Keeps Simmering." *Globe and Mail*, 29 Feb., A1.

Hutchison, Bruce. 1942. *The Unknown Country: Canada and Her People.* Toronto: Longmans, Green and Company.

Innis, Harold. 1930. *The Fur Trade in Canada: An Introduction to Canadian Economic History.* New Haven: Yale University Press.

Jedwab, Jack. 2014. "What Keeps Canada Together: No Clear Majority, but Charter of Rights and Healthcare Still Tops." At: www.acs-aec.ca/pdf/polls/What%20keeps%20Canada%20Together%20(7).pdf.

Khondaker, Jafar. 2007. "Canada's Trade with China: 1997 to 2006." *Canada Trade Highlight Series*, No. 1. Statistics Canada Catalogue no. 65-508-XWE. At: www.statcan.gc.ca/pub/65-508-x/65-508-x2007001-eng.htm.

Knight, Angela. 2015. "Are You a Calgarian—Or Do You Just Live Here?" CBC News, 30 Nov. At: http://www.cbc.ca/news/canada/calgary/calgarian-fakin-it-calgary-at-a-crossroads-1.3340478.

Konrad, Victor, and Heather Nicol. 2008. *Beyond Walls: Reinventing the Canada–US Borderlands*. Aldershot, UK: Ashgate.

Laliberté, Nicole, John Paul Catungal, Heather Castleden, Arn Keeling, Bernard Momer, and Catherine Nash. 2015. "Teaching the Geographies of Canada: Reflections on Pedagogy, Curriculum, and the Politics of Teaching and Learning." *Canadian Geographer* 59, 4: 519–31.

Lemon, James T. 1996. *Liberal Dreams and Nature's Limits: Great Cities of North America Since 1600*. Toronto: Oxford University Press.

Lipset, Seymour M. 1990. *Continental Divide: The Values and Institutions of the United States and Canada*. New York: Routledge.

Macdonald, Neil. 2009. "Interview with US Homeland Security Secretary Janet Napolitano." CBC News, 20 Apr. At: www.cbc.ca/canada/story/2009/04/20/f-transcript-napolitano-macdonald-interview.html.

McParland, Kelly. 2012. "Dalton McGuinty Blames Dog for Eating Province." *National Post*, 28 Feb. At: fullcomment.nationalpost.com/2012/02/28/dalton-mcguinty-blames-the-dog-for-eating-his-province/.

Norcliffe, Glen. 2001. "Canada in a Global Economy." *Canadian Geographer* 45: 14–30.

Northwest Territories. 2011. *Statistics Quarterly* 33, 2. At: www.stats.gov.nt.ca/publications/statistics-quarterly/sqsep2011.pdf.

Northwest Territories, Bureau of Statistics. 2006. *Northwest Territories—2005 . . . By the Numbers*. At: www.stats.gov.nt.ca/Statinfo/Generalstats/bythenumbers/BTNhome(dvo).html.

Norton, William. 2010. *Human Geography*, 7th edn. Toronto: Oxford University Press.

Paasi, Anssi. 2003. "Region and Place: Regional Identity in Question." *Progress in Human Geography* 27, 4: 475–85.

Parkinson, David. 2009. "Despite Some Price Woes, Commodities Bull Market Is Thriving." *Globe and Mail*, 17 July, B8.

Peet, Richard, and Elaine Hartwick. 2009. *Theories of Development: Contentions, Arguments, Alternatives*, 2nd edn. New York: Guilford.

Potter, Mitch. 2010. "Secretive Family and a Vital U.S. Link Create International Span of Mystery." *Toronto Star*, 16 Feb., A1, A17.

R. v. N.S., 2012 SCC 72, [2012] 3 S.C.R. 726

Relph, E.C. 1976. *Place and Placelessness*. London: Pion.

Resnick, Philip. 2000. *The Politics of Resentment: British Columbia Regionalism and Canadian Unity*. Vancouver: University of British Columbia Press.

Rumney, Thomas A. 2010. *Canadian Geography: A Scholarly Bibliography*. Lanham, Md: Scarecrow Press.

Samuelson, Paul. 1976. *Economics*. New York: McGraw-Hill.

Saul, John Ralston. 1997. *Reflections of a Siamese Twin: Canada at the End of the Twentieth Century*. Toronto: Viking.

Simco, Luke. 2009. "Wallin Addresses SARM Convention." *StarPhoenix* (Saskatoon), 13 Mar., A5.

Simpson, Jeffrey. 1993. *Faultlines: Struggling for a Canadian Vision*. Toronto: HarperCollins.

———. 2011. "An Eagle with Clipped Talons." *Globe and Mail*, 12 Oct., A15.

Statistics Canada. 1871. 1871 Census (Canada) - Library and Archives of Canada. http://www.bac-lac.gc.ca/eng/census/1871/Pages/about-census.aspx.

Statistics Canada. 2012a. "Population by Mother Tongue and Age Groups (Total), Percentage Distribution (2011) for Canada, Provinces and Territories," 24 Oct. At: www12.statcan.gc.ca/census-recensement/2011/dp-pd/hlt-fst/lang/Pages/highlight.cfm?TabID=1&Lang=E&Asc=1&PRCode=01&OrderBy=999&View=2&tableID=401&queryID=1&Ag.

———. 2012b. "Population and Dwelling Counts, for Canada, Provinces and Territories, 2011 and 2006 Censuses." 2011 Census, Jan. At: www12.statcan.gc.ca/census-recensement/2011/dp-pd/hlt-fst/pd-pl/Table-Tableau.cfm?LANG=Eng&T=101&S=50&O=A.

———. 2013. "Number and Distribution of the Population Reporting an Aboriginal Identity and Percentage of Aboriginal People in the Population, Canada, Provinces and Territories." National Household Survey (NHS). Table 2. 13 May. At: http://www12.statcan.gc.ca/nhs-enm/2011/as-sa/99-011-x/99-011-x2011001-eng.cfm.

———. 2016a. "Estimates of Population, Canada, Provinces and Territories." CANSIM Table 051-0005, 16 Mar. At: http://www5.statcan.gc.ca/cansim/a26?lang=eng&id=510005.

———. 2016b. "Gross Domestic Product (GDP) at Basic Prices, by North American Industry Classification System (NAICS), Provinces and Territories Annual (dollars × 1,000,000)." CANSIM Table 379-0030. 12 May. At: http://www5.statcan.gc.ca/cansim/a26?lang=eng&retrLang=eng&id=3790030&&pattern=&stByVal=1&p1=1&p2=31&tabMode=dataTable&csid=.

Tuan, Yi-Fu. 1977. *Space and Place: The Perspective of Experience*. Minneapolis: University of Minnesota Press.

———. 1980. *Landscapes of Fear*. Oxford: Blackwell.

Tucker, Brian, and Reuben Rose-Redwood. 2015. "Decolonizing the Map? Toponymic Politics and the Rescaling of the Salish Sea." *Canadian Geographer* 59, 2: 194–206.

VanderKlippe, Nathan. 2009. "T. Boone Pickens Bets on Natural Gas." *Globe and Mail*, 19 June. At: www.theglobeandmail.com/globe-investor/t-boone-pickens-bets-on-natural-gas/article1186003/.

Wallerstein, Immanuel. 1974. *The Modern World System: Capitalist Agriculture and the Origins of the European World Economy in the Sixteenth Century*. New York: Academic Press.

———. 1979. *The Capitalist World Economy*. Cambridge: Cambridge University Press.

Watkins, M.H. 1963. "A Staple Theory of Economic Growth." *Canadian Journal of Economics and Political Science* 29, 2: 141–58.

———. 1977. "The Staple Theory Revisited." *Journal of Canadian Studies* 12, 5: 83–95.

Wente, Margaret. 2015. "We Embrace Our Syrian Refugees—For Now." *Globe and Mail*, 17 Dec. At: http://www.theglobeandmail.com/globe-debate/we-embrace-our-syrian-refugees-for-now/article27791333/.

Wei, Y.D. 2006. "Geographers and Globalization: The Future of Regional Geography." *Environment and Planning A* 38, 8: 1395–1400.

Yukon. 2006. *Yukon Labour Force Survey Review, 2005*. At: www.eco.gov.yk.ca/stats/onetime/lforcerev05.pdf.

———. 2011. *Yukon Economic Outlook, 2011*. 17 May. At: economics.gov.yk.ca/Files/Economic%20Outlook/Outlook2011.pdf.

CHAPTER 2

BBC News. 2010. "Q & A: Professor Phil Jones." 13 Feb. At: news.bbc.co.uk/2/hi/8511670.stm.

Bone, Robert M., Shane Long, and Peter McPherson. 1997. "Settlements in the Mackenzie Basin: Now and in the Future 2050." In Cohen (1997: 265–74).

Bonsal, B. R., R. Aider, P. Gachon, and S. Lapp, 2013: An Assessment of Canadian Prairie Drought: Past, Present, and Future, *Climate Dynamics* 41: 501–516, DOI 10.1007/s00382-012-1422-0.

Bouchard, Mireille. 2001. "Un défi environnemental complexe du XXIe siècle au Canada: L'identification et la compréhension de la réponse des environnements face aux changements climatiques globaux." *Canadian Geographer* 45, 1: 54–70.

Broecker, Wally. 1975. "Are We on the Brink of a Pronounced Global Warming?" *Science* 189: 460–3.

CBC News. 2004. "Inside Walkerton: Canada's Worst-ever E. Coli Contamination." 20 Dec. At: canadaonline.about.com/gi/dynamic/offsite.htm?site=http://www.cbc.ca/news/background/walkerton/.

———. 2014. "Mount Polley Mine Tailings Spill: Imperial Metals Could Face $1M Fine." 6 Aug. At: http://www.cbc.ca/news/canada/british-columbia/mount-polley-spill-blamed-on-design-of-embankment-1.2937387.

———. 2015. "N.W.T. Scientists Predict 'Catastrophic Lake Drainage' Due to Thawing Permafrost." 15 July. At: http://www.cbc.ca/news/canada/north/n-w-t-scientists-predict-catastrophic-lake-drainage-due-to-thawing-permafrost-1.3158206.

Christopherson, Robert W. 1998. *Geosystems: An Introduction to Physical Geography*, 3rd edn. Upper Saddle River, NJ: Prentice-Hall.

Clarke, Garry K.C., Alexander H. Jarosch, Faron S. Anslow, Valentina Radić, and Brian Menounos. 2015. "Projected Deglaciation of Western Canada in the Twenty-First Century." *Nature Geoscience.* doi:10.1038/ngeo2407.

Cohen, Stewart J., ed. 1997. *The Final Report of the Mackenzie Basin Impact Study.* Downsview, Ont.: Environment Canada.

Conrad, Cathy T. 2009. *Severe and Hazardous Weather in Canada: The Geography of Extreme Events.* Toronto: Oxford University Press.

Cutforth, H.W., O.O. Akinremi, and S.M. McGinn. 2000. "Seasonal and Spatial Patterns of Rainfall Trends on the Canadian Prairies." *Journal of Climate* 14: 2177–82.

Dearden, Philip, and Bruce Mitchell. 2012. *Environmental Change and Challenge: A Canadian Perspective*, 4th edn. Toronto: Oxford University Press.

de Loë, R. 2000. "Floodplain Management in Canada: Overview and Prospects." *Canadian Geographer* 44, 4: 354–68.

Environment Canada and Climate Change Canada. 2016a. "Greenhouse Gas Emissions." 14 Apr. At: https://ec.gc.ca/indicateurs-indicators/default.asp?lang=en&n=FBF8455E-1.

———. 2016b. "Greenhouse Gas Emissions by Province and Territory." 14 Apr. At: https://ec.gc.ca/indicateurs-indicators/default.asp?lang=en&n=18F3BB9C-1.

European Space Agency. 2015. "Cool Summer Boosts Arctic Ice." 20 July. At: http://www.esa.int/Our_Activities/Observing_the_Earth/CryoSat/Cool_summer_boosts_Arctic_ice.

Fisheries and Oceans Canada. 2003. "Fast Facts." At: www.dfo-mpo.gc.ca/communic/facts-info/facts-info_c.htm.

French, H.M., and O. Slaymaker, eds. 1993. *Canada's Cold Environments.* Montréal and Kingston: McGill-Queen's University Press.

Global News. 2015. "Mount Polley Mine." At: http://globalnews.ca/tag/mount-polley-mine/.

Hamelin, Louis-Edmond. 1979. *Canadian Nordicity: It's Your North, Too.* Trans. William Barr. Montréal: Harvest House.

Hare, F. Kenneth, and Morley K. Thomas. 1974. *Climate Canada.* Toronto: Wiley.

Harris, Kathleen. 2016. "Justin Trudeau Gives Provinces until 2018 to Adopt Carbon Price Plan." CBC News, 3 Oct. At: http://www.cbc.ca/news/politics/canada-trudeau-climate-change-1.3788825.

Hoekstra, Gordon. 2014. "Imperial Metals Pegs Mount Polley Clean Up Cost at $67 Million." *Vancouver Sun*, 16 Nov. At: http://www.vancouversun.com/technology/Imperial+Metals+pegs+Mount+Polley+cleanup+cost+million/10389778/story.html.

Intergovernmental Panel on Climate Change (IPCC). 2010. *The IPCC Assessment Reports.* At: www.ipcc.ch/.

Kokelj, Steve, Jon F. Tunnicliffe, Denis Lacelle, Trevor C. Lantz, and Robert H. Fraser. 2015. "Retrogressive Thaw Slumps: From Slope Process to the Landscape Sensitivity of Northwestern Canada." GeoQuèbec 2015 Conference. At: https://www.researchgate.net/publication/283307961_Retrogressive_thaw_slumps_From_slope_process_to_the_landscape_sensitivity_of_northwestern_Canada.

Laycock, A.H. 1987. "The Amount of Canadian Water and Its Distribution." In M.C. Healey and R.R. Wallace, eds, *Canadian Arctic Resources.* Ottawa: Department of Fisheries and Oceans, 13–42.

McKibben, Bill. 2010. *Earth: Making a Life on a Tough Planet.* New York: Times Books.

Menounos, B., G. Osborn, J. J. Clague, and B.B. Luckman. 2009. "Latest Pleistocene and Holocene Glacier Fluctuations in Western Canada." *Quaternary Science Review* 28: 2049–74.

Miller, G.H., et al. 2012. "Abrupt Onset of the Little Ice Age Triggered by Volcanism and Sustained by Sea-Ice/Ocean Feedbacks." *Geophysics Research Letters* 39 (Jan.). At: www.agu.org/pubs/crossref/2012/2011gl050168.shtml.

Mount Polley Independent Expert Engineering Investigation and Review Panel. 2015. *Report on Mount Polley Tailings Storage Facility Breach.* Jan. At: https://www.mountpolleyreviewpanel.ca/sites/default/files/report/ReportonMountPolleyTailingsStorageFacilityBreach.pdf.

Muller, Richard A. 2012. "The Conversion of a Climate-Change Skeptic." *New York Times*, 28 July. At: www.nytimes.com/2012/07/30/opinion/the-conversion-of-a-climate-change-skeptic.html?pagewanted=all.

NASA. 2008. "Arctic Sea Ice Reaches Lowest Coverage for 2008." At: www.nasa.gov/topics/earth/sea_ice_nsidc.html.

Norton, William. 2010. *Human Geography*, 7th edn. Toronto: Oxford University Press.

Pachauri, R.K., and A. Reisinger, eds. 2007. *Climate Change 2007: Synthesis Report.* Geneva: IPCC Secretariat.

Pacheco-Vega, Raul. 2015. "Transnational Environmental Activism in North America: Wielding Soft Power through Knowledge Sharing?" *Review of Policy Research* 32, 1: 146–62.

Petticrew, Ellen L., et al. 2015. "The Impact of a Catastrophic Mine Tailings Impoundment Spill into One of North America's Largest Fjord Lakes: Quesnel Lake, British Columbia, Canada." *Geophysical Research Letters.* doi: 10.1002/2015GL063345.

Rasid, Harun, Wolfgang Haider, and Len Hunt. 2000. "Post-flood Assessment of Emergency Evacuation Policies in the Red River Basin, Southern Manitoba." *Canadian Geographer* 44, 4: 369–86.

Shabbar, Amir, Barrie Bonsal, and Madhav Khandekar. 1997. "Canadian Precipitation Patterns Associated with Southern Oscillation." *Journal of Climate* 10: 3016–27.

Slocombe, D. Scott, and Phillip Dearden. 2009. "Protected Areas and Ecosystem-Based Management." In Dearden and Rick Rollins, eds, *Parks and Protected Areas in Canada: Planning and Management*, 3rd edn. Toronto: Oxford University Press, 342–70.

Smith, Laurence C. 2010. *The World in 2050: Four Forces Shaping Civilization's Northern Future.* London: Dutton.

Statistics Canada. 2013. "Aboriginal Identity Population, Canada, 2011." National Household Survey (NHS). Table 1. 13 May. At: http://www12.statcan.gc.ca/nhs-enm/2011/as-sa/99-011-x/99-011-x2011001-eng.cfm.

UN Climate Change Newsroom. 2015. "Historic Paris Agreement on Climate Change." At: http://newsroom.unfccc.int/unfccc-newsroom/finale-cop21/.

US Energy Information Administration (USEIA). 2014. "China Produces Almost as Much Coal as the Rest of the World Combined." 14 May. At: http://www.eia.gov/todayinenergy/detail.cfm?id=16271.

Vaughan, Scott. 2012. *2012 Spring Report of the Commissioner of the Environment and Sustainable Development.* 8 May. At: www.oag-bvg.gc.ca/internet/English/parl_cesd_201205_00_e_36772.html.

Warren, F.J., and D.S. Lemmen, eds. 2014. *Canada in a Changing Climate: Sector Perspectives on Impacts and Adaptations.* Ottawa: Natural Resources Canada. At: http://www.nrcan.gc.ca/sites/www.nrcan.gc.ca/files/earthsciences/pdf/assess/2014/pdf/Full-Report_Eng.pdf.

Weart, Spencer R. 2008. *The Discovery of Global Warming.* Cambridge, Mass.: Harvard University Press.

Weber, Bob. 2015. "Timelapse Video Shows Lake Falling Off a Cliff in Northwest Territories, creating a Large Temporary Waterfall." *National Post,* 10 Dec. At: http://news.nationalpost.com/news/canada/timelapse-video-shows-lake-falling-off-a-cliff-in-northwest-territories-creating-a-large-temporary-waterfall.

Zhang, Xuebin, Lucie A. Vincent, W.D. Hogg, and Ain Niitsoo. 2000. "Temperature and Precipitation Trends in Canada during the 20th Century." *Atmosphere-Ocean* 38, 3: 395–429. doi: 10.1080/07055900.2000.9649654.

CHAPTER 3

Aboriginal Affairs and Northern Development Canada. 2013. "Registered Indian Population by Sex and Residence, 2011." 6 Feb. At: www.aadnc-aandc.gc.ca/eng/1351001356714/1351001514619#chp9_1.

———. 2014a. "FAQs: Bill C-33, First Nations Control of First Nations Education Act." 4 Oct. At: https://www.aadnc-aandc.gc.ca/eng/1381841473896/1381841548486.

———. 2014b. "Urban Aboriginal Peoples." 4 Oct. At: https://www.aadnc-aandc.gc.ca/eng/1100100014265/1369225120949.

Bartlett, Richard H. 1990. *Indian Reserves and Aboriginal Lands in Canada: A Homeland.* Saskatoon: University of Saskatchewan, Native Law Centre.

Bélanger, Claude. 2007. "North-West Rebellion—Canadian History." *The Quebec History Encyclopedia.* At: faculty.marianopolis.edu/c.belanger/quebechistory/encyclopedia/North-WestRebellion-CanadianHistory.htm.

Bone, Robert M. 2012. *The Canadian North: Issues and Challenges.* Fourth Edition. Toronto: Oxford University Press.

———. 2016. *The Canadian North: Issues and Challenges,* 5th edn. Toronto: Oxford University Press.

——— and Robert B. Anderson. 2017. *Natural Resources and Indigenous Peoples in Canada,* 3rd edn. Toronto: Captus Press.

Brownlie, Robin Jarvis. 2003. *A Fatherly Eye: Indian Agents, Government Power, and Aboriginal Resistance in Ontario, 1918–1939.* Toronto: Oxford University Press.

Bumsted, J.M. 2007. *A History of the Canadian Peoples,* 3rd edn. Toronto: Oxford University Press.

Cairns, Alan. 2000. *Citizens Plus: Aboriginal Peoples and the Canadian State.* Vancouver: University of British Columbia Press.

Canada. 1882. *Census of Canada 1880–81,* vol. 1. Ottawa: MacLean, Rogers & Company.

———. 1892. *Census of Canada 1890–91,* vol. 1. Ottawa.

Canada, Department of Finance. 2009a. "Equalization Program." At: www.fin.gc.ca/fedprov/eqp-eng.asp.

———. 2009b. "Federal Transfers to Provinces and Territories." At: www.fin.gc.ca/access/fedprov-eng.asp#Major.

———. 2011. "Equalization Program," 19 Dec. At: www.fin.gc.ca/fedprov/eqp-eng.asp.

Cardinal, Harold. 1969. *The Unjust Society: The Tragedy of Canada's Indians.* Edmonton: Hurtig.

Carter, Sarah. 2004. "'We Must Farm to Enable Us to Live': The Plains Cree and Agriculture to 1900." In R. Bruce Morrison and C. Roderick Wilson, eds, *Native Peoples: The Canadian Experience.* Toronto: Oxford University Press, 320–40.

CBC News. 2011. "Quebec Inuit Vote against Self-Government Plan." 29 Apr. At: www.cbc.ca/news/canada/north/story/2011/04/29/nunavik-government-referendum.html.

———. 2013a. "At Least 3,000 Died in Residential Schools, Research Shows." 18 Feb. At: www.cbc.ca/news/canada/story/2013/02/18/residential-schools-student-deaths.html.

———. 2013b. "Métis Celebrate Historic Supreme Court Land Ruling." 8 Mar. At: www.cbc.ca/news/politics.story/2013/03/08/pol-metis-supreme-court-land-dispute.html.

———. 2016. "Canada and Manitoba Métis Federation Sign MOU Following Historic Supreme Court Land Ruling." 27 May. At: http://www.cbc.ca/news/canada/manitoba/metis-federation-of-manitoba-signs-mou-1.3604370.

Cook, Ramsay. 1993. *The Voyages of Jacques Cartier.* Toronto: University of Toronto Press.

Cuthand, Doug. 2012. "Time to Move On for Sake of Future Generations." *StarPhoenix* (Saskatoon), 22 June, A11.

Delacourt, Susan. 2010. "Ontario to Get 18 New MPs." *Toronto Star,* 2 Apr., A1, A19.

Dickason, Olive Patricia, with David T. McNab. 2009. *Canada's First Nations: A History of Founding Peoples from Earliest Times,* 4th edn. Toronto: Oxford University Press.

——— and William Newbigging. 2015. *A Concise History of Canada's First Nations,* 3rd edn. Toronto: Oxford University Press.

Dyck, Noel. 1985. *Indigenous Peoples and the Nation-State.* St John's: ISER Books.

Favel, Blaine, and Ken S. Coates. 2016. *Understanding UNDRIP: Choosing Action on Priorities over Sweeping Claims about the United Nations Declaration on the Rights of Indigenous Peoples.* Aboriginal Canada and the Natural Resource Economy Series No. 10. Macdonald/Laurier Institute. At: http://www.macdonaldlaurier.ca/files/pdf/MLI-10-UNDRIPCoates-Favel05-16-WebReadyV4.pdf.

Flanagan, Thomas. 1991. *Métis Lands in Manitoba.* Calgary: University of Calgary Press.

Galloway, Gloria. 2016. 2016. "Liberals to Reassess First Nations Education Funds after Removal from Last Year's Ledgers." *Globe and Mail,* 21 Mar. At: http://www.theglobeandmail.com/news/politics/trudeau-looking-to-improve-state-of-first-nations-education/article29166291/.

——— and Sean Fine. 2016. "Métis, Non-Status Indians Win Supreme Court Battle Over Rights." *Globe and Mail,* 14 Apr. At: http://www.theglobeandmail.com/news/national/metis-ruling/article29628869/.

Garreau, Joel. 1981. *The Nine Nations of North America.* Boston: Houghton Mifflin.

Globe and Mail. 1995. "No—by a Whisker." 31 Oct., A1.

Halligan, Jessi J., et al. 2016. "Pre-Clovis Occupation 14,550 Years Ago at the Page-Ladson Site, Florida, and the Peopling of the Americas." *Science Advances* 2, 5 (13 May): e1600375. doi: 10.1126/sciadv.1600375.

Harris, R. Cole. 1997. *The Resettlement of British Columbia: Essays on Colonialism and Geographical Change.* Vancouver: University of British Columbia Press.

———. 2002. *Making Native Space: Colonialism, Resistance, and Reserves in British Columbia.* Vancouver: University of British Columbia Press.

———. 2009. *The Reluctant Land: Society, Space, and Environment in Canada before Confederation.* Vancouver: University of British Columbia Press.

——— and John Warkentin. 1991. *Canada before Confederation: A Study in Historical Geography.* Ottawa: Carleton University Press.

Henderson, Gordon, executive producer. 2015. *Franklin's Lost Ships.* Film documentary about the 2014 discovery of Sir John Franklin's *Erebus.* Toronto: 90th Parallel Products.

Indian and Northern Affairs Canada (INAC). 2009. "Registered Indian Population by Sex and Residence 2007." At: www.ainc-inac.gc.ca/ai/rs/pubs/sts/ni/rip/rip07/rip07-eng.asp#Sum.

Indigenous and Northern Affairs Canada (INAC). 2015. "Fact Sheet: Implementation of Final Agreements." 13 Aug. At: https://www.aadnc-aandc.gc.ca/eng/1100100030580/1100100030581.

Innis, Harold. 1923. *A History of the Canadian Pacific Railway*. Toronto: McClelland and Stewart. Online at http://www.gutenberg.ca/ebooks/innis-historyofthecpr/innis-historyofthecpr-00-h.html.

Kerr, Donald, and Deryck W. Holdsworth, eds. 1990. *Historical Atlas of Canada, Volume III: Addressing the Twentieth Century 1891–1961*. Toronto: University of Toronto Press.

Kulchyski, Peter. 2013. *Aboriginal Rights Are Not Human Rights: In Defence of Indigenous Struggles*. Winnipeg: Arbeiter Ring Publishing.

Laxer, James. 2012. *Tecumseh and Brock: The War of 1812*. Toronto: Anansi.

Lewis, Mike, and Sara-Jane Brocklehurst. 2009. *Aboriginal Mining Guide*. Canadian Centre for Community Renewal. At: http://www.sdsg.org/wp-content/uploads/2011/06/AboriginalMiningGuide_online_complete_0.pdf.

Library and Archives of Canada. 2012. "Métis Scrip Records." 1 Mar. At: www.collectionscanada.gc.ca/metis-scrip/005005-3100-e.html.

Lower, J. Arthur. 1983. *Western Canada: An Outline History*. Vancouver: Douglas & McIntyre.

McVey, Wayne W., and W.E. Kalbach. 1995. *Canadian Population*. Toronto: Nelson Canada.

Manuel, George. 1974. *The Fourth World: An Indian Reality*. Toronto: Collier/Macmillan.

Miller, J.R. 2000. *Skyscrapers Hide the Heavens: A History of Indian–White Relations in Canada*, 3rd edn. Toronto: University of Toronto Press.

Milloy, John S. 1999. *A National Crime: The Canadian Government and the Residential School System*. Winnipeg: University of Manitoba Press.

Milne, Brad. 1995. "The Historiography of Métis Land Dispersal." *Manitoba History* 30: 30–41.

Moffat, Ben. 2002. "Geographic Antecedents of Discontent: Power and Western Canadian Regions 1870 to 1935." *Prairie Perspectives* 5: 202–28.

Morrison, William. 2003. "Forging the National Dream." At: https://www.youtube.com/watch?v=DRuwCrQ7Qkw.

Nadasdy, Paul. 1999. "The Politics of TEK: Power and the Introduction of Knowledge." *Arctic Anthropology* 36(1/2): 1–18.

———. 2003. *Hunters and Bureaucrats: Power, Knowledge, and Aboriginal–State Relations in the Southwest Yukon*. Vancouver: University of British Columbia Press.

Nemni, Max. 1994. "The Case against Quebec Nationalism." *American Review of Canadian Studies* 24, 2: 171–96.

Nepinak, Chief Derek. 2014. "New First Nations Education Act an 'Illusion of control'." CBC News, 11 Apr. At: http://www.cbc.ca/news/aboriginal/new-first-nations-education-act-an-illusion-of-control-1.2607178.

Pedersen, Mikkel W., et al. 2016."Postglacial Viability and Colonization in North America's Ice-Free Corridor." *Nature* (10 Aug.). doi: 10.1038/nature19085.

Porter, Jody. 2013. "First Nations Must 'Learn from' De Beers Deal." CBC News, 13 Feb. At: http://www.cbc.ca/news/canada/thunder-bay/first-nations-must-learn-from-de-beers-deal-1.1327592.

Romaniuc, Anatole. 2000. "Aboriginal Population of Canada: Growth Dynamics under Conditions of Encounter of Civilisations." *Canadian Journal of Native Studies* 20: 95–137.

Saul, John Ralston. 1997. *Reflections of a Siamese Twin: Canada at the End of the Twentieth Century*. Toronto: Viking.

Sifton, Clifford. 1922. "The Immigrants Canada Wants." *Maclean's* 35, 7: 16.

Simpson, Jeffrey. 1993. *Faultlines: Struggling for a Canadian Vision*. Toronto: HarperCollins.

Sinclair, Senator Murray. 2015. Truth and Reconciliation Report: Executive Summary. http://www.trc.ca/websites/trcinstitution/File/2015/Honouring_the_Truth_Reconciling_for_the_Future_July_23_2015.pdf

Smith, P.J. 1982. "Alberta Since 1945: The Maturing Settlement System." In L.D. McCann, ed., *Heartland and Hinterland: A Regional Geography of Canada*. Scarborough, Ont.: Prentice-Hall.

Sprague, D.N. 1988. *Canada and Métis, 1869–1885*. Waterloo, Ont.: Wilfrid Laurier University Press.

Statistics Canada. 2003. *Historical Statistics of Canada*. Ottawa: Statistics Canada Catalogue no. 11-516-XIE. At: www.statcan.ca/english/freepub/11-516-XIE/sectiona/sectiona.htm.

———. 2008. "Aboriginal Identity Population by Age Groups, Median Age and Sex, 2006 Counts, for Canada, Provinces and Territories." At: www12.statcan.gc.ca/english/census06/data/highlights/Aboriginal/pages/Page.cfm?Lang=E&Geo=PR&Code=01&Table=1&Data=Count&Sex=1&Age=1&StartRec=1&Sort=2&Display=Page.

Taylor, Charles. 1993. *Reconciling the Solitudes*. Montréal and Kingston: McGill-Queen's University Press.

Thomas, David Hurst. 1999. *Exploring Ancient Native America: An Archaeological Guide*. New York: Routledge.

Tough, Frank. 1996. *As Their Natural Resources Fail: Native Peoples and the Economic History of Northern Manitoba, 1870–1930*. Vancouver: University of British Columbia Press.

Tracie, Carl J. 1996. *Toil and Peaceful Life: Doukhobor Village Settlement in Saskatchewan, 1899–1918*. Regina: Canadian Plains Research Centre, University of Regina.

Villeneuve, Paul. 1993. "Allocution présidentielle: L'invention de l'avenir au nord de l'amérique." *Le géographe canadien* 37, 2: 98–104.

White, Graham. 2006. "Cultures in Collision: Traditional Knowledge and Euro-Canadian Governance Processes in Northern Land-Claim Boards." *Arctic* 59, 4: 401–14.

Williams, Glyndwr. 1983. "The Hudson's Bay Company and the Fur Trade, 1670–1870." *The Beaver* (Autumn): 4–81.

Willow, Anna J. 2014. "The New Politics of Environmental Degradation: Un/expected Landscapes of Disempowerment and Vulnerability." *Journal of Political Ecology* 21: 237–57.

CHAPTER 4

Adserà, Alícia, and Ana Ferrer. 2014. "The Fertility of Married Immigrant Women to Canada." *International Migration Review*. 2 Sept. doi: 10.1111/imre.12114.

Azia, Omer. 2015. "Banning the Niqab Harms an Open Society. So Does Wearing It." *Globe and Mail*, 16 Mar. At: http://www.theglobeandmail.com/globe-debate/banning-the-niqab-harms-an-open-society-so-does-wearing-it/article23469409/.

Beaujot, Roderic. 1991. *Population Change in Canada: The Challenges of Policy Adaptation*. Toronto: McClelland & Stewart.

Bélanger, Alain, and Stéphane Gilbert. 2006. "The Fertility of Immigrant Women and Their Canadian-born Daughters." *Report on the Demographic Situation in Canada 2002*. Sept. Statistics Canada Catalogue no. 91-209-XPE. At: www.statcan.gc.ca/pub/91-209-x/91-209-x2002000-eng.pdf.

Bernier, Jacques. 1991. "Social Cohesion and Conflicts in Quebec." In Guy M. Robinson, ed., *A Social Geography of Canada*. Toronto: Dundurn Press.

Bohnert, Nora, Jonathan Chagnon, and Patrice Dion. 2014. *Population Projections for Canada (2013 to 2063)*. Statistics Canada Catalogue no. 91-529-X. 17 Oct. At: http://www.statcan.gc.ca/pub/91-520-x/91-520-x2014001-eng.htm.

Bone, Robert M. 2016. *The Canadian North: Issues and Challenges*, 5th edn. Toronto: Oxford University Press.

Bourne, Larry S., Tom Hutton, Richard Shearmur, and Jim Simmons. 2011. *Canadian Urban Regions: Trajectories of Growth and Change.* Toronto: Oxford University Press.

——— and Damaris Rose. 2001. "The Changing Face of Canada: The Uneven Geographies of Population and Social Change." *Canadian Geographer* 45, 1: 105–19.

Boyd, Erman. 2009. "S&P Launches Canadian Sharia Compliant Index." *Globe and Mail,* 27 May. At: www.theglobeandmail.com/globe-investor/funds-and-etfs/sp-launches-canadian-sharia-compliant-index/article1198352/.

Brean, Joseph. 2012. "The Changing Meaning of Citizenship in Canada." *National Post,* 16 Mar. At: news.nationalpost.com/2012/03/16/the-changing-meaning-of-citizenship-in-canada/.

Bunting, Trudi, Pierre Filion, and Ryan Walker, eds. 2010. *Canadian Cities in Transition: New Directions in the Twenty-First Century,* 4th edn. Toronto: Oxford University Press.

Canada. 1884. *Census of Canada, 1880–1881.* Ottawa: Department of Agriculture.

Canadian Magazine of Immigration. 2016. "Canada: Immigration by Source Country (2015)." At: http://canadaimmigrants.com/canada-immigration-by-source-country-2015/.

Cardinal, Harold. 1969. *The Unjust Society: The Tragedy of Canada's Indians.* Edmonton: Hurtig.

Chui, Tina, Kelly Tran, and Hélène Maheux. 2008. "Immigration in Canada: A Portrait of the Foreign-born Population, 2006 Census: Immigration: Driver of Population Growth." At: www12.statcan.ca/census-recensement/2006/as-sa/97-557/figures/c1-eng.cfm.

CIA. 2007. *The World Fact Book: Canada.* Washington. At: www.cia.gov/library/publications/the-world-factbook/index.html.

Citizenship and Immigration Canada. 2011a. *Annual Report to Parliament on Immigration 2011.* 27 Oct. At: www.cic.gc.ca/english/resources/publications/annual-report-2011/section2.asp#part2_1.

———. 2011b. "Canada—Permanent Residents by Source Country." *Facts and Figures 2010 Overview.* 30 Sept. At: www.cic.gc.ca/english/resources/statistics/facts2010/permanent/10.asp#countries.

———. 2015. *Facts and Figures 2013—Immigration Overview: Permanent and Temporary Residents.* 19 Mar. At: http://www.cic.gc.ca/english/resources/statistics/menu-fact.asp.

———. 2016. "New Report Reveals Popular Destination Provinces for New Immigrants to Canada." *CIC Newsletter* (Apr.). At: http://www.cicnews.com/2016/04/report-reveals-popular-destination-provinces-immigrants-canada-047644.html#z6J8QI0vxvzpBIZb.99.

Coates, Ken S. 2015. *Sharing the Wealth: How Resource Revenue Agreements Can Honour Treaties, Improve Communities and Facilitate Canadian Development.* Aboriginal Canada and the Natural Resource Economy Series 6. Ottawa: Macdonald-Laurier Institute. At: http://www.macdonaldlaurier.ca/files/pdf/MLIresourcerevenuesharingweb.pdf.

Curry, Bill, and Gloria Galloway. 2012. "PM Sees Jobs as Key to First Nations' Future." *Globe and Mail,* 25 Jan., A6.

Denevan, William M. 1992. "The Pristine Myth: The Landscape of the Americas in 1492." *Annals, Association of American Geographers* 82, 3: 369–85.

Dickason, Olive Patricia, with David T. McNab. 2009. *Canada's First Nations: A History of Founding Peoples from Earliest Times,* 4th edn. Toronto: Oxford University Press.

——— and William Newbigging. 2015. *A Concise History of Canada's First Nations,* 3rd edn. Toronto: Oxford University Press.

Drucker, Peter. 1969. *The Age of Discontinuity.* London: Heinemann.

Fife, Robert. 2002. "Migrants Must Spread Out: Ottawa." *National Post,* 22 June, A1, A9.

Foot, David, with D. Stoffman. 1996. *Boom, Bust and Echo: How to Profit from the Coming Demographic Shift.* Toronto: Macfarlane, Walter & Ross.

Gee, Ellen, and Gloria Gutman, eds. 2000. *The Overselling of Population Aging: Apocalyptic Demography, Intergenerational Challenges, and Social Policy.* Toronto: Oxford University Press.

Gilbert, Anne. 2001. "Le français au Canada, entre droits et géographie." *Canadian Geographer* 45, 1: 175–9.

Gionet, Linda. 2009. "First Nations People: Selected Findings of the 2006 Census." *Canadian Social Trends* no. 87. At: www.statcan.gc.ca/pub/11-008-x/2009001/article/10864-eng.htm.

Hare, Kenneth. 1968. "Canada." In John Warkinton, ed., *Canada: A Geographical Interpretation.* Toronto: Methuen, 3–12.

Harvey, David. 1989. *The Urban Experience.* Baltimore: Johns Hopkins University Press.

Herberg, Edward N. 1989. "Identity, Cultural Production and the Vitality of Francophone Communities outside Quebec." In Leen d'Haenens, ed., *Images of Canadianness: Visions on Canada's Politics, Culture, Economics.* Ottawa: University of Ottawa Press.

Hiebert, Daniel. 2000. "Immigration and the Changing Canadian City." *Canadian Geographer* 44, 1: 25–43.

——— and David Ley. 2003. "Assimilation, Cultural Pluralism and Social Exclusion among Ethnocultural Groups in Vancouver." *Urban Geography* 24, 1: 16–44.

Human Resources and Development Canada, Employment and Social Development. 2015. "Canadians in Context—Aging Population." *Indicators of Well-being in Canada* (18 Mar.). At: http://www4.hrsdc.gc.ca/.3ndic.1t.4r@-eng.jsp?iid=33.

Ibbitson, John. 2012. "Tories Prepare New Native Land Plan." *Globe and Mail,* 25 Aug., A1, A4.

Innes, Robert Alexander. 2015. "Moose on the Loose: Indigenous Men, Violence, and the Colonial Excuse." *Aboriginal Policy Studies* 4, 1: 46–56.

Innis, Harold. 1930. *The Fur Trade in Canada: An Introduction to Canadian Economic History.* New Haven: Yale University Press.

Ishaq, Zunera. 2015. "Why I Intend to Wear a Niqab at My Citizenship Ceremony." *Toronto Star,* 16 Mar. At: http://www.thestar.com/opinion/commentary/2015/03/16/why-i-intend-to-wear-a-niqab-at-my-citizenship-ceremony.html.

Javed, Noor. 2010. "'Visible Minority' Will Mean 'White' by 2031." *Toronto Star,* 10 Mar., A3.

Jiminez, Marina, and Kim Lunman. 2004. "Canada's Biggest Cities See Influx of New Immigrants." *Globe and Mail,* 19 Aug.

Leo, Geoff. 2012. "Blind Spot: What Happened to Canada's Aboriginal Fathers?" CBC TV, 12 Jan. At: www.cbc.ca/sask/community/mt/2012/03/blind-spot---what-happened-to-canadas-aboriginal-fathers.html.

Lewington, Jennifer. 2007. "Immigrants and Integration—Is the City Ready to Listen?" *Globe and Mail,* 29 Jan. At: www.theglobeandmail.com/servlet/story/RTGAM.20070116.wimmig16home/BNStory/National/home.

Ley, David. 1999. "Myths and Meanings of Immigration and the Metropolis." *Canadian Geographer* 43, 1: 2–18.

——— and Daniel Hiebert. 2001. "Immigration Policy as Population Policy." *Canadian Geographer* 45, 1: 120–5.

Li, Peter S. 2003. *Destination Canada: Immigration Debates and Issues.* Toronto: Oxford University Press.

McGrath, John Michael. 2016. "How the Waters of Grassy Narrows Were Poisoned." TVO, 23 Sept. At: http://tvo.org/article/current-affairs/shared-values/how-the-waters-of-grassy-narrows-were-poisoned.

McLachlin, Beverley, Rt. Hon., P.C. 2015. "Reconciling Unity and Diversity in the Modern Era: Tolerance and Intolerance." Remarks made at the Aga Khan Museum, Toronto, Ontario, 28 May. At: http://www.theglobeandmail.com/news/national/unity-diversity-and-cultural-genocide-chief-justice-mclachlins-complete-text/article24698710/.

McVey, Wayne W., and W.E. Kalbach. 1995. *Canadian Population*. Toronto: Nelson Canada.

Martin, Don. 2005. "The Paycheque Exiles." *National Post*, 6 Sept., A18.

Mooney, James. 1928. *The Aboriginal Population of America North of Mexico*. Smithsonian Miscellaneous Collections. Washington: Smithsonian Institution.

Newhouse, David R. 2000. "From the Tribal to the Modern: The Development of Modern Aboriginal Societies." In Ron F. Laliberté et al., eds, *Expressions in Canadian Native Studies*. Saskatoon: University of Saskatchewan Extension Press, 395–409.

——. 2007. "Aboriginal Languages in Canada: Emerging Trends and Perspectives on Second Language Acquisition." *Canadian Social Trends*, no. 83. Statistics Canada, Catalogue no. 11–008.

Ostry, Bernard. 2005. "Canada's Ethnic Makeup Is Branching Out in New Directions." *Globe and Mail*, 15 Nov., A25.

Peters, Evelyn J. 2010. "Aboriginal People in Canadian Cities." In Trudi Bunting, Pierre Filion, and Ryan Walker, eds, *Canadian Cities in Transition: New Directions in the Twenty-First Century*, 4th edn. Toronto: Oxford University Press, ch. 22.

Ravenstein, Ernest George. 1885. "The Laws of Migration." *Journal of the Statistical Society of London* 48, 2: 167–235.

——. 1889. "The Laws of Migration." *Journal of the Royal Statistical Society* 52, 2: 241–305.

Royal Commission on Bilingualism and Biculturalism. 1970. *Report. Book IV: Cultural Contributions of the Other Ethnic Groups*. Ottawa: Queen's Printer.

Saul, John Ralston. 1997. *Reflections of a Siamese Twin: Canada at the End of the Twentieth Century*. Toronto: Viking.

Saunders, Doug. 2012. *The Myth of the Muslim Tide: Do Immigrants Threaten the West?* Toronto: Knopf Canada.

Shkilnyk, Anastasia, M. 1985. *A Poison Stronger Than Love: The Destruction of an Ojibwa Community*. New Haven: Yale University Press.

Smith, Laurence C. 2010. *The World in 2050: Four Forces Shaping Civilization's Northern Future*. New York: Dutton.

Statistics Canada. 1997. *Mortality—Summary List of Causes, 1995*. Catalogue no. 84-209-XPB. Ottawa: Minister of Industry.

——. 2002. *Census of Canada 2001—Census Geography. Highlights and Analysis: Canada's 2001 Population*. Ottawa. At: www12.statcan.ca/English/census01/.

——. 2003a. "Components of Population Growth." 28 Feb. Ottawa. At: www.statcan.ca/English/Pgdb/demo33a.htm.

——. 2003b. *Census of Canada 2001—Aboriginal Peoples of Canada: A Demographic Profile*. Analysis series 96F0030XIE2001007. Ottawa, 21 Jan. At: www12.statcan.ca/english/census01/products/analytic/companion/abor/contents.cfm.

——. 2003c. *Census of Canada 2001—Religions in Canada*. Analysis series 96F0030XIE2001015. At: www12.statcan.ca/english/census01/products/analytic/companion/rel/contents.cfm.

——. 2005. "Population by Religion, by Province and Territory (2001 Census)." 25 Jan. At: http://www.statcan.gc.ca/tables-tableaux/sum-som/l01/cst01/demo30a-eng.htm.

——. 2006a. "Components of Population Growth, by Province and Territory, July 1, 2005 to June 30, 2006." At: www40.statcan.ca/l01/cst01/demo33c.htm.

——. 2006b. *Annual Demographic Statistics 2005*. Catalogue no. 91-213-XIB. At: www.statcan.ca/english/freepub/91-213-XIB/0000591-213-XIB.pdf.

——. 2006c. "Labour Force Survey." *The Daily*, 10 Feb. At: www.statcan.ca/Daily/English/060210/d060210a.htm.

——. 2006d. "Canada's Population by Age and Sex." *The Daily*, 26 Oct. At: www.statcan.ca/Daily/English/061026/d061026b.htm.

——. 2007a. "Immigrant Population by Place of Birth, by Province and Territory (2006 Census)." 11 Dec. At: http://www.statcan.gc.ca/tables-tableaux/sum-som/l01/cst01/demo34a-eng.htm.

——. 2007b. "Births and Birth Rate, by Province and Territory." At: www40.statcan.ca/l01/cst01/demo04b.htm.

——. 2007c. "Deaths and Death Rate, by Province and Territory." At: www40.statcan.ca/l01/cst01/demo07b.htm.

——. 2007d. "Portrait of the Canadian Population in 2006: Subprovincial Population Dynamics: Canada's Population Becoming More Urban." At: www12.statcan.ca/english/census06/analysis/popdwell/Subprov1.cfm.

——. 2008a. "Aboriginal Peoples in Canada in 2006: Inuit, Métis and First Nations, 2006 Census." *The Daily*, 15 Jan. At: www.statcan.gc.ca/daily-quotidien/080115/tdq080115-eng.htm.

——. 2008b. "Language (including Language of Work)." Releases no. 4 and 6. At: www12.statcan.gc.ca/census-recensement/2006/rt-td/lng-eng.cfm.

——. 2008c. "Aboriginal Identity Population, 2006 Counts, Percentage Distribution, Percentage Change for Both Sexes, for Canada, Provinces and Territories—20% Sample Data." *Aboriginal Peoples Highlight Tables*. 2006 Census. Statistics Canada Catalogue no. 97-558-XWE2006002. At: www12.statcan.ca/english/census06/data/highlights/aboriginal/index.cfm?Lang=E.

——. 2008d. "The Evolving Linguistic Portrait, 2006 Census: The Proportion of Francophones and of French Continue to Decline." At: www12.statcan.ca/census-recensement/2006/as-sa/97-555/p6-eng.cfm.

——. 2008e. "Mandate, Responsibilities and Objectives." At: www.statcan.gc.ca/about-apercu/mandate-mandat-eng.htm.

——. 2009a. "Components of Population Growth, by Province and Territory, 2007–2008." At: http://www.statcan.gc.ca/tables-tableaux/sum-som/l01/cst01/demo33a-eng.htm.

——. 2009b. "Ethnocultural Portrait of Canada: Ethnic Origins, 2006 Counts, for Canada, Provinces and Territories." At: www12.statcan.ca/english/census06/data/highlights/ethnic/pages/Page.cfm?Lang=E&Geo=PR&Code=01&Data=Count&Table=2&StartRec=1&Sort=3&Display=All&CSDFilter=5000.

——. 2009c. "Table 2. Quarterly Demographic Estimates." At: www.statcan.gc.ca/daily-quotidien/090326/t090326a2-eng.htm.

——. 2009d. "Annual Demographic Estimates: Canada, Provinces and Territories." At: www.statcan.gc.ca/pub/91-215-x/2008000/5200700-eng.htm.

——. 2009e. "Labour Force, Employed and Unemployed, Numbers and Rates, by Province." At: www.statcan.gc.ca/tables-tableaux/sum-som/l01/cst01/labor07c-eng.htm.

——. 2009f. "Gross Domestic Product, Expenditure-based, by Province and Territory." At: www.statcan.gc.ca/tables-tableaux/sum-som/l01/cst01/econ15-eng.htm.

——. 2009g. "Population, Age Distribution and Median Age by Province and Territory, as of July 1, 2008." At: www.statcan.gc.ca/daily-quotidien/090115/t090115c1-eng.htm.

——. 2009h. *Aboriginal Peoples in Canada in 2006: Inuit, Métis and First Nations, 2006 Census*. 2006 Analysis Series. At: www12.statcan.gc.ca/census-recensement/2006/as-sa/97-558/p2-eng.cfm#02.

——. 2009i. "Births." *The Daily*, 22 Sept. At: www.statcan.gc.ca/daily-quotidien/090922/dq090922b-eng.htm.

——. 2009j. *Immigration in Canada: A Portrait of the Foreign-born Population, 2006 Census: Immigrants Came from Many Countries*. At: www12.statcan.ca/census-recensement/2006/as-sa/97-557/figures/c2-eng.cfm.

——. 2009k. *Canadian Demographics at a Glance: Population Growth in Canada*. At: www.statcan.gc.ca/pub/91-003-x/2007001/figures/4129879-eng.htm.

——. 2009l. *2006 Census: Aboriginal Peoples in Canada in 2006: Inuit, Métis and First Nations, 2006 Census*. Catalogue no. 97-558-XIE2006001. At: http://www12.statcan.ca/census-recensement/2006/as-sa/97-558/p2-eng.cfm.

————. 2010a. "Ethnocultural Portrait of Canada." Highlight Tables, 2006 Census. At: www12.statcan.ca/census-recensement/2006/dp-pd/hlt/97-562/sel_geo.cfm?Lang=E&Geo=PR&Table=2.

————. 2010b. "Projections of the Diversity of the Canadian Population: Analysis of Results." 9 Mar. At: www.statcan.gc.ca/pub/91-551-x/2010001/ana-eng.htm.

————. 2011a. "Birth and Total Fertility Rate, by Province and Territory." 20 Dec. At: www.statcan.gc.ca/tables-tableaux/sum-som/l01/cst01/hlth85b-eng.htm.

————. 2011b. "Crude Birth Rate, Age-Specific and Total Fertility Rates (Live Births), Canada, Provinces and Territories." 19 Dec. At: www5.statcan.gc.ca/cansim/pick-choisir?lang=eng&p2=33&id=1024505.

————. 2011c. "Components of Population Growth, by Province and Territory." 28 Sept. At: www.statcan.gc.ca/tables-tableaux/sum-som/l01/cst01/demo33a-eng.htm.

————. 2011d. *Ethnic Origin Reference Guide, 2006 Census.* Catalogue no. 97-562-GWE200625, 5 May. At: www12.statcan.gc.ca/census-recensement/2006/ref/rp-guides/ethnic-ethnique-eng.cfm.

————. 2011e. *2011 Census of Population.* Statistics Canada Catalogue no. 98-314-XCB2011043. At: http://www12.statcan.gc.ca/census-recensement/2011/dp-pd/tbt-tt/Rp-eng.cfm?TABID=2&LANG=E&APATH=3&DETAIL=0&DIM=0&FL=A&FREE=0&GC=0&GK=0&GRP=1&PID=103395&PRID=0&PTYPE=101955&S=0&SHOWALL=0&SUB=0&Temporal=2011&THEME=90&VID=0&VNAMEE=&VNAMEF=.

————. 2012a. "Population and Dwelling Counts for Canada, Provinces and Territories, 2011 and 2006 censuses." 11 Apr. At: www12.statcan.gc.ca/census-recensement/2011/dp-pd/hlt-fst/pd-pl/Table-Tableau.cfm?LANG=Eng&T=101&S=50&O=A.

————. 2012b. "Population and Dwelling Counts, for Population Centres, 2011 and 2006 Censuses." 11 Apr. At: www12.statcan.gc.ca/census-recensement/2011/dp-pd/hlt-fst/pd-pl/Table-Tableau.cfm?LANG=Eng&T=801&SR=1&S=51&O=A&RPP=25&PR=0&CMA=0.

————. 2012c. "Population of Census Metropolitan Areas." 3 July. At: www.statcan.gc.ca/tables-tableaux/sum-som/l01/cst01/demo05a-eng.htm.

————. 2012d. "The Canadian Population in 2011: Population Counts and Growth." 30 May. At: www12.statcan.gc.ca/census-recensement/2011/as-sa/98-310-x/2011001/fig/fig2-eng.cfm.

————. 2012e. "Population by Broad Age Groups and Sex, 2011 Counts for Both Sexes, for Canada, Provinces and Territories." 17 July. At: www12.statcan.gc.ca/census-recensement/2011/dp-pd/hlt-fst/as-sa/Pages/highlight.cfm?TabID=1&Lang=E&Asc=1&PRCode=01&OrderBy=999&Sex=1&View=1&tableID=21&queryID=1.

————. 2012f. "Figure 2.4, Number of Children Age 14 and Under and Persons Aged 65 and Over, Canada, 1921 to 2011." Visual Census—Age and Sex, Canada, 5 July. At: www12.statcan.gc.ca/census-recensement/2011/dp-pd/vc-rv/index.cfm?Lang=eng.

————. 2012g. "Population by Broad Age Groups and Sex, Counts, Including Median Age, 1921 to 2011 for Both Sexes—Canada." 25 July. At: www12.statcan.gc.ca/census-recensement/2011/dp-pd/hlt-fst/as-sa/Pages/highlight.cfm?TabID=1&Lang=E&PRCode=01&Asc=0&OrderBy=1&Sex=1&View=1&tableID=22.

————. 2012h. *Immigrant Languages in Canada.* Oct. At: www12.statcan.gc.ca/census-recensement/2011/as-sa/98-314-x/98-314-X2011003_2-eng.pdf.

————. 2012i. "Population by Mother Tongue and Age Groups (Total), 2011 Counts, for Canada, Provinces and Territories." 24 Oct. At: www12.statcan.gc.ca/census-recensement/2011/dp-pd/hlt-fst/lang/Pages/highlight.cfm?TabID=1&Lang=E&Asc=1&PRCode=01&OrderBy=999&View=1&tableID=401&queryID=1&Age=1.

————. 2013a. "Population and Growth Rate of Metropolitan and Non-Metropolitan Canada, 2006 and 2011." 24 Jan. At: www12.statcan.gc.ca/census-recensement/2011/as-sa/98-310-x/2011001/tbl/tbl2-eng.cfm.

————. 2013b. "Number and Distribution of Population Reporting an Aboriginal Identity and Percentage of Aboriginal People in the Population, Canada, Provinces and Territories, 2011." *Aboriginal Peoples in Canada: First Nations People, Métis and Inuit.* National Household Survey document 99-011-x. Table 2. 7 May. At: http://www12.statcan.gc.ca/nhs-enm/2011/as-sa/99-011-x/2011001/tbl/tbl02-eng.cfm.

————. 2014a. "Population by Marital Status and Sex." 13 Nov. At: http://www.statcan.gc.ca/tables-tableaux/sum-som/l01/cst01/famil01-eng.htm.

————. 2014b. "Population Growth: Migratory Increase Overtakes Natural Increase." *Canadian Megatrends.* Catalogue no. 11-630-X. 9 Oct. At: http://www5.statcan.gc.ca/olccel/olc.action?objId=11-630-X2014001&objType=46&lang=en&limit=0.

————. 2014c. "Dependency Ratio (2011 Census and Administrative Data), by Age Group for July 1st, Canada, Provinces, Territories, Health Regions (2013 Boundaries) and Peer Groups." 12 June. At: http://www5.statcan.gc.ca/cansim/pick-choisir?lang=eng&p2=33&id=1095336, p. 24.

————. 2014d. "National Household Survey, Ethic Origin." Catalogue no. 99-010-X2011028. 4 Mar. At: http://www12.statcan.gc.ca/nhs-enm/2011/dp-pd/dt-td/Rp-eng.cfm?LANG=E&APATH=3&DETAIL=0&DIM=0&FL=A&FREE=0&GC=0&GID=0&GK=0&GRP=0&PID=105396&PRID=0&PTYPE=105277&S=0&SHOWALL=0&SUB=0&Temporal=2013&THEME=95&VID=0&VNAMEE=&VNAMEF=.

————. 2014e. "Immigration and Ethnocultural Diversity in Canada." Catalogue no. 99-010-X. 14 Jan. At: http://www12.statcan.gc.ca/nhs-enm/2011/as-sa/99-010-x/99-010-x2011001-eng.cfm#a6.

————. 2015a. "Quarterly Population Estimates National Perspective—Population," Table 1-1. Catalogue no. 91-002-X. 18 Mar. At: http://www.statcan.gc.ca/pub/91-002-x/2014004/t007-eng.htm.

————. 2015b. "Birth and Total Fertility Rate, by Province and Territory." 19 Mar. At: http://www.statcan.gc.ca/tables-tableaux/sum-som/l01/cst01/hlth85b-eng.htm.

————. 2015c. "Visual Census—Language, Canada." Tables 4.1 and 4.2. Catalogue no. 98-315-XWE. 23 Jan. At: http://www12.statcan.gc.ca/census-recensement/2011/dp-pd/vc-rv/index.cfm?LANG=ENG&VIEW=D&TOPIC_ID=4&GEOCODE=01&CFORMAT=jpg#fd4_1.

————. 2015d. "Total Projected Population of Canada (in thousands) in 2025 and 2050 According to Various Projection Scenarios." Table 2.2. 30 Nov. At: http://www.statcan.gc.ca/pub/91-520-x/2014001/tbl/tbl2.2-eng.htm.

————. 2015e. "Dependency Ratio." Modified 27 Nov. 2015. At: http://www.statcan.gc.ca/pub/82-229-x/2009001/demo/dep-eng.htm.

————. 2016a. "Estimates of Population, Canada, Provinces and Territories." CANSIM Table 051-0005. 16 Mar. At: http://www5.statcan.gc.ca/cansim/a26?lang=eng&id=510005.

————. 2016b. "Population of Census Metropolitan Areas. 10 Feb. At: http://www.statcan.gc.ca/tables-tableaux/sum-som/l01/cst01/demo05a-eng.htm.

————. 2016c. "Religion (108), Immigrant Status and Period of Immigration (11), Age Groups (10) and Sex (3) for the Population in Private Households of Canada, Provinces, Territories, Census Metropolitan Areas and Census Agglomerations, 2011 National Household Survey." Catalogue no. 99-010-X2011032. 7 Jan. At: http://www12.statcan.gc.ca/nhs-enm/2011/dp-pd/dt-td/Rp-eng.cfm?TABID=2&LANG=E&APATH=3&DETAIL=0&DIM=0&FL=A&

FREE=0&GC=0&GK=0&GRP=0&PID=105399&PRID=0&PTYPE
=105277&S=0&SHOWALL=0&SUB=0&Temporal=2013&THEME=
95&VID=0&VNAMEE=&VNAMEF=.

————. 2016d. "Components of Population Growth, Canada, Provinces and Territories, Annual (Persons)." CANSIM Table 051-0004, 4 Oct. At: http://www5.statcan.gc.ca/cansim/a21.

————. 2016e. "Estimates of Population, Canada, Provinces and Territories." CANSIM Table 051-0005, 16 Mar. At: http://www5.statcan.gc.ca/cansim/a26?lang=eng&id=510005.

————. 2016f. Focus on Geography Series, 2011 Census. "Census Subdivision of Timmins, CY—Ontario." 21 Sept. At: https://www12.statcan.gc.ca/census-recensement/2011/as-sa/fogs-spg/Facts-csd-eng.cfm?LANG=Eng&GK=CSD&GC=3556027.

————. 2016g. "The Evolution of English–French Bilingualism in Canada from 1901 to 2011." Megatrends. 28 Sept. At: http://www.statcan.gc.ca/pub/11-630-x/11-630-x2016001-eng.htm.

————. 2016h. "Birth and Total Fertility Rates, by Province and Territory." 26 Nov. At: http://www.statcan.gc.ca/tables-tableaux/sum-som/l01/cst01/hlth85b-eng.htm.

Steyn, Mark. 2006. America Alone: The End of the World As We Know It. Washington: Regnery Publishing.

Swift, John, and Lee Maracle. 2016. "Indigenous Men: Masculinity and Leadership." In David Long and Olive Patricia Dickason, eds, Visions of the Heart: Issues Involving Aboriginal Peoples in Canada, 4th edn. Toronto: Oxford University Press, 152–78.

Taylor, Charles. 1994. Multiculturalism: Examining the Politics of Recognition. Princeton, NJ: Princeton University Press.

Trewartha, G.T., A.H. Robinson, and E.H. Hammond. 1967. Elements of Geography, 5th edn. New York: McGraw-Hill.

Walks, R. Alan, and Larry S. Bourne. 2006. "Ghettos in Canada's Cities? Racial Segregation, Ethnic Enclaves and Poverty Concentration in Canadian Urban Areas." Canadian Geographer 50, 3: 273–97.

Woods, Alan. 2006. "Dual Citizenship Faces Review." National Post, 21 Sept. At: www.canada.com/nationalpost/news/story.html?id=fb2d75ab-8880-4945-8537-1508186a4964&k=61921.

CHAPTER 5

Adams, Christopher. 2016. "Breaking: NEB Cancels Energy East Hearing in Montreal as Protesters Stage Sit-in." National Observer. 29 Aug. At: http://nationalobserver.com/2016/08/29/news/breaking-neb-cancels-energy-east-hearing-montreal-protesters-storm-room.

Agrell, Siri. 2011. "Calgary Mayor Spreads a Gospel of Revenue Sharing," Globe and Mail, 22 Sept., A6.

Atkin, David. 2000. "In a Hot-Wired World, Everything's Personal." National Post, 15 Nov., C1, C6–C7.

Bank of Canada. 2016. Monetary Policy Report, July. At: http://www.bankofcanada.ca/wp-content/uploads/2016/07/mpr-2016-07-13.pdf.

BBC News. 2016. "G20 Leaders Told 'Avoid Empty Talk' by China's Xi Jinping." 4 Sept. At: http://www.bbc.com/news/business-37269954.

Bélanger-Barrette, Mathieu. 2014. "Top 5 Robotic Applications in the Automotive Industry." Robotiq, 4 Feb. At: http://blog.robotiq.com/bid/69722/Top-5-Robotic-Applications-in-the-Automotive-Industry.

Bell, Daniel. 1976. The Coming of the Post-Industrial Society. New York: Basic Books.

Bernard, André. 2009. "Trends in Manufacturing Employment." Perspective. Statistics Canada Catalogue no. 75-001xs. At: www.statcan.gc.ca/pub/75-001-x/2009102/pdf/10788-eng.pdf.

Britton, John N.H., ed. 1996. Canada and the Global Economy: The Geography of Structural and Technological Change. Montréal and Kingston: McGill-Queen's University Press.

Brooks, Stephen. 2012. Canadian Democracy, 7th edn. Toronto: Oxford University Press.

Burney, Derek and Fen Osler Hampson. 2012. "The Last Thing We Need Is Another Foreign Policy Review." Globe and Mail, 20 Jan., A13.

Canada. 2016. "Canada and the United States: Trade and Investment." 9 June. At: http://can-am.gc.ca/relations/commercial_relations_commerciales.aspx?lang=eng.

Canadian Press. 2016. "Enbridge's Northern Gateway Pipeline Approval Overturned by Federal Court." 30 June. At: http://www.bnn.ca/enbridge-s-northern-gateway-pipeline-approval-overturned-by-federal-court-1.518578.

Conference Board of Canada. 2015. "Conference Board of Canada Further Downgrades Canada's Growth Forecast." 29 July. At: http://www.conferenceboard.ca/press/newsrelease/15-07-29/conference_board_of_canada_further_downgrades_canada_s_growth_forecast.aspx.

Courchene, Thomas J., with Colin R. Telmer. 1998. From Heartland to North American Region State: The Social, Fiscal and Federal Evolution of Ontario. Monograph Series on Public Policy, Centre for Public Management. Toronto: Faculty of Management, University of Toronto.

Department of Finance. 2015. "Federal Support to Provinces and Territories." 30 Oct. At: http://www.fin.gc.ca/fedprov/mtp-eng.asp.

Dragicevic, Nevena. 2014. "How Ontario Lost 300,000 Manufacturing Jobs (and Why Most Aren't Coming Back)." Mowat Centre. 29 July. At: https://mowatcentre.ca/how-ontario-lost-300000-manufacturing-jobs/.

Drucker, Peter. 1969. The Age of Discontinuity. London: Heinemann.

EIA. 2016. Annual Energy Outlook 2016, 7 July. At: https://www.eia.gov/outlooks/aeo/er/.

Evans, Pete. 2016. "Canadian Housing Market Hits $508,097 Average Price in April as Sales Rise to Record." CBC News, 16 May. At: http://www.cbc.ca/news/business/crea-housing-april-1.3583942.

Feehan, Jim. 2014. "Canada's Equalization Formula: Peering Inside the Black Box . . . and Beyond." SSP Research Papers, vol. 7, issue 24. School of Public Policy, University of Calgary. At: http://policyschool.ucalgary.ca/sites/default/files/research/feehan-equalization.pdf.

Florida, Richard. 2002a. "The Economic Geography of Talent." Annals, Association of American Geographers 92: 743–55.

————. 2002b. The Rise of the Creative Class: And How It's Transforming Work, Leisure, Community and Everyday Life. New York: Basic Books.

————. 2005. Cities and the Creative Class. London: Routledge.

————. 2008. Who's Your City? How the Creative Economy Is Making Where to Live the Most Important Decision of Your Life. New York: Basic Books.

————. 2012. The Rise of the Creative Class—Revisited. New York: Basic Books.

———— and S. Jackson. 2010. "Sonic City: The Evolving Economic Geography of the Music Industry." Journal of Planning, Education and Research 29, 3: 310–21.

————, C. Mellander, and K. Stolarick. 2010. "Talent, Technology, and Tolerance in Canadian Regional Development." Canadian Geographer 54, 3: 277–304.

Ford, Martin. 2015. Rise of the Robots: Technology and the Threat of a Jobless Future. New York: Basic Books.

Gollom, Mark. 2016. "Black Lives Matter Got Attention, but Did Its Pride Tactics Hurt or Help Its Cause? CBC News, 5 July. At: http://www.cbc.ca/news/canada/toronto/black-lives-matter-toronto-pride-parade-1.3663659?cmp=rss.

Gordon, Robert J. 2016. The Rise and Fall of American Growth. Princeton, NJ: Princeton University Press.

Harvey, David. 1989. The Urban Experience. Baltimore: Johns Hopkins University Press.

Heap, Alan. 2005. "China—The Engine of a Commodities Super Cycle." Citigroup, 31 Mar. At: www.fallstreet.com/Commodities_China_Engine0331.pdf.

Hodgson, Glen. 2016. "Change of Course Needed to Revive Canada's Manufacturing." Conference Board of Canada. 14 Jan. At: http://www.conferenceboard.ca/press/speech_oped/15-01-16/change_of_course_needed_to_revive_canadian_manufacturing.aspx.

Hracs, Brian J., Jill L. Grant, Jeffry Haggett, and Jesse Morton. 2011. "Tale of Two Scenes: Civic Capital and Retaining Musical Talent in Toronto and Halifax." *Canadian Geographer* 55, 3: 365–82.

International Monetary Fund (IMF). 2016. "Subdued Demand: Symptoms and Remedies." *World Economic Outlook*. Oct. At: http://www.imf.org/external/pubs/ft/weo/2016/02/.

Keenan, Greg. 2012. "In Tough Times, Cut Auto Workers' Wages, Report Urges," *Globe and Mail*, 21 Mar., B3.

———. 2015. "Made in Mexico: An Emerging Auto Giant Powers Past Canada." *Globe and Mail*, 13 Feb. At: http://www.theglobeandmail.com/report-on-business/international-business/latin-american-business/mexico-feature/article22987307/.

La Caixa. 2015. "Has the Commodity Supercycle Come to an End?" La Caixa Economic Research Department. 22 June. At: http://www.fxstreet.com/analysis/economic-monthly-report/2015/06/22/.

McGregor, Janyce. 2016. "U.S. Lumber Coalition Files Petition, Restarting Canada–U.S. Softwood Lumber Hostilities." CBC News, 25 Nov. At: http://www.cbc.ca/news/politics/softwood-lumber-canada-united-states-filing-friday-1.3868117.

McKenna, Barrie. 2016. "Business Hiring, Speeding Plans at Lowest since 2009: Bank of Canada." *Globe and Mail*, 11 Jan. At: http://www.theglobeandmail.com/report-on-business/economy/businesses-outside-oil-patch-now-feeling-sting-of-commodity-price-rout-boc/article28105709/.

McVey, Wayne W., and W.E. Kalbach. 1995. *Canadian Population*. Toronto: Nelson Canada.

Mann, Catherine L. 2016. "Policymakers: Act Now to Break out of the Low-Growth Trap and Deliver on Our Promises." OECD *Ecoscope*. 1 June. At: https://oecdecoscope.wordpress.com/2016/06/01/policymakers-act-now-to-break-out-of-the-low-growth-trap-and-deliver-on-our-promises/.

Milner, Brian. 2016. "How to diversify an economy: Four lessons for Canada." *Globe and Mail*, 26 Aug. B8.

Rostow, W.W. 1960. *The Stages of Economic Growth: A Non-Communist Manifesto*. Cambridge: Cambridge University Press.

Royal Bank. 2016. "Canadian Federal and Provincial Fiscal Tables." 4 Aug. At: http://www.rbc.com/economics/economic-reports/pdf/provincial-forecasts/prov_fiscal.pdf.

Sachs, Jeffery D. 2015. *The End of Poverty: Economic Possibilities for Our Times*. New York: Penguin Books.

Schwab, Klaus. 2016. *The Fourth Industrial Revolution*. Geneva: World Economic Forum.

Smith, Matt. 2016. "Oil Prices in Freefall as Fundamentals Worsen." *OilPrice.com*. 31 Aug. At: http://oilprice.com/Energy/Energy-General/Oil-Prices-In-Freefall-As-Fundamentals-Worsen.html.

Statistics Canada. 2006. "Labour Force Survey." *The Daily*, 10 Feb. At: http://www.statcan.ca/Daily/English/060210/d060210a.htm.

———. 2009. "Chart 21.1 (data) Unemployment Rate," 16 Jan. At: www41.statcan.gc.ca/2008/2621/grafx/htm/ceb2621_000_1-eng.htm#table.

———. 2010. "Labour Force, Employed and Unemployed, Numbers and Rates, by Province." 29 Jan. At: http://www.statcan.gc.ca/tables-tableaux/sum-som/l01/cst01/labor07b-eng.htm.

———. 2011. "Canada's International Merchandise Trade: Annual Review." *The Daily*, 7 Apr., Table 1. At: www.statcan.gc.ca/daily-quotidien/110407/t110407b1-eng.htm.

———. 2012a. "Labour Force Survey Estimates (LFS), by North American Industrial Classification System (NAICS), Sex and Age Group, Unadjusted for Seasonability, May 1977 to June 2012." 6 July. CANSIM Table 282–007. At: www5.statcan.gc.ca/cansim/a26?lang=eng&retrLang=eng&id=2820007&pattern=282-0001..282-0042&tabMode=dataTable&srchLan=-1&p1=-1&p2=-1.

———. 2012b. "Canada Economic Accounts First Quarter 2012 and March 2012." *The Daily*, 1 June, Chart 1. At: www.statcan.gc.ca/daily-quotidien/120601/dq120601a-eng.htm.

———. 2015a. "Merchandise Exports and Imports, by Origin and Destination, 1977 to 2011." Table 20.3. 20 Dec. At: www.statcan.gc.ca/;pub/11-402-x/2012000/chap/international/tb1/tb103-eng.htm.

———. 2015b. "Annual Average Unemployment Rate Canada and Provinces 1976–2014." 28 Jan. At: http://www.stats.gov.nl.ca/statistics/Labour/PDF/UnempRate.pdf.

———. 2015c. "Employment by Industry." 28 Jan. At: http://www.statcan.gc.ca/tables-tableaux/sum-som/l01/cst01/econ40-eng.htm.

———. 2016a. "Labour Force Characteristics, Seasonally Adjusted, by Province (Monthly)." 4 Nov. At: http://www.statcan.gc.ca/tables-tableaux/sum-som/l01/cst01/lfss01a-eng.htm.

———. 2016b. "Imports, Exports and Trade Balance of Goods on a Balance-of-Payments Basis, by Country or Country Grouping." 1 Mar. At: http://www.statcan.gc.ca/tables-tableaux/sum-som/l01/cst01/gblec02a-eng.htm.

———. 2016c. "Distribution of Employed People, by Industry, by Province." 8 Jan. At: http://www.statcan.gc.ca/tables-tableaux/sum-som/l01/cst01/labor21a-eng.htm.

———. 2016d. "Annual Merchandise Trade: Canada's Top 10 Principal Trading Partners, Seasonally Adjusted, Current Dollars." Table 3. 6 Apr. At: http://www.statcan.gc.ca/daily-quotidien/160406/t003a-eng.htm.

———. 2016e. "Gross Domestic Product, Expenditure-based." Table 380-0064. 31 Aug. At: http://www5.statcan.gc.ca/cansim/a46?lang=eng&childId=3800064&CORId=3764&viewId=3.

———. 2016f. "Gross Domestic Product by Industry: Provinces and Territories, 2015." *The Daily*, 12 May. At: http://www.statcan.gc.ca/daily-quotidien/160512/dq160512b-eng.htm.

Tang, Justin. 2016. "Timing of Economic Rebound from Alberta Wildfire Hard to Forecast, Stephen Poloz Says." CBC News, 4 June. At: http://www.cbc.ca/news/business/alberta-wildfire-economy-poloz-1.3616894.

Taxpayers.com. 2016. "Debt Clock." At: http://www.debtclock.ca.

Trading Economics. 2016. "Canada GDP Annual Growth Rate: 1962–2016." At: http://www.tradingeconomics.com/canada/gdp-growth-annual.

US Energy Information Administration. 2016. "Crude Oil Prices Started 2015 Relatively Low, Ended the Year Lower." 6 Jan. At: http://www.eia.gov/todayinenergy/detail.cfm?id=24432.

Wherry, Aaron. 2016a. "Trudeau Touts Canada's Diversity and Resourcefulness in Davos." CBC News, 20 Jan. At: http://www.cbc.ca/news/politics/trudeau-davos-future-look-economy-harper-1.3412182.

———. 2016b. "For Trudeau and Trans Mountain, It Could Be All Over but the Shouting." CBC News, 29 Nov. At: http://www.cbc.ca/news/politics/wherry-trudeau-pipelines-1.3873174.

Wilkins, Carolyn, and Stephen S. Poloz. 2016. "Monetary Policy Report Press Conference Opening Statement." 13 July. At: http://www.bankofcanada.ca/2016/07/opening-statement-130716/.

Younglai, Rachelle. 2014. "Wabush Woes: Labrador Town Reels from China Slowdown." *Globe and Mail*, 28 Nov. At: http://www.theglobeandmail.com/report-on-business/industry-news/energy-and-resources/wabush-woes-labrador-mining-town-reels-from-a-china-slowdown/article21836552/.

CHAPTER 6

Arcand, Alan, Robin Wiebe, Jane McIntyre, and Constantinos Bougas. 2015. "Hamilton's Economy Continues Its Recovery in 2015." Conference Board of Canada. 14 May. At: http://www.conferenceboard.ca/press/newsrelease/15-0514/hamilton_s_economy_continues_its_recovery_in_2015.aspx.

Berman, David. 2016a. 'In-branch Tellers Bear the Brunt of RBC Cost Cuts." *Globe and Mail*, 7 Sept. At: http://www.theglobeandmail.com/report-on-business/streetwise/in-branch-tellers-bear-the-brunt-of-rbc-cost-cuts/article31751181/.

——. 2016b. "Laurentian Bank to Shut Down Dozens of Branches, Cut 300 Jobs." *Globe and Mail*, 28 Sept. At: http://www.theglobeandmail.com/report-on-business/laurentian-bank-to-shut-down-dozens-of-branches-cut-300-jobs/article32110758/.

—— and Tim Kiladze. 2016. "Shaking up Scotiabank: Brian Porter's Vision for a Bank of the Future." *Globe and Mail*, 22 July. At: http://www.theglobeandmail.com/report-on-business/shaking-up-scotiabank-brian-porters-vision-for-a-bank-of-the-future/article31085736/.

Bernard, Andre. 2013. "Recent Trends in Canadian Automobile Industries 1992 to 2012." *Economic Insights*. Statistics Canada Catalogue no. 11-626-x-26. At: http://www.statcan.gc.ca/pub/11-626-x/11-626-x2013026-eng.htm.

——and Jeannine Usalcas. 2014. "The Labour Market in Canada and the United States since the Last Recession." *Economic Insights*. Statistics Canada Catalogue no. 11-626-x-36. At: http://www.statcan.gc.ca/pub/11-626-x/11-626-x2014036-eng.pdf.

Bone, Robert M. 2012. *The Canadian North: Issues and Challenges*. Fourth Edition. Toronto: Oxford University Press.

Bone, Robert M. 2016. *The Canadian North: Issues and Challenges*, 5th edn. Toronto: Oxford University Press.

Brennan, Richard J. 2015. "Liberals Failing to Deliver on Ring of Fire, Opposition Says." *Toronto Star*, 23 June. At: http://www.thestar.com/news/queenspark/2015/06/23/liberals-failing-to-deliver-on-ring-of-fire-opposition-says.html.

Britton, John N.H. 1996. "High-Tech Canada." In Britton, ed., *Canada and the Global Economy: The Geography of Structural and Technological Change*. Montréal and Kingston: McGill-Queen's University Press.

Canadian Auto Workers Union. 2012. *Re-thinking Canada's Auto Industry: A Policy Vision to Escape the Race to the Bottom*, Apr. At: https://d3n8a8pro7vhmx.cloudfront.net/caw/pages/29/attachments/original/1335189435/554AutoPolicyDocumentweb.pdf?1335189435.

Canadian Press. 2016. "GM Workers Accept Tentative Agreement." *Toronto Star*, 25 Sept. At: https://www.thestar.com/business/2016/09/25/gm-workers-vote-on-tentative-agreement-sunday.html.

CBC News. 2006. "Caledonia Land Claim: Historical Timeline." 1 Nov. At: www.cbc.ca/news/background/caledonia-landclaim/historical-timeline.html.

Chubb, Christine. 2015. "Breathe Easier: Smog-free Days the Norm as City's Air Quality Improves." City News, 17 Aug. At: http://www.citynews.ca/2015/08/17/breathe-easier-smog-free-days-the-norm-as-citys-air-quality-improves/.

Church, Elizabeth. 2012. "MIT to Honour Two Professors Transforming the World from Toronto." *Globe and Mail*, 21 Aug., A5.

Cleroux, N., and M. Woods. 2012. "The Plasco Energy Group's Plasma Gasification System." 22 May. At: wiki.telfer.uottawa.ca/ci-wiki/index.php/The_Plasco_Energy_Group's_Plasma_Gasification_System.

Cole, Trevor. 2009. "Hamilton's Dead. Or Is It?" *Globe and Mail*, 28 Aug. At: http://www.theglobeandmail.com/report-on-business/rob-magazine/hamiltons-dead-or-is-it/article1264739/.

Courchene, Thomas J., with Colin R. Telmer. 1998. *From Heartland to North American Region State: The Social, Fiscal and Federal Evolution of Ontario*. Monograph Series on Public Policy, Centre for Public Management. Toronto: Faculty of Management, University of Toronto.

CTV News. 2006. "Canada, U.S. Agree on Softwood Framework." 26 Apr. At: www.ctv.ca/servlet/ArticleNews/story/CTVNews/20060426/softwood_deal_060426/20060426?hub=Canada.

Cuddy, James. 2015. "From Laggard to Leader (Almost)." *Commentary* 5. Northern Policy Institute, Thunder Bay. At: http://www.northernpolicy.ca/upload/documents/publications/commentaries/paper-from-laggard-to-leader--almost--no.pdf.

Curry, Bill. 2016. "Road to Ring of Fire Could Cost up to $550-Million." *Globe and Mail*, 26 Aug. At: http://www.theglobeandmail.com/news/politics/road-to-ring-of-fire-could-cost-up-to-550-million/article31585443/.

Darling, Graham. 2007. "Land Claims and the Six Nations in Caledonia Ontario." Centre for Constitutional Studies. At: www.law.ualberta.ca/centres/ccs/Current-Constitutional-Issues/Land-Claims-and-the-Six-Nations-in-Caledonia-Ontario.php.

Department of Finance Canada. 2015. "Federal Support to Provinces and Territories." 30 Oct. At: https://www.fin.gc.ca/fedprov/mtp-eng.asp.

Dickason, Olive Patricia, with David T. McNab. 2009. *Canada's First Nations: A History of Founding Peoples from Earliest Times*, 4th edn. Toronto: Oxford University Press.

Dicken, Peter. 1992. *Global Shift: The Internationalization of Economic Activity*, 2nd edn. New York: Guilford Press.

Di Matteo, Livio. 2006. "Breakaway Country." *National Post*, 6 Sept., FP19.

——. 2012. "2011 Census Results for Population In: Northern Ontario Declines." *Northern Economist 2.0*. 8 Feb. At: http://northerneconomist.blogspot.ca/2012/02/2011-census-results-for-population-in.html.

Dragicevic, Nevena. 2014. "How Ontario Lost 300,000 Manufacturing Jobs (and Why Most Aren't Coming Back)." Mowat Centre. 29 July. At: https://mowatcentre.ca/how-ontario-lost-300000-manufacturing-jobs/.

Drummond, Don, and Derek Burleton. 2008. "Time for a Vision of Ontario's Economy." At: http://www.td.com/document/PDF/economics/special/td-economics-special-db0908-ont.pdf.

Economist, The. 2015. "Canada's Car Industry: The Road to Nowhere." 9 Apr. At: economist.com/news/business-and-finance/21648065-canadian-government-no-longer-propping-up-carmakers-dead-not-forgotten.

Environment Canada. 2006. "Information on Greenhouse Gas Sources and Sinks." At: www.ec.gc.ca/pdb/ghg/onlineData/dataAndReports_e.cfm.

Flavelle, Dana. 2012. "Canadian Auto Workers at Ford Accept Contract." *Toronto Star*, 23 Sept. At: www.thestar.com/business/2012/09/23/canadian_auto_workers_at_ford_accept_contract.html.

——. 2016. "General Motors to Create 700 Technical Jobs in Ontario." *Toronto Star*, 10 June. At: https://www.thestar.com/business/2016/06/10/general-motors-to-create-700-technical-jobs-in-ontario.html.

Florida, Richard. 2002. *The Rise of the Creative Class: And How It's Transforming Work, Leisure, Community and Everyday Life*. New York: Basic Books.

——. 2012. *The Rise of the Creative Class—Revisited*. New York: Basic Books.

—— and S. Jackson. 2010. "Sonic City: The Evolving Economic Geography of the Music Industry." *Journal of Planning, Education and Research* 29, 3: 310–21.

——, C. Mellander, and K. Stolarick. 2010. "Talent, Technology, and Tolerance in Canadian Regional Development." *Canadian Geographer* 54, 3: 277–304.

Green, Kenneth P., Taylor Jackson, and Ian Herzog. 2016. "High Electricity Prices Putting Rural Ontario in Energy Poverty." *Fraser Forum*. Fraser Institute. 6 July. At: https://www.fraserinstitute.org/blogs/high-electricity-prices-putting-rural-ontario-in-energy-poverty.

Hodgson, Glen. 2016. "Signs of Optimism? The Canadian Economy Entering 2017—Insights from the Chief Economist." Conference Board of Canada, 24 Aug. At: http://www.conferenceboard.ca/e-library/abstract.aspx?did=8073.

Hracs, Brian J., Jill L. Grant, Jeffry Haggett, and Jesse Morton. 2011. "Tale of Two Scenes: Civic Capital and Retaining Musical Talent in Toronto and Halifax." *Canadian Geographer* 55, 3: 365–82.

Hunter, Julie. 2016. "Electric Vehicle Sales in Canada: Q3 2016 Update." Fleetcarma. Nov. At: http://www.fleetcarma.com/ev-sales-canada-2016-q3/.

Indigenous and Northern Affairs Canada (INAC). 2009. "Chronology of Events at Caledonia." At: www.ainc-inac.gc.ca/ai/mr/is/eac-eng.asp.

Industry Canada. 2015a. "Assembly Plants in Canada—2015." 16 May. At: https://www.ic.gc.ca/eic/site/auto-auto.nsf/eng/am00767.html.

———. 2015b. "Motor Vehicle Manufacturing (NAICS 3361): Employment." 21 July. At: https://www.ic.gc.ca/app/scr/sbms/sbb/cis/employment.html?code=3361&lang=eng.

———. 2015c. "Motor Vehicle Parts Manufacturing (NAICS 3363): Employment." 7 July. At: https://www.ic.gc.ca/app/scr/sbms/sbb/cis/employment.html?code=3363&lang=eng.

International Great Lakes Study. 2012. *Final Report to the International Joint Commission: Lake Superior Regulation: Addressing Uncertainty in Upper Great Lakes Water Levels.* Mar. At: www.ijc.org/iuglsreport/wp-content/report-pdfs/Lake_Superior_Regulation_Full_Report.pdf.

Ipperwash Inquiry (Ont.), and Sidney B. Linden. 2007. *Report of the Ipperwash Inquiry.* Toronto: Published by Ministry of the Attorney General, Queen's Printer for Ontario.

JAMA Canada. 2010. "Monthly and Annual Statistics for JAMA Canada Member Companies." 18 Mar. At: www.jama.ca/jamastats/.

Jamasmie, Cecilia. 2014. "De Beers Not Ruling Out Expansion of Its Victor Diamond Mine in Canada." Mining.com. At: http://www.mining.com/de-beers-not-ruling-out-expansion-of-its-victor-diamond-mine-in-canada-68578/.

Keenan, Greg. 2015. "Made in Mexico: An Emerging Auto Giant Powers Past Canada." *Globe and Mail*, 13 Feb. At: http://www.theglobeandmail.com/report-on-business/international-business/latin-american-business/mexico-feature/article22987307/.

———. 2016a. "GM Switches Gears by Adding Engineering Muscle to Canada." *Globe and Mail*, 19 June. At: http://www.theglobeandmail.com/report-on-business/international-business/us-business/gm-switches-gears-by-adding-engineering-muscle-to-canada/article30396906/.

———. 2016b. "GM in Line for $200-Million in Support from Ontario, Ottawa." *Globe and Mail*, 26 Sept. At: http://www.theglobeandmail.com/report-on-business/industry-news/gm-in-line-for-200-million-in-support-from-ontario-ottawa/article32060730/.

——— and Steven Chase. 2013. "Auto Makers Get $250-Million as Ottawa Renews Innovation Fund." *Globe and Mail*, 4 Jan. At: www.theglobeandmail.com/report-on-business/economy/auto-makers-get-250-million-as-ottawa-renews-innovation-fund/article6934817/.

Klasing, Amanda. 2016. "Why Is Canada Denying Its Indigenous Peoples Clean Water?" *Globe and Mail*, 30 Aug. At: http://www.theglobeandmail.com/opinion/why-is-canada-denying-its-indigenous-peoples-clean-water/article31599791/.

Leslie, Keith. 2012. "TransCanada Inks Deal to operate Controversial Ontario Power Plant," *Globe and Mail*, 17 Dec. At www.theglobeandmail.com/news/national/transcanada-inks-deal-to-operate-controversial-ontario-power-plant/article6480885/.

———. 2014. "Ottawa Urged to Settle Six Nations Land Claim in Caledonia." CTV News, 11 July. At: http://ctvnews.ca/politics/ottawa-urged-to-settle-six-nations-land-claim-in-caledonia-1.1909627.

McCarthy, Shawn. 2013. "As Cost Pressures Mount, Ontario's Wholesale Power Prices to Soar." *Globe and Mail*, 30 Jan. At: www.theglobeandmail.com/report-on-business/industry-news/energy-and-resources/as-cost-pressures-mount-ontarios-wholesale-power-prices-set-to-soar/article8025566/.

Macaluso, Grace. 2016. "Unifor's GM Investment Win 'Miraculous,' Says Pupatello." *Windsor Star*, 27 Sept.. At: http://windsorstar.com/business/local-business/unifors-gm-,investment-win-miraculous-says-pupatello.

Mehta, Diana. 2016. "Ottawa, Ontario First Nation Sign Settlement over Camp Ipperwash." *Globe and Mail*, 14 Apr. At: http://www.theglobeandmail.com/new/politics/ottawa-ontario-first-nation-sign-settlement-over-camp-ipperwash/article29640093/.

Milke, Mark, and Youri Chassin. 2016. "Viewpoint—Is Ontario the New Quebec?" Montreal Economic Institute (MEI). 11 Aug. At: http://www.iedm.org/62775-viewpoint-is-ontario-the-new-quebec.

Moro, Teviah. 2016. "Native Claims on Caledonia Housing Land Heat Up." *Hamilton Spectator*, 13 Jan. At: http://www.thespec.com/news-story/6230665-native-claims-on-caledonia-housing-land -heat-up/.

National Post. 2007. "Ipperwash Report." 1 June, A14.

Natural Resources Canada. 2012. "Table 2: Revised Statistics of the Mineral Production of Canada, by Province, 2012." At: http://publications.gc.ca/collections/collection_2014/rncan-nrcan/M31-12-2012.pdf.

———. 2015a. *The State of Canada's Forests: Annual Report 2014.* At: http://cfs.nrcan.gc.ca/pubwarehouse/pdfs/35713.pdf.

———. 2015b. "Current Lumber, Pulp and Panel Prices." 28 July. At: http://www.nrcan.gc.ca/forests/industry/current-prices/13309#softwood.

———. 2015c. "Preliminary Estimate of the Mineral Production of Canada, by Province, 2014." 16 Aug. At: http://sead.nrcan.gc.ca/prod-prod/2014p-eng.aspx.

———. 2016. *Minerals and Metals Fact Book—2016.* At: http://www.nrcan.gc.ca/sites/www.nrcan.gc.ca/files/mineralsmetals/pdf/mms-smm/Minerals%20and%20Metals_factbook_En.pdf.

OICA (International Organization of Motor Vehicle Manufacturers). 2015. "Production Statistics." At: http://www.oica.net/category/production-statistics/2015-statistics/.

Ontario Energy Board. 2015. "Electricity Data: First Quarter 2015." *Ontario Energy Report.* At: http://www.ontarioenergyreport.ca.

Ontario Ministry of Agriculture. 2016. "Statistical Summary of Ontario Agriculture." 6 Jan. At: http://www.omafra.gov.on.ca/english/stats/agriculture_summary.htm#first.

Ontario Ministry of Finance. 2014. "Ontario Budget 2014: Ontario Jobs and Economy Plan—Creating Jobs for Today and Tomorrow." 1 May. At: http://www.fin.gov.on.ca/en/budget/ontariobudgets/2014/budhi1.html.

———. 2015a. *2015 Ontario Budget: Building Ontario Up.* 30 Apr. At: http://www.fin.gov.on.ca/en/budget/ontariobudgets/2015/.

———. 2015b. "Ontario Economic Accounts—First Quarter of 2015." 14 July. At: http://www.fin.gov.on.ca/en/economy/ecaccts/.

———. 2015c. "Ontario Real GDP Per Capita." *Ontario's Long-Term Report on the Economy: Chapter 2: Long-Term Ontario Economic Projection*, Chart 2.11. At: http://www.fin.gov.on.ca/en/economy/ltr/2014/ch2.html#ch2_c10.

———. 2016a. "Population Projections Update, 2015–2041." 20 June. At: http://www.fin.gov.on.ca/en/economy/demographics/projections/#s3cc.

———. 2016b. "Ontario Trade Fact Sheet." May. At: http://www.sourcefromontario.com/tradefactsheet/en/page/tradefactsheet_ontario.php.

Ontario Ministry of Natural Resources. 2012. "The Value of Ontario's Forest Sector." At: www.mnr.gov.on.ca/en/Business/Forests/2ColumnSubPage/STEL02_167493.h.

Patrick, Robert. 2017. "Indigenizing Source Water Protection." In Robert M. Bone and Robert B. Anderson, eds, *Indigenous Peoples and Resource Development in Canada.* Toronto: Captus Press.

Porter, Jody. 2013. "First Nations Must 'Learn from' De Beers Deal." CBC News, 13 Feb. At: http://www.cbc.ca/news/canada/thunder-bay/first-nations-must-learn-from-de-beers-deal-1.1327592.

Preston, Valerie, and Lucia Lo. 2000. "Canadian Urban Landscape Examples—21: 'Asian Theme' Malls in Suburban Toronto: Land Use Conflicts in Richmond Hill." *Canadian Geographer* 44, 2: 182–90.

Pulp and Paper Canada. 2013. "Domtar Sells Former E.B. Eddy Sites in Ottawa and Gatineau." 11 Dec. At: http://www.pulpandpaper canada.com/sustainability/domtar-sells-former-mill-site-in-ottawa-1002792504.

Royal Bank of Canada. 2012. *Provincial Outlook: Ontario.* Sept. At: www.rbc.com/newsroom/pdf/provfcst-09-2012.pdf.

Scotiabank. 2013. *Global Forecast Update.* 28 Feb. At: www.gbm.scotiabank.com/English/bns_econ/forecast.pdf.

Shecter, Barbara. 2015. "Bank of Montreal Tests New Smaller Branches without Physical Tellers." *Financial Post,* 30 Mar. At: http://business.financialpost.com/news/fp-street/bank-of-montreal-tests-new-smaller-branches-without-physical-tellers.

Shiell, Leslie, and Robin Somerville. 2012. *Bailouts and Subsidies: The Economics of Assisting the Automotive Sector in Canada.* IRPP Study No. 28, Mar. At: www.irpp.org/pubs/IRPPstudy/IRPP_Study_no28.pdf.

Shkilnyk, A.M. 1985. *A Poison Stronger Than Love: The Destruction of an Ojibwa Community.* New Haven: Yale University Press.

Siekierska, Alicia. 2016. "Signs in Toronto Urge White People to Join 'Alt-Right'." *Toronto Star,* 14 Nov. At: https://www.thestar.com/news/gta/2016/11/14/signs-in-toronto-urge-white-people-to-join-alt-right.html.

Spears, John. 2013. "Ontario Coal-burning Power Plants to Close This Year." *Toronto Star,* 28 Feb. At: www.thestar.com/business/2013/01/10/ontario_coalburning_power_plants_to_close_this_year.html.

Statista. 2016. "Statistics on Vehicle Production." *Statista: The Statistics Portal.* At: https://www.statista.com/search/?q=vehicle+production&qKat=tag.

Statistics Canada. 2002. "2001 Census: Population and Dwelling Counts, for Census Metropolitan Areas and Census Agglomerations, 2001 and 1996 Censuses." 16 July. At: www.statcan.ca/English/IPS/Data/93F0050XCB2001013.htm.

———. 2006. "Canadian Statistics: Distribution of Employed People, by Industry, by Province." At: www40.statcan.ca/101/cst01/labor21c.htm.

———. 2007a. "Population Urban and Rural, by Province and Territory: 1851 to 2001." At: www40.statcan.ca/l01/cst01/demo62g.htm.

———. 2007b. "Population and Dwelling Counts, for Census Metropolitan Areas and Census Agglomerations, 2006 and 2001 Censuses—100% Data." At: www12.statcan.ca/english/census06/data/popdwell/Table.cfm?T=201&S=3&O=D&RPP=150.

———. 2012a. "Labour Force Survey, July 2012." *The Daily,* 10 Aug. At: www.statcan.gc.ca/daily-quotidien/120810/dq120810a-eng.htm.

———. 2012b. "Unemployment Rate, Canada, Provinces, Health Regions (2011 Boundaries) and Peer Groups." 24 May. At: www5.statcan.gc.ca/cansim/pick-choisir?lang=eng&p2=33&id=1095324.

———. 2012c. "Population by Broad Age Groups and Sex, 2011 Counts for Both Sexes, for Canada, Provinces and Territories, and Census Divisions." 25 July. At: www12.statcan.gc.ca/census-recensement/2011/dp-pd/hlt-fst/as-sa/Pages/highlight.cfm?TabID=1&Lang=E&Asc=1&OrderBy=1&Sex=1&View=1&tableID=21&queryID=5&PRCode=35.

———. 2012d. "Census of Agriculture." *The Daily,* 10 May. At: www.statcan.gc.ca/daily-quotidien/120510/dq120510a-eng.htm.

———. 2012e. "Distribution of Employed People, by Industry, by Province." 1 June. At: www.statcan.gc.ca/tables-tableaux/sum-som/l01/cst01/labor21a-eng.htm.

———. 2012f. "Export of Goods on a Balance-of-Payments Basis, by Product." 10 May. At: www.statcan.gc.ca/tables-tableaux/sum-som/l01/cst01/gblec04-eng.htm.

———. 2012g. "Population and Dwelling Counts, for Census Metropolitan Areas and Census Agglomerations, 2011 and 2006 Censuses." 11 Apr. At: www12.statcan.gc.ca/census-recensement/2011/dp-pd/hlt-fst/pd-pl/Table-Tableau.cfm?LANG=Eng&T=201&S=3&O=D&RPP=150.

———. 2013. "Number and Distribution of Population Reporting an Aboriginal Identity and Percentage of Aboriginal People in the Population, Canada, Provinces and Territories, 2011." *Aboriginal Peoples in Canada: First Nations People, Métis and Inuit.* National Household Survey document 99-011-x. Table 2. 7 May. At: http://www12.statcan.gc.ca/nhs-enm/2011/as-sa/99-011-x/2011001/tbl/tbl02-eng.cfm.

———. 2014. "NHS Focus on Geography Series—Thunder Bay." 17 Apr. At: http://www12.statcan.gc.ca/nhs-enm/2011/as-sa/fogs-spg/Pages/FOG.cfm?lang=E&level=3&GeoCode=595.

———. 2016a. "Farm Cash Receipts." CANSIM Table 002-0001. 25 May. At: http://www5.statcan.gc.ca/cansim/a26.

———. 2016b. "Population of Census Metropolitan Areas." 10 Feb. At: http://www.statcan.gc.ca/tables-tableaux/sum-som/l01/cst01/demo05a-eng.htm.

———. 2016c. "Employment by Major Industry Group, Seasonally Adjusted, by Province." 10 June. At: http://www.statcan.gc.ca/tables-tableaux/sum-som/l01/cst01/labr67a-eng.htm.

The Economist. 2016. "The most livable cities". 18 Aug. At: http://www.economist.com/blogs/graphicdetail/2016/08/daily-chart-14

Talaga, Tanya. 2015. "Cree Community Looks on Warily as De Beers Eyes New Diamond Mine." *Toronto Star,* 10 Oct. At: http://www.thestar.com/news/insight/2015/10/10/cree-community-looks-on-warily-as-de-beers-eyes-new-diamond-mine.html.

Wallace, Don. 2016. "Showdown at the Ring: Which Route Will Win Out: North–South or East–West?" *Chronicle Journal.* 11 June. At: http://www.chroniclejournal.com/opinion/letters_to_editor/showdown-at-the-ring-which-route-will-win-out-north/article_7543c2f6-2f4e-11e6-8d9a-3bb125894d25.html.

Windmill Developments. 2015. *Zibi: Domtar Lands Redevelopment.* 30 Mar. At: http://www.windmilldevelopments.com/wp-content/uploads/2015/05/Zibi_ExecutiveSummary_Final.pdf.

Wine Country Ontario. n.d. "All About Icewine." At: http://wine countryontario.ca/wine-101/story-icewine.

Wingrove, Josh. 2016. "GM Canada to Hire 700 Engineers in Oshawa, Markham to Drive Research in Self-driving Cars." *Financial Post,* 10 June. At: http://business.financialpost.com/news/transportation/gm-canada-to-hire-700-engineers-to-drive-research-in-self-driving-cars.

CHAPTER 7

Alcoa. 2015. "Baie-Comeau Smelter, Manicouagan Power Stations." At: https://www.alcoa.com/canada/en/info_page/sr_vision_corp_profile_abc.asp.

Arcand, Alan, Jane McIntyre, Robin Wiebe, Henry Diaz, Christopher Heschl, and Constantinos Bougas. 2016. "Metropolitan Outlook

1: Economic Insights into 13 Canadian Metropolitan Economies, Autumn 2016." Conference Board of Canada. At: http://www.conferenceboard.ca/e-library/abstract.aspx?did=8271.

ArcelorMittal. 2015. "Transforming Tomorrow." Aug. At: http://corporate.arcelormittal.com/who-we-are/interactive-map#/N_America/canada/mount_wright_mining_complex.

Aubin, Henry. 2013. "Henry Aubin: Taxes, Bill 101 Drive People Away." *Montreal Gazette*, 19 Feb. At: www.montrealgazette.com/news/Henry+Aubin+Taxes+Bill+drive+people+away/7981947/story.html#ixzz2Mn1IOTOD.

Blackwell, Richard. 2015. "Bombardier's C Series on Track for Delivery Next Year." *Globe and Mail*, 10 Sept. At: http://www.theglobeandmail.com/report-on-business/bombardiers-c-series-on-track-for-delivery-next-year/article26307431/.

Bone, Robert M. 2016. *The Canadian North: Issues and Challenges*, 5th edn. Toronto: Oxford University Press.

Boone, Marilyn. 2016. "From Bad to Worse: Churchill Contract Renewal Means Even Less Revenue for N.L." CBC News, 1 Sept. At: http://www.cbc.ca/news/canada/newfoundland-labrador/upper-churchill-contract-renewal-means-less-money-for-newfoundland-1.3451376.

Bouchard, Gérard, and Charles Taylor. 2008. *Building the Future: A Time for Reconciliation, Abridged Report*. Québec: Gouvernement du Québec. At: http://red.pucp.edu.pe/wp-content/uploads/biblioteca/building thefutureGerard Bocuhardycharlestaylor.pdf.

Bumsted, J.M. 2007. *A History of the Canadian Peoples*, 3rd edn. Toronto: Oxford University Press.

Canadian Dairy Information Centre. 2015. "Provincial Share of the National Market Sharing Quota (MSQ)." 15 Aug. At: http://www.dairyinfo.gc.ca/index_e.php?s1=dff-fcil&s2=quota&s3=prov.

Canadian Manufacturing. 2016. "SNC-Lavalin Wins $21.7 Million Mine Construction Contract in Mozambique." 25 Aug. At: http://www.canadianmanufacturing.com/procurement/snc-lavalin-wins-21-7m-mine-construction-contract-in-mozambique-174578/.

Cousineau, Sophie. 2012. "Decision to Close Nuclear Plant Expected to Cost Quebec $1.3-Billion." *Globe and Mail*, 6 Oct., A15.

Cryderman, Kelly, and Shawn McCarthy. 2016. "Anti-Pipeline Accord Could Deepen Divide in Indigenous Communities." *Globe and Mail*, 23 Sept., B3.

CTV News. 2015a. "Fate of Bombardier's Sole C Series Jet Order in Canada in Question." 13 Nov. At: http://www.ctvnews.ca/business/fate-of-bombardier-s-sole-cseries-jet-order-in-canada-in-question-1.2657016.

———. 2015b. "Quebec City Restaurant in Trouble with Language Police over Grilled Cheese." At: http://www.ctvnews.ca/canada/quebec-restaurant-in-trouble-with-language-police-over-grilled-cheese-1.2739809.

De Courcy, Diane, Minister responsible for the Charter of the French Language. 2012. Bill 14: *An Act to Amend the Charter of the French Language, the Charter of Human Rights and Freedoms and Other Legislative Provisions*. National Assembly, First Session, 40th Legislature. At: www.assnat.qc.ca/en/travaux-parlementaires/projets-loi/projets-loi-40-1.html.

Department of Finance. 2014. *The Federal Gas Tax Fund*. 21 Oct. At: http://www.fin.gc.ca/afr-rfa/2015/report-rapport-eng.asp.

Dick-Agnew, David. 2011. "A New Home for the Montreal Symphony Orchestra." *Azure*, 26 Sept. At: http://www.azuremagazine.com/article/a-new-home-for-the-montreal-symphony-orchestra/.

Duhaime, Gérard, Nick Bernard, and Robert Comtois. 2005. "An Inventory of Abandoned Mining Exploration Sites in Nunavik, Canada." *Canadian Geographer* 49, 3: 260–71.

Economist, The. 2016. "The World's Most Liveable Cities." 18 Aug. At: http://www.economist.com/blogs/graphicdetail/2016/08/daily-chart-14.

Finances Québec. 2005. "Québec's Clothing and Textile Industries: The Difficult Path Ahead." *Economic Fiscal and Budget Studies* 1, 4. At: http://www.finances.gouv.qc.ca/documents/EEFB/en/eefb_vol1_no4a.pdf.

Fischer, David Hackett. 2008. *Champlain's Dream*. New York: Simon & Schuster.

Gerbel, Thomas. 2015. "Montreal to Dump 8 Billion Litres of Sewage into St. Lawrence River." CBC News, 29 Sept. At: http://www.cbc.ca/news/canada/montreal/st-lawrence-river-sewage-bonaventure-mill-interceptor-1.3248937.

Havard, Gilles. 2001. *The Great Peace of Montréal*. Montréal and Kingston: McGill-Queen's Press.

Hogue, Robert. 2016. "Provincial Outlook", RBC Economics. June. At: http://www.rbc.com/economics/economic-reports/pdf/provincial-forecasts/provfcst-jun2016.pdf.

Hornig, James F., ed. 1999. *Social and Environmental Impacts of the James Bay Hydroelectric Project*. Montréal and Kingston: McGill-Queen's University Press.

Hutchinson, Brian. 2015. "Inside the Clandestine World of SNC Lavalin's Fallen Star, Riadh Ben Aissa." *Financial Post*, 18 Mar. At: http://business.financialpost.com/legal-post/inside-the-clandestine-world-of-snc-lavalins-fallen-star-riadh-ben-aissa.

Hydro-Québec. 2016a. "Technological Innovations." At: http://www.hydroquebec.com/innovation/en/innovations.html.

———. 2016b. "Louis Vézina, Export Advisor." At: http://welcome.hydroquebec.com.

Institut de la statistique du Québec. 2016. *Québec Handy Numbers*. At: http://www.stat.gouv.qc.ca/quebec-chiffre-main/pdf/qcm2016_an.pdf.

Iron Ore Company of Canada. 2013. "The Company." At: http://www.ironore.ca/en/the-company_1/.

———. 2015. "Our Business." At: http://www.ironore.ca/en/our-business_291/.

Jarislowsky, Stephen. 2012. "The French Myth Isolates Quebec." *Globe and Mail*, 28 Sept., A19.

Kativik Regional Government. 2009. *Proposed Timeline for the Creation of the Nunavik Regional Government*. At: www.nunavikgovernment.ca/en/documents/NRG_Timeline_En_Oct_09.pdf.

Keenan, Greg. 2013. "Bombardier Targets Big Rivals as C Series Makes Its Debut." *Globe and Mail*, 8 Mar., B1, B4.

Lammam, Charles, Milagros Palacios, Hugh MacIntyre, and Feixue Ren. 2016. "The Cost of Government Debt in Canada, 2016." *Fraser Bulletin*, Jan. At: https://www.fraserinstitute.org/sites/default/files/cost-of-government-debt-in-canada-2016.pdf.

La Presse. "Élections Québec 2014." 2 Juin. At: http://www.lapresse.ca/actualites/elections-quebec-2014/resultats-des-elections-quebec-2014/#qc.

Lemay, Martin. 2010. "Francophones Have Reason to Be Paranoid." *Montreal Gazette*, 30 Apr. At: www.vigile.net/Francophones-have-reason-to-be.

Lucas, C.P. 1912. *Lord Durham's Report of the Affairs of British North America*, vol. 1. Oxford: Clarendon Press.

McArthur, Greg, and Graeme Smith. 2012. "SNC-Lavalin's Gadhafi Disaster: The Inside Story." *Globe and Mail*, 27 Sept. At: www.theglobeandmail.com/report-on-business/rob-magazine/snc-lavalins-gadhafi-disaster-the-inside-story/article4570115/?page=all.

McCutcheon, Sean. 1991. *Electric Rivers: The Story of the James Bay Project*. Montréal: Black Rose Books.

Macpherson, Don. 2015. "Montreal's (and Quebec's) Response to a 'Radical' Muslim Preacher May Be Worse Than the Problem." *Montreal Gazette*, 2 Feb. At: http://montrealgazette.com/news/quebec/don-macpherson-montreals-and-quebecs-response-to-a-radical-muslim-preacher-may-be-worse-than-the-problem.

Marotte, Bertrand. 2016. "SNC-Lavalin Strikes Deal to Build Nuclear Reactor in China." *Globe and Mail*, 22 Sept. At: http://www.theglobeandmail.com/report-on-business/industry-news/energy-and-resources/snc-lavalin-strikes-deal-to-build-nuclear-reactors-in-china/article32000350/.

Marowits, Ross. 2010. "SNC-Lavalin Focuses on Global Growth." *Globe and Mail*, 17 Mar., B3.

Mills, David. 1988. "Durham Report." In James H. Marsh, ed., *The Canadian Encyclopedia*, 2nd edn. Edmonton: Hurtig, 637–8.

Montreal Economic Institute. 2015. "Quebec 'Debt Clock'." At: http://www.iedm.org/27-quebec-debt-clock.

Moreault, Éric. 2009. "Le Saint-Laurent encore 'vulnérable' à la pollution." *Le Soleil*, 30 juin. At: www.cyberpresse.ca/le-soleil/actualites/environnement/200906/30/01-880288-le-saint-laurent-encore-vulnerable-a-la-pollution.php.

Municipalité de Baie-James. 2015. "Territory of James Bay." At: http://www.villembj.ca/html/mbj/territoire_bj_en.php.

National Post. 2015. "Anti-democracy Imam Gets Cold Reception from Politicians over Montreal Community Centre Plan." 30 Jan. At: http://news.nationalpost.com/2015/01/30/anti-democracy-imam-gets-cold-reception-over-montreal-community-centre-plan/.

Natural Resources Canada. 2016a. *Minerals and Metals Fact Book—2016*. At: http://www.nrcan.gc.ca/sites/www.nrcan.gc.ca/files/mineralsmetals/pdf/mms-smm/Minerals%20and%20Metals_factbook_En.pdf.

———. 2016b. "Forest Inventory." 21 Sept. At: http://cfs.nrcan.gc.ca/statsprofile.

Osisko. 2013. "Canadian Malartic at a Glance." At: www.osisko.com/mines-and-projects/canadian-malartic/canadian-malartic-in-brief/.

Owram, Kristine. 2016. "Bombardier Inc to Get US$1 Billion from Quebec Government to Rescue Troubled C Series." *Financial Post*, 29 Oct. At: http://business.financialpost.com/investing/global-investor/bombardier-inc-to-get-1-billion-from-quebec-government-to-rescue-troubled-cseries.

Pittis, Don. 2015. "Bombardier Investment Launches Quebec into Battle with Aerospace Giants." CBC News, 30 Oct. At: http://www.cbc.ca/news/business/quebec-bombardier-investment-analysis-1.3294257.

Port of Montréal. 2014. "Statistics: Traffic Summary." At: http://www.port-montreal.com/PMStats/html/frontend/statistics.jsp?lang=en&context=about.

Québec and Canada. 2012. *The St. Lawrence Action Plan: 2011–2026.* At: planstlaurent.qc.ca/en/home/about_us.html.

———. 2015. *Overview of the State of the St. Lawrence River.* 6 Mar. At: http://planstlaurent.qc.ca/en/state_monitoring/overview_of_the_state_of_the_st_lawrence.html.

Richardson, Boyce. 1975. *Strangers Devour the Land: The Cree Hunters of the James Bay Area versus Premier Bourassa and the James Bay Development Corporation.* Toronto: Macmillan.

Robitaille, Antoine. 2008. "Charest mise sur le Nord." *Le Devoir*, 29 Apr. At: http://www.ledevoir.com/politique/quebec/208131/charest-mise-sur-le-nord.

Rogers, Sarah. 2015. "The Raglan Agreement at 20: How It's Shaped Nunavik's Mining Industry." *Nunatsiaq Online*. 11 Dec. At: http://www.nunatsiaqonline.ca/stories/article/65674the_raglan_agreement_at_20_how_its_shaped_nunaviks_mining_industry/.

Roslin, Alex. 2001. "Cree Deal a Model or Betrayal?" *National Post*, 10 Nov., FP7.

St Lawrence Seaway Management Corporation. 2012. "Delivering Economic Value," *Annual Report 2011–2012*. At: www.greatlakes-seaway.com/en/pdf/slsmc_ar2012_nar_en.pdf.

Salisbury, Richard Frank. 1986. *A Homeland for the Cree: Regional Development in James Bay, 1971–1981*. Montréal and Kingston: McGill-Queen's University Press.

Séguin, Rhéal. 2009. "Tiny Quebec Town Is Sitting on a Gold Mine." *Globe and Mail*, 14 July. At: www.theglobeandmail.com/news/national/tiny-quebec-town-is-sitting-on-a-gold-mine/article1217078.

Sinclair, Murray. 2015. *Honouring the Truth, Reconciling for the Future: Summary of the Final Report of the Truth and Reconciliation Commission of Canada.* At: http://nctr.ca/assets/reports/Final%20Reports/Executive_Summary_English_Web.pdf.

Smee, Michael. 2016. "Bombardier Has 'No Comments' on New Questions about TTC Streetcar Delivery." CBC News, 29 Sept. At: http://www.cbc.ca/news/canada/toronto/bombardier-has-no-comments-on-new-questions-about-ttc-streetcar-delivery-1.3784418.

SNC-Lavalin. 2016. "About Us." At: http://www.lavalin.com/en/about-us/.

Statistics Canada. 2002. *2001 Census of Population.* Statistics Canada Catalogue nos. 97F0007XCB2001004 and 97F0007XCB2001010 (Quebec—Québec, Code24).

———. 2006. "Distribution of Employed People, by Industry, by Province." At: www40.statcan.ca/l01/cst01/labor21c.htm.

———. 2007. "Population and Dwelling Counts, for Census Metropolitan Areas and Census Agglomerations, 2006 and 2001 censuses—100% Data." At: www12.statcan.ca/english/census06/data/popdwell/Table.cfm?T=201&S=3&O=D&RPP=150.

———. 2011. "Births and Total Fertility Rate, by Province and Territory." 20 Dec. At: www.statcan.gc.ca/tables-tableaux/sum-som/l01/cst01/hlth85b-eng.htm.

———. 2012a. "Distribution of Employed People, by Industry, by Province." 1 June. At: www.statcan.gc.ca/tables-tableaux/sum-som/l01/cst01/labor21a-eng.htm.

———. 2012b. "Population and Dwelling Counts, for Quebec, by Census Metropolitan Areas and Census Agglomerations, 2011 and 2006 Census." 11 May. At: www12.statcan.gc.ca/census-recensement/2011/dp-pd/hlt-fst/pd-pl/Table-Tableau.cfm?LANG=Eng&T=202&PR=24&S=0&O=D&RPP=50.

———. 2013. *Linguistic Characteristics of Canadians*. At: www12.statcan.gc.ca/census-recensement/2011/as-sa/98-314-x/98-314-x2011001-eng.cfm.

———. 2015a. "Gross Domestic Product: Provinces and Territories, 2014." *The Daily*, 22 June. At: http://www.statcan.gc.ca/daily-quotidien/150428/dq150428a-eng.htm.

———. 2015b. "Employment by Major Industry Group by Province (Quebec)." 9 Nov. At: http://www.statcan.gc.ca/tables-tableaux/sum-som/l01/cst01/labr67f-eng.htm.

———. 2015c. "Annual Population Estimates by Census Metropolitan Area, July 1, 2014." CANSIM Table 051-0056. 11 Feb. At: http://www5.statcan.gc.ca/cansim/a26?lang=eng&retrLang=eng&id=0510056&&pattern=&stByVal=1&p1=1&p2=49&tabMode=dataTable&csid=.

———. 2016a. "Labour Force, Employment and Unemployment, Levels and Ages, by Province." At: http://www.statcan.gc.ca/tables-tableaux/sum-som/l01/cst01/labor07a-eng.htm.

———. 2016b. "Estimates of Population, Canada, Provinces and Territories." CANSIM Table 051-0005. 16 Mar. At: http://www5.statcan.gc.ca/cansim/a26?lang=eng&id=510005.

———. 2016c. "Gross Domestic Product by Industry: Provinces and Territories, 2015." 12 May. At: http://www.statcan.gc.ca/daily-quotidien/160512/dq160512b-eng.htm.

———. 2016d. "Employment by Major Industry Group, Seasonally Adjusted, by Province." 10 June. At: http://www.statcan.gc.ca/tables-tableaux/sum-som/l01/cst01/labr67a-eng.htm.

Toronto Transit Commission. 2013. "New Subway Train: The Toronto Rocket." At: www.ttc.ca/About_the_TTC/Projects_and_initiatives/New_Subway_Train/index.jsp.

Yakabuski, Konrad. 2015. "Big Hydro's Big Days Are Behind It." *Globe and Mail*, 5 Jan. At: http://www.theglobeandmail.com/globe-debate/big-hydros-big-days-are-behind-it/article22288577/.

CHAPTER 8

Agriculture and Agri-Food Canada. 2016. "Trade Balance for Beef and Hogs." 7 Oct. At: http://www.agr.gc.ca/eng/industry-markets-and-trade/statistics-and-market-information/by-product-sector/red-meat-and-livestock/red-meat-and-livestock-market-information/trade-balance/?id=1415860000005.

Akinremi, O.O., S.M. McGinn, and H.W. Cutforth. 2001. "Seasonal and Spatial Patterns of Rainfall on the Canadian Prairies." *Journal of Climate* 14, 9: 2177–82.

Alberta. 2007. "Oil Reserves." At: www.energy.gov.ab.ca/docs/oil/pdfs/AB_OilReserves.pdf.

———. 2012. *Budget 2012: Investing in People.* At: www.finance.alberta.ca/publications/budget/budget2012/fiscal-plan-revenue.pdf.

Alberta Energy. 2012. "Facts and Statistics." At: www.energy.alberta.ca/oilsands/791.asp.

———. 2016. "Economic Dashboard." 30 Sept. At: http://economicdashboard.alberta.ca/OilPrice.

Bakx, Kyle. 2016a. "Pulse Crop Prices Jump in Canada, Even as Supply Grows." CBC News, 18 Feb. At: http://www.cbc.ca/news/business/pulse-crops-lentils-canada-prices-agriculture-1.3450271.

———. 2016b. "Oilpatch Lowers Expectations for Future Growth." CBC News, 23 June. At: http://www.cbc.ca/news/business/capp-oilsands-2016-forecast-1.3648752.

Bell, Ian. 1999. "Dancing with Elephants." *Western Producer*, 2 Sept., 60–1.

Biber, Francois. 2016. "University of Saskatchewan Engineer Says Cause of Husky Oil Spill Not a 1-time Event." CBC News, 18 Nov. At: http://www.cbc.ca/news/canada/saskatoon/university-of-saskatchewan-engineer-husky-oil-spill-instability-1.3858200.

Bickis, Ian. 2016. "Ground Movement to Blame for Oil Spill into North Saskatchewan River: Husky Energy." Global News, 17 Nov. At: http://globalnews.ca/news/3073921/husky-energy-says-ground-movement-to-blame-for-spill-into-north-saskatchewan-river/.

Bonsal, B.R., X. Zhang, and W.D. Hogg. 1999. "Canadian Prairie Growing Season Precipitation Variability and Associated Atmospheric Circulation." *Climate Research* 11: 191–208.

Bramley, Matthew, Pierre Sadik, and Dale Marshall. 2008. *Climate Leadership, Economic Prosperity: Final Report on an Economic Study of Greenhouse Gas Targets and Policies for Canada.* Pembina Institute and David Suzuki Foundation. At: pubs.pembina.org/reports/climate-leadership-report-en.pdf.

Buchanan, Peter. 2013. "Changing Global Realities Buffet Canada's Oil Patch." *Economic Insights* (CIBC World Markets), 3 Apr. At: research.cibcwm.com/economic_public/download/feature2.pdf.

Canadian Association of Petroleum Producers. 2012a. "Crude Oil: Forecasts, Markets & Pipelines." June. At: www.capp.ca/getdoc.aspx?DocId=209546&DT=NTV.

———. 2012b. "Safeguarding the Public." At: www.capp.ca/ENVIRONMENTCOMMUNITY/HEALTHSAFETY/Pages/Public.aspx.

Canadian Grain Commission. 2012. "Quality of Western Canadian Canola 2011." 6 Mar. At: www.grainscanada.gc.ca/canola/harvest-recolte/2011/hqc11-qrc11-03-eng.htm.

Canadian Nuclear Safety Commission. 2017. "Northern Saskatchewan." 27 Jan. At: nuclearsafety.gc.ca/eng/resources/nuclear-facilities/index.cfm.

———. 2015. "Uranium Mines and Mills." 30 Apr. At: https://www.cnsc-ccsn.gc.ca/eng/uranium/mines-and-mills/index.cfm#RegulatingUraniumMinesandMills.

Canola Council of Canada. 2016. "Harvest Acreage." At: http://www.canolacouncil.org/markets-stats/statistics/harvest-acreage/.

D'Aliesio, Renata. 2012. "Brooks, Alberta on the Brink as It Awaits Fate of XL Plant." *Globe and Mail*, 22 Oct. At: www.theglobeandmail.com/news/national/brooks-alberta-on-the-brink-as-it-awaits-fate-of-xl-plant/article4627920/.

Davenport, Coral. 2015. "Citing Climate Change, Obama Rejects Construction of Keystone XL Oil Pipeline." *New York Times*, 6 Nov. At: http://www.nytimes.com/2015/11/07/us/obama-expected-to-reject-construction-of-keystone-xl-oil-pipeline.html?_r=0.

Folk, Mark. 2011. "Farm Ownership." Farmland Security Board. At: www.farmland.gov.sk.ca/ownership/overview.shtml.

Food and Agriculture Organization of the United Nations (FAO). 2016. "FAO Food Price Index." 4 Feb. At: http://www.fao.org/worldfoodsituation/foodpricesindex/en/.

Forbes. 2016. "Oil Production by Country." At: https://www.reference.com/web?qsrc=999&qo=semQuery&ad=semD&o=37042&l=sem&askid=6c8c0fe5-f5b5-40fe-ab27-7d93aafca881-0-rf_msb&q=world%20oil%20production&dqi=&am=broad&an=msn_s.

Gerein, Keith. 2016. "Alberta Government Moves to Scrap External Environmental Monitoring Agency." *Edmonton Journal*, 17 May. At: http://edmontonjournal.com/news/politics/alberta-government-moves-to-scrap-external-environmental-monitoring-agency.

Greenwood, John. 2007. "Surging Prices Separate Wheat from the Chaff." *National Post*, 15 June, FP1.

Healing, Dan. 2016. "Low Oil Prices Cast Doubt on Just Approved Alberta Oil Sands Projects." *Toronto Star*, 16 Sept. At: https://www.thestar.com/business/2016/09/16/low-oil-prices-cast-doubt-on-just-approved-alberta-oilsands-projects.html.

Hodson, Peter V. 2013. "History of Environmental Contamination by Oil Sands Extraction." *Proceedings of the National Academy of Sciences* 110, 5: 1569–70. doi: 10.1073/pnas.1221660110.

Hugenholtz, D.H., and S.A. Wolfe. 2005. "Biogeomorphic Model of Dune Activation and Stabilization on the Northern Great Plains." *Geomorphology* 70: 53–70.

Imperial Oil. 2012a. "Cold Lake." At: www.imperialoil.ca/Canada-English/operations_sands_cold.aspx.

———. 2012b. "Oil Sands 101." At: www.imperialoil.ca/Canada-English/operations_sands_glance_101.aspx.

Jones, David C. 1987. *Empire of Dust: Settling and Abandoning the Prairie Dry Belt.* Edmonton: University of Alberta Press.

Kroeger, Arthur. 2007. *Hard Passage: A Mennonite Family's Long Journey from Russia to Canada.* Edmonton: University of Alberta Press.

———. 2009. *Retiring the Crow Rate: A Narrative of Political Management.* Edmonton: University of Alberta Press.

Kurek, Joshua, Jane L. Kirk, Derek C.G. Muir, Xiaowa Wang, Marlene S. Evans, and John P. Smol. 2013. "Legacy of a Half Century of Athabasca Oil Sands Development Recorded by Lake Ecosystems." *Proceedings of the National Academy of Sciences* 110, 5: 1761–6.

Lewis, Jeff. 2016. "Suncor Reaches $4.2-Billion Deal with Canadian Oil Sands." *Globe and Mail*, 18 Jan. At: http://www.theglobeandmail.com/report-on-business/industry-news/energy-and-resources/suncor-hikes-bid-for-canadian-oil-sands/article28236158/.

McGlade, Christophe, and Paul Ekins. 2015. "Research Suggests a Large Share of Fossil Fuel Reserves Will Need to Stay in the Ground to Keep Warming below 2°C—But Achieving This Will Be a Daunting Challenge." *Nature* 517: 187–90. doi:101038/nature14016.

MacLachlan, Ian. 2001. *Kill and Chill: Restructuring Canada's Beef Commodity Chain.* Toronto: University of Toronto Press.

Manitoba Finance. 2016. "Manitoba Economic Highlights." 13 Sept. At: https://www.gov.mb.ca/finance/pubs/highlights.pdf.

Mas, Susana, and Catherine Cullen. 2016. "Justin Trudeau Signs Paris Climate Treaty at UN, Vows to Harness Renewable Energy." CBC News, 22 Apr. At: http://www.cbc.ca/news/politics/paris=agreement-trudeau sign-1.3547822.

Minsky, Amy. 2016. "Will Paris Climate Agreement Become Another Kyoto?" Global News, 5 Oct. At: http://globalnews.ca/news/2984699/will-paris-climate-agreement-become-another-kyoto/.

Monsanto Canada. 2012. "Monsanto Canada Unveils DEKALB® Canola Seed Processing Plant in Lethbridge, Alberta." Monsanto in the News, 7 Oct. At: www.monsanto.ca/newsviews/Pages/NR-2012-07-10.aspx.

National Energy Board. 2016. "Estimated Production of Canadian Crude Oil and Equivalent." 4 Oct. At: https://www.neb-one.gc.ca/nrg/sttstc/crdlndptrlmprdct/stt/stmtdprdctn-eng.html.

Natural Resources Canada. 2010. Canada in a Changing Climate, "Prairies." 20 Aug. At: www.nrcan.gc.ca/earth-sciences/climate-change/community-adaptation/642.

———. 2016a. "Preliminary Estimate of the Mineral Production of Canada, by Province, 2015." 29 Aug. At: http://sead.nrcan.gc.ca/prod-prod/ann-data-en.aspx?FileT=2015&Lang=en.

———. 2016b. Minerals and Metals Fact Book—2016. At: http://www.nrcan.gc.ca/sites/www.nrcan.gc.ca/files/mineralsmetals/pdf/mms-smm/Minerals%20and%20Metals_factbook_En.pdf.

———. 2016c. The State of Canada's Forest Report: Annual Report 2016. 7 Oct. At: http://www.nrcan.gc.ca/forests/report/16496.

Oilsands Developers Group. 2009. "Oilsands Projects." 30 June. At: www.oilsandsdevelopers.ca/index.php/test-project-table/.

Paul, Alec H. 1997. "Shortlines, Mainlines, Branchlines, Dead Lines: Rural Railways in Southwestern Saskatchewan in the 1990s." In John Welsted and John Everitt, eds, The Yorkton Papers: Research by Prairie Geographers. Brandon Geographical Studies No. 2. Brandon, Man.: Brandon University.

Pembina Institute. 2007. "Athabasca River Expedition: Connecting the Drops." At: http://www.connectingthedrops.ca/river/stresses.

Peters, E.J. 2010. "Aboriginal People in Canadian Cities." In Trudi Bunting, Pierre Filion, and Ryan Walker, eds, Canadian Cities in Transition: New Directions in the Twenty-First Century, 4th edn. Toronto: Oxford University Press.

——— and Chris Anderson, eds. 2013. Indigenous in the City: Contemporary Identities and Cultural Innovations. Vancouver: University of British Columbia Press.

Price, Jacqueline D. 2003. "Are Factory Farms Fouling Our Water?" Alberta Views (May–June): 34–9.

Proctor, Jason. 2016. "Northern Gateway Pipeline Approval Overturned." CBC News, 30 June. At: http://www.cbc.ca/news/canada/british-columbia/northern-gateway-pipeline-federal-court-of-appeal-1.3659561.

Rapier, Robert. 2016. "World Sets Record for Fossil Fuel Consumption." Forbes. At: http://www.forbes.com/sites/rrapier/2016/06/08/world-sets-record-for-fossil-fuel-consumption/#153c330d1ea6.

Richards, J. Howard. 1968. "The Prairie Region." In John Warkentin, ed., Canada: A Geographical Interpretation. Toronto: Methuen, ch. 12.

Rodrigue, Jean-Paul, Claude Comtois, and Brian Slack. 2009. The Geography of Transport Systems. Toronto: Routledge.

Saskatchewan Ministry of Agriculture. 2009. "Crop Statistics." At: www.agriculture.gov.sk.ca/agriculture_statistics/HBv5_P2.asp.

———. 2015. "Statistics Fact Sheet." Dec. At: http://publications.gov.sk.ca/documents/20/83874-Ag%20Stat%20Fact%20Sheet%20-%202015.pdf.

Saskatchewan Ministry of Energy and Resources. 2016. Annual Report, 2015/2016. July. At: http://www.finance.gov.sk.ca/PlanningAndReporting/2015-16/2015-16EconomyAnnualReport.pdf.

Saskatchewan Research Council. 2012. "Project CLEANS (Cleanup of Abandoned Northern Sites)." At: www.src.sk.ca/About/Featured-Projects/Pages/Project-CLEANS.aspx.

———. 2016. "Project CLEANS." At: http://www.src.sk.ca/about/featured-projects/pages/project-cleans.aspx.

Shell Canada. 2015. "Shell Launches Quest Carbon Capture and Storage Project." 6 Nov. At: http://www.shell.ca/en/aboutshell/media-centre/news-and-media-releases/2015/oil-sands/shell-launches-quest-carbon-capture-and-storage-project.html.

Shrivastava, Meenal, and Lorna Stefanick, eds. 2015. Alberta Oil and the Decline of Democracy in Canada. Edmonton: University of Alberta Press.

Spry, Irene M. 1963. The Palliser Expedition: An Account of John Palliser's British North American Expedition 1857–1860. Toronto: Macmillan.

Stanley, George F.G. 1936. The Birth of Western Canada: A History of The Riel Rebellions. Reprint (1992) U. of Toronto Press.

Statistics Canada. 2006. "Canadian Statistics: Distribution of Employed People, by Industry, by Province." At: www40.statcan.ca/101/cst01/labour21c.htm.

———. 2007. "Population and Dwelling Counts, for Canada, Provinces and Territories, 2006 and 2001 Censuses—100% Data." At: www12.statcan.ca/english/cnesus06/data/popdwell/Table.cfm?T=101.

———. 2011. "Forest Land by Province and Territory." At: http://www.statcan.gc.ca/tables-tableaux/sum-som/l01/cst01/envi34a-eng.htm

———. 2012a. "Population by Mother Tongue and Age Groups (Total), Percentage Distribution (2011) for Canada, Provinces and Territories." 24 Oct. At: www12.statcan.gc.ca/census-recensement/2011/dp-pd/hlt-fst/lang/Pages/ highlight.cfm?TabID=1&Lang=E&Asc=1&PRCode=01&OrderBy=999&View=2&tableID=401&queryID=1&Ag.

———. 2012b. "Farm and Farm Operator Data." 2011 Census of Agriculture, 5 June. At: www.statcan.gc.ca/pub/95-640-x/2012002-eng.htm.

———. 2012c. "2011 Census of Agriculture." The Daily, 10 May. At: www.statcan.gc.ca/daily-quotidien/120510/t120510a001-eng.htm.

———. 2012d. "Population and Dwelling Counts, 2011 Census." At: www5.statcan.gc.ca/bsolc/olc-cel/olc-cel?catno=98-310-XWE2011002&lang=eng.

———. 2013a. "Population and Dwelling Counts, for Canada, Provinces and Territories, 2011 and 2006 Censuses." 2011 Census, Jan. At: http://www12.statcan.gc.ca/census-recensement/2011/as-sa/98-310-x/98-310-x2011001-eng.cfm.

———. 2013b. "Number and Distribution of Population Reporting an Aboriginal Identity and Percentage of Aboriginal People in the Population, Canada, Provinces and Territories, 2011." Aboriginal Peoples in Canada: First Nations People, Métis and Inuit. National Household Survey document 99-011-x. Table 2. 7 May. At: http://www12.statcan.gc.ca/nhs-enm/2011/as-sa/99-011-x/2011001/tbl/tbl02-eng.cfm.

———. 2013c. "Aboriginal Ancestry by Canada, Province, Territory, CMA and Census Agglomeration." 2011 National Household Survey: Data Tables. Catalogue no. 99-011-X2011029. At: http://www12.statcan.gc.ca/nhs-enm/2011/dp-pd/dt-td/Ap-eng.cfm?LANG=E&APATH=3&DETAIL=0&DIM=0&FL=A&FREE=0&GC=0&GID=0&GK=0&GRP=1&PID=105402&PRID=0&PTYPE=105277&S=0&SHOWALL=0&SUB=0&Temporal=2013&THEME=94&VID=0&VNAMEE=&VNAMEF=.

———. 2015a. "Estimates of Population for Canada, Provinces, and Territories." CANSIM Table 051-0005. At: http://www5.statcan.gc.ca/cansim/pick-choisir?lang=eng&p2=33&id=0510005.

———. 2015b. "Principal Field Crop Areas, June 2015." 30 June. At: http://www.statcan.gc.ca/daily-quotidien/150630/dq150630b-eng.htm.

————. 2015c. "Population of Census Metropolitan Areas." 11 Feb. At: http://www.statcan.gc.ca/tables-tableaux/sum-som/l01/cst01/demo05a-eng.htm.

————. 2016a. "Distribution of Employed People, by Industry, by Province." 16 Jan. At: http://www.statcan.gc.ca/tables-tableaux/sum-som/l01/cst01/labr67k-eng.htm.

————. 2016b. "Census Metropolitan Areas (CMAs), Census Agglomerations (CAs) Grouped by Provinces and Territories." NHS Focus on Geography Series. 7 Jan. At: http://www12.statcan.gc.ca/nhs-enm/2011/as-sa/fogs-spg/Pages/CMACASelector.cfm?lang=E&level=3.

————. 2016d. "Estimates of Population, Canada, Provinces and Territories." CANSIM Table 051-0005, 16 Mar. At: http://www5.statcan.gc.ca/cansim/a26?lang=eng&id=510005.

————. 2016e. "Gross Domestic Product by Industry: Provinces and Territories, 2015." The Daily, 12 May. At: http://www.statcan.gc.ca/daily-quotidien/160512/dq160512b-eng.htm.

————. 2016f. "Farm Cash Receipts." CANSIM Table 002-0001. 25 May. At: http://www5.statcan.gc.ca/cansim/a26.

————. 2016g. "Population of Census Metropolitan Areas." 10 Feb. At: http://www.statcan.gc.ca/tables-tableaux/sum-som/l01/cst01/demo05a-eng.htm.

————. 2016h. "Employment by Major Industry Group, Seasonally Adjusted, by Province." At: http://www.statcan.gc.ca/tables-tableaux/sum-som/l01/cst01/labr67a-eng.htm.

————. 2016i. "Snapshot of Canadian Agriculture." Table 2. 25 Jan. At: http://www.statcan.gc.ca/pub/95-640-x/2011001/p1/p1-01-eng.htm.

————. 2016j. "Estimated Areas, Yield, Production, Average Farm Price and Total Farm Value of Principal Field Crops, in Imperial Units, Annual." CANSIM Table 001-0017. 29 June. At: http://www5.statcan.gc.ca/cansim/a47.

————. 2016k. "Census Subdivision of Airdrie, CY—Alberta." Focus on Geography Series, 2011 Census. 21 Sept. At https://www12.statcan.gc.ca/census-recensement/2011/as-sa/fogs-spg/Facts-csd-eng.cfm?LANG=Eng&GK=CSD&GC=4806021.

————. 2016l. "Population and Dwelling Counts, for Census Agglomerations, 2011 and 2006 Censuses." Population and Dwelling Counts Highlight Tables, 2011 Census. 9 Aug. At: http://www12.statcan.gc.ca/census-recensement/2011/dp-pd/hlt-fst/pd-pl/Table-Tableau.cfm?LANG=Eng&T=206&SR=1&S=3&O=D&RPP=100&PR=0&CMA=0.

Tasker, John Paul. 2016. "Ottawa Won't Appeal Court Decision Blocking Northern Gateway Pipeline." CBC News, 20 Sept. At: http:www.cbc.ca/news/politics/enbridge-northern-gateway-federal-court-1.3770543.

TransCanada. 2016. "Energy East Pipeline Project." At: http://www.transcanada.com/energy-east-pipeline.html.

Vanderhaeghe, Guy. 1996. The Englishman's Boy. Toronto: McClelland & Stewart.

VanderKlippe, Nathan. 2012. "Shell Launches First Canadian Oil Sands Carbon-Capture Project." Globe and Mail, 5 Sept. At: www.theglobeandmail.com/globe-investor/shell-launches-first-canadian-oil-sands-carbon-capture-project/article4520968/.

Wiebe, Rudy. 1973. The Temptations of Big Bear. Toronto: McClelland & Stewart.

Wilkins, Charles. 2013. "This Little Piggy Went to Market . . . and the Farmer Lost Money." Report on Business, The Globe and Mail (Mar.): 32–41.

Wilt, James. 2016. "After Three Decades in Canada, Is Carbon Capture Technology Doomed?" Alberta Oil, 9 Feb. At: http://www.albertaoilmagazine.com/2016/02/is-carbon-capture-technology-doomed/.

Winnipeg, City of. 2016. "Aboriginal Persons Highlights." Economic and Demographic Information. At: http://winnipeg.ca/cao/pdfs/2011Aboriginal_Persons_Highlights_National_Household_Survey.pdf.

Wolfe, S.A., C.H. Hugenholtz, C.P. Evans, D.J. Huntley, and J. Ollerhead. 2007. "Potential Aboriginal-Occupation-Induced Dune Activity, Elbow Sand Hills, Northern Great Plains, Canada." Great Plains Research 17: 173–92.

WTRG Economics. 2012. "Oil Price History and Analysis." At: www.wtrg.com/prices.htm.

CHAPTER 9

Alldritt, Benjamin. 2012. "This Is Going to Be a Boom: Seaspan CEO." 25 Apr. At: www.nsnews.com/story.html?id=6514682.

Bailey, Ian. 2015. "B.C. Film Industry Booming, but Insiders Warn It May Not Last." Globe and Mail, 16 May. At: http://www.theglobeandmail.com/news/british-columbia/bc-film/article24462867/.

Barnes, Alex. 2015. "BC Forest Product Exports." Ministry of Forests, Lands, and Natural Resource Operations. At: https://www.for.gov.bc.ca/ftp/het/external/!publish/web/exports/Exports-Report-2015-07.pdf.

Barnes, Trevor, and Roger Hayter. 1997. Trouble in the Rainforest: British Columbia's Forest Economy in Transition. Canadian Western Geographical Series, vol. 33. Victoria: Western Geographical Press.

BC Government. 2012. "Requirements for British Columbia to Consider Support for Heavy Oil Pipelines." At: http://www.env.gov.bc.ca/main/docs/2012/TechnicalAnalysis-HeavyOilPipeline_120723.pdf.

BC Hydro. 2015a. "Peace Region." At: https://www.bchydro.com/energy-in-bc/our_system/generation/our_facilities/peace.html.

————. 2015b. "Columbia Region." At: https://www.bchydro.com/energy-in-bc/our_system/generation/our_facilities/columbia.html.

BC Ministry of Forests, Lands and Natural Resource Operations. 2016. "Great Bear Rainforest Land Use Zones." 20 Oct. At: https://www.for.gov.bc.ca/tasb/slrp/lrmp/nanaimo/CLUDI/GBR/Orders/GBR_LandUseZones_20161020.pdf.

BC Ministry of Transportation. 2007. "Pacific Gateway." At: www.th.gov.bc.ca/PacificGateway/index.htm.

BC Stats. 2012. "Annual data for BC Exports with Selected Destinations and Commodity Details." Aug. At: www.bcstats.gov.bc.ca/StatisticsBySubject/ExportsImports/Data.aspx.

————. 2016a. "BC Exports: Data Tables." At: http://www.bcstats.gov.bc.ca/StatisticsBySubject/ExportsImports.aspx.

————. 2016b. "Annual Data for B.C. Exports with Selected Destination and Commodity Detail." 5 Aug. At: http://www.bcstats.gov.bc.ca/StatisticsBySubject/ExportsImports/Data.aspx.

————. 2016c. "2015 Production Estimates for Major Commodities Mined in B.C." At: http://www2.gov.bc.ca/gov/content/industry/mineral-exploration-mining/further-information/statistics/production.

Bone, Robert M. 2016. The Canadian North: Issues and Challenges, 5th edn. Toronto: Oxford University Press.

Boulton, Matthew. 2010. "Financial Vulnerability Assessment: Who Would Pay for Oil Tanker Spills Associated with the Northern Gateway Pipeline?" Environmental Law Centre, University of Victoria, Oct. At: http://www.elc.uvic.ca/press/documents/2010-02-06-Tanker-Spill-Financial-Vulnerability-Assessment_Jan15%2011.pdf.

Cassidy, Frank. 1992. "Aboriginal Land Claims in British Columbia: A Regional Perspective." In K. Coates, ed., Aboriginal Land Claims. Toronto: Copp Clark, 10–43.

CBC News. 2009. "Queen Charlotte Islands Renamed Haida Gwaii in Historic Deal." 11 Dec. At: www.cbc.ca/canada/british-columbia/story/2009/12/11/bc-queen-charlotte-islands-renamed-haida=gwaii.html.

————. 2012. "Tests Confirm Virus at B.C. Salmon Farm." 30 May. At: www.cbc.ca/news/canada/british-columbia/story/2012/05/30/bc-salmon-virus-dixon-bay.html.

————. 2016. "City of Vancouver Approves Empty Homes Tax." 16 Nov. At: http://www.cbc.ca/news/canada/british-columbia/city-of-vancouver-approves-empty-homes-tax-1.3853542.

Chase, Steven, and Bertrand Marotte. 2011. "Halifax, Vancouver Win $33-Billion in Shipbuilding Sweepstakes." Globe and Mail, 20 Oct., A1.

Christensen, Bev. 1995. Too Good to Be True: Alcan's Kemano Completion Project. Vancouver: Talonbooks.

Clapp, R.A. 2008. "The Resource Cycle in Forestry and Fishing," Canadian Geographer 42, 2:129–44.

Clark, Christy. 2012. "Premier Christy Clark's Letter to Alison Redford." 26 Sept. At: www.newsroom.gov.bc.ca/2012/09/premier-christy-clarks-letter-to-alberta-premier-alison-redford.html.

Council of Forest Industries. 2015. BC Forest Industry: Economic Impact Study. Jan. At: http://www.cofi.org/wp-content/uploads/2015/01/bc_industry_impact_01-2015.pdf.

Crowley, Brian Lee. 2016. "For Eco-warriors: No Amount of Tinkering Will Make Pipelines Acceptable." Macdonald-Laurier Institute. 29 Jan. At: http://www.macdonaldlaurier.ca/for-eco-warriors-no-amount-of-tinkering-will-make-pipelines-acceptable-brian-lee-crowley-in-the-citizen/#.

David Suzuki Foundation. 2005. Clearcutting Canada's Rainforest, Status Report 2005: Canada's Rainforests under Threat. At: www.davidsuzuki.org/files/Forests/DSF-rainforests-2005-5.pdf.

Destination British Columbia. 2015. The Value of Tourism in BC. Feb. At: http://www.destinationbc.ca/getattachment/Research/Industry-Performance/Value-of-Tourism/Value-of-Tourism-in-British-Columbia-(2013)/Value-of-Tourism_2013_Full-Report.pdf.aspx.

Deutsch, Jeremy. 2015. "City Tries to Prevent Burrard Thermal Closure." Tri-City News, 12 Feb. At: http://www.tricitynews.com/news/city-tries-to-prevent-burrard-thermal-closure-1.1761726.

Economist Intelligence Unit. 2012. "Melbourne, Vienna and Vancouver Named World's Most Liveable Cities." 15 Aug. At: www.citymayors.com/environment/eiu_bestcities.html.

Fisheries and Oceans Canada.2009. "Pacific Salmon Treaty Renewal." 5 Jan. At: www.dfo-mpo.gc.ca/media/back-fiche/2009/pr01-eng.htm.

————. 2015. "Canada's Fisheries Fast Facts, 2014." At: http://www.dfo-mpo.gc.ca/stats/facts-Info-14-eng.htm.

Fletcher, Tom. 2016. "U.S. Lumber Trade Faces Uncertain Future." BC Local News, 13 Oct. At: http://www.bclocalnews.com/business/396966791.html.

Harris, Cole. 1997. The Resettlement of British Columbia: Essays on Colonialism and Geographical Change. Vancouver: University of British Columbia Press.

Hasemyer, David. 2016. "Enbridge's Kalamazoo Spill Saga Ends in $177 Million Settlement." Inside Climate News. 20 July. At: https://insideclimatenews.org/news/20072016/enbridge-saga-end-department-justice-fine-epa-kalamazoo-river-michigan-dilbit-spill.

Hume, Mark. 2009. "Millions of Missing Fish Signal Crisis on the Fraser River." Globe and Mail, 12 Aug., B1.

Hume, Stephen. 2000. "Did Francis Drake Discover B.C.?" National Post, 5 Aug., B1–B2.

Hunter, Justine. 2016. "Key Players in Great Bear Rainforest Deal Find Common Ground." Globe and Mail, 1 Feb. At: http://www.theglobeandmail.com/news/british-columbia/key-players-in-great-bear-rainforest-deal-find-common-ground/article28475126/.

Industry Advisory Group. 2006. Pacific Gateway Strategy Action Plan 2006–2020. Vancouver. At: www.th.gov.bc.ca/PacificGateway/documents/PGS_Action_Plan_043006.pdf.

Johnson, Lisa. 2016. "Seaspan's Vancouver Shipyards Gets $65M to Build Navy Supply and Science Ships." CBC News, 14 Mar. At: http://www.cbc.ca/news/canada/british-columbia/vancouver-shipyards-national-shipbuilding-strategy-1.3490792.

Johnson, Tracy. 2016. "What the Pacific NorthWest LNG Decision Could Mean for Trans Mountain." CBC News, 29 Sept. At: http://www.cbc.ca/news/business/whats-coming-for-transmountain-1.3782549.

Katz, Diane. 2010. "The Agricultural Land Reserve Doesn't Work—So Let's Get Rid of It." BC Business Online, 6 Jan. At: www.bcbusinessonline.ca/bcb/business-sense/2010/01/06/alr-tear-down-wall.

Keyzer, Wendy. 2016. "MDA to Deliver a Broad-Area Maritime Surveillance System Using the RADARSAT Constellation Mission." 17 June: At: http://mdacorporation.com/news/pr/pr2016061702.html.

Kheraj, Sean. 2015. "Burrard Inlet, Beaches and Oil Spills: A Historical Perspective." 16 Apr. At: http://niche-canada.org/2015/04/16/burrard-inlet-beaches-and-oil-spills-a-historical-perspective/.

Kinder Morgan. 2015. "Trans Mountain: Maps." At: http://www.transmountain.com.

Loki, Reynard. 2015. "8 Dangerous Side Effects of Fracking That the Industry Doesn't Want You to Hear About." AlterNet, 28 Apr. At: http://www.alternet.org/environment/8-dangerous-side-effects-fracking-industry-doesnt-want-you-hear-about.

MacDonald, John. 2012. "Cuts Threaten Canada's Satellite Eye on the Arctic." Vancouver Sun, 24 Apr. At: http://democracyastray.blogspot.ca/2012/04/cuts-threaten-canadas-satellite-eye-on.html.

McCullough, Michael. 1998. Granville Island: An Urban Oasis. Vancouver: CMHC.

McKenna, Barrie. 2016. "Canada, U.S. Poised to Reignite Softwood Lumber War." Globe and Mail, 9 Oct. At: http://www.theglobeandmail.com/report-on-business/rob-commentary/executive-insight/canada-us-poised-to-reignite-softwood-war/article32311586/.

Metro Vancouver. 2015. "About Us." At: http://www.metrovancouver.org/about/Pages/default.aspx.

Morgan, Geoffrey. 2016. "NEB Approves Kinder Morgan's Trans Mountain Pipeline Expansion with 157 Conditions." Financial Post, 19 May. At: http://business.financialpost.com/news/energy/national-energy-board-recommends-approval-of-kinder-morgans-trans-mountain-pipeline-expansion?__lsa=a3a3-f506.

Meissner, Dirk. 2015. "B.C. Megathrust Earthquake Could Rupture Like a Zipper, Expert Says." CBC News, 18 Jan. At: http://www.cbc.ca/news/canada/british-columbia/b-c-megathrust-earthquake-could-rupture-like-a-zipper-expert-says-1.2917261.

————. 2016. "Mount Polley Mine Disaster Hits 2-Year Mark, Fallout Still Causes Divisions." CBC News, 4 Aug. At: http://www.cbc.ca/news/canada/british-columbia/mount-polley-anniversary-1.3706850.

Mineral Resources Education Program of BC. 2009. At: www.bcminerals.ca/files/bc_mine_information.php.

Ministry of Forests, Lands and Natural Resource Operations. 2011. The Forest Industry Snapshot: A Selection of Monthly Economic Statistics, Mar. At: www.for.gov.bc.ca/ftp/het/external/!publish/web/snapshot/201103.pdf.

National Energy Board. 2015. "Frequently Asked Questions: An Assessment of the Unconventional Petroleum Resources in the Montney Formation, West-Central Alberta and East-Central British Columbia." 16 Oct. At: https://www.neb-one.gc.ca/nrg/sttstc/ntrlgs/rprt/ltmtptntlmntnyfrmtn2013/ltmtptntlmntnyfrmtn2013fq-eng.html.

Natural Resources Canada. 2015. "Simplified Seismic Hazard Map for Canada, the Provinces and Territories." 12 Apr. at: http://www.earthquakescanada.nrcan.gc.ca/hazard-alea/simphaz-en.php.

Nemetz, Peter N. 1990. The Pacific Rim Investment, Development and Trade, 2nd rev. edn. Vancouver: University of British Columbia Press.

Nisga'a Nation. n.d. "Nisga'a History." At: www.schoolnet.ca/aboriginal/nisga1/hist-e.html.

O'Neil, Peter. 2012. "Former Exec Calls for Oil Spill Insurance." *StarPhoenix* (Saskatoon), 6 July, C5.

Padova, Allison. 2004. *Trends in Containerization at Canadian Ports*. Ottawa: Library of Parliament. At: www.parl.gc.ca/information/library/PRBpubs/prb0575-e.htm.

Paper Excellence. 2015. "Mackenzie Mill." At: http://www.paperexcellence.com/mills/mackenzie/.

Port Metro Vancouver. 2015. "Statistics Overview." At: http://www.portmetrovancouver.com/wp-content/uploads/2015/03/2014-statistics-overview.pdf.

Port of Prince Rupert. 2016. "Cargo Performance Proves Port's Resilience in Shifting Economic Conditions." At: http://www.rupertport.com/news/releases/2015-performance-volumes.

Provincial Agricultural Land Commission. 2014. "About the ALC." At: http://www.alc.gov.bc.ca/commission/alc/content/about-the-alc.

Rio Tinto Alcan. 2010. "Kitimat Works Modernization." At: www.kitimatworksmodernization.com/pages/modernization-project/about-kitimat-modernization.php.

Roy, Patricia E. 1989. *White Man's Province*. Vancouver: University of British Columbia Press.

Saqib, Naj, and Dan Schrier. 2015. *A Profile of British Columbia's Manufacturing Sector*. BC Stats, June. At: http://www.bcstats.gov.bc.ca/StatisticsBySubject/BusinessIndustry/Manufacturing.aspx.

Schmunk, Rhianna. 2016. "Vancouver's Housing Market Is World's 3rd Most-Unaffordable: Study." *Huffington Post*, 27 Jan. At: http://www.huffingtonpost.ca/2016/01/26/vancouver-housing-unaffordable-study_n_9081516.html.

Schrier, Dan. 2012. "BC Exports Moving Out of the Wood." BC Stats, 11 May. At: www.bcstats.gov.bc.ca/Publications/AnalyticalReports.aspx.

——— and Lillian Hallin. 2016. "Profile of the British Columbia Technology Sector 2015." BC Stats, June. At: www.bcstats.gov.bc.ca/Publications/RecentReleases.aspx.

Seaspan. 2015. "Seaspan's Vancouver Shipyards Celebrates Start of Construction of First NSPS Vessel." 24 June. At: http://www.seaspan.com/seaspans-vancouver-shipyards-celebrates-start-of-construction-on-first-nsps-vessel.

Statistics Canada. 2006. "Distribution of Employed People by Industry, by Province, 2005." At: www40.statcan.ca/l01/cst01/labor21c.htm.

———. 2007. "Population and Dwelling Counts, for Census Metropolitan Areas and Census Agglomerations, 2006 and 2001 Censuses—100% Data." At: www12.statcan.ca/english/census06/data/popdwell/Table.cfm?T=201&S=3&O=D&RPP=150.

———. 2011. "Population and Dwelling Counts, for Canada, Provinces and Territories, Census Metropolitan Areas and Census Agglomerations, 2011 and 2006 Censuses." At: www12.statcan.gc.ca/census-recensement/2011/dp-pd/hlt-fst/pd-pl/Table-Tableau.cfm?LANG=Eng&T=202&PR=59&S=0&O=D&RPP=50.

———. 2012. "Principal Statistics for Manufacturing Industries." CANSIM table 301-0006, 2 Mar. At: www5.statcan.gc.ca/cansim/a26?lang=eng&retrLang=eng&id=3010006.

———. 2013. "Number and Distribution of Population Reporting an Aboriginal Identity and Percentage of Aboriginal People in the Population, Canada, Provinces and Territories, 2011." *Aboriginal Peoples in Canada: First Nations People, Métis and Inuit*. National Household Survey document 99-011-x. Table 2. 7 May. At: http://www12.statcan.gc.ca/nhs-enm/2011/as-sa/99-011-x/2011001/tbl/tbl02-eng.cfm.

———. 2015. "Population of Census Metropolitan Areas." 11 Feb. At: http://www.statcan.gc.ca/tables-tableaux/sum-som/l01/cst01/demo05a-eng.htm.

———. 2016a. "Labour Force, Employment and Unemployment, Levels and Rates, by Province." At: http://www.statcan.gc.ca/tables-tableaux/sum-som/l01/cst01/labor07a-eng.htm.

———. 2016b. "Estimates of Population, Canada, Provinces and Territories." CANSIM table 051-0005, 16 Mar. At: http://www5.statcan.gc.ca/cansim/a26?lang=eng&id=510005.

———. 2016c. "Gross Domestic Product by Industry: Provinces and Territories, 2015." 12 May. At: http://www.statcan.gc.ca/daily-quotidien/160512/dq160512b-eng.htm.

———. 2016d. "Farm Cash Receipts." CANSIM table 002-0001. 25 May. At: http://www5.statcan.gc.ca/cansim/a26.

———. 2016e. "Population of Census Metropolitan Areas." 10 Feb. At: http://www.statcan.gc.ca/tables-tableaux/sum-som/l01/cst01/demo05a-eng.htm.

———. 2016f. "Employment by Major Industry Group, Seasonally Adjusted, by Province." At: http://www.statcan.gc.ca/tables-tableaux/sum-som/l01/cst01/labr67a-eng.htm.

Structural Engineers Association of British Columbia (SEABC). n.d. "British Columbia Earthquake Fact Sheet." At: https://www.apeg.bc.ca/getmedia/4278c069-0374-4cc2-9e73-2b454a0f978a/SEABC-Earthquake-Fact-Sheet.pdf.aspx.

Todd, Douglas. 2014. "Vancouver Is the Most 'Asian' City outside Asia. What Are the Ramifications?" *Vancouver Sun*, 28 Mar. At: http://vancouversun.com/life/vancouver-is-most-asian-city-outside-asia-what-are-the-ramifications.

Tomlinson, Kathy. 2016. "On B.C.'s Farmland, Mega-Mansions and Speculators Reap the Rewards of Lucrative Tax Breaks." *Globe and Mail*, 20 Nov. At: http://www.theglobeandmail.com/news/investigations/farmland-and-real-estate-in-british-columbia/article32923810/.

TransCanada. 2016. "Energy East Pipeline." At: http://www.energyeastpipeline.com/about-2/the-project/.

Wagstaffe, Johanna. 2016. "Why the Risk of the 'Big One' in B.C. Is Heightened Every 14 Months." CBC News, 28 Mar. At: http://www.cbc.ca/news/canada/british-columbia/earthquakes-bc-slow-slip-1.3794192.

CHAPTER 10

Bailey, Sue. 2016. "N.L. Premier to Meet with Aboriginal Leaders over Muskrat Falls Protests." CTV News, 25 Oct. At: http://www.ctvnews.ca/canada/n-l-premier-to-meet-with-aboriginal-leaders-over-muskrat-falls-protests-1.3130434.

Bennett, Margaret. 1989. *The Last Stronghold: Scottish Gaelic Traditions in Newfoundland*. Edinburgh: Canongate.

Beswick, Aaron. 2015. "Week-end Focus: Marshall Decision Still Ripples through Native Fishery." *Chronicle Herald* (Halifax), 27 Jan. At: http://thechronicleherald.ca/novascotia/1265170-weekend-focus-marshall-decision-still-ripples-through-native-fishery.

Blades, Kent. 1995. *Net Destruction: The Death of Atlantic Canada's Fishery*. Halifax: Nimbus.

Bradfield, Michael. 1991. *Maritime Economic Union: Sounding Brass and Tinkling Symbolism*. Halifax: Canadian Centre for Policy Alternatives.

Budgel, Richard, and Michael Stavely. 1987. *The Labrador Boundary*. Labrador Institute of Northern Studies, Memorial University of Newfoundland. At: www.mun.ca/labradorinstitute/projects/labrador_boundary2.pdf.

Campbell, Darren. 2015. "Vale Facility Ramps Up Processing of Voisey's Bay Nickel Motherlode." *Natural Resources Magazine* (3 July). At: http://www.naturalresourcesmagazine.net/?article=homeward-bound.

Canada, Department of Finance. 2009. "Equalization Program." At: www.fin.gc.ca/fedprov/eqp-eng.asp.

———. 2015. "Federal Transfers to Provinces and Territories." 30 Oct. At: https://www.fin.gc.ca/fedprov/mtp-eng.asp.

Canada Forest Service. 2016. "Statistical Data." 27 Jan. At: http://cfs .nrcan.gc.ca/statsprofile/overview/nl.

Canada–Nova Scotia Offshore Petroleum Board. 2016. At: http://www .cnsopb.ns.ca/offshore-activity/offshore-projects/deep-panuke.

Canadian Association of Petroleum Producers. 2015. *Statistical Handbook.* At: http://www.capp.ca/publications-and-statistics/statistics/statistical-handbook.

Canadian Human Rights Commission. 2003. *Report to the Canadian Human Rights Commission on the Treatment of the Innu of Canada by the Government of Canada,* by Professors Constance Backhouse and Donald M. McRae. At: www.chrc-ccdp.ca/publications/Rapport_Innu_Report/Rapport InnuReport_Page3.asp?l=e.

Canadian Press. 2016. "Good Faith Appeal on Churchill Falls Power Contract Falls Flat." *The Telegram* (St John's), 1 Aug. At: http:// www.thetelegram.com/Business/2016-08-01/article-4603516/ Good-faith-appeal-on-Churchill-Falls-power-contract-falls-flat/1.

Cashin, Richard. 1993. *Charting a New Course: Towards the Fishery of the Future.* Ottawa: Department of Fisheries and Oceans.

CBC News. 2007. "Long Commute, Huge Rewards." 29 Oct. At: www .cbc.ca/canada/newfoundland-labrador/story/2007/10/29/big-commute.html.

———. 2009. "The Big Commute." 29 Oct. At: www.cbc.ca/nl/ features/bigcommute/.

———. 2012. "Final Plan for Sidney Tar Ponds Clean-up Announced." 28 Oct. At: www.cbc.ca/news/canada/nova-scotia/story/2012/10/28/ ns-tarpond-announcement.html.

———. 2016. "Battle over Muskrat Falls: What You Need to Know." 27 Oct. At: http://www.cbc.ca/news/indigenous/ muskrat-falls-what-you-need-to-know-1.3822898.

Chaundry, David. 2012. *Meeting the Skills Challenge: Five Key Labour Market Issues Facing Atlantic Canada.* Report of Atlantic Provinces Economic Council, Oct. At: www.apec-econ.ca/files/pubs/%7BBA615AD5-336A-4448-980F-A121DD036733%7D.pdf?title=Meeting%20the%20 Skills%20Challenge%3A%20Five%20Key%20Labour%20Market %20Issues%20Facing%20Atlantic%20Canada&publicationtype= Research%20Reports.

Clapp, R.A. 1998. "The Resource Cycle in Forestry and Fishing." *Canadian Geographer* 42, 2: 129–44.

Coates, Ken S. 2000. *The Marshall Decision and Native Rights.* Montréal and Kingston: McGill-Queen's University Press.

———. 2015. "Sharing the Wealth: How Resource Revenue Agreements Can Honour Treaties, Improve Communities, and Facilitate Canadian Development." Macdonald/Laurier Institute. At: http://www. macdonaldlaurier.ca/files/pdf/MLIresourcerevenuesharing web.pdf.

Conrad, Cathy T. 2009. *Severe and Hazardous Weather in Canada: The Geography of Extreme Events.* Toronto: Oxford University Press.

Council of Canadians. 2013. "Saint John Mayor Boasts of Energy East Pipeline Export Options in the Bay of Fundy." 15 May. At: http:// canadians.org/fr/node/9530.

Cox, Kevin. 1994. "How Hibernia Will Cast Off." *Globe and Mail,* 12 Nov., D8.

Department of Natural Resources, Newfoundland and Labrador. 2011. *Strategic Plan 2011–14.* At: www.nr.gov.nl.ca/nr/publications/2011-14_ StrategicPlan.pdf.

Doucette, Keith. 2013. "$288-Million Deal Will Kick-start Design of Arctic Patrol Ships, Ottawa Announces." *National Post,* 7 Mar. At: news .nationalpost.com/2013/03/07/288-million-deal-will-kick-start-design-of-arctic-patrol-ships-ottawa-announces/.

Erskine, David. 1968. "The Atlantic Region." In John Warkentin, ed., *Canada: A Geographical Interpretation.* Toronto: Methuen, 231–80.

Faragher, John Mack. 2005. *A Great and Noble Scheme: The Tragic Story of the Expulsion of the French Acadians from Their American Homeland.* New York: Norton.

Feehan, James P., and Melvin Baker. 2005. *The Renewal Clause in the Churchill Falls Contract: The Origins of a Coming Crisis,* Papers in Political Economy No. 96. London, Ont.: University of Western Ontario, Political Economy Research Group.

Fisheries and Oceans Canada. 2015a. "Commercial Fisheries: Landings Seafisheries." 9 Dec. At: http://www.dfo-mpo.gc.ca/stats/commercial/ sea-maritimes-eng.htm.

———. 2015b. *2014 4X5Yb Atlantic Cod Stock Status Update.* DFO Can. Sci. Advis. Sec. Sci. Resp. 2015/010.

———. 2015c. "Facts on Canadian Fisheries: Lobster." 6 Mar. At: http:// www.dfo-mpo.gc.ca/fm-gp/sustainable-durable/fisheries-peches/ lobster-homard-eng.htm.

———. 2016. "Seafisheries Landings." 6 Oct. At: http://www.dfo-mpo .gc.ca/stats/commercial/sea-maritimes-eng.htm.

Fish, Food & Allied Workers (FFAW). 2016. "Lobster Prices 2015: Nova Scotia, PEI and New Brunswick." At: http://ffaw.nf.ca/en/lobster-prices-2015-ns-pei-nb#.Vst0hWB9nww.

Griffiths, N.E.S. 2005. *From Migrant to Acadian: A North American Border People 1604–1755.* Montréal and Kingston: McGill-Queen's University Press.

Hardin, Garrett. 1968. "The Tragedy of the Commons." *Science* 162: 1243–8.

Hiller, J.K. 1997. "The Debate: Confederation Rejected, 1864–1869." *Newfoundland and Canada: 1864–1949.* At: www.heritage.nf.ca/law/ debate.html.

Holden, Michael. 2008. *Canada's New Equalization Formula.* Ottawa: Library of Parliament, PRB 08–20E.

Hydro-Québec. 2015. "Rates." At: http://welcome.hydroquebec.com/ video/2/rates.

Index Mundi. 2013. "Crude Oil (Petroleum); Dated Brent Daily Price." 11 Mar. At: www.indexmundi.com/commodities/?commodity= crude-oil-brent&months=120.

Irving Shipbuilding. 2016. "Canadian Impact." At: http://shipsforcanada .ca/canadian-impact/#CA.

MacDonald, Michael. 2012a. "Irving Shipbuilding Sets Deadline of January for Arctic Patrol Ship Work." *Vancouver Sun,* 19 Oct. At: www .vancouversun.com/news/national/Irving+Shipbuilding+sets+ deadline+January+Arctic+patrol+ship+work/7417496/story.html.

———. 2012b. "Cod Making a Comeback in Newfoundland, Research Shows." *Globe and Mail,* 2 July. At: www.theglobeandmail .com/news/national/cod-making-a-comeback-in-newfoundland-research-shows/article4385506/.

Macpherson, Alan G., ed. 1972. *The Atlantic Provinces: Studies in Canadian Geography.* Toronto: University of Toronto Press.

Macpherson, Joyce. 1997. "Cold Ocean." Newfoundland and Labrador Heritage, Memorial University of Newfoundland. At: www.heritage .nf.ca/environment/ocean.html#amherst.

McLellan, David A. 2014. "Opinion: Why Building New Refineries in Canada Is Uneconomic and Undesirable." *Financial Post,* 17 Jan. At: http://business.financialpost.com/news/energy/opinion-why-building-new-refineries-in-canada-is-uneconomic-and-undesirable?__lsa=a3a3-f506.

Massell, David. 2016. "History Lingers at Muskrat Falls." *Niche,* 21 Sept. At: http://niche-canada.org/2016/09/21/history-lingers-at-muskrat-falls/.

Matthews, Ralph. 1983. *The Creation of Regional Dependency.* Toronto: University of Toronto Press.

Moore, Oliver. 2009. "Innu Reach Deal on Lower Churchill Project." *Globe and Mail,* 26 Sept., B1.

National Energy Board (NEB). 2016. *Canada's Energy Future 2016: Energy Supply and Demand Projections to 2040.* At: https://www.neb-one.gc.ca/nrg/ntgrtd/ftr/2016/index-eng.html.

Natural Resources Canada. 2015. "Preliminary Estimate of the Mineral Production of Canada, by Province, 2014." 16 Aug. At: http://sead.nrcan.gc.ca/prod-prod/2014p-eng.aspx.

———. 2016. "Statistical Data: Forests." At: https://cfs.nrcan.gc.ca/statsprofile/overview/ca.

Newfoundland Power. 2016. "Rate Comparison." At: http://www.newfoundlandpower.com/aboutus/electricalrates/pdf/ComparisonOfRates2016.pdf.

Ong, Yunita, and Lydia Mulvany. 2015. "Lobster Prices Exports Skyrocket as China's Hunger for the Lucky Canadian Crustacean Soars." *Bloomberg News*, 4 Aug. At: http://business.financialpost.com/news/economy/lobster-prices-exports-skyrocket-as-chinas-hunger-for-the-lucky-canadian-crustacean-soars.

Phillips, David. 1993. The Day Niagara Falls Ran Dry! Toronto: Canadian Geographic and Key Porter Books.

Power, Thomas P., ed. 1991. *The Irish in Atlantic Canada, 1780–1900.* Fredericton: New Ireland Press.

Prince Edward Island, Department of Agriculture and Forestry. 2012. "Farm Cash Receipts." At: www.gov.pe.ca/photos/original/af_stat_tab2.pdf.

Quinn, Greg, 2012. "Long-Distance Commutes the Normal Life for Many Canadians." *Financial Post*, 1 Aug. At: business.financialpost.com/2012/08/01/long-distance-commutes-the-new-normal-for-many-canadians/.

Roberts, Terry. 2016a. "Bursting of Alberta's Oil Bubble on Display at St. John's Airport." CBC News, 16 Feb. At: http://www.cbc.ca/news/canada/newfoundland-labrador/airport-st-johns-alberta-downturn-1.3443452.

———. 2016b. "It's Official: Muskrat Falls a Boondoggle, Says Stan Marshall." CBC News, 24 June. At: http://www.cbc.ca/news/canada/newfoundland-labrador/stan-marshall-muskrat-falls-update-1.3649540.

Royal Canadian Navy. 2015. "Arctic/Offshore Patrol Ships." 21 July. At: http://www.navy-marine.forces.gc.ca/en/fleet-units/aops-home.page.

Samson, Colin. 2003. *A Way of Life That Does Not Exist: Canada and the Extinguishment of the Innu.* St John's: ISER Books.

Statistics Canada. 2002a. *Census of Canada 2001—Census Geography. Highlights and Analysis: Canada's 2001 Population.* At: www12.statcan.ca/English/census01.

———. 2002b. "Population and Dwelling Counts, 2001 Census." 16 July. Catalogue no. 93F0050XCB2001013.

———. 2006. "Canadian Statistics: Distribution of Employed People, by Industry, by Province." At: www40.statcan.ca/l01/cst01/labor21c.htm.

———. 2007. "Population and Dwelling Counts, for Census Metropolitan Areas and Census Agglomerations, 2006 and 2001 Censuses—100% Data." At: www12.statcan.ca/english/census06/data/popdwell/Table.cfm?T=201&S=3&O=D&RPP=150.

———. 2012a. "Population and Dwelling Counts, for Canada, Provinces and Territories, 2011 and 2006 Censuses." 24 Jan. At: www12.statcan.gc.ca/census-recensement/2011/dp-pd/ hlt-fst/pd-pl/index-eng.cfm.

———. 2012b. "Gross Domestic Product, Expenditure-based, by Province and Territory." 19 Nov. At: www.statcan.gc.ca/tables-tableaux/sum-som/l01/cst01/econ15-eng.htm.

———. 2012c. "Unemployment Rate, Canada, Provinces, Health Regions and Peer Groups, CANSIM table 109–5324, 24 May. At: www5.statcan.gc.ca/cansim/pick-choisir?lang=eng&p2=33&id=1095324.

———. 2012d. "Great Harbour Deep." Census Profile. 17 Oct. At: www12.statcan.gc.ca/census-recensement/2011/dp-pd/prof/ search-recherche/frm_res.cfm?Lang=E&TABID=1&G=1&Geo1=PR&Code1=10&Geo2=0&Code2=0&SearchType=Begins&SearchText=great+harbour+deep&PR=10.

———. 2015a. "Estimates of Population for Canada, Provinces, and Territories." CANSIM table 051-0005. At: http://www5.statcan.gc.ca/cansim/pick-choisir?lang=eng&p2=33&id=0510005.

———. 2015b. "Gross Domestic Product and Final Domestic Demand." 29 June. At: http://www.statcan.gc.ca/daily-quotidien/150529/cg-a001-png-eng.htm.

———. 2015c. "Farm Cash Receipts, by Province." At: http://www.statcan.gc.ca/tables-tableaux/sum-som/l01/cst01/agri04e-eng.htm.

———. 2016a. "Labour Force, Employment and Unemployment, Levels and Rates, by Province." 8 Jan. At: http://www.statcan.gc.ca/tables-tableaux/sum-som/l01/cst01/labor07c-eng.htm.

———. 2016b. "Sales of Natural Gas, Monthly." CANSIM (database), table 129-0003. At: http://www5.statcan.gc.ca/cansim/a26?lang=eng&retrLang=eng&id=1290003&&pattern=&stByVal=1&p1=1&p2=-1&tabMode=dataTable&csid=.

———. 2016c. *Visual Census. 2011 Census.* Ottawa. Released 24 Oct. 2012. At: http://www12.statcan.gc.ca/census-recensement/2011/dp-pd/vc-rv/index.cfm?Lang=ENG&TOPIC_ID=1&GEOCODE=310.

———. 2016d. "Labour Force, Employment and Unemployment, Levels and Rates, by Province." At: http://www.statcan.gc.ca/tables-tableaux/sum-som/l01/cst01/labor07a-eng.htm.

———. 2016e. "Estimates of Population, Canada, Provinces and Territories." CANSIM table 051-0005, 16 Mar. At: http://www5.statcan.gc.ca/cansim/a26?lang=eng&id=510005.

———. 2016f. "Gross Domestic Product by Industry: Provinces and Territories, 2015." 12 May. At: http://www.statcan.gc.ca/daily-quotidien/160512/dq160512b-eng.htm.

———. 2016g. "Annual Population Estimates by Census Metropolitan Area, July 1, 2014." Table 1. At: http://www.statcan.gc.ca/daily-quotidien/150211/t150211a001-eng.htm.

Storey, Keith. 2009. "Help Wanted: Demographics, Labor Supply and Economic Change in Newfoundland and Labrador." *Challenged by Demography: A NORA Conference on the Demographic Challenges of the North Atlantic Region*, Alta, Norway, 20 Oct.

Tait, Carrie. 2013. "East Coast's Hebron Offshore Play Gets the Nod from Exxon." *Globe and Mail*, 4 Jan. At: www.theglobeandmail.com/globe-investor/east-coasts-hebron-offshore-play-gets-the-nod-from-exxon/article6942298/.

Ware, Beverley. 2012. "Time Runs Out for Bowater Mill." *Chronicle Herald* (Halifax), 14 June. At: thechronicleherald.ca/novascotia/107146-time-runs-out-for-bowater-mill.

Wente, Margaret. 2016. "Please Forgive Me, and Slap Me with a Cod." *Globe and Mail*, 24 Sept., F7.

Withers, Paul. 2016. "Nova Scotia Exports Continue to Be Buoyed by Lobster Sales to China." CBC News, 18 May. At: http://www.cbc.ca/news/canada/nova-scotia/lobster-sales-china-buoy-ns-exports-1.3586699.

CHAPTER 11

Abele, Frances, Thomas J. Courchene, F. Leslie Seidle, and France St-Hilaire, eds. 2009. *Northern Exposure: Peoples, Powers and Prospects in Canada's North.* Montréal: Institute for Research on Public Policy.

Agnew, John. 2005. "Sovereignty Regimes: Territoriality and Authority in Contemporary World Politics." *Annals, Association of American Geographers* 95, 2: 437–61.

Baffin Fisheries. 2016. "Baffin Fisheries on Track to Harvest 100% of Quota with Inuit-owned Vessels in 2016." 3 Aug. At: http://www.baffinfisheries.ca/media/.

Barz, Sandra B., and Bente Roed. 2008. "Inuit Printmaking." *The Canadian Encyclopedia*. At: http://www.thecanadianencyclopedia.ca/en/article/inuit-printmaking/.

BBC News. 2007. "Canada to Strengthen Arctic Claim," 10 Aug. At: news.bbc.co.uk/2/hi/Americas/6941426.stm.

————. 2015. "Denmark Challenges Russia and Canada over North Pole." 15 Dec. At: http://www.bbc.com/news/world-europe-30481309.

Berger, Thomas R. 1977. *Northern Frontier, Northern Homeland: The Report of the Mackenzie Valley Pipeline Inquiry*, 2 vols. Ottawa: Minister of Supply and Services.

Bone, Robert M. 2016. *The Canadian North: Issues and Challenges*, 5th edn. Toronto: Oxford University Press.

———— and Robert B. Anderson, eds. 2017. *Indigenous Peoples and Resource Development*. Toronto: Captus Press.

Brown, Chris. 2016. "Massive Cruise Ship Brings New Era of Arctic Tourism to Cambridge Bay." CBC News, 29 Aug. At: http://www.cbc.ca/news/canada/north/massive-cruise-ship-brings-new-era-of-arctic-tourism-to-cambridge-bay-1.3739491.

Bumsted, J.M. 2010. *The Peoples of Canada: A Pre-Confederation History*, 3rd edn. Toronto: Oxford University Press.

Byers, Michael. 2009. *Who Owns the Arctic? Understanding Sovereignty Disputes in Canada's North*. Vancouver: Douglas & McIntyre.

Canada. 1985. *The Western Arctic Claim: The Inuvialuit Final Agreement*. Ottawa: Department of Indian Affairs and Northern Development.

————. 1991. "Comprehensive Land Claim Agreement Initialled with Gwich'in of the Mackenzie Delta in the Northwest Territories." Communiqué 1-9171. Ottawa: Department of Indian Affairs and Northern Development.

————. 1993a. "Formal Signing of Tungavik Federation of Nunavut Final Agreement." Communiqué 1–9324. Ottawa: Department of Indian Affairs and Northern Development.

————. 1993b. *Umbrella Final Agreement between the Government of Canada, Council for Yukon Indians and the Government of the Yukon*. Ottawa: Department of Indian Affairs and Northern Development.

————. 2004. "Agreements." Ottawa: Department of Indian and Northern Affairs. At: www.ainc-inac.gc.ca/pr/agr/index_e.html#Comprehensive%20Claims%20Agreements.

CBC News. 2007. "Mackenzie Gas Line Still 'Leading Case' Despite Bloating $16.2B Cost Outlook." 12 Mar. At: www.cbc.ca/cp/business/070312/b031292A.html#skip300x250.

Chan, Laurie H.M. 2006. "Food Safety and Food Security in the Canadian Arctic." Meridian (Publication of the Canadian Polar Commission): 1–3.

Coates, Ken, P. Whitney Lackenbauer, William Morrison, and Greg Poelzer. 2008. *Arctic Front: Defending Canada in the Far North*. Toronto: Thomas Allen.

Conference Board of Canada. 2015. "Education and Skills in the Territories." How Canada Performs. At: http://www.conferenceboard.ca/hcp/provincial/education/edu-territories.aspx#10.

Contenta, Sandra. 2015. "Nunavut's Youth Suicide Epidemic—'Who is next? How do we stop this?'" Toronto Star, 4 Apr. At: https://www.thestar.com/news/insight/2015/04/04/nunavuts-youth-suicide-epidemic-who-is-next-how-do-we-stop-this.html.

Crowe, Keith J. 1991. *A History of the Original Peoples of Northern Canada*, 2nd edn. Montréal and Kingston: McGill-Queen's University Press.

Danylchuk, Jack. 2007. "Giant, Glittering and Tarnished." Up Here, 18 Dec. At: www.uphere.ca/node/175.

Dickason, Olive Patricia. 2002. *Canada's First Nations: A History of Founding Peoples from Earliest Times*, 3rd edn. Toronto: Oxford University Press.

Drummond, K.J. 2009. *Northern Canada Distribution of Ultimate Oil and Gas Resources*. At: drummondconsulting.com/NCAN09Report.pdf.

Elias, Peter Douglas. 1995. *Northern Aboriginal Communities: Economies and Development*. North York, Ont: Captus Press.

Environment Canada. 2012. "Canadian Arctic Sea Ice Reached Record Low in Summer 2012." 5 Nov. At: http://www.ec.gc.ca/glaces-ice/default.asp?lang=En&n=765F63E4-1.

Flyvbjerg, Bent. 2014. "What You Should Know about Megaprojects and Why: An Overview." Project Management Journal 45, 2: 6–19.

George, Jane. 2016. "Western Nunavut's Crystal Serenity Encounter Runs Smoothly." Nunatsiaq Online, 30 Aug. At: http://www.nunatsiaqonline.ca/stories/article/65674no_problems_mar_huge_cruise_ship_visit_in_western_nunavut/.

Griffiths, Franklyn. 2009. "Canadian Arctic Sovereignty: Time to Take Yes for an Answer on the Northwest Passage." In Abele et al. (2009: 107–36).

Hamelin, Louis-Edmond. 1978. *Canadian Nordicity: It's Your North, Too*, trans. William Barr. Montréal: Harvest House.

Indigenous and Northern Affairs Canada (INAC). 2007. *Northern Oil and Gas Annual Report 2006*. At: www.ainc-inac.gc.ca/oil/ann/ann2006/dev_e.html.

————. 2009. *Northern Oil and Gas Annual Report 2008*. At: www.ainc-inac.gc.ca/nth/og/pubs/ann/ann2008/ann2008-eng.pdf.

————. 2010. "The History of Land Claims and Self-government in the Yukon." 15 Oct. At: www.aadnc-aandc.gc.ca/eng/1100100028417/1100100028418.

————, Northern Oil and Gas Branch. 2012. *Northern Oil and Gas Annual Report 2011*. 2 May. At: www.aadnc-aandc.gc.ca/eng/1335971994893/1335972853094.

————. 2015. "Backgrounder—Déline Final Self-Government Agreement." At: https://www.aadnc-aandc.gc.ca/eng/1387314654000/1387314707746.

————. 2016. "General Briefing Note on Canada's Self-government and Comprehensive Land Claims Policies and the Status of Negotiations." At: https://www.aadnc-aandc.gc.ca/eng/1373385502190/1373385561540.

Inuvialuit Regional Corporation (IRC). 2014. "IRC Provides Distribution Payments to Beneficiaries." 16 Apr. At: http://www.irc.inuvialuit.com/publications/pdf/News%20Release%20-%202014%20Distribution%20Apr%2016%2014.pdf.

Irlbacher-Fox, Stephanie. 2014. "Traditional Knowledge, Co-existence and Co-resistance." Decolonization: Indigeneity, Education & Society 3, 3: 145–58.

Jordan, Pav. 2012. "Nunavut Mining Rush Attracts China's MMG." Globe and Mail, 5 Sept., B3.

————. 2013. "Baffinland Iron Mines Sharply Scales Back Mary River Project." Globe and Mail, 11 Jan. At: www.theglobeandmail.com/globe-investor/baffinland-iron-mines-sharply-scales-back-mary-river-project/article7227358/.

Koring, Paul. 2012. "In the Arctic, Drones Could Close the Gap." Globe and Mail, 9 July, A13.

Légaré, André. 2008. "Canada's Experiment with Aboriginal Self-determination in Nunavut: From Vision to Illusion." International Journal on Minority and Group Rights 15: 335–67.

McGhee, Robert. 1996. *Ancient People of the Arctic*. Vancouver: University of British Columbia Press.

MacLachlan, Letha. 1996. *NWT Diamonds Project: Report of the Environmental Assessment Panel*. Ottawa: Canadian Environmental Assessment Agency.

McRae, Donald. 2008. "An Arctic Agenda for Canada and the United States." In From Correct to Inspired: A Blueprint for Canada–US Engagement. At: www.carleton.ca/ctpl/conferences/documents/BackgroundPapers-Final.pdf.

Manuel, George, and Michael Posluns. 1974. *The Fourth World: An Indian Reality*. Toronto: Collier-Macmillan Canada.

Marcus, Alan R. 1995. *Relocating Eden: The Image and Politics of Inuit Exile in the Canadian Arctic*. Hanover, NH: University Press of New England.

Milne, Richard. 2016. "Denmark Rejects Russia Call for Swift Talks on Arctic Rights." *Financial Times*, 12 Sept. At: https://www.ft.com/content/d1810bd4-77e5-11e6-97ae-647294649b28.

National Snow & Ice Data Center (NSIDC). 2016. "Sluggish Ice Growth in Arctic." 2 Nov. At: http://nsidc.org/arcticseaicenews/.

Natural Resources Canada. 2015. "Preliminary Estimate of the Mineral Production of Canada, by Province, 2014." 16 Aug. At: http://sead.nrcan.gc.ca/prod-prod/2014p-eng.aspx.

Northern Gas Pipelines. 2009. *Northern Gas Pipelines: Mackenzie Valley Pipeline Project*. At: www.arcticgaspipeline.com/Delta%20Route.htm.

NWT Bureau of Statistics. 1990. "Fur Production and Value." *Statistical Quarterly* 12.

———. 2014. *2014 NWT Survey of Mining Employees*. Dec. At: http://www.iti.gov.nt.ca/sites/www.iti.gov.nt.ca/files/2014_nwt_survey_of_mining_employees_overall_report.pdf.

———. 2015. "Fuel Production." *Northwest Territories—2014 . . . by the numbers*. At: http://www.statsnwt.ca/publications/bythenos/2014NWT%20by%20the%20nos.pdf.

———. 2016a. "Fur Production and Value." *Statistical Quarterly* (Sept.). At: http://www.statsnwt.ca/publications/statistics-quarterly/index.html.

———. 2016b. "Population." *Statistical Quarterly* (Sept.) At: http://www.statsnwt.ca/publications/statistics-quarterly/index.html.

Nunavut. 1999. *The Bathurst Mandate Pinasuaqtavut: What We've Set Out to Do*. Iqaluit: Legislative Assembly.

Nunavut Statistics Bureau. 2016. "Nunavut Population Estimates, 2015." At: http://www.stats.gov.nu.ca/en/home.aspx.

Page, Robert. 1986. *Northern Development: The Canadian Dilemma*. Toronto: McClelland & Stewart.

Pehora, Brian. 2016. "Coast Guard: New $1.3 Billion Arctic Icebreaker to be Ready by 2022." *Nunatsiaq Online*. 28 Jan. At: http://www.nunatsiaqonline.ca/stories/article/65674coast_guard_new_1.3_billion_arctic_icebreaker_to_be_ready_by_2022/.

Quenneville, Guy. 2014. "Fly-in, Fly-out and Fed-up." *Up Here Business*. At: http://upherebusiness.ca/post/97075639467.

———. 2015a. "Snap Lake Mine Could Close If Dissolved Solid Limit Not Raised: De Beers." CBC News, 13 Mar. At: http://www.cbc.ca/news/canada/north/snap-lake-mine-could-close-if-dissolved-solid-limit-not-raised-de-beers-1.2993214.

———. 2015b. "N.W.T. Braces for Economic Sting of Snap Lake Mine Shut Down." CBC News, 7 Dec. At: http://www.cbc.ca/news/canada/north/snap-lake-shutdown-layoffs-1.3353295.

Reuters. 2016. "De Beers Puts Canadian Snap Lake Diamond Mine Up for Sale." 23 July. At: http://www.rcinet.ca/eye-on-the-arctic/category/general/general-politics/.

Rowley, Graham W. 1996. *Cold Comfort: My Love Affair with the Arctic*. Montreal and Kingston: McGill-Queen's University Press.

Royal Canadian Navy. 2015. "Arctic/Offshore Patrol Ships." 21 Aug. At: http://www.navy-marine.forces.gc.ca/en/fleet-units/aops-home.page.

Sevunts, Levon. 2016. "Canada to Submit Its Arctic Continental Shelf Claim in 2018." Radio Canada International, 3 May. At: http://www.rcinet.ca/2016/05/03/canada-to-submit-its-arctic-continental-shelf-claim-in-2018/.

Shadian, Jessica. 2007. "In Search of an Identity Canada Looks North." *American Review of Canadian Studies* 37, 3: 323–53.

Skura, Elyse. 2016. "Baffinland Not Meeting Inuit Employment Goals at Mary River: QIA." CBC News, 12 Oct. At: http://www.cbc.ca/news/canada/north/baffinland-qia-mary-river-review-1.3800652.

Statistics Canada. 2004. "Study: Diamonds Are Adding Lustre to the Canadian Economy." *The Daily*, 13 Jan. At: www.statcan.gc.ca/Daily/English/040113/d040113a.htm.

———. 2008. "Aboriginal Identity Population by Age Groups, Median Age and Sex, 2006 Counts, for Canada, Provinces and Territories." At: www12.statcan.gc.ca/english/census06/data/highlights/Aboriginal/pages/Page.cfm?Lang=E&Geo=PR&Code=01&Table=1&Data=Count&Sex=1&Age=1&StartRec=1&Sort=2&Display=Page.

———. 2012a. "Population and Dwelling Counts, for Canada, Provinces and Territories and Population Centres." 11 Apr. At: www12.statcan.gc.ca/census-recensement/2011/dp-pd/hlt-fst/pd-pl/Tables-Tableaux.cfm?LANG=Eng&T=800.

———. 2012b. "Components of Population Growth, Canada, Provinces and Territories." CANSIM table 051-0004, 27 Oct. At: www.statcan.gc.ca/tables-tableaux/sum-som/l01/cst01/demo33c-eng.htm.

———. 2013. "Number and Distribution of Population Reporting an Aboriginal Identity and Percentage of Aboriginal People in the Population, Canada, Provinces and Territories, 2011." *Aboriginal Peoples in Canada: First Nations People, Métis and Inuit*. National Household Survey document 99-011-x, Table 2. 7 May. At: http://www12.statcan.gc.ca/nhs-enm/2011/as-sa/99-011-x/2011001/tbl/tbl02-eng.cfm.

———. 2014a. "Aboriginal Peoples in Canada: First Nations People, Métis and Inuit." National Household Survey. 28 Mar. At: http://www12.statcan.gc.ca/nhs-enm/2011/as-sa/99-011-x/99-011-x2011001-eng.cfm#a1.

———. 2014b. "Population by Year, Province and Territory." 26 Sept. At: http://www12.statcan.gc.ca/tables-tableaux/sum-som/l01/cst01/demo02a-eng.htm.

———. 2016a. "Estimates of Population, Canada, Provinces and Territories." CANSIM table 051-0005, 16 Mar. At: http://www5.statcan.gc.ca/cansim/a26?lang=eng&id=510005.

———. 2016b. "Components of Population Growth, Canada, Provinces and Territories, Annual (Persons)." Table 051-0004. 4 Oct. At: http://www5.statcan.gc.ca/cansim/a21.

Weber, Bob. 2012. "Ottawa Set to Eye China's Nunavut Mine Plan." *Globe and Mail*, 28 Dec., B1.

Williams, Glyn. 2009. *Arctic Labyrinth*. Toronto: Viking Canada.

Williamson, Robert G. 1974. *Eskimo Underground: Socio-Cultural Change in the Canadian Central Arctic*. Occasional Papers II. Uppsala, Sweden: Almqvist & Wiksell.

World Atlas. 2015. "Hans Offs! Canada and Denmark's Arctic Dispute." 1 June. At: http://www.worldatlas.com/articles/hans-island-boundary-dispute-canada-denmark-territorial-conflict.html.

Young, Oran. 2009. "Whither the Arctic: Conflict or Cooperation in the Circumpolar North." *Polar Record* 45, 232: 73–82.

Young, T. Kue, Boris Revich, and Leena Soininen. 2015. "Suicide in Circumpolar Regions: An Introduction and Overview." *International Journal of Circumpolar Health* 74. At: http://www.circumpolarhealthjournal.net/index.php/ijch/article/view/27349.

Yukon Bureau of Statistics. 2016. *Yukon Statistical Review, 2015*. At: http://www.eco.gov.yk.ca/stats/pdf/Annual_Review_2015.pdf.

CHAPTER 12

Adams, Michael. 2007. *Unlikely Utopia: The Surprising Triumph of Canadian Pluralism*. Toronto: Viking Press.

Bailey, Sue. 2016. "Cathy Bennett, N.L. Finance Minister, Says She's Endured 'Vile' Online Harassment." *Huffington Post*, 12 Dec. At: http://www.huffingtonpost.ca/2016/12/12/body-shamed-threatened-and-bullied-finance-minister-exposes-online-abuse_n_13589558.html.

Byers, Michael. 2016. "Why It's Worth It for Canada to Talk to the Russian Bear." *Globe and Mail*, 19 Oct. At: http://www.theglobeandmail.com/opinion/why-its-worth-it-for-canada-to-talk-to-the-russian-bear/article32429843/.

Canadian Press. 2016. "New Alberta NDP Member Sandra Jansen Urges Colleagues to Fight Harassment." Global News, 22 Nov. At: http://globalnews.ca/news/3082784/new-alberta-ndp-member-sandra-jansen-urges-colleagues-to-fight-harassment/.

Conway, Sir Gordon. 2009. "Geographical Crises of the Twenty-First Century." Geographical Journal 175, 3: 221–8.

Dobson, Wendy. 2009. Gravity Shift: How Asia's New Economic Powerhouses Will Shape the Twenty-First Century. Toronto: University of Toronto Press.

Florida, Richard. 2002. The Rise of the Creative Class: And How It's Transforming Work, Leisure, Community and Everyday Life. New York: Basic Books.

———. 2012. The Rise of the Creative Class—Revisited. New York: Basic Books.

Ford, Martin. 2015. Rise of the Robots: Technology and the Threat of a Jobless Future. New York: Basic Books.

Frye, Northrop. 1971. The Bush Garden: Essays on the Canadian Imagination. Toronto: Anansi Press.

Hare, F. Kenneth. 1968. "Canada." In John Warkentin, ed., Canada: A Geographical Interpretation. Toronto: Methuen.

Li, Wei. 2009. Ethnoburb: The New Ethnic Community in Urban America. Honolulu: University of Hawaii Press.

McCarthy, Shawn. 2009. "Canada's Race for a High-Tech Strategy." Globe and Mail, 1 Aug., B1, B3.

McKenna, Barrie. 2016. "To Fix the Economy, Trudeau Taps Global Star in Corporate World." Globe and Mail, 26 Feb. At: http://www.theglobeandmail.com/news/politics/globe-politics-insider/to-fix-the-economy-trudeau-taps-global-star-of-corporate-world/article28937535/.

Martin, Lawrence. 2016. "On Energy, PM Needs to Lead with His Head, Not Heart." Globe and Mail, 9 Sept. At: http://www.theglobeandmail.com/opinion/on-energy-pm-needs-to-lead-with-his-head-not-heart/article31727993/.

Magnier, Mark. 2016. "China's Economic Growth Is the Slowest in 25 Years." Wall Street Journal, 19 Jan. At: http://www.wsj.com/articles/china-economic-growth-slows-to-6-9-on-year-in-2015-1453169398.

Pawson, Chad. 2016. "Justin Trudeau Steals the Show at the Vancouver Pride Parade." CBC News, 1 Aug. At: http://www.cbc.ca/news/canada/british-columbia/justin-trudeau-vancouver-pride-parade-1.3702613.

Saul, John Ralston. 1997. Reflections of a Siamese Twin: Canada at the End of the Twentieth Century. Toronto: Viking.

———. 2009. The Collapse of Globalism and the Reinvention of the World, 2nd edn. Toronto: Penguin Canada.

Schwab, Klaus. 2016. The Fourth Industrial Revolution. World Economic Forum: Geneva.

Sinclair, Murray, Chair. 2015. Honouring the Truth, Reconciling for the Future: Summary of the Final Report of the Truth and Reconciliation Commission of Canada. At: http://www.trc.ca/websites/trcinstitution/index.php?p=890.

Statistics Canada. 2017. Exports of goods on a balance-of-payments basis, by product. May 5. At: http://www.statcan.gc.ca/tables-tableaux/sum-som/l01/cst01/gblec04-eng.htm.

TransCanada Pipelines. 2016. "Energy East Pipeline." At: http://www.energyeastpipeline.com/home/route-map/.

Wallace, Alan. 2016. "Alan Wallace: Saskatoon's Next Mayor Must Move Minds." StarPhoenix (Saskatoon), 22 Oct. At: http://thestarphoenix.com/news/local-news/alan-wallace-saskatoons-next-mayor-must-move-minds.

Wallerstein, Immanuel. 1979. The Capitalist World Economy. Cambridge: Cambridge University Press.

———. 1998. "Contemporary Capitalist Dilemmas, the Social Sciences, and the Geopolitics of the Twenty-First Century." Canadian Journal of Sociology 23, 2 and 3: 141–58.

Index